Τοιοῦτος οὖν μοι ὁ συγγραφεὺς ἔστω, . . .
ξένος ἐν τοῖς βιβλίοις καὶ ἄπολις.

—Lucian.

A HISTORY OF
EUROPEAN THOUGHT
IN THE NINETEENTH CENTURY

BY

JOHN THEODORE MERZ

in Four Volumes

VOLUME II

DOVER PUBLICATIONS, INC., NEW YORK

Published in Canada by General Publishing Company, Ltd., 30 Lesmill Road, Don Mills, Toronto, Ontario.

Published in the United Kingdom by Constable and Company, Ltd., 10 Orange Street, London W.C.2.

This Dover edition, first published in 1965, is an unabridged and unaltered republication of the work first published by William Blackwood & Sons, between 1904 and 1912.

Library of Congress Catalog Card Number 64-18363

Manufactured in the United States of America

Dover Publications, Inc.
180 Varick Street
New York 14, N.Y.

PREFACE.

In this second volume I have carried out the programme which I put forward in the preface to the first volume, thus finishing the first portion of my undertaking—The History of Scientific Thought in the Nineteenth Century. The two volumes form a work complete in itself, and for this reason I have attached an alphabetical index.

In addition to the names I mentioned in the preface to the first volume, I have to add those of other friends who have been of great help to me in the course of my work. With Professor Sampson, F.R.S., of Durham University, I have had many helpful discussions on the subjects of this volume, notably on chapters viii. and xiii., which he read in proof. Mr Arthur Berry, M.A., of King's College, Cambridge, has read over chapter xiii., and made valuable suggestions. Mr Archibald S. Percival, M.B., of Cambridge, has read over chapters vi. and x. Professor F. G. Weiss, D.Sc., of Victoria University, has read chapters viii. and ix. Mr Thomas Whittaker has continued his revision, much to the benefit of the book; and Dr Spence Watson has given the finishing touches to the last pages, in which I endeavour to secure in advance the interest of my readers for the subsequent portions of this work. To all these friends I wish to express my sense of obligation and my sincere thanks. I find it impossible to express how much this book owes to my beloved wife, my constant helpmate on the long course of this arduous enterprise.

It is unnecessary for me to lighten the work of my critics by pointing out the many defects of which I myself am painfully conscious; but, in the case of the last chapter on "The Development of Mathematical Thought," I wish to say that this is—so far as I know—the first attempt to give to this abstract region of thought a place in a general history of intellectual progress. I sincerely hope that it will be followed by other and more successful attempts to perform this very difficult task. It is now abundantly clear that mathematical thought will play an increasingly important part in the progress of science and culture, and it is no longer permissible to consider it merely an interesting specialty apart from the general course of intellectual development. A due appreciation of its importance and power will in future be expected, not only from the practical thinker who applies science, but likewise from the philosopher who assigns to science its place in the comprehensive scheme of human culture.

J. THEO. MERZ.

The Quarries,
Newcastle-upon-Tyne, *October* 1903.

CONTENTS OF THE SECOND VOLUME.

CHAPTER VI.

ON THE KINETIC OR MECHANICAL VIEW OF NATURE.

CHAPTER VII.

ON THE PHYSICAL VIEW OF NATURE.

CHAPTER VIII.

ON THE MORPHOLOGICAL VIEW OF NATURE.

CHAPTER IX.

ON THE GENETIC VIEW OF NATURE.

CHAPTER X.

ON THE VITALISTIC VIEW OF NATURE.

CHAPTER XI.

ON THE PSYCHO-PHYSICAL VIEW OF NATURE.

CHAPTER XII.

ON THE STATISTICAL VIEW OF NATURE.

CHAPTER XIII.

ON THE DEVELOPMENT OF MATHEMATICAL THOUGHT DURING THE NINETEENTH CENTURY.

RETROSPECT AND PROSPECT.

A HISTORY OF EUROPEAN THOUGHT IN THE NINETEENTH CENTURY

PART I.

SCIENTIFIC THOUGHT

(CONCLUDED).

CHAPTER VI.

ON THE KINETIC OR MECHANICAL VIEW OF NATURE.

IT was a favourite idea with the philosophers of antiquity that everything is in motion, that rest is to be found nowhere in nature, and that the entire process of life and sensation in particular is brought about by the communication and transference of minute movements of a purely mechanical kind. Out of the deep conviction that everything around us and in us is in a perpetual flux—a doctrine which is usually fathered upon Heraclitus of Ephesus [1]—two distinct problems resulted, and occupied the thinkers of antiquity: the problem of explaining the apparent rest and permanency of many observable pheno-

---

[1] The doctrine of Heraclitus (B.C. 500) is placed by Zeller ('Philosophie der Griechen,' vol. i.) in direct opposition to that of the Eleatic School (Parmenides, Zeno) and of Pythagoras. The Eleatics argued from the unity of all existence to the impossibility of the multiplicity and the change of things. Heraclitus sets out from the conception that everything is in continual motion and flow ($\kappa\iota\nu\epsilon\hat{\iota}\sigma\theta\alpha\iota$, $\dot{\epsilon}\nu$ $\kappa\iota\nu\dot{\eta}\sigma\epsilon\iota$ $\epsilon\hat{\iota}\nu\alpha\iota$). Our knowledge of Heraclitus is derived mainly from references in the writings of Plato and Aristotle. A very full account is given by Zeller, and by E. Pfleiderer ('Die Philosophie des Heraklit von Ephesus,' Berlin, 1886), who sums up the fundamental idea in the beautiful verses of Goethe (Gedichte, "Eins und Alles"):—

" Und umzuschaffen das Geschaffne
Damit sich's nicht zum Starren waffne,
Wirkt ewiges, lebendiges Thun.
Und was nicht war, nun will es werden,
Zu reinen Sonnen, farbigen Erden.
In keinem Falle darf es ruhn.
    Es soll sich regen, schaffend handeln,
Erst sich gestalten, dann verwandeln ;
Nur scheinbar steht's Momente still.
Das Ewige regt sich fort in Allen :
Denn Alles muss in Nichts zerfallen,
Wenn es im Sein beharren will."

mena and properties of natural objects, and the higher
ethical problem of fixing upon that which is lastingly
real and important in the continuous change of sensation
and opinion.   The latter formed the central interest of
that course of reasoning which began with Socrates and
culminated in Plato and Aristotle; the former was the
problem of natural philosophy of which Epicurus and
Lucretius stand out as the great representatives.   In
a well-known passage of the second book of his great
poem, Lucretius explains the apparent rest of natural
things by the simile of a flock of lustily dancing sheep,
which at a distance looks like a white spot on a green
hillside.[1]   This tendency of philosophic reasoning to see
motion where common-sense only sees rest, to reduce
theoretically the apparently permanent properties of
things to a play of intricate but imperceptible modes
of motion, has governed still more markedly modern
scientific thought.   I shall comprise all efforts to give
more definite[2] expression to this general idea under

---

[1] 'De Natura Rerum,' ii. 308—
"Illud in his rebus non est mirabile,
quare,
Omnia cum rerum primordia sint in motu,
Summa tamen summa videatur stare
quiete,
Præterquam siquid proprio dat corpore
motus.
Omnis enim longe nostris ab sensibus
infra
Primorum natura jacet; quapropter, ubi
ipsa
Cernere jam nequeas, motus quoque sur-
pere debent;
Præsertim cum, quæ possimus cernere,
celent
Sæpe tamen motus spatio diducta lo-
corum.
Nam sæpe in colli tondentes pabula læta
Lanigeræ reptant pecudes quo quamque
vocantes
Invitant herbæ gemmantes rore recenti,
Et satiati agni ludunt blandeque corus-
cant;

Omnia quæ nobis longe confusa videntur
Et velut in viridi candor consistere
colli."

[2] This more definite expression is
entirely a question of mathematics.
It is interesting to note how Le
Sage, in his 'Lucrèce Neutonien'
(Berlin Acad., 1782), "argues that
if Epicurus had had but a part of
the geometrical knowledge of his
contemporary Euclid, and conceptions of cosmography the same as
those of many then living, he might
have discovered the laws of universal gravity, and not only the
laws, but, what was the despair of
Newton, its mechanical cause"
(Munro, 'Lucretius,' vol. ii. p. 135).
Lionardo da Vinci (1452-1519) says :

the name of the kinetic [1] theory or view of nature. It has frequently been placed in opposition to the atomic theory, and the history of the natural philosophy of the earlier ages, down to Newton, has in recent years been written from this point of view.[2] If everything is motion, there must still be something that moves, and the question arises, What is it that moves? The system of Epicurus, and the great poem in which it has found a classical expression, are really more occupied with describing the final elements of matter—the so-called nature of things—than with studying the different modes of their motion. In the atomic theory, in the conception of an infinite number of moving particles, the kinetic tendency of thought repeatedly found both in ancient

"There is no certainty in science where some mathematics are not applicable" (quoted by Lasswitz, 'Geschichte der Atomistik,' 1890, vol. ii. p. 11); and Leibniz, in a letter to Foucher dated 1693, condemns his earlier tract entitled 'Hypothesis Physica' as a "juvenile attempt of one who had not yet fathomed mathematics" (Gerhardt's edition of Leibniz's 'Philosophische Schriften,' vol. i. p. 415).

[1] The word "kinetic" seems to have been introduced into scientific literature by Ampère, who uses the term "cinématique" to denote that portion of mechanics where "les mouvements sont considérés en euxmêmes, tels que nous les observons dans les corps qui nous environnent, et spécialement dans les appareils appelés machines" ('Essai sur la Philosophie des Sciences,' 1834). In English text-books the term kinematics, following Thomson and Tait ('Natural Philosophy,' Preface), is used to denote what French writers call "cinématique

pure," formerly called "phoronomie," the doctrine of the purely geometrical properties of motion, without reference to the cause of motion ; the consideration of the latter being the special study of "kinetics," which, together with "statics," is comprised in the term "dynamics." The acceptance of the word "kinetic" to denote the view that motion is at the bottom of all natural processes dates probably from the writings of Thomson (Lord Kelvin), Tait, and Clerk Maxwell, who, under the influence of Newton and the great French school of Lagrange, Ampère, Poinsot, Poncelet, and others, have reformed English, and subsequent'y also German, thought and nomenclature in these subjects.

[2] I refer to the highly interesting and important work of Professor Kurd Lasswitz, 'Geschichte der Atomistik vom Mittelalter bis Newton,' 2 vols., Hamburg and Leipzig, 1890.

and modern times a convenient resting-place; but the repose which it afforded has never been long enjoyed; every new attempt to attach permanent, ultimate, or intrinsic properties to matter, or to its particles, has provoked the desire to explain these properties by going still farther back, and to see in them, through the dissecting microscope of the mind's eye, a still more hidden motion. Two of the most suggestive ideas by which physical science has benefited in the nineteenth century are the successful explanation of the dead pressure of gases by a rapid translational, and of the rigidity of solid bodies by a rapid rotational, motion of matter. The second of these suggestions is far from being exhausted in its capabilities; the working out of the ultimate problems which it suggests will be one of the principal tasks of the coming age.

2.
Descartes'
develop-
ment of
the kinetic
view.

The kinetic view of nature, however useful and suggestive it may have shown itself to be in recent times, did not yield any fruits of real knowledge either in the hands of the ancients or even in those of the first great philosopher of modern times, in those of Descartes. Just like attraction and atomism, the kinetic theory had to be worked out by the instruments of measurement and calculation, by the exact method, before it led to any actual results. The kinetic view of nature was made scientifically possible when Newton, in the First Book of the 'Principia,' laid down for all time the laws of motion. And yet we can hardly say that Newton himself developed this promising vein of exploration; for, even while opening out an endless vista of research, he also, in the enunciation of the so-called law of gravitation, afforded only one of those convenient resting-places, those preliminary or provisional bases of thought, from which definite problems could be attacked and solved. His immediate influence lay, therefore, rather in discountenancing the attempts towards a kinetic view of nature, which belonged to the school of Descartes, and found an eminent exponent in Huygens as well as in others of his contemporaries and rivals;[1] in fact, he launched into existence what I have termed the astronomical view of nature, under the sway of which the promising beginnings of the kinetic view were for a long period almost forgotten, but which has the merit of having built up the most perfect of all physical sciences, namely, physical astronomy.

3. Huygens and Newton.

The sporadic beginnings of a genuine kinetic view of natural phenomena, after having been cultivated with more or less success by Huygens and Euler,[2] and early

4. Revival of the kinetic view in the nineteenth century.

[1] Among these, of whom Lasswitz gives an exhaustive account, must be mentioned specially Robert Hooke (1635-1703). "In the history of the corpuscular theory Hooke represents quite an original idea, which would have been of the most far-reaching importance if Hooke himself had got beyond a mere sketch to an exhaustive theory, or if his conceptions had, through Huygens' principles of dynamics, been domiciled in science. The deviation from kinetic theories caused by Newton's discoveries brushed away, with much useless hypothetical rubbish, likewise Hooke's more valuable and legitimate suggestions. The doctrine owing to which we place Hooke between Borelli and Huygens is his vibratory theory of matter. It is given in various writings, but most clearly in his Lectures ' De Potentia Restitutiva, or of Spring explaining the Power of Springing Bodies,' London, 1678 " (op. cit., vol. ii. p. 329 sq.)

[2] Leonhard Euler (1707-83), one of the greatest analytical talents of all times, whose writings contain the beginnings of a very large portion of subsequent mathematical work in pure and applied science, was in physics a great opponent of Newton's philosophy as it was then generally expounded on the continent of Europe. There it was identified in mechanics with the theory of action at a distance, and, in optics, with the corpuscular theory of light. To both Euler opposed his ether theory, of which he gave a popular account in his celebrated ' Lettres à une princesse d'Allemagne [Princess of Anhalt - Dessau] sur quelques sujets de physique et de philosophie' (Petersburg, 1768-72, 3 parts). He had given a scientific exposi-

Young and
Fresnel. in the nineteenth century by Rumford and Young, were united into a consistent physical theory by Augustin Fresnel, who has been termed the Newton of optics, and who consistently, and all but completely, worked out one great example of this kind of reasoning. He has the glory of having not only established the undulatory theory of light on a firm foundation, but still more of having impressed natural philosophers with the importance of studying the laws of regular vibratory motion and the phenomena of periodicity in the most general manner. His work was carried through, as was that of Newton, by a combination of observation, measurement, and calculation; of experimental skill with mathematical ability.

tion of the same twenty-five years before in his Berlin memoir, "Sur la lumière et les couleurs" (1745). Euler was as much opposed to Descartes' and Leibniz's views as he was to those of Newton, and though he admits having forerunners, he hardly refers to the principal one, viz., Huygens, whose well-known and useful principle he absolutely ignores. In fact, in spite of his great name and reputation, his ideas on the ether as continuously filling space, and his attempts to explain the phenomena of light, heat, magnetism, and even gravitation by means of this continuum remained isolated, and had hardly any influence on physical science. His great friend and correspondent, Daniel Bernoulli, remained a firm believer in action at a distance, and thought Euler had put forward his hypotheses with too much assurance. It is, nevertheless, remarkable how closely the terms in which Euler, in his posthumous work 'Anleitung zur Naturlehre' (edited by the Petersburg Academy in the second volume of the "Opera posthuma . . . anno 1844 detecta," 1862), describes his ether as continuously filling empty space and existing in a strained (*gewaltsam*) condition, agree with quite modern ideas on the subject. Accordingly Euler's ether theory has in recent times been studied again by several writers abroad, of whom I will only mention E. Cherbuliez, 'Ueber einige physikalische Arbeiten Eulers' (Bern, 1872); F. Rosenberger, 'Die Geschichte der Physik' (vol. ii. 1884, p. 333 *sqq.*); C. Isenkrahe in 'Zeitschrift für Mathematik und Physik' (Hist. Lit. Abth., vol. xxvi.) and ('Abhandlungen zur Geschichte der Mathematik,' vi.; and E. Miething, 'L. Eulers Lehre vom Aether' (Berlin, 1894). The first-mentioned author tries to answer the question why Euler's ideas remained so isolated. He says (p. 49): "If we combine the results of Huygens' and Euler's investigations, we see that in the 'fifties of the eighteenth century the undulatory system formed a largely developed scientific doctrine. . . .

There is not, indeed, to be found in Fresnel's work any central and simple formula—like the gravitation formula of Newton—out of which everything else flows with mathematical necessity. His work lay rather in combining a number of fruitful suggestions thrown out by contemporary or earlier writers into a consistent whole, correcting and enlarging them as was found necessary, and following them out into their logical consequences. Thus he was able to reveal in a special branch of physical science new phenomena which had remained unobserved or unexplained till that time. In order to understand how the kinetic view of nature has become firmly established in the minds of physicists it will be useful to enum-

In a certain sense Euler carried further the work of Huygens, . . . but as he neglected the useful idea of a wave-surface and anxiously avoided Huygens' principle, he made the theory which he wished to defend unfruitful. . . . We think that Euler did more harm than good to the progress of that theory. . . . Euler's theory of light had no great number of followers." In England Euler's theory was known and generally condemned. Priestley, in his 'History of Optics' (1772), refers to it at some length. In the well-known attacks in which Lord Brougham treated so unfairly and superficially the discoveries of Dr Young, it is suggested that the latter borrowed his ideas from Euler, whose natural philosophy is held in little esteem. The fact is that Young really went back to Huygens and Newton, and that he well knew that his own opinion, as stated in the first Bakerian Lecture (1802), "was precisely the theory of Hooke and Huygens, with the adoption of some suggestions made by Newton himself as not in themselves improbable" (Young's 'Miscellaneous Works,' ed. Peacock, vol. i. p. 200). In spite of the great admiration which Young had for Euler as a mathematician, he admits that Euler "added no argumentative evidence whatever to the [undulatory] theory, but has done a real injury to the cause which he endeavoured to support" ('Lectures on Natural Philosophy,' ed. Kelland, vol. i. p. 380). A more recent and well-informed writer on this subject, M. Verdet, says of Euler: "Bien qu'il a donné de la plupart des phénomènes connus de son temps les explications les plus inexactes, il ne mérite pas moins de conserver dans l'histoire de l'optique une place éminente pour avoir dit d'une manière expresse que les ondulations lumineuses sont périodiques comme les vibrations sonores, et que la cause des différences de coloration est au fond la même, que la cause des différences de tonalité" ('Œuvres de Fresnel,' vol. i. p. xix).

erate shortly the different suggestions which Fresnel
assimilated and worked up into his celebrated physical
theory of light.

That light consisted in the motion of something was
in the beginning of the nineteenth century a generally
accepted notion among natural philosophers. It had
been so ever since Olaus Römer [1] in the seventeenth
century, from the observation of the hitherto unexplained
delay in the disappearance of Jupiter's satellites during
eclipses, had inferred, and Bradley [2] had later on con-

[1] The moons of Jupiter, of which two are visible to the naked eye, were clearly seen and described as one of the first discoveries with his telescope by Galileo in 1610, and published in his 'Sidereus Nuncius.' Owing to their continual and rapid change of position and their frequent eclipses, they were very soon considered to furnish a valuable means of determining the longitude at sea, and were repeatedly and very minutely observed. In the course of such observations by Cassini and Römer at Paris, the latter found, in 1675, that the period of occultation of the nearest moon varied. This variation he traced to the fact that the earth was moving towards or away from Jupiter. If light takes time to travel, the visibility of the phenomenon is necessarily thus anticipated or postponed. This was the first occasion on which data for the calculation of the velocity of light were forthcoming; the terrestrial experiments of Galileo having been inconclusive. Römer's explanation and calculation were accepted by most astronomers; they were confirmed by

[2] the phenomenon of aberration, discovered by Bradley. It is analogous to the observation we can make in a moving railway train if it rains; the drops at the window, though they be descending perpendicularly, yet appearing in a slanting direction, in proportion to the velocity of the train. Both phenomena involve the motion of light itself and the motion of the observer, who receives the luminous impression and locates it in space and time. The principle involved in Römer's discovery was later enunciated by Doppler, who maintained that the very short periods which belong to different colours of the spectrum, according to the undulatory theory, must suffer (like the longer periods in Römer's occultations) by the motion of the luminous object or of the observer in the line of sight. Although this theory was admitted in acoustics, it took some time before it was admitted in optics. Bolzano, Professor of Religious Philosophy and a colleague of Doppler at Prague, foretold as early as 1842 the great utility of the principle, and wrote: "I foresee with confidence that use will be hereafter made of it in order to solve—by observing the changes which the colour of stars undergoes in time —the questions whether and in which direction and with what

firmed, that light takes time to travel from one point in space to another. Wherever time is involved in a phenomenon, motion of something is suggested, and this something, as well as the nature of its motion, become subjects of speculation. At the beginning of the nineteenth century two distinct theories existed regarding these matters. Both had succeeded in explaining and calculating satisfactorily a large number of the phenomena of light as exhibited by mirrors and lenses, as well as in optical instruments and crystals. One of these theories, the so-called emission, emanation, or corpuscular theory of light, held that luminous bodies send out minute particles which travel in straight lines, and, impinging upon the eye, create the sensation of light. The rival hypothesis, the undulatory or vibratory theory, held light to consist in the periodic wave-motion of a substance called ether, which was supposed to exist everywhere, filling all space and interpenetrating all ponderable matter. Both theories are kinetic or mechanical theories, and for their development require the analysis of certain modes of motion. Both had to formulate their respective notions as to the something that moved. Both could point to analogies in other domains of natural science. There existed at that time similar corpuscular explanations of the phenomena of heat, of electricity

5.
Undulatory and emission theories.

6.
Both theories kinetic.

velocity they move, how distant they are from us, and much else besides," a prediction which, since the invention of spectrum analysis and various controversies connected with the subject, has been brilliantly verified by the discoveries of Sir William Huggins (1868), Fox-Talbot, and others. That Doppler's principle is really none other than Römer's was remarked by P. G. Tait in 'Light' (2nd ed. p. 220). See also Rosenberger, 'Gesch. d. Physik,' vol. iii. p. 708 *sqq.*

and of magnetism. On the other side there was the highly developed theory of sound, which had succeeded in explaining and analysing the properties of sounding bodies by studying experimentally and mathematically the vibrations of sounding strings, membranes and plates, and also of the air in organ-pipes and other

7.
Undulatory
theory
prepared by
acoustics.

musical instruments. Acoustics, the branch of science which treats of these phenomena, was, next to physical astronomy, the furthest developed and best founded of the physical sciences. By following up the elementary and primitive experience, known already to the ancients, that sound is everywhere to be traced to the vibrations or the tremor of some body which has been struck or otherwise excited, a very complete theory, substantiated by many experiments, had been built up. Common-sense and everyday experience had originally suggested this line of inquiry and explanation.[1] No other physical science was so early in possession of the right road of inquiry. In astronomy and optics the suggestion of common-sense, which regards the earth as stationary and light as an emission travelling in straight lines, had indeed allowed a certain amount of definite knowledge, based upon measurement and cal-

---

[1] Acoustics is probably the only physical science where this has been the case; as is well remarked by Whewell in his ' History of the Inductive Sciences.' He there contrasts acoustics with astronomy and optics. He might have added dynamics, where Galileo's principle of inertia similarly reversed the dicta of common-sense. Whewell says (vol. ii. p. 237) of acoustics : "Instead of having to travel gradually towards a great discovery, like universal gravitation, or luminiferous undulations, we take our stand upon acknowledged truths, the production and propagation of sound by the motion of bodies and of air; and we connect these with other truths, the laws of motion, and the known properties of bodies, as for instance their elasticity. Instead of epochs of discovery, we have solutions of problems."

culation, to be accumulated.   A real physical theory, however, was impossible until the notions suggested by common - sense were completely reversed, and an ideal construction put in the place of a seemingly obvious theory.   This was done in astronomy at one stroke by Copernicus; in optics only gradually, tentatively, and hesitatingly.   The purely geometrical relations of straight lines, which light seemed to resemble; of pencils of rays, which were bent back or altered in their direction at the surface of plane or curved mirrors and of transparent bodies; seemed to flow quite easily and naturally when in the seventeenth century the simple law of refraction had been added to that of reflexion, known already to the ancients.   The sciences of catoptrics and dioptrics, with their application to the telescope and microscope, were thus so complete and useful that to many it must have seemed difficult and unnecessary to plunge into a new theory; [1] especially

[1] It has always been the aim of "geometrical optics" to free itself from every hypothesis on the physical nature of light, and to deduce properties of light from a few simple geometrical constructions. Precisely in the same way all geometrical and many physical properties of the stellar system can be deduced from the kinematical formula of attraction, without discussing the nature of gravitation. This desideratum —so far as optics is concerned— was before the mind of Sir W. R. Hamilton, when, during the years 1824-33, he discovered and elaborated the theory of the "characteristic function, by the help of which all optical problems, whether on the corpuscular or on the undulatory theory, are solved by one common process" (Tait, 'Light,' 2nd ed., p. 160). Owing to the difficulties which have more and more presented themselves in the fundamental conceptions of the wave-theory and the vibrating ether, of which we shall learn more in the sequel of this chapter, the desire to bring the phenomena of refraction under a purely geometrical formula, and to emancipate the optics of crystals from physical hypotheses, has become very pronounced. Huygens' geometrical construction of the ordinary and extraordinary rays in uniaxial crystals answered well. For biaxial crystals Fresnel had introduced the wave-surface, to which corresponds Hamilton's characteristic function. For didactic purposes, and for the practical applica-

as that theory failed for a long time to explain the apparently fundamental fact, viz., that light travels in straight lines, accompanied by well-marked shadows. The contrary view, according to which light is a tremor propagated like sound, was unable to explain the existence of clearly marked shadows. And so it came about that Newton, to whom both theories were quite familiar, and to whom we owe great discoveries telling severally in favour of each of these theories, in the end threw the weight of his authority into the scale of the corpuscular or emission theory. For many this was quite sufficient to suppress for a long time all claims which the tremor or wave theory put forward, the fact being forgotten or overlooked that Newton himself had pronounced the pure emission theory to be insufficient, and had modified and complicated it by

8. Newton's authority on the side of the emission theory,

tion to crystallography, it became a desideratum to reach the geometrical conception of the wave-surface by purely geometrical methods. This has been done in an admirable treatise entitled 'The Optical Indicatrix,' by Mr L. Fletcher. He has shown that the construction of the ray, a conception easily defined geometrically, gives an easier approach than the construction of the wave, which introduces physically doubtful definitions; and he demonstrates how "a simple generalisation, involving no reference either to the constitution of the luminiferous ether or to the nature of the physical change involved in the transmission of light," will lead to the ray surface (p. 18). For his purpose he starts from a surface of reference, which in singly refractive substance is a sphere, in uniaxial crystals a spheroid, and by inference in biaxial crystals an ellipsoid with three unequal axes. This beautiful construction was arrived at, as the author tells us, before the detailed history of Fresnel's theory had come to his notice. It is now known through Verdet, one of the editors of Fresnel's 'Works' (1868), that Fresnel arrived at his wave-surface by a purely geometrical generalisation of Huygens' construction, and that the conception of the ether was subsequently fixed so as to allow the wave-surface to be deduced therefrom (p. 24); surely an interesting case in the history of scientific thought. As to the insufficiency of purely geometrical optics for explaining the phenomena connected with optical instruments, see Czapski, 'Theorie der optischen Instrumente,' Breslau, 1893, p. 2.

suggesting that the rays of light were possessed of fits of easy transmission and reflexion, *i.e.*, of regular periodic changes which could be measured and numbered. To this amplification of the simple geometrical emission theory Newton was driven by his own immortal researches, which revealed the wonderful regularly arranged colours of thin plates known as Newton's rings. In reading, after the lapse of nearly two centuries, the reflections of Newton on the nature of light, reflections which he never gathered up into a compact and exhaustive treatise, as he did the theory of gravitation,[1] we recognise that he had clearly before his mind the two fundamental phenomena peculiar to light, namely, its property of travelling in straight lines, and its periodicity, as revealed by certain delicate experiments of his own. Which of the two theories should in the end prevail depended on the more intimate knowledge—to be gained by experiment and calculation—of the two kinds of motion involved; of rectilinear motion of particles under the influence of contending forces, and of the more complicated periodic motion peculiar to waves, tremors, or oscillations. The first kind of motion, being more easily studied and also more nearly related to other prevailing studies, received earlier attention; the second—especially so

9.
but also
suggests
the other
theory.

---

[1] It is now sufficiently known and recognised that Newton, both in the theory of gravitation and that of light, did not propose to do more than give a preliminary formulation which was applicable as a basis for experiment and calculation. His further speculations are contained mostly in the well-known 'Queries' to the 'Opticks,' which were extended in later editions, and among which, "to show that" he "did not take gravity for an essential property of bodies," he added one question concerning its cause, choosing to propose it by way of a question, because "he was not yet satisfied about it for want of experiments" (Advertisement to second edition, 1717).

far as the mathematical side was concerned — was studied later. The former theory has been furthered more by the ingenuity of physical observers, the latter more by mathematical reasoning applied to the invention of crucial experiments which pure observation would probably never have suggested. Since the time of Newton, whose name has been used in a one-sided way to discredit the vibratory theory, although, as already stated, his discoveries contributed equally to the formation of both views, the development of the corpuscular theory owes most to the experimental labours of Biot in France and Brewster in this country; whilst no doubt Laplace's great predilection for atomic and astronomical explanation of all natural phenomena gave it great support in the eyes of his many followers and admirers. The vibratory theory was first made the subject of detailed study by Huygens, Newton's contemporary; it was accepted on purely mathematical grounds by Euler; the lines of reasoning on which its ultimate success depended were elaborated by Lagrange's and d'Alembert's mathematical study of vibrations; but the first great step in advance, based upon experiment and calculation alike, was taken by Dr Young, who from 1793 onward studied the subject, and who in 1801 published his 'Principle of Interferences.' Young was led to his reflections on the phenomena of light by an inquiry into the nature of sound,[1] a province where

10.
Biot,
Brewster,
and Laplace
against the
undulatory
theory.

11.
Euler the
successor
of Huygens.

12.
Young.

[1] In his 'Reply to the Edinburgh Reviewers' (published as a pamphlet in 1804, see Works, ed. Peacock, vol. i. pp. 192-215), Young gives the following history of his speculations: "When I took a degree in physic at Göttingen, it was necessary, besides publishing a medical dissertation, to deliver a lecture upon some subject connected with medical studies, and I chose for this the Formation of the Human

the theory of vibrations had already achieved so much. He was thus more interested in the physical nature than in the geometrical properties of rays of light. He was impressed by the analogies which exist between many phenomena of sound and light, and acquainted with the writings of the Continental mathematicians, among whom Euler was conspicuous as favouring the undulatory or ether theory of Huygens. He noticed that in Newton's writings were to be found the germs of both theories, also that the arguments by which Newton convinced himself that a theory of undulations could not explain the rectilinear propagation of light, were untenable.[1] On reflecting in May 1801 on Newton's beautiful experiments,

Voice. . . . When I began the outline of an essay on the human voice, I found myself at a loss for a perfect conception of what sound was, and during the three years that I passed at Emmanuel College, Cambridge, I collected all the information relating to it that I could procure from books, and I made a variety of original experiments on sounds of all kinds, and on the motions of fluids in general. In the course of these inquiries I learned to my surprise how much further our neighbours on the Continent were advanced in the investigation of the motions of sounding bodies and of elastic fluids than any of our countrymen ; and in making some experiments on the production of sounds, I was so forcibly impressed with the resemblance of the phenomena that I saw to those of the colours of thin plates, with which I was already acquainted, that I began to suspect the existence of a closer analogy between them than I could before have easily believed " (p. 199). This led to his ' Outlines of Experiments and Inquiries respecting Sound and Light ' (ibid., p. 64).

[1] Works, vol. i. p. 200. "Newton's arguments from experiment appear to me to have been sufficiently obviated by what Lambert has advanced in the 'Memoirs of Berlin.' . . . The demonstration is attempted in the ' Principia ' : to me it appears to be defective. . . . The celebrated Laplace, in comparing the opinions respecting light, is contented to call the Newtonian doctrine a hypothesis, which, on account of the facility of its application to the phenomena, is extremely probable. If he had considered the undulatory system as demonstrably absurd, he would not have expressed himself in so undecided a manner. . . . Much as I venerate the name of Newton, I am not therefore obliged to believe that he was infallible. I see . . . with regret that he was liable to err, and that his authority has, perhaps, sometimes even retarded the progress of science," &c., &c.

he " discovered a law which appeared to account for a greater variety of interesting phenomena than any other optical principle that had yet been made known." [1] This principle he familiarly illustrated by the well-known observation that two series of waves of water entering a channel reinforce or destroy each other according as their elevations coincide or alternate in time. He maintained that similar effects take place whenever two portions of light are thus mixed, and this he called

13.
His " general law of the interference of light."

" the general law of the interference of light." He showed [2] " that this law agrees most accurately with the measures recorded in Newton's ' Opticks,' relative to the colours of transparent substances, and with a great diversity of other experiments never before explained." [3] In three papers Young entered " minutely into the consequences of the law of the interference of light." Especially in the case of the remarkable phenomena discovered by Grimaldi, where light seems to bend round the edge of screening surfaces, he showed how under certain conditions light added to light would create darkness, and, if removed, would leave light; and he

14.
Theory of the luminiferous ether.

boldly generalised the undulatory theory by maintaining that [4] " a luminiferous ether pervades the universe, rare and elastic in a high degree," that the sensation of

[1] Works, vol. i. p. 202.
[2] Ibid., p. 203.
[3] " This, I assert, is a most powerful argument in favour of the theory which I had before revived : there was nothing that could have led to it in any author with whom I am acquainted, except some imperfect hints in those inexhaustible but neglected mines of nascent inventions, the works of the great Dr Robert Hooke, which had never occurred to me at the time that I discovered the law " (ibid., p. 203).
[4] The sentences in quotation marks are the headings of the different paragraphs in the " Bakerian Lecture " of November 12, 1801. Works, vol. i. p. 140 sqq.

different colours depends on the different frequency of vibrations excited by light in the retina, and " that all material bodies have an attraction for the ethereal medium by means of which it is accumulated within their substance." In all his conclusions, while differing from Newton's doctrines, he sees the strongest proofs of the admirable accuracy of Newton's experiments, " but scarcely any remaining hope to explain the affections of light by a comparison with the motions of projectiles." [1] Although Young thus established " a theory of the nature of light which satisfactorily removes almost every difficulty that has hitherto attended the subject," [2] his view was only tardily accepted. Wollaston,[3] with the hesitancy which also characterised his adhesion to the atomic theory of Dalton, did not avowedly adopt Young's views, though he furnished some capital experimental support for the vibratory theory of light.[4]

Brougham, in the 'Edinburgh Review,' ridiculed Young's theories, and persuaded the public that they stood in contradiction with Newton's discoveries, on which they were really as much founded as those of the opposite school. Through such disfavour, arising largely from a want of skill in grasping the intricate mathematical problems which were involved, the doctrine of the interference of light, the mainstay of the undula-

15.
Brougham's attack on Young.

[1] Works, vol. i. p. 169.
[2] 'Lectures,' ed. Kelland, Preface, p. ix.
[3] " Whatever disposition Dr Wollaston may have felt to view this theory with favour, he was restrained from adopting its conclusions by the habitual caution of his character, or rather by the want of that bold and enterprising spirit of speculation which is more or less essential to those who make great revolutions in science " (Peacock, 'Life of Young,' p. 375).
[4] Ibid., p. 374.

tory theory was, like the atomic theory of Dalton, driven
out of the country.   Little was heard of it, or of Young's
great contribution, till it was taken up abroad, and in the
very place where the brilliant development by Laplace of
one side of Newton's suggestions had given plausibility
to that form of the projectile theory of light according to which its material particles were supposed subject to attractive forces when they arrived in the
neighbourhood of ponderable matter.   Young had
indeed shown that the introduction of such forces
could easily be dispensed with as a basis of many of
Laplace's calculations, and that the results could be
got without making use of molecular attraction.   He had
emancipated himself from a belief in the infallibility of
Laplace's methods.[1]   He was also one of the first to

[1] On the 20th December 1804,
Young presented to the Royal
Society his important "Memoir on
the Cohesion of the Fluids." It was
printed in the 'Transactions' in 1805.
In December 1805 Laplace read
before the Institute of France, and
subsequently published in a supplement to the 'Mécanique céleste,'
his celebrated theory of capillary
attraction. Young bases his investigation entirely on the existence
of a surface tension, an observable
and measurable property ; whereas
Laplace falls back upon the hypothesis of an attraction of the
smallest particles of matter, just
as he had employed the idea of
an attraction of matter on the
smallest particles of light to explain
atmospheric refraction according to
the projectile theory adopted by
him. In the sequel this attraction
is reduced to an action which is
insensible at sensible distances. In
a supplement to his memoir, which
appeared anonymously in the first
number of the 'Quarterly Review'
(1809), Young, evidently annoyed
that some of his results had been
reproduced without acknowledg-
ment (see Peacock, 'Life of Young,'
p. 205), reviewed the treatise of
Laplace "with a severity which,
though excessive, can hardly be
considered unprovoked or un-
merited" (ibid., p. 206). *Inter
alia* he says : " The point on which
M. Laplace seems to rest the most
material part of his claim to originality is the deduction of all the
phenomena of capillary action from
the simple consideration of molecular attraction. To us it does
not appear that the fundamental
principle from which he sets out
is at all a necessary consequence
of the established properties of
matter ; and we conceive that this
mode of stating the question is but
partially justified by the coincidence
of the results derived from it with

emancipate himself from the astronomical view of phenomena. In France the matter stood quite differently, and nothing better proves the genius of Augustin Fresnel than the fact that he ventured against the opposition of great authorities to go his own way, starting from the beginning and devising many ingenious appeals to nature herself—*i.e.*, to experiment—in order to establish a correct view. It is well known that his labours had to wait many years for their deserved appreciation.[1] It is, however, only just to remark that Arago, an admirer of Laplace and an intimate friend of Biot, the great supporter of the projectile theory of light, was the first to recognise the importance of Fresnel's work, and that it was largely owing to his co-operation and influence that the undulatory theory of light triumphed in the end. Fresnel's own labours began with the study of the same phenomena which had led Young to the discovery of "interference"—viz., the bands and coloured fringes observable round the shadows of small screening objects, or the images of small apertures through which rays of light are allowed to enter: the phenomena of diffraction or inflection of light. But whilst Young still explained these phenomena as arising from the interference of direct "portions" of light and such as were reflected at the edge of the screening obstacle, Fresnel showed that the principle of interference had a much wider application, that it was adequate to explain why a periodic wave-motion, such as was conceived by Huygens, only sent out rays of

16.
Augustin
Fresnel.

experiment, since he has not de-monstrated that a similar coinci-dence might not be obtained by proceeding on totally different grounds " (' Quarterly Review,' No. 1, p. 109).

[1] See the first volume of this work, p. 241 note[2].

light in the direction which was in a straight line from the origin or centre of light; that the lateral or secondary waves destroyed each other almost entirely by interference or overlapping; and that the so-called inflection, bending, or lateral spreading of light, was occasioned by an incomplete coincidence or overlapping of these lateral undulations. It appears that about the year 1815 Fresnel had, through a study of the phenomena of diffraction, arrived at a conviction, entertained by Young fifteen years earlier, that the projectile theory of light could not explain them. He had also, by a more rigorous and minute study of Young's principle of interference, explained the reason of the rectilinear propagation of light. Yet these results did not materially affect the adherents of the projectile theory, who had been during late years very active in studying another class of optical phenomena, those of polarisation—the power which light possesses of acquiring, either by refraction or reflexion, a difference not discernible merely by the eye. This difference consists in the fact that a ray of light very frequently—as Newton had already expressed it—possesses "sides," just as a flat strip or narrow tape has sides if compared with an ordinary thread or wire, which has no sides; or as a wire drawn through a specially shaped die acquires sides or edges. This property was later termed polarity,[1] a term which implies that the particles of light

17.
Difficulties presented by the polarisation of light.

---

[1] The word "polarity" was introduced by Malus in 1810. It is unfortunate, as it suggests the corpuscular nature of light. Newton's conception of "sidedness" ("laterality," formed by analogy on Lord Kelvin's term "chirality" to describe right- or left-handedness, see vol. i. p. 432) is a better description of the phenomenon. It is contained in the 26th query to the second edition of the 'Opticks' (1717). Huygens had long before, in his 'Traité de la Lumière' (written in 1678, published in 1690), after having given a correct rule for

have unequal properties in different directions; and the process of revealing it was termed polarisation. Huygens had discovered this property, which he found was given to rays of light if they passed through certain crystals, notably through Iceland spar, which has the capacity of dividing the rays so that objects seen through them appear double. He could not explain it on his hypothesis of undulations, though he had invented a geometrical construction of the double refraction which had led him to its discovery. Malus showed in 1808 that double refraction was not a necessary accompaniment of polarisation, but that ordinary reflexion was enough to give these sides to rays of light. Although the projectile theory gave no complete explanation of this property, still the supposition that this one- or many-sidedness was owing to certain geometrical shapes of the projected particles suggested that double refraction might be explained by the different attraction or repulsion which these particles suffered according to the aspect

determining the course of the ordinary and extraordinary rays in Iceland spar, described the phenomenon fully, admitting at the same time that he could not explain it. When Malus discovered that light might acquire this peculiar property by reflexion, Young wrote in a review ('Quarterly Review,' May 1810): "The discovery . . . appears to us to be by far the most important and interesting that has been made in France, concerning the properties of light, at least since the time of Huygens; and it is so much the more deserving of notice, as it greatly influences the general balance of evidence in the comparison of the undulatory and the projectile theories of the nature of light" (Works, vol. i. p. 247). And Malus himself, in writing to Young as Foreign Secretary of the Royal Society, by whom he had been awarded the Rumford Medal, says: "Je ne regarde pas la connaissance de ces phénomènes comme plus favorable au système de l'émission qu'à celui des ondulations. Ils démontrent également l'insuffisance des deux hypothèses; en effet comment expliquer dans l'une ou dans l'autre pourquoi un rayon polarisé peut traverser sous une certaine inclinaison un corps diaphane, en se dérobant totalement à la réflexion partielle qui a lieu à la surface de ces corps dans les cas ordinaires?" (quoted by Peacock, 'Life of Young,' p. 248 note).

which they presented when approaching ponderable or
attracting substances.   Nothing of this kind seemed
imaginable on the undulatory theory, which, reasoning
from the analogy of sound, considered light to consist
in a rapid to-and-fro motion of the ether in the direction of the rays of light. Sidedness or "laterality"
seemed inconceivable.   Rays of light possessing this
property would (as Fresnel and Arago showed in 1816)
eventually even lose their capability of interference, that
main property discovered by Young, the principal argument for the vibratory theory.   "Every day in that
remarkable period—when so many great observers were
endeavouring to outstrip each other in the career of
discovery—was making known modifications and phenomena of polarised light which no existing theory was
yet competent to explain. It was polarisation which
still continued to cast a dark cloud over the hopes and
fortunes of the undulating theory." [1]   Thus it was
natural that the representatives of the astronomical view
of nature, who, headed by Laplace, had given so many
real and some apparent explanations of complicated phenomena, and to whom the conceptions of the projectile
theory of light seemed more promising, should think it
time to attack the very stronghold of the vibratory theory,
namely, the phenomena of interference, exhibited mainly
in diffraction, and, by a minute experimental and mathematical analysis, show whether these phenomena could
not be brought within the pale of their fundamental conceptions.   For the discoveries of Young and Fresnel had
not shaken them.   Accordingly the Paris Academy of

[1] Peacock in 'Life of Young,' p. 383.

Sciences in 1817 issued for the competition on the grand
mathematical prize for 1819 the subject of Diffraction,
"persuaded that a deeper investigation of these phenomena,
which seemed opposed to their cherished doctrine, would
give occasion for new triumphs." [1]   In this they were
doomed to disappointment. At the request of Arago and
Ampère, Fresnel entered for this competition, and his
'Mémoire sur la Diffraction' was crowned the following
year. In it he viewed the subject from a much more
general point of view, examining the two rival systems—
that of emission and that of undulations—as to their
capacity for explaining the phenomena of diffraction.
The result seemed decisive in favour of the latter theory,
and the impression produced was all the greater because
Poisson,[2] one of the judges and a believer in the emission
theory, drew certain apparently very paradoxical conse-

18.
Fresnel's
Memoir on
Diffraction.

[1] Verdet in ' Œuvres de Fresnel,'
vol. i., Preface, p. xxxv., &c.

[2] The commission consisted of
Biot, Arago, Laplace, Gay-Lussac,
and Poisson. Arago drew up the
report, which is published in the
first volume of the ' Œuvres de
Fresnel,' No. 13. It closes with
the following note : " M. Poisson,
depuis le rapport de la commission,
ayant fait remarquer à M. Fresnel
que l'intégrale qui représente
l'intensité de la lumière diffractie
peut aisément s'obtenir pour le
centre de l'ombre d'un écran ou
d'une ouverture circulaires, celui-ci
fit le calcul pour ce dernier cas, et
trouva que l'expression générale
d'intensité devenait alors semblable
à celle de la lumière réfléchie dans
le phénomène des anneaux colorés ;
que ses minima étaient tout à fait
nul et devaient présenter ainsi un
noir à peu près parfait dans une
lumière sensiblement homogène ; du
moins pour les trois premiers ordres,
où le défaut d'homogénéité de la
lumière rouge employée ne se faisait pas encore trop sentir : c'est
aussi ce que l'expérience a confirmé ;
en plaçant le foyer de la loupe du
micromètre aux distances calculées
on appercevait comme une tache
d'encre au centre de l'ouverture
circulaire. . . . On peut regarder
cette expérience comme une vérifi-
cation des formules de M. Fresnel,"
&c. ('Œuvres,' vol. i. p. 245).
See also the note which Fresnel
attached to his memoir (ibid., p.
365). The memoir was crowned in
1819, but not published till 1826.
An abstract of the first and a reprint of the second part had been
published in the 11th vol. of the
' Annales de Chimie et de Physique.'
Fresnel sent two copies to Young,
19th September 1819.

quences from Fresnel's calculations : Fresnel was invited
to prove by experiment these astonishing results, and he
found them actually confirmed. So far as the phenomena
of diffraction—erroneously termed inflection—are concerned, this work of Fresnel established the fact " that
the theory of undulations foretells the phenomena as
exactly as the theory of gravitation foretells the movements of the heavenly bodies." [1] It was, however,
quite different if we consider that other larger class of
phenomena [2] which revealed the fact that rays of light

[1] See Schwerd, 'Die Beugungs-
erscheinnugen aus den Fundamental-
gesetzen der Undulations - theorie
analytisch entwickelt' (Mannheim,
1835), Preface, p. x.

[2] The history of the final establishment of the wave theory of
light has been written by Whewell
in the second volume of the
'History of the Inductive Sciences.'
The main sources which existed at
that time were the memoirs of
Young and Fresnel, and the 'Life
of Dr Young' by Peacock. This
history has been written again with
ampler materials by M. Verdet as
an introduction to the edition of
the complete works of Fresnel, published in 1866. It is well to read
both accounts, as some points which
remain obscure in the earlier are
fully explained in the later. There
is no doubt that Young suggested
that the phenomena of "sidedness," which rays of light exhibit,
lead to the conception of a lateral
or transverse movement ; he also
hinted that in biaxial crystals the
shape of the wave might be that
of an almond or an amygdaloid
(article "Chromatics," reprinted in
Works, vol. i. pp. 317, 322), what we
now call an ellipsoid ; but M. Verdet is right in characterising Young's
suggestions as vague, and vindicat-

ing for Fresnel the full merit of
having defined transverse vibrations
and of having introduced the ellipsoid of elasticity as a geometrically
perfect means of finding by construction the paths of rays in biaxial
crystals. The method was quite
independent of the theoretical views
regarding light which were contained in the same memoir, the
consideration of which was referred
to a commission consisting of
Ampère, Arago, Fourier, and Poisson. Of these Ampère had suggested transverse vibrations as a
means of explaining the phenomena
of polarisation ('Œuvres de Fresnel,'
vol. i. p. 394). Arago, though a great
friend of Fresnel and a believer
in the wave theory, never to the
end of his life accepted the
hypothesis of transverse vibrations
(ibid., p. lv.) Poisson, a supporter
of Laplace's molecular theory, re-
tired from the commission ; and
Arago, who composed the Report
to the Academy, confined himself
to pronouncing on the experimental
portion, which fully confirmed the
general law of double refraction announced by the author ; refraining
from the expression of any opinion as
to the theoretical portion, it being
premature to do so (see 'Œuvres
de Fresnel,' vol. ii. p. 463). Im-

have sides, the phenomena of "laterality" (misleadingly called polarisation). The believers in the emission theory studied them with predilection, Biot at their head. Although to Young their explanations were unconvincing, their results were so perplexing that he wrote to Brewster in September 1815, "With respect to my own fundamental hypotheses respecting the nature of light, I become less and less fond of dwelling on them, as I learn more and more facts like those which Mr Malus discovered; because, although they may not be incompatible with these facts, they certainly give us no assistance in explaining them."[1]   When Young wrote this, Fresnel had not yet presented his first memoir on Diffraction to the Institute; his own labours on that matter were more than ten years old; the phenomena of polarisation had meantime absorbed the attention of opticians.   In the summer of 1816 Arago and Gay-Lussac paid a visit to

mediately after the reading of Arago's report, Laplace, "who had thought for a long time that his analysis had made the phenomena of double refraction depend on his emission theory," proclaimed the great importance of the memoir, and declared that he placed these researches above anything that had for a long time been communicated to the Academy (' Œuvres de Fresnel,' vol. i. p. lxxxvi., and vol. ii. p. 459). We are indebted to M. Verdet for having shown that the discovery of this law by Fresnel is independent of the theoretical considerations by which he tried synthetically to prove it. On this point he says: "En révélant la série de généralisations et de conjectures par lesquelles Fresnel est arrivé peu à peu à la découverte des lois générales de la double ré-

fraction, ils font disparaître une difficulté qui ne pouvait manquer de résulter de toute étude tant soit peu approfondie de ses écrits imprimés. . . . On a vu au contraire que cette loi s'est manifesté à Fresnel comme le résultat d'une généralisation toute semblable aux généralisations qui ont amené la plupart des grandes découvertes.   Lorsqu'il a voulu ensuite se rendre compte de la loi par une théorie mécanique, il n'est pas étonnant qu'il ait, peut-être à son insu, conduit cette théorie vers le but qu'il connaissait d'avance, et qu'il ait été déterminé, dans le choix des hypothèses auxiliaires moins par leur vraisemblance intrinsèque que par leur accord avec ce qu'il. était en droit de considérer comme la verité" (ibid., vol. ii. p. 327. Cf. vol. i. p. lxxxiv.)

[1] Works, vol. i. p. 361.

England and to Young, who learnt from them that, mainly owing to Fresnel's labours, his own researches had "attracted much more notice in Paris than in London, . . . leading to some very warm discussions among the members of the Institute on some public occasions."[1] It is likely that this visit, as well as the discovery of Arago that rays of light when polarised —*i.e.*, possessed of laterality—lose under certain conditions their power of interference, induced Young to resume seriously the consideration of the subject. In January 1817, long before Fresnel had made up his mind to adopt a similar conclusion (suggested to him by Ampère), Young announced in a letter to Arago that in the assumption of transverse vibrations, after the manner of the vibrations of a stretched string, lay the possibility of explaining polarisation or "laterality," and the non - interference of rays whose sides are perpendicular to each other. By introducing this conception of a lateral or transverse movement into physical optics —a conception shortly afterwards adopted by Fresnel— the data were provided for a complete mechanical or kinetic explanation of all phenomena of homogeneous rays of light—*i.e.*, of such rays as, on passing through refracting substances, are not divided into several colours.

Two great problems now presented themselves, one of which Fresnel attacked with great success. The other is hardly yet solved. Inasmuch as these two problems have largely occupied physicists and mathematicians all through the century, and guided their reasonings in other

[1] Peacock, 'Life of Young,' p. 389.

branches of research, it will be useful to define them more clearly.

Ever since Newton laid down the general laws of motion, it has been seen with increasing clearness to be the object of mathematical physics to describe the existing observable or supposed forms of motion in nature by having recourse to the fundamental laws of motion coupled with the smallest possible number of assumptions as to the ultimate constitution of matter or of the moving substance. As soon as any definite assumption was made, it became necessary to follow it into all possible consequences, and not to make any new assumptions so long as the capabilities of the old ones were unexhausted, or so long as it was not shown either that the new assumption was based upon observable facts, or did not involve latent contradictions with those already admitted. Newton had led the way by making one great assumption in addition to laying down the laws of motion. This was the property of gravitation. Heedless of Newton's warning that this assumption, though proved by experiment, did involve certain seeming absurdities which called for further examination, philosophers like Boscovich, and mathematicians like Laplace, busied themselves with drawing all the consequences of the assumption, and they saw the most hopeful way of further progress in an extension of it into the realm of molecular physics. Young was probably one of the first to see the futility or the mere semblance of truth in the astronomical view of nature. He approached both by experiment and mathematically the great class of phenomena of small, extremely rapid, periodic movements; and he applied his results for the purpose of gaining a new basis for the theory of light. His speculations were, however, not confined to this. He had started by studying sound and had shown its analogy with light; but when he ultimately ventured on the bold assumption of a lateral to-and-fro tremor, he showed where the nature of light differed from that of sound.

20. Mechanical difference between light and sound.

It was in this: that the tremor of sound was that of an elastic fluid such as air, or of any substance in which the movement is carried forward by alternate compression and expansion. But the phenomena of light seemed to require for their explanation two seemingly incompatible assumptions: first, a substance more subtle than air, incapable of impeding the motion of matter in it; and, secondly, a substance having vibrations resembling the tremors of what we term solid bodies, e.g., stretched strings. Young is one of the founders of the theory of elasticity.[1]

---

[1] The history of the theories of elasticity has been written by Isaac Todhunter and continued by Professor Karl Pearson. A perusal of the earlier portion of the work shows how imperfect were the ideas which existed at the time when Fresnel approached the problem in the interest of the wave theory of light. The greatest mathematicians, like Euler, had handled the subject, and had damaged their reputation, especially in this country, by serious errors or by conclusions which agreed ill with experience. Young was one of the earliest writers on elasticity in the nineteenth century; having given considerable attention to the subject in his Lectures on Natural Philosophy (delivered in 1802, published in 1807). He there introduces the modulus of elasticity, a term which, with some change of meaning, survives in modern treatises. His name, as well as that of Hooke ("Ut tensio sic vis"), appears accordingly at the portal of the science. Young, though Todhunter has a significant remark on his obscurity of style, stands out prominently, if compared with contemporary writers in this country, by his thorough knowledge of the labours of Continental mathematicians, among whom he assigns special merit to Coulomb. In general, Todhunter has little to say in praise of English science in this department during the earlier part of the century, and he considers the "perusal of English text-books on practical mechanics published in the first half of the century a dispiriting task," in consequence of a "want of clear thinking, of scientific accuracy, and of knowledge of the work ac-

He must have fully realised the difficulty of imagining a substance more subtle than air and yet endowed with the property of rigidity, known to us only in solid bodies. The elaboration of the theory of light pressed upon physicists and mathematicians a more careful study of the different states in which matter can exist. The different properties which this hypothetical substance called ether must possess had to be mathematically defined; and, further, it had to be shown whether it would be physically possible for a body, subject to the empirical laws of motion, to possess certain of the properties of what we term solids, and yet to be in other respects the very opposite of a solid. The solution of the first problem was a purely mathematical performance, in which many eminent mathematicians, such as Cauchy, Neumann, Green, M'Cullagh, and Stokes,[1] have been

21.
The properties of the ether.

complished abroad" (vol. i. p. 105). "It is difficult to picture the remarkable scientific ignorance of practical men in England in the first quarter of the century. One can only trust that there may be a closer union of practice and theory in our own day" (p. 106). This passage was probably written in the 'seventies.

According to Todhunter, the true theory of elasticity was founded in France between the years 1820 and 1830, by Navier, Poisson, and Cauchy on the one side ; by the experimental work of Savart on the other. It had been allied with theoretical acoustics since Euler's time. Chladni in Germany furthered that branch of the subject in three celebrated works : 'Theorie des Klanges' (1787), 'Akustik' (1802), 'Beiträge zur Akustik' (1817). Chladni influenced the

brothers Weber, whose 'Wellenlehre auf Experimente gegründet' appeared in 1825. In it wave-motion, such as the theories of sound and light had made specially interesting and important, was experimentally examined and illustrated. The theory of elasticity now received a new ally, viz., the elastic theory of light or of the ether. Though suggested by Fresnel, its real founder was Cauchy.

[1] The natural philosopher to whom we are most indebted for bringing clearness and definiteness into our ideas and our language in these very intricate subjects is Sir George Stokes. In two papers, published respectively in 1845 and 1849 (see 'Mathematical and Physical Papers,' vol. i. pp. 75-129, and vol. ii. pp. 8-13), he has done more than any other writer to fix for nearly half a century the conceptions and the

engaged. The solution of the latter problem involved experiment as well as calculation. The different states and properties of matter had to be studied from quite novel points of view: they had to be defined in terms of the different kinds of motion and of inertia, *i.e.*, resistance to motion or capacity for motion. The popular conceptions of solidity, rigidity, fluidity, expansion, pressure, weight, required to be translated into the language of ordinary dynamics, that it might appear to what

vocabulary of physical optics. He has, however, whilst working independently, been careful to point out to what extent his views agree with or are anticipated by the important writings of Cauchy and Poisson in France. Up to his time the ether was universally spoken of as a fluid. Stokes led up to the "elastic solid" and the "jelly" theory of the ether. "Undoubtedly," he says, "it does violence to the ideas that we should have been likely to form *a priori* of the nature of the ether to assert that it must be regarded as an elastic solid in treating of the vibrations of light. When, however, we consider . . . the difficulty of explaining these phenomena by any vibrations due to the condensation and rarefaction of an elastic fluid such as air, it seems reasonable to suspend our judgment and be content to learn from phenomena the existence of forces which we should not beforehand have expected. . . . The following illustration is advanced, not so much as explaining the real nature of the ether, as for the sake of offering a plausible mode of conceiving how the apparently opposite properties of solidity and fluidity which we must attribute to the ether may be reconciled. Suppose a small quantity of glue dissolved in a little water so as to form a stiff jelly. This jelly forms, in fact, an elastic solid: it may be constrained . . . and return to its original form when the constraining force is removed, by virtue of its elasticity ; but if we constrain it too far it will break. Suppose now the quantity of water to be 'increased' . . . till we have a pint or a quart of glue-water. The jelly will then become thinner. . . . At last it will become so far fluid as to mend itself again as soon as it is dislocated. Yet there seems hardly sufficient reason for supposing that at a certain stage of the dilution the tangential force whereby it resists constraint ceases all of a sudden. In order that the medium . . . should have to be treated as an elastic solid, it is only necessary that the amount of constraint should be very small. The medium would, however, be what we should call a fluid as regards the motion of solid bodies through it. . . . Conceive now a medium having similar properties, but incomparably rarer than air, and we have a medium such as we may conceive the ether to be, a fluid as regards the motion of the earth and planets through it, an elastic solid as regards the small vibrations which constitute light" ('Papers,' vol. ii. p. 11 *sqq.*)

extent these various properties could exist separately or were mutually dependent.[1]

In the domain of sound and light the early part of the century was thus, as we have seen, witness of a useful interpretation of these various modifications as merely different kinds of motion : both were considered to be vibrations, the frequency of which marked the position of a note or a tint in the musical or chromatic

[1] That is to say, the number of independent constants had to be fixed which would permit isotropic or anisotropic bodies (*i.e.*, bodies which are either equal in all directions, or unequal in the three directions) to be mathematically defined, and in consequence their behaviour studied, if subjected to strains and displacements. Over these definitions there arose the great controversies of those who believed in a small number of constants (one constant in isotropic and fifteen in anisotropic bodies against two and twenty-one respectively). A good account of these controversies and of their mathematical and physical significance will be found in the first volume of Todhunter's ' History of Elasticity,' by Professor Karl Pearson, p. 496 *sqq.* The former theory is termed the rari- (few) constant theory, the latter the multi- (many) constant theory. The rari-constant theory is based upon the assumption that a body consists of molecules, and that the action between two molecules . . . is in the line joining them. It is an outcome of the atomic and action - at - a - distance theory in vogue on the Continent, and is accordingly mainly represented by Naiver, Poisson, Cauchy, and others, notably Saint-Venant. The other school, mainly represented by mathematical physicists in this country, starts not from a mathematical formula (which,

after all, loses its precision as the active forces are reduced to the vague statement that they act sensibly only at insensible distances) but from physical data. It is an analogue to Young's theory of capillarity as against Laplace (see above, p. 20, note). "The somewhat unsatisfactory nature of the results of those investigations produced, especially in this country, a reaction in favour of the opposite method of treating bodies as if they were, so far at least as our experiments are concerned, truly continuous. This method, in the hands of Green, Stokes, and others, has led to results the value of which does not at all depend on what theory we adopt as to the ultimate constitution of bodies " (Clerk Maxwell, ' Scientific Papers,' vol. ii. p. 253). "After the French mathematicians had attempted, with more or less ingenuity, to construct a theory of elastic solids from the hypothesis that they consist of atoms in equilibrium under the action of their mutual forces, Stokes and others showed that all the results of this hypothesis, so far at least as they agreed with facts, might be deduced from the postulate that elastic bodies exist, and from the hypothesis that the smallest portions into which we can divide them are sensibly homogeneous " (id. ibid., p. 449).

scale, and the amplitude or height of the wave-motion of which decided its intensity. There was floating about the vague idea that heat also was to be interpreted as a mode of motion; still vaguer were the kinetic notions as to electricity and magnetism; whilst some early attempts to explain gravity, not as an inherent property of matter, but as a consequence of the motion of matter itself, which was possessed merely of inertia, had been half forgotten.

There is no doubt that the successful development of the undulatory theory of light induced many minds to dream of an ultimate kinetic explanation or interpretation of all natural phenomena, when in the course of the third quarter of the century this direction of thought received a great impetus through three independent branches of research of a purely theoretical kind. These have led to a very remarkable development of the kinetic view of nature; in fact it is mainly through them that this view has become possible not only in special departments, but on a universal scale. They have, each in its own way, led to a great extension of our experimental knowledge; one of them has likewise led to many practical applications. What most interests us here is the peculiar direction which they have given to a great volume of mathematical and physical thought of our day.

The first of these lines of research was connected with, and grew out of, the atomic hypothesis. It culminated in the kinetic theory of gases, in which the names of Joule, Clausius, and Clerk Maxwell are prominent. Of this I have treated already in the fifth chapter. It rests on a study of the average effect produced by a

22.
Other
kinetic
theories.

23.
Kinetic
theory of
gases.

swarm of bodies, subject to a transverse movement in
straight lines like projectiles, and continually encountering each other on their way.   The second line of research
in question is the study of bodies subject to rapid movement round an axis, but immersed in a medium which
is itself movable like water, but not in a rotary but
merely in a flowing motion.   The whole series of investigations which started by defining vortex or whirling
motion as distinct from transverse, flowing, or projectile
motion, and from vibratory to - and - fro motion, was
initiated by Helmholtz in 1857 in a purely mathematical paper, and then applied and greatly extended
by Sir William Thomson in the conception of the vortex
atom.   The third branch of research had its origin in
experimental investigations carried on for many years on
peculiar lines, and quite independently, by Faraday; it
was put into mathematical language by Clerk Maxwell
in his celebrated treatise on electricity and magnetism
which appeared in 1872.   It will be my object to show
in how far these different investigations have confirmed
and developed the kinetic view of natural phenomena.
But before doing this it will be well to realise what
specific problems presented themselves to theoretical
physicists when once the undulatory conception of light
had taken hold of their minds ; what peculiar difficulties
were involved; and into what distinct new lines of
reasoning they were conducted.

We saw above that when the gravitational explanation of a large class of phenomena had a century earlier
gradually gained ground, a great variety of researches
was suggested by it, and new lines of reasoning opened

24.
Vortex
motion.

25.
Faraday's
researches.

out, which in the course of the eighteenth century combined to establish what I termed the astronomical view
of nature. The undulatory theory of light, established
by Young and Fresnel during the first quarter of the
nineteenth century, was a breaking away from what
then seemed to many Continental philosophers a promising line of thought, a unifying principle in natural
philosophy. As long as light was thought to consist of
particles, however minute, which were projected from
luminous centres, the mechanical laws of impact, of attraction and repulsion, could be applied; and they went
a considerable way in apparently explaining the ordinary
phenomena of light, such as motion in straight lines, reflexion, and refraction. They failed indeed in the case
of diffraction or inflection, and still more in those phenomena which were misleadingly grouped under the term
polarisation. The new theory seemed specially adapted
to these more recently discovered phenomena, but it had
to be admitted that the explanation of reflexion and
refraction of light at the surface of polished, transparent,
or opaque bodies met with considerable difficulties. The
new theory had introduced the conception of an all-
pervading, apparently imponderable substance, the ether.
The reintroduction of this conception into physical
science was repugnant to many thinkers of the then
prevailing school,[1] and it became more so when it had—

26.
Problems
as to the
nature of
the ether.

---

[1] One of the crucial tests for
deciding between the corpuscular
and the wave theory of light was
the relative speed with which light
travels in air and in water, i.e., in
a refracting substance. Foucault,
in 1850, by a very ingenious method,
improved since by Mitchelson,
measured the speed of light in
various media. He proved that
light moves faster in air than in
water, whereas on the corpuscular
theory the speed of light in water
must be to its speed in air as 4 to 3
approximately. "This finally disposed of the corpuscular theory"

for the purpose of serving as the carrier of a definite kind of wave - motion—to be endowed with most mysterious, seemingly contradictory properties.[1] Nevertheless the development of this conception, the desire to define more minutely the properties of this fictitious substance of which we have no direct perception, came in the course of the century to guide more and more the work of experimentalists as well as theorists. We meet with objections in the beginning, when the conception was first introduced, such as were urged by many chemical philosophers when Dalton reintroduced and formulated

(Tait, 'Light,' p. 192). Sir G. G. Stokes tells us "that in a course of conversation with Sir David Brewster, who had just returned from France, where he witnessed the celebrated experiment by which Foucault had just proved experimentally that light travels faster in air than in water, he asked him what his objection was to the theory of undulations, and he found he was staggered by the idea *in limine* of filling space with some substance merely in order that ' that little twinkling star,' as he expressed himself, should be able to send his light to us" ('Burnett Lectures on Light,' p. 15).

[1] It is known that the two philosophers who in the middle of the century did more than any others to introduce the positive or exact spirit into general thinking and into philosophical literature, Auguste Comte and John Stuart Mill, were both opposed to the theory of an ether. Huxley, in speaking of Comte, exclaims: "What is to be thought of the contemporary of Young and of Fresnel who never misses an opportunity of casting scorn upon the hypothesis of an ether—the fundamental basis not only of the undulatory theory of light, but of so much else in modern physics, and whose contempt for the intellects of some of the strongest men of his generation was such that he puts forward the mere existence of night as a refutation of the undulatory theory?" (See 'Philosophie Positive,' vol. ii. p. 440, and Huxley, 'Lay Sermons,' p. 134.) The fourteenth chapter of Mill's 'System of Logic,' written originally in the beginning of the 'forties, but subsequently annotated with reference to some of Whewell's criticisms, contains a lengthy discussion of the hypothesis of an ether. Mill says (vol. ii. p. 21, seventh edition) : "What has most contributed to accredit the hypothesis of a physical medium for the conveyance of light is the certain fact that light travels, that its communication is not instantaneous but requires time, and that it is intercepted by intervening objects. There are analogies between its phenomena and those of the mechanical motion of a solid or fluid substance. But we are not entitled to assume that mechanical motion is the only power in nature capable of exhibiting these attributes."

the atomic view of matter. Similar uncertainties in
the definitions exist in both theories all through the
century, down to the most recent times. There are
those who still look upon both conceptions as merely
convenient symbolisms, as ideal instruments of thought
or scientific shorthand; and on the other side we have it
as emphatically stated, that the question, What is ether?
"is *the* question of the physical world at the present
time," "that it is not unanswerable," in fact, "that it
is not far from being answered," that "it is probably
a simpler question" than the other question, What is
matter? [1] The whole domain of physical science is even
divided into two portions, the physics of matter and the
physics of ether,[2] and the older, more empirical, and
common - sense divisions, treating separately of light,
electricity, and magnetism, are assembled in one great
doctrine, the "doctrine of the ether." It is, indeed,
somewhat astounding, if not disheartening, to hear at the
same time from an authority who has done more than
any other living philosopher to enlighten us in these

[1] Professor O. Lodge, in the
Preface to the first edition of
'Modern Views of Electricity,'
p. xi. "It is simpler," he continues, "partly because ether is
one, while matter is apparently
many; partly because the presence
of matter so modifies the ether that
no complete theory of the properties
of matter can possibly be given
without a preliminary and fairly
complete knowledge of the properties and constitution of undisturbed ether in free space. When
this has been attained, the resultant
and combined effect we call matter
may begin to be understood."

[2] See *inter alia* Professor Paul
Drude's 'Physik des Aethers'
(Stuttgart, 1894). In the Preface,
p. vi, he speaks of the philosophical
"desire of using the same fundamental conceptions for the physics
of the æther as for the physics of
matter, whereby it remains an open
question whether it is more service-
able to reduce the equations in the
physics of the æther to those expressions which can be got from
the observable phenomena in the
physics of matter (the equations
of dynamics), or whether the
opposite road can be chosen with
advantage."

matters, that at the present moment he knows as little as to the true nature of these agencies or substances as he did fifty years ago.[1]

Viewed from the position which we occupy in this history of thought—*i.e.*, in relation to the development of ideas—the conception of an ether has, however, like the atomic theory, had the most marked influence on scientific research and reasoning.   In digging for a hidden treasure, in trying to describe the atoms or the ether, many practically useful conceptions, applicable to tangible phenomena, have been discovered.   The atomic theory led at once to an enormous increase of our knowledge of different forms of matter, the knowledge of the elements, and of their innumerable possible compounds.   The conception of the ether has led similarly to an enormous extension of knowledge of the different possible forms of motion.   It is in this sense that we are greatly indebted to these abstract conceptions : both have guided our ideas in trying to understand and grasp the endless variety of phenomena.   Let us see how from the early years of the undulatory theory of light our knowledge regarding the different forms of motion has grown, how that theory has contributed to the kinetic view of nature.

---

[1] Lord Kelvin, in referring to fifty years of scientific labour, said (see the publication by James Maclehose & Sons of the proceedings at his jubilee in 1896, p. 70): "I know no more of electric and magnetic force, or of the relation between ether, electricity, and ponderable matter, or of chemical affinity, than I knew and tried to teach to my students of natural philosophy fifty years ago in my first session as professor. Something of sadness must come of failure ; but . . . what splendid compensation for philosophical failures we have had in the admirable discoveries by observation and experiment on the properties of matter, and in the exquisitely beneficent applications of science to the use of mankind with which these fifty years have so abounded."

It was recognised by Young, and still more clearly by Fresnel, that the medium which they supposed to be the carrier of light could not have the ordinary properties of either a solid, a liquid, or a gas. It offered apparently no resistance to the motion of the heavenly bodies, 'its waves were not like those which in air produced sound ; it propagated its waves at a speed much greater than any other velocity known at that time ; at the same time the wave-motion was not that of a body possessing the properties of a gas—*i.e.*, an elastic, compressible fluid : it was that of a body offering resistance to change of form rather than to change of bulk. It was evident that the different properties, which we see roughly assembled to constitute the three forms of ponderable matter with which we are practically acquainted, the solid, the liquid, and the gaseous, cannot be assembled in any similar manner in this imponderable substance, the ether. It was bound to have inertia—*i.e.*, mass—otherwise the laws of motion could not be employed in dealing with it, and mathematical thinking about it would be impossible. A more perfect description of the elementary movements which constituted light evidently required a minute experimental study, and a closer mathematical definition of the different properties of matter, known popularly but not very clearly under the terms compressibility, rigidity, mobility, elasticity, viscosity, &c., and of the inter-dependence of these clearly defined properties one on the other. Just about the time when the vibratory theory of light began to be seriously entertained by natural philosophers, a beginning had also been made in this study : the theory of elasticity had been founded in

27.
The theory
of elasticity.

France by Navier and Poisson. One of the greatest
analysts of the century, Augustin Cauchy, had likewise applied himself to it; and when Fresnel, in the
year 1826, brought out his great memoir on double
refraction in crystals, in which he was obliged to enter
more closely into the properties of the luminiferous ether
and its relation to ponderable matter, Cauchy was induced
to devote himself more specially to the mathematical
problems which presented themselves. Before his time
the theory of elasticity had been studied more as connected with questions of practical engineering, such as
the strength of materials, the stability of buildings, the
construction of machines, or with the properties of musical
and sounding bodies. A new interest was created by
Fresnel's researches.[1] The question arose, How are we
to describe the vibrations of an imponderable substance,
endowed with mass (density) and rigidity, and what conceptions can we form of the change of these vibrations
if there is present likewise ponderable matter? Evidently upon the clearness and correctness of these
notions depends the explanation of the phenomena observable when rays of light fall upon the surfaces of transparent or opaque bodies. We have to ask: In what
terms (viz., of different kinds of motion) can we define
and describe, and accordingly calculate the phenomena
of reflexion, refraction, scattering (*i.e.*, dispersion), and
absorption (*i.e.*, extinction) of light? A tolerably clear

---

[1] See Verdet in 'Œuvres de
Fresnel,' vol. i. p. lxxx : "Les
seuls écrits antérieurs à Fresnel
où l'on trouve des notions justes
sur les inégalités d'élasticité qui
peuvent exister dans les corps et
sur leur répartition régulière par
rapport à certains axes ou plans de
symétrie sont ceux du grand miné-
ralogiste allemand Samuel Christian
Weis " ('Mém. de l'Acad. de Berlin,'
1815).

definition of the kind of motion constituting a pencil of
homogeneous light in the free ether or in atmospheric
air had been given by Fresnel. Experimentally the
velocity of a wave-motion of this kind was known ; it
was subsequently ascertained that this speed was not
the same in air as in the free ether, the so-called
vacuum. It was also known that this speed in an
elastic medium, such as the ether was supposed to be,
depends upon the density and the rigidity of the medium.
But when rays of light—*i.e.*, the wave-motions of the
ether—arrive at the surface of liquid or solid bodies,
various changes are known to take place. These changes
had been to some extent described and brought into
measurable terms by experiment, and it had been shown
in a general way by Huygens, and more completely by
Fresnel, how these observed changes of reflexion, refraction, and dispersion could be translated into the language
of the vibratory theory. Complicated and yet very elegant
geometrical constructions, at which Fresnel arrived by an
intuitive or tentative process,[1] enabled the course of rays
inside transparent, doubly-refracting substances, such as
crystals, to be calculated ; a whole geometry of rays was
developed out of these representations ; now phenomena

---

[1] The equation of the wave-surface was not explicitly given by
Fresnel himself. M. Verdet says
(' Œuvres de Fresnel,' vol. i. p.
lxxv) : "Fresnel n'a pu lui-même
venir à bout de ces difficultés et n'a
su obtenir l'équation de la surface
de l'onde qu'en la supposant *a priori*
du quatrième degré, et calculant la
valeur de ses coefficients de manière
qu'ils satisfissent à certaines conditions faciles à déduire de la con-
sidération des ondes planes normales
aux trois plans de symétrie du
milieu. Ampère est le premier qui
ait effectué le calcul d'une manière
rigoureuse." However, "the construction yields the wave-surface in
such a way that its singularities
are not obvious, and were only remarked by Sir W. R. Hamilton
several years after Fresnel's death"
(Fletcher, 'The Optical Indicatrix,' p. 31).

of refraction, such as conical refraction, were mathematically foretold and experimentally verified.[1] The
real physical question, however, remained unanswered;
and it remains only partially answered up to the present
day.[2] How is it that the luminiferous ether, when existing inside ponderable matter, like air permeating a
grove of trees—as Young put it—is so changed that its
waves travel with variously altered speeds, that in
different directions the rays acquire different properties, are differently maintained or partially extinguished (absorbed)? It was natural to suppose that
the particles of ponderable matter must in some way
affect the ether, changing its density or its rigidity, and
that they themselves are affected by the movements
of the ether which fills their interstices. The question
can only be exhaustively answered by a complete know-

[1] The subsequent suggestion of
the phenomena of inner and outer
conical refraction, experimentally
verified by Humphrey Lloyd in
1833 (see his ' Miscellaneous Papers,'
No. 1, or Transactions, Royal Irish
Academy, vol. xvii.), was popularly
regarded as a complete proof of
the correctness of the wave-surface,
and of Fresnel's entire theory. But
as to the first point, Sir G. G.
Stokes showed (Brit. Assoc. Report
on Double Refraction, 1862, p.
270) that conical refraction "must
be a property of the wave-surface resulting from any reasonable
theory." And as the wave-surface
itself can be geometrically constructed without any reference to
the mechanical theory of the ether
(as Mr Fletcher has most exhaustively shown), the prediction of
conical refraction cannot be regarded as a proof of Fresnel's

theory. Todhunter-Pearson says :
" But for Cauchy's magnificent
molecular researches, it might have
been possible for Fresnel to completely sacrifice the infant theory
of elasticity to that flimsy superstition, the mechanical dogma, on
which he has endeavoured to base
his great discoveries in light.
Cauchy inspired Green, and Green
and his followers have done something, if not all, to reconcile Fresnel's results with the now fully
developed theory of elasticity, the
growth of which his dogma at one
time seriously threatened to check "
('Hist. of Elasticity,' vol. i. p.
167).

[2] In 1862 Sir G. G. Stokes " expressed his belief that the true
dynamical theory of double refraction had yet to be found " (Report,
p. 268).

ledge of the mechanism of the ether on the one side, of
ponderable matter on the other.   Two ways are open by
which a solution of this ultimate or fundamental problem

28.
The problem
of the ether
may be
treated
mathe-
matically,

can be solved.   The one is purely mathematical.   It
means the analysis of all the possible modes of motion of
a given mechanical system, and of the mutual influence
which two interconnected mechanical systems, that of the
ether and that of ponderable matter, exert on each other.
This is a perfectly definite though a very intricate problem.   It is a problem which can be compared with—
though it transcends in complexity—the analytical problem suggested by the gravitational view of physical
astronomy : to calculate mathematically the movements
of any number of bodies attracting each other according

29.
or experi-
mentally.

to Newton's formula.   The other way is the experimental method — to observe how under methodically
altered conditions rays of light are modified in colour
(wave-frequency), in direction, in intensity (amplitude of
wave-motion), in laterality (polarisation), and in other
ways ; and then to translate these conditions and alterations into the now fairly well-established language of
the vibratory theory ; gaining in this way indications as
to the changes which the wave-motion is capable of, and
inferring from these possible changes the original constitution (usually called the constants) of the primary
substances—the ether and the ponderable matter which
come into interaction.

30.
Necessity of
combining
the two
methods.

It may in general be stated that neither of these two
methods has for any length of time been pursued alone,
but that progress has nearly always depended upon an
alternating employment or a combination of both.   On

the one side we have a great volume of purely analytical reasoning begun by Cauchy in France, and pursued under varying assumptions by Green and MacCullagh in England, by F. Neumann and others in Germany. On the other side we have the purely experimental work beginning with Wollaston and Brewster in England, the refined methods for measuring the speed of light invented by Fizeau and Foucault, the beautiful contrivances for experimental research and verification of Jamin and many others. Out of so many fruitful conceptions which have resulted in an enormous accumulation of new knowledge of actual .phenomena of light and wave-motion —the real and sole end and aim of all theory—I will for the purpose of illustration single out one which in the middle of the century opened out an entirely new field of inquiry, forming almost a new science by itself. I refer to spectrum analysis.

31.
Spectrum
analysis.

The phenomena of dispersion (rainbow scattering) and absorption (partial or complete extinction) of light were among the earliest known, and had been among the longest studied, properties of bodies. Being, besides, connected with the physiological, subjective, and artistic effects of light, they have always commanded special interest.   And yet, so far as either the emission or the undulatory theory is concerned, they have always presented special difficulties.   When the wave theory was first propounded, it was generally understood on the analogy of the phenomenon of sound that difference of colour depends upon difference of frequency, or where the velocity of propagation (as *in vacuo* or in atmospheric air) is the same, on the length of the waves.   The difficulty arose of explaining how in refracting substances, be they fluid, amorphous (singly refracting), or crystalline (including doubly refracting), these different rays, with different wave-lengths, come to travel with different velocities, and hence take different courses; how, further, some of these rays come to be extinguished or reflected (or both) in varying degrees.

Now, although the complete answer to this general question has not yet been given, a principle has been recognised which gives us a clue to the possible explanation of a large class of phenomena, and which is thus of remarkable fruitfulness. It was first laid down by Euler,[1] a pure mathematician, whose physical reasoning was frequently suggestive but never particularly clear and definite; it was probably first applied to optical phenomena by Sir George Stokes;[2] and it was later on used by him

[1] In the last section of his treatise on light and colours ('Berlin Memoirs,' 1745; published in Latin, 1746), Euler treats of luminous, reflecting, refracting, and opaque bodies, and he there mentions the analogy which exists with musical resonance. "The smallest particles [of opaque bodies] are similar to stretched strings, which are, as it were, specially receptive for certain vibrations, which they can assume without being struck, if only they are affected by the undulatory movement of the air. "In his expositions upon light and colours, Euler always starts with the analogy of sound and light; he follows it with absolute consistency" (Cherbuliez, 'Euler's physicalische Arbeiten,' p. 44). This analogy was exactly what was absent in the investigations of Brewster, who remained to the end an adherent of the

projectile theory. Balfour Stewart came nearest to the true explanation in his memoir of 1858 ('Trans. of the Royal Society of Edinburgh,' 1861); but this referred to radiant heat and to Prévost's theory of exchanges. It contains the words: "The absorption of a plate equals its radiation, and that for every description of heat" (p. 13). Had this statement been distinctly applied to luminous rays, spectrum analysis would have been his discovery, although his theoretical proof might be regarded as insufficient (see Scheiner's treatise on Astronomical Spectroscopy, transl. by Frost, 1894, p. 112; also Rosenberger's 'Geschichte der Physik,' vol. iii., 1890, p. 482 sq.)

[2] See the references given on p. 277 of the first volume of this history.

in giving a mechanical explanation of the dark and bright lines of the spectrum, upon which Kirchhoff and Bunsen founded spectrum analysis about the year 1860.

32.
The clue
furnished
by the
phenomena
on which it
depends.

Wollaston[1] had in 1802, on examining the solar spectrum (the succession of rainbow colours expanded on a white screen placed behind a prism of white glass through which a narrow beam of sunlight is made to pass), noticed that with a sufficient enlargement black lines in great number could be detected. Fraunhofer,[2] in Munich, made a special study of them, named them by letters of the alphabet, and compared the solar spectrum with the spectra of artificial terrestrial sources where light is created by combustion or incandescence. He found that these spectra differed, the peculiar colour exhibited by various flames being defined in the spectra by special bright lines of different colours. Thus notably the two dark lines called by him D in the solar spectrum were replaced in the spectrum of a flame in which a volatile salt of sodium was present, by two bright lines : Brewster found the same coincidence of others of Fraunhofer's lines with the bright lines of a flame in which nitre was volatilised. Very similar and very accurate observations of A. Miller as to the identity of the dark lines D in the solar spectrum with the two bright lines of the sodium flame were explained by Sir G. Stokes about the year 1850 by the following theoretical reasoning : The sodium

[1] "A method of examining refractive and dispersive powers by prismatic reflection" ('Trans. of the Royal Society,' 1802).

[2] Fraunhofer, whose epitaph, "approximavit sidera," describes beautifully his life-work, was led to the discovery of the lines named after him in his investigations of the "refractive and dispersive powers of various kinds of glass" for the purpose of improving the achromatic telescope ('Denkschriften der Münchener Akademie,' vol. i., 1814-15).

flame which emits the two bright lines in its own spectrum destroys them (replacing them by two dark lines) in the spectrum of a ray of light which passes through the sodium flame.[1] Foucault had in 1849 already shown the direct reversal of the sodium line in the spectrum of the electric arc. These earlier anticipations remained partly unnoticed, partly unknown, or were looked upon as isolated cases, and it was reserved for Gustav Kirchhoff to put this remarkable property of emission and absorption of special colours by coloured flames into practical language, and express it in a general way. He wrote in 1859 :[2] "I conclude that coloured flames in the spectra of which bright lines present themselves, so weaken rays of the colour of these lines, when such rays pass through them, that in place of the bright lines, dark ones appear as soon as there is brought behind the flame a source of light of sufficient intensity, in which these lines are otherwise wanting." And when he concluded further that the dark lines of the solar spectrum which are not evoked by the atmosphere of the earth, exist in consequence of the presence in the sun's atmosphere of those substances which in the spectrum of a flame produce bright lines at the same place, " he at once gave

34.
Gustav
Kirchhoff.

---

[1] From this he inferred that the presence of sodium vapour in the atmosphere of the sun would explain by absorption the two dark lines in the solar spectrum. Lord Kelvin reports that in consequence of this observation of Stokes he regularly taught his Glasgow students that sodium must be in the sun's atmosphere. See the reprint of the correspondence on this subject in the ' Gesammelte Abhandlungen ' of Kirchhoff, 1882, p. 639, where it will also be seen that Sir W. Crookes claimed a similar anticipation for Miller in 1846. See also Sir W. Thomson's ninth Baltimore Lecture.

[2] See the translations of Foucault's and Kirchhoff's memoirs sent by Sir G. Stokes to the ' Philosophical Magazine ' of March 1860, p. 194 *sqq.*

birth to two great applications of his principle—the
search, through the study of the spectra of distant stellar
sources of light, after the ingredients which are present
in those distant luminaries, and the search, through the
study of the flames of terrestrial substances, for new
spectral lines announcing yet undiscovered elements." [1]
Whilst in these two independent directions an enormous
amount of new knowledge has been accumulated, the
mechanical explanation through which Sir G. Stokes
anticipated these phenomena, and the further applications
of this principle by him, have done much to confirm the
conviction, that in looking upon light as a vibratory mode
of motion, we are on the road towards an adequate
description of these phenomena.

[1] To this principle we owe the spectrum analysis of stellar atmospheres and the discovery of new chemical elements, of which no fewer than six have been identified by this method, beginning with cæsium and rubidium (found by Kirchhoff and Bunsen in the waters of some mineral springs). The suggestion of Doppler, mentioned above (p. 10, note), has only become fruitful through the invention of the spectroscope. Colour differences originating through the change of the frequency of vibrations depending on cosmical velocities in the line of sight, could not be discovered by the most sensitive eye. In the spectrum, however, shown by the spectroscope, "not only the colours of the bright lines have been altered, but their position in the spectrum relatively to a fixed point of reference as well. . . . The measurement of the displacement of spectral lines in consequence of the altered refrangibility of the rays is the only method yet known which possesses sufficient accuracy for determining the motions of objects in the line of sight. Thus far it has not been possible to produce in the laboratory velocities high enough to occasion a perceptible displacement of the lines" (Scheiner, loc. cit., p. 148). And as Doppler's principle in acoustics was proved directly by Buys Ballot through the whistle on moving railway trains, so it has been proved directly in optics by observing the displacement in the lines of the solar spectrum, when this is derived from the outer rays of the sun's disc, the light-giving parts moving in the line of sight towards or away from the observer in consequence of the rotation of the sun round its axis. "The resulting velocity of the surface of the sun is found to agree very closely with the results of direct observations of the revolution of the spots, thus practically furnishing a proof of the correctness of Doppler's principle" (ibid., p. 149).

We have seen above how the vibratory theory of light was arrived at—mainly in the hands of Young—through dwelling on the analogy of certain optical phenomena, notably those of interference, with the properties exhibited by sound. Among the latter none were more remarkable than those known popularly as consonance and resonance. Sir George Stokes, on the appearance of Kirchhoff's memoir on the relation of emission and absorption of certain rays of light, gave the mechanical explanation in the following words : [1] " In describing the result of a prismatic analysis of the voltaic arc formed between charcoal poles, M. Foucault ' found that the arc presents us with a medium which emits the rays D on its own account, and which at the same time absorbs them when they come from another quarter.' . . . The remarkable phenomena discovered by Foucault, and rediscovered and extended by Kirchhoff, that a body may be at the same time a source of light, giving out rays of a definite refrangibility, and an absorbing medium extinguishing rays of the same refrangibility which traverse it, seems readily to admit of a dynamical illustration borrowed from sound. We know that a stretched string which on being struck gives out a certain note, is capable of being thrown into the same state of vibration by aerial vibrations corresponding to the same note. Suppose now a portion of space to contain a great number of such stretched strings, forming thus the analogue of a ' medium.' It is evident that such a medium, on being agitated, would give out the note above mentioned, while on the other hand, if that note were sounded in air at a distance, the incident vibrations would

[1] 'Phil. Mag.,' March 1860, pp. 194, 196.

throw the strings into vibration, and consequently would themselves be gradually extinguished, since otherwise there would be a creation of *vis viva.* The optical application of this illustration is too obvious to need comment."

Already ten years before Kirchhoff gave to the researches into the spectrum their popular celebrity and practical importance, Stokes [1] had made an extensive ex-

---

[1] The memoir of Sir G. Stokes "on the change of the refrangibility of light," in the 'Philos. Transactions' (May 1852), forms a landmark in optical science, and whilst dealing with the less obvious —though very frequent and general —phenomena of fluorescence and phosphorescence, really indicated the line of reasoning which has become so fruitful and suggestive in his own hands and in those of other eminent natural philosophers. On page 549 of that memoir he wrote : "All believers in the undulatory theory of light are agreed in regarding the production of light in the first instance as due to vibratory movements among the molecules of the self-luminous body. . . . Nothing then seems more natural than to suppose that the incident vibrations of the luminiferous ether produce vibratory movements among the ultimate molecules of sensitive substances, and that the molecules in turn, swinging on their own account, produce vibrations in the luminiferous ether, and thus cause the sensation of light. The periodic times of these vibrations depend upon the periods in which the molecules are disposed to swing, not upon the periodic time of the incident vibrations." Referring, then, to the dynamical difficulties which attach to such a view, he proceeds to point out "that we have no right to regard the molecular vibrations as indefinitely small. The excursions of the atoms may be, and doubtless are, excessively small compared with the linear dimensions of a complex molecule. It is well known that chemical changes take place under the influence of light, especially the more refrangible rays, which would not otherwise happen. In such cases it is plain that the molecular disturbances must not be regarded as indefinitely small. But vibrations may very well take place which do not go to the length of complete disruption and yet which ought by no means to be regarded as indefinitely small. . . . Certainly we cannot affirm that in the disturbance communicated back again to the luminiferous ether none but periodic vibrations would be produced having the same period as the incident vibrations. Rather, it seems that a sort of irregular motion must be produced in the molecules, periodic only in the sense that the molecules retain the same mean state ; and that the disturbance which the molecules in turn communicate to the ether must be such as cannot be expressed by circular functions of a given period, namely, that of the incident vibrations." Stokes then refers to the probable internal vibration of the atoms in the compound molecules, as "it is chiefly among organic compounds . . . having a complicated structure that internal dispersion (fluorescence) is found."

amination into the question how vibrations of the luminiferous medium can be mechanically transferred to the compound molecules of a transparent body, and retransferred again to those of the ether itself — *i.e.*, the question of the absorption and emission of light. He showed that vibrations of a certain period, corresponding to a definite tint of colour, could eventually give rise to vibrations of altered period in the emitted light; that this period, however, must always be longer—*i.e.*, that the new colour must always be of a lower order in the

35.
Explana-
tion of
fluorescence.

scale of refrangibility. He was thus not only able to explain mechanically the peculiar luminosity which he termed fluorescence,[1] and which had been observed by Herschel and Brewster in certain minerals and solutions, and independently studied by E. Becquerel in France, but he also showed how, by means of such substances, rays of light which, owing to the frequency of their vibrations, transcend the perceptive powers of the human eye, can be made visible by giving rise to secondary waves of less frequency. The line of reason-

---

[1] The term fluorescence was coined by Sir G. Stokes by analogy with opalescence as involving no theoretical suggestion, in place of the earlier names of "internal dispersion" or "epipolised light" used by Brewster and Herschel. He, however, very soon favoured the term "degraded light," suggested by William Thomson (Lord Kelvin) (see the second memoir, 1853, p. 387). The latter was at that time occupied with his celebrated and not less epoch-making researches referring to the dissipation or degradation of energy, of which more in the next chapter. If we remember that fifty years ago the term radiation was not yet generally used to embrace the invisible chemical (ultra-violet) and caloric (infra-red) rays ; that photography, which more than any other process has familiarised us with chemical radiation, was a comparatively recent invention ; that the ideas of conservation, conversion, and degradation of energy were quite new ; that the general term energy had not even been invented, —we must indeed regard the words of Sir G. Stokes as containing a prophetic programme of the ideas and problems of the whole subsequent period down to quite recent times.

ing here employed gave the clue to all subsequent attempts to deal with the difficult problem of the interaction of the ether and ponderable matter; of the possible alteration of the density or the rigidity (called the elastic constants) of the ether when filling the interstices of transparent bodies ; of the mechanical differences which make some bodies transparent for some and opaque for other rays of light. Many possible modifications were theoretically foreseen, giving rise to remarkable unexpected phenomena, and these were frequently verified by subsequent experience. The whole theory of light entered upon a new phase as it became more and more evident that the study of the vibrations of the elastic medium was not sufficient, but that it must be supplemented by that of the interaction of two vibrating systems, the ether and the molecules of the ponderable substance, which give rise to the phenomena of partial reflexion, refraction, dispersion, and partial or complete absorption. This more complicated problem in the theory of elasticity had already presented itself in its simpler form in the theory of the pendulum. To the principle of optical consonance which had been employed to explain the phenomena of absorption of light was added, in order to explain the phenomena of dispersion, the principle of the free and forced vibrations of a vibrating system.[1]

[1] "If to the bob of a pendulum, executing horizontal vibrations, another pendulum be attached, executing vibrations of a slightly shorter period, the effect of the latter will be to increase the period of the former and *vice versâ*" (see A. S. Percival, 'Optics,' 1899, p. 181).

Anomalous dispersion such as was foreseen by Sellmeier and Lord Kelvin and discovered by Christiansen and Kundt depends on the change of wave frequency independent of the change of wave length in refracting media.

36.
View of the
ether as an
"elastic
solid."

The latest discussion of this form of the elastic-solid theory of light, which was gradually developed from independent beginnings in the three countries,[1] is to be

[1] In France and Germany, where even in the middle of the century the labours of English natural philosophers like Green, M'Cullagh, Stokes, were only very imperfectly known, the necessity was equally felt of studying the interaction of the ether and ponderable matter. In France the school of the eminent "elastician," Barré de St Venant, produced in M. Boussinesq the author of the earliest published attempt to solve the difficulties which the older methods of Cauchy had not overcome. In a lucid review of the state of physical optics, Saint Venant himself ('Ann. de chimie et de Physique," 4me série, vol. 25, 1872) hails with delight the researches of M. Boussinesq from 1865 onward, where the idea that the ether in the interstices of transparent bodies has different elastic constants is given up, and the participation of the ponderable matter in the vibrations is introduced in its place. "En effet," he says, "il est bien difficile de concevoir, d'une part, que l'éther puisse être agité au sein d'un corps dont la densité est probablement bien supérieure à la sienne, sans lui communiquer une fraction sensible de sa quantité de mouvement, et d'autre part, que les ondes ne soient pas bientôt éteintes par cette participation de la matière pondérable au mouvement s'il n'y a pas concordance entre les oscillations imprimées à chaque molécule et celles de l'éther qui l'environne." It was the problem of the continuity at the interface of reflecting and refracting substances and the problem of absorption which the older simple ether theories could not explain.

In Germany a similar impulse was given to the study of the interaction of elastic systems—as indeed to many problems of mathematical physics—by Franz Neumann, who was the centre of a numerous and influential school. He taught at Königsberg together with Richelot and Bessel. His lectures have been edited by his pupils. Prof. Karl Pearson, in his continuation of Todhunter's 'History of the Theory of Elasticity,' does ample justice to the labours of Neumann, who, "in his investigations on photo-elasticity and the elasticity of crystals, breaks almost untrodden ground, which both physicists and mathematicians have hardly yet exhausted" (loc. cit., vol. ii. 2, p. 183). "Neumann was among the first (1841, 'Abh. der Berliner Akademie') to attribute dispersion to the influence of the ponderable particles on the particles of the ether" (ibid., p. 31). The most important original contributions of Neumann's pupils are the researches of Sellmeier, who had been led by theoretical considerations in 1866 to expect certain anomalies in the phenomena of dispersion, such as were in 1870 actually discovered by Christiansen, and fully investigated by Kundt. Surface coloration was shown to be intimately connected with the absorptive powers in substances showing these anomalous phenomena. A full report on these and other theories, based upon what has been termed abroad the "Bessel-Sellmeier hypothesis" (see Ketteler, 'Theoretische Optik,' 1885), will be found in Prof. Glazebrook's "Report on Optical Theories," Brit. Assoc. Reports, 1885.

found in Lord Kelvin's celebrated Baltimore Lectures,[1]
where with unlimited resourcefulness the methods of
analogy, analysis, and experiment are employed to solve
or to define the intricate problems of physical optics.
Nor is it a merely fortuitous coincidence for the history
of thought that, whilst his mind must have been filled
with the many illustrations and mechanical devices, and
all the wealth of suggestions contained in the Baltimore
Lectures, Lord Kelvin should have delivered the opening
address to the mathematical section of the British Association, entitled, " Steps towards a Kinetic Theory of
Matter." Following—as did also Clerk Maxwell—on
the lines indicated by Stokes's earlier papers, he has done
much to change our fundamental conceptions as to the
properties of matter, and this in two distinct ways.
The first consisted in breaking down the rigid barriers
which popular definitions had set up between the different forms of aggregation—the solid, liquid, and gaseous
states of matter ; whilst the second tended to show how

[1] The Baltimore Lectures were delivered by Lord Kelvin (then Sir W. Thomson) after the meeting of the British Association at Montreal in the month of October 1884, at the Johns Hopkins University, before a company of physicists. The final edition of these important and highly suggestive conferences is in the press as the fourth volume of the collected mathematical and physical papers. The completion of this publication is eagerly ex-pected, as containing the most mature exposition of the elastic-solid theory of light, towards which the author has in the course of the last fifteen years made various valu-able additions. Notably in a paper dated 1888, published in the 'Phil-osophical Magazine,' he has, as it has been said, " extricated the elastic theory from the position of deadlock, according to which the ether must be both compressible and incompressible," by showing that the difficulty can be met, " pro-vided we either suppose the medium to extend all through boundless space, or give it a fixed containing vessel as its boundary." Prof. Glazebrook has further worked out the consequences of this suggestion. See vols. 26 and 27 of the 5th series of the 'Phil. Mag.,' also 'Nature,' vol. 40, 1889, p. 32, and Fletcher, the 'Optical Indicatrix,' p. 6, &c.

the supposed static properties of matter could be explained by different modes of motion, translational, periodic, or rotational. The mathematical and experimental investigations connected with the theory of radiations and vibrations had thus an influence[1] on our general views of the nature of physical processes which far exceeded the aims for which they were originally undertaken. That a substance so attenuated as the ether should have the properties of a solid ; that brittle substances like pitch should flow like liquids, if only sufficient time were given ; that towards very rapid impulses gases and liquids might behave as solids—all these observations resulted in a complete revolution of our scientific notions as well as of our vocabulary. The great turning-point, indeed, lay in the kinetic theory of gases, which about the middle of the century had introduced quite novel considerations by showing how the dead pressure of gases and vapours could be explained on the hypothesis of a very rapid but disorderly translational movement of the smallest particles in every possible direction. Pressure of gases having been explained by a very rapid motion of the minute particles of matter, heat was immediately conceived to be merely a "mode of motion." As no event did more to spread modern views in the theory of light, and to popularise modern scientific methods, than Kirchhoff's

[1] It has been asserted that the theory of elasticity received a great impulse when Fresnel was forced to make assumptions as to the mode of vibrations of the ether which were quite incompatible with the then accepted laws of the vibrations of an elastic medium. To this view of the origin of the modern theory of elasticity Prof. Karl Pearson takes exception, as Navier's memoir of 1827 was not suggested by optical investigations (Todhunter-Pearson, vol. ii. 2, p. 5).

and Bunsen's spectrum analysis, so in the closely related doctrine of heat, probably no publication did more to establish a general kinetic view of matter and of natural phenomena than Tyndall's celebrated treatise, 'Heat as a Mode of Motion.' In spite of the criticisms which have been levelled against this expression,[1] the book, which appeared in 1863, was to the popular mind a revelation ; it was translated into many foreign languages, ran through many editions, was recommended by thinkers of the first order, and the title coveted as " manifesting far and wide through the world one of the greatest discoveries of modern philosophy." [2]   It is the popular herald of the kinetic or mechanical view of nature.

38. Tyndall's 'Heat.'

The same great authority who has so generously referred to Tyndall's treatise—Lord Kelvin—had been inspired from quite a different quarter to suggest the most advanced conception, in this line of thought, of which the human mind has so far been capable : the

39. Lord Kelvin's vortex theory of matter.

[1] Notably by Prof. P. G. Tait ; see his volume on 'Heat,' p. 350, also his 'Recent Advances of Physical Science,' which contains as an appendix his lecture on " Force," delivered in Glasgow on the occasion of the meeting of the British Association. He says there : " Heat and kinetic energy in general are no more *modes of motion* than potential energy of every kind is a *mode of rest.*' " Heat is not the mere motions, but the energy of these motions." There is no doubt that the terms force and motion can be used in very different meanings, and that the early expounders of the mechanical theory of heat have not been always consistent in the use of words ; though their ideas, wherever they appeared in mathematical expressions, were definite enough. A good deal of vagueness has accordingly crept into popular textbooks and into philosophical treatises, and criticisms such as those of Prof. Tait have been useful in helping us towards clearer conceptions. We shall come across more of these instances in the next chapter when dealing with the gradual evolution of the conception of energy.

[2] See Lord Kelvin's abstract of lecture, " Elasticity viewed as possibly a Mode of Motion," 1881 ; 'Popular Lectures,' &c., vol. i. p. 142. "I have always admired it" (viz., Tyndall's title) ; " I have long coveted it for elasticity, and now, by kind permission of its inventor, I have borrowed it for this discourse."

vortex theory of matter. As this is one of the most remarkable instances of the fruitful reaction of abstract mathematical reasoning on the progress of physical research, it will be useful to consider for a moment by what gradual steps this novel idea was evolved or suggested. The immediate occasion which led to it was the publication, in 1858, by Helmholtz of a purely mathematical investigation of some peculiar forms of fluid motion.[1] About a hundred years before Helmholtz published his memoir, Euler had laid the foundation of theoretical hydrodynamics—*i.e.*, of the theory of the motion of fluids. In doing so, it was necessary to define

40.
Helmholtz's
investiga-
tions.

---

[1] Helmholtz's memoir, "Ueber Integrale der hydrodynamischen Gleichungen welche den Wirbelbewegungen entsprechen," appeared in the 55th volume of Crelle's 'Journal für die reine und angewandte Mathematik.' It was translated into English by Prof. Tait in the 'Philosophical Magazine' for 1867. Helmholtz's occupation with the subject had originated in the acoustical researches which he was carrying on at the time. These necessitated an analysis of the more complicated conditions which the motion of incompressible and elastic fluids presents in actual experience. The hydrodynamical equations had been solved under certain simplifying assumptions. Discontinuity of motion and internal friction had been left out of consideration. Helmholtz's researches led him to the study of these more complicated phenomena; and he successfully applied the mathematical methods which had proved useful in other branches of physical science for the solution of these problems. Notably in the paper on whirling motion, he came

upon very remarkable and unexpected results, which ten years later led in this country to the novel speculations of Lord Kelvin. It is interesting to note how at that time researches in England or Germany could for many years remain unnoticed in the other country. The result was that the same problems were frequently taken up in ignorance of the fact that they had been treated before. See Hicks's "Report on Hydrodynamics," 'Brit. Assoc. Reports,' 1881-82. Especially the labours of Stokes seem to have been little known to German writers, who usually started from the better-known French researches. Stokes had anticipated some of Helmholtz's results referring to whirling and discontinuous motion of fluids. About the middle of the century the periodical "Fortschritte der Physik" was started by the "Physikalische Gesellschaft" of Berlin. Helmholtz himself contributed several valuable reports on acoustical subjects. See the 'Wissenschaftliche Abhandlungen,' vol. i. *passim.*

mathematically what is meant by a fluid. The chief property of a fluid, as compared with a solid body, is the perfect mobility of its parts, the absence of rigidity. Thus there were two possible kinds of fluids—those which retained their bulk or volume, whilst offering no resistance to change of shape, and those which tried to expand, and could be compressed by means of external forces. These latter were called gases. In dealing with the former, incompressibility had to be defined mathematically, as also perfect mobility. These properties constitute what is called a perfect fluid. Such perfect fluids do not exist in nature; but the method of reasoning was to begin with an ideal, simple case, and approach the explanation of natural phenomena by a process of correction, introducing more and more complications. The phenomena of the flow of liquids, practically by far the most important, could be studied to a great extent by means of the simplest form of the hydrodynamical conception, and up to the middle of the century such problems, as well as those of the propagation of small displacements under the action of external forces,—notably the motion of waves,—formed the principal problems which were treated mathematically. The idea of the friction of fluids, also called viscosity, had been excluded in the definition of a fluid, inasmuch as friction opposed the notion of perfect mobility of the parts, which was the mathematical definition of a fluid. Now it is a matter of experience that in all liquids with which we are acquainted friction can produce rotational motion, such as whirls and eddies; it was also found that other forces, such as magnetic forces, are, under certain conditions, able to produce these rotations. It was therefore of interest to study the nature of rotational or whirling motion, if such could exist in a perfect liquid, and to see what would be likely to happen to these whirls. Though it might be difficult to understand how in a perfect liquid rotation of any portion could be produced, calculation might determine what would be the nature and fate of such whirls, if they did exist. The problem was a purely mathematical one. Can a rotational motion, a whirl, exist in a perfect fluid, as defined by the mathematical conception? If it can, what are the properties of such whirls, and what becomes of them? Helmholtz solved these questions in his now celebrated treatise, showing that whirls (called by English writers vortices) can exist, but only under certain conditions, such as can be experimentally represented by smoke-rings issuing from an orifice; that, if they existed in a perfect liquid, they would be indestructible and would possess a motion of their own, giving them a special individual character as to permanence and movement. The treatise, like the problem, was a purely mathematical one,[1] and in the mind of the celebrated author was probably connected more with the problem of the formation of drops, and with that of the friction or viscosity of fluids, which he attacked subsequently, than with the nature of matter. In this country vortex motion had already been studied by natural philosophers with very different ends in view.

It was known that solid bodies which are in a rapid

---

[1] It revealed incidentally the analogy of hydrodynamical and electrical phenomena.

rotary motion acquire properties which they do not 41. Earlier researches on vortex motion. possess otherwise—viz., rigidity—*i.e.*, reaction against change of shape (the stiffness of a travelling rope thrown off a pulley is a familiar illustration); stability—*i.e.*, reaction against change of position and motion, as in a spinning-top or a bicycle; elasticity—*i.e.*, tendency to revert to the same position, if violently disturbed. The gyroscope[1] had been invented in 1852 by Foucault, and used by him and other physicists in France and Germany to illustrate the rotation of the earth. It was now shown that portions of a perfect fluid—*i.e.*, of a body which possesses neither rigidity, nor stability, nor elasticity —when in a state of rapid rotational motion, acquire these gyrostatic properties; that whirling portions cannot be naturally created, but that if once in existence they preserve their identity, being permanently differentiated from the surrounding fluid, which may be at rest or in the state of flow. These differentiated portions of the liquid were called by Helmholtz vortex filaments; he showed that in a liquid without a boundary they must run back into themselves, forming rings which might be knotted and linked together in many ways.

---

[1] A much older invention was that of Bohnenberger (1817), known by his name. The name "gyroscope" was introduced by Foucault; and that of "gyrostat," as defining an apparatus which acquires stability through rotational (whirling or gyrating) motion, was used first by Lord Kelvin. An extensive treatment of the subject is to be found in the first part of Thomson and Tait's 'Natural Philosophy' (2nd ed.), pp. 314-415. It is mainly through the influence of this work, and through the inexhaustible wealth of experimental illustrations contained in many of Lord Kelvin's addresses (see 'Popular Lectures and Addresses,' vol. i. pp. 143 *sqq.*, 218 *sqq.*; iii. 165 *sqq.* 245), that gyrostatic and vortex motion has become in this country a favourite study of mathematicians and natural philosophers, and forms an important feature in almost every recent attempt to describe the properties of matter and ether.

It does not seem that Helmholtz's speculations were much taken up abroad ; in this country, however, they fell on more fruitful soil:[1] they led first of all to

[1] It is a remarkable fact that the country which produced the great theory that finally destroyed the older vortex theory of Descartes, was the one in which, a century after Newton, the modern views on vortex-motion were first and almost exclusively developed. Notably the scientific atmosphere in which Thomson and Tait moved was, *inter alia*, charged with the bold ideas and the suggestive nomenclature of Macquorn Rankine. He owes his permanent place in the history of science to being side by side with Lord Kelvin and Clausius, one of the three founders of theoretical thermodynamics. But he was in addition to this perhaps the earliest and purest representative of the kinetic or mechanical view of natural phenomena, and of the scientific tendency or habit—derived from his profession as an engineer—of constructing for every phenomenon to be explained a mechanical model. In a succession of memoirs beginning in 1850, Rankine put forward his theory of "molecular vortices," "which assumes that each atom of matter consists of a nucleus or central point enveloped by an elastic atmosphere" ('Scientific Papers of Macquorn Rankine,' ed. Miller, London, 1881, p. 17). Clerk Maxwell in 1878 wrote of Rankine's theory : "Whatever he imagined about molecular vortices was so clearly imaged in his mind's eye that he, as a practical engineer, could see how it would work. However intricate, therefore, the machinery might be which he imagined to exist in the minute parts of bodies, there was no danger of his going on to explain natural phenomena by any mode of action of this machinery which was not consistent with the general laws of mechanism. Hence, though the construction and distribution of his vortices may seem to us as complicated and arbitrary as the Cartesian system, his final deductions are simple, necessary, and consistent with facts. Certain phenomena were to be explained. Rankine set himself to imagine the mechanism by which they might be produced. Being an accomplished engineer, he succeeded in specifying a particulur arrangement of mechanism competent to do the work." Maxwell goes on to say : "As long as the training of the naturalist enables him to trace the action only of particular material systems, without giving him the power of dealing with the general properties of all such systems, he must proceed by the method so often described in histories of science — he must imagine model after model of hypothetical apparatus, till he finds one which will do the required work. . . . The theory of molecular vortices was distinguished from other theories which attribute motion to bodies apparently at rest, by the further assumption that this motion is like that of very small vortices, each whirling about its own axis " (Clerk Maxwell in 'Nature,' 1878 ; 'Scientific Papers,' vol. ii. p. 662, &c. ; and Prof. Tait's memoir of Rankine in the 'Collected Papers,' p. xxix). In the most recent attempt to reconcile the two fundamental ideas without which we do not seem to be able to proceed in a description of natural phenomena — viz., that space is a *plenum*, filled by a continuous something, and that matter

many experimental contrivances, by which the remarkable phenomena known as "gyrostatic" — i.e., the stable properties of bodies in rapid rotary motion [1] —could be studied, as also to the development of the theory of knots and linkage.[2]   In the resourceful brain

(and electricity) is atomic (discrete, grained), Dr Larmor has traced the modern vortex theory further back beyond Rankine to James MacCullagh, who in his 'Essay towards a Dynamical Theory of Crystalline Reflexion and Refraction' (Trans. Irish Academy, 1839), "arrived at a type of elasticity (of the ether) which was wholly rotational, . . . somewhat after the manner that a spinning flywheel resists any angular deflection of its axis" (p. 26 of his Adams prize essay 'Æther and Matter,' 1900). "Rankine, never timid in his speculations, expounded MacCullagh's analytical scheme soundly and clearly, in full contrast with the elastic properties of matter, as representing a uniform medium or *plenum* endowed with ordinary inertia, but with elasticity of purely rotational type" (ibid., p. 77; cf. p. 73); but he also remarks that "up to the period of Lord Kelvin's vortex atoms . . . the earlier theories . . . could only have been hypothetical speculations" (p. 25 note).

[1] Helmholtz himself did not give many practical illustrations of his remarkable theories. Such were first given by W. B. Rogers ('Amer. Journ. of Science' (2), vol. 26, p. 246) in 1858, without knowledge of Helmholtz's theoretical investigations. In this country such illustrations have become quite favourite popular lecture experiments (see Sir Rob. S. Ball's memoir). Smoke-rings, solid and liquid gyrostats, and a host of similar contrivances, have impressed on us the hidden resources of whirling motion. Prof.

Tait, in his 'Recent Advances of Physical Science' (3rd ed., 1885, p. 296), states that experiments on smoke-rings which he performed, suggested to Lord Kelvin the vortex theory of matter. The various papers of the latter have, so far, not been collected in a convenient form. The earliest is contained in the 'Proceedings of the Royal Society of Edinburgh,' February 1867. Then followed a memoir in the 'Transactions' (April 1867) on vortex statics (Proc. R. S. E., December 1875) ; "Vibrations of a Columnar Vortex" (Proc., March 1880). Prof. Hicks, and especially Prof. J. J. Thomson (Trans. R. Soc., 1884 ; 1881), have contributed to the theory, and the latter, in his Adams prize essay for 1882, has further tested the conception in its application to chemical statics. See Hicks, 'Recent Progress in Hydrodynamics' (Brit. Assoc. Rep., 1881, p. 63, &c.), and J. J. Thomson 'On the Motion of Vortex Rings' (1883, p. 114, &c.)

[2] The creator of this branch of purely positional geometry is doubtless Johann Benedict Listing, who was led to his researches by some suggestions of Gauss. Gauss refers to the subject in connection with his unpublished researches into electrodynamics (1833, posthumously published in 'Werke,' vol. v. p. 605). Listing called this branch of geometry "Topologie" (cf. Listing, 'Vorstudien zur Topologie,' Göttingen, 1847). In the meantime Riemann had been (1851) led in his mathematical representation of functions on the surface called

of Lord Kelvin this theory led to the conception that
in an all-pervading, boundless fluid, such as physicists
imagined for the purposes of the theory of light, differentiated portions might exist in the form of whirling
rings (vortex rings), which would possess most of the
properties of ponderable matter—identity and permanence of quantity of substance, stability, rigidity, elasticity.

**43.
Difficulties
of the vortex
ring theory.** It was indeed soon found that although eminently suggestive in this way, and pointing in the direction of a
general kinetic theory of natural phenomena, the vortex
ring theory presented two fundamental difficulties. How
does whirling matter acquire weight, and how does it
acquire immensely increased inertia? In the explanation of these two properties the progress has been small,
—if indeed any glimpse at all has as yet been got.[1]
But by suggesting numberless experiments through which
our knowledge of things natural has been enormously increased, by placing before the minds of mathematicians
a great number of problems of practical importance and
physical interest, and generally by familiarising the minds
of philosophers with an ultimate kinetic explanation of
nature,[2] the vortex-atom theory has marked an epoch in

after him, to distinguish between
singly, doubly, triply, &c., connected surfaces ('Werke,' 1876,
pp. 18, 88, 448). These studies,
which for a long time were looked
upon merely as *curiosa* or of purely
abstract interest, were independently taken up in the practical
interest of the vortex-atom theory
by Prof. Tait in 1876 ("On Knots,"
Trans. Roy. Soc. Edinb., 1877, vol.
28, p. 145. &c.), and continued in
1884-85. To him we owe a convenient notation and vocabulary.
For the history of the subject and

further developments, see Din-
geldey, 'Topologische Studien.'
Leipzig, 1890.
[1] See Clerk Maxwell's article
"Atom" in the 9th ed. of the
'Ency. Brit.,' reprinted in 'Scientific Papers,' vol. ii., and the account
given there of Le Sage's theory.
[2] See Dr Larmor's Address to
Section A of the Brit. Assoc. at
Bradford in 1890 (Report, p. 625):
"The vortex-atom theory has been
a main source of physical suggestion,
because it presents, on a simple
basis, a dynamical picture of an

the history of thought. As the study of stable motion or dynamical equilibrium, it has joined hands with the kinetic theory of gases—*i.e.*, the study of the motion of a swarm of bodies in rectilinear motion, and with the mechanical theory of heat—*i.e.*, of irregular infinitesimal motion of any kind; and it has certainly, through the remarkable results gained by Professor J. J. Thomson, afforded a clue to the explanation of chemical linkage, showing how it comes about that stability of chemical compounds is dependent on, and limited to, a small number of combinations or linkages.[1] The mathematical difficulties in the way of progress are enormous, sufficient to tax the brains of many generations to come, but as it

---

ideal material system, atomically constituted, which could go on automatically without extraneous support. The value of such a picture may be held to lie, not in any supposition that this is the mechanism of the actual world laid bare, but in the vivid illustration it affords of the fundamental postulate of physical science, that mechanical phenomena are not parts of a scheme too involved for us to explore, but rather present themselves in definite and consistent correlations, which we are able to disentangle and apprehend with continually increasing precision."

[1] See his essay on the "Motion of Vortex Rings": "Let us suppose that the atoms of the different chemical elements are made up of vortex rings all of the same strength, but that some of these elements consist of only one of these rings, others of two of the rings linked together, or else of a continuous curve with two loops, others of three, and so on. Our investigation shows that no element can consist of more than six of these rings if they are arranged in the symmetrical way there described" (p. 119). "Each vortex ring in the atom would correspond to a unit of affinity in the chemical theory of quantivalence. If we regard the vortex rings in those, atoms consisting of more vortex rings than one as linked together in the most symmetrical way, then no element could have an atom consisting of more than six vortex rings at the most, so that no single atom would be capable of uniting with more than six atoms of another element so as to form a stable compound. This agrees with chemical facts, as Lothar Meyer in his 'Moderne Theorien der Chemie,' 4th ed., p. 196, states that no compound consisting of more than six atoms of one element combined with only one of another is known to exist in the gaseous state, and that a gaseous compound of tungsten, consisting of six atoms of chlorine united to one of tungsten, does exist" (p. 120).

has been remarked, " the glory of surmounting them would be unique." [1]

The vortex-atom theory is the most advanced chapter in the kinetic theory of matter, the most exalted glimpse into the mechanical view of nature. Though suggested by Helmholtz, it has, as already stated, been limited almost exclusively to this country. If science still shows international differences and patriotic predilections, this affords one of the few remaining examples. Another step first taken in this country, the last and most important contribution to the science of physical motion, the greatest support of the kinetic or mechanical view of nature, has, in union with the undulatory theory of light, been now all but universally accepted in the scientific world : I refer to the modern view of electric phenomena, which for a long time was supported by the solitary labours and genius of Faraday.

44.
Modern
view of
electrical
phenomena:
Faraday.

His great discoveries of magneto-electricity, of induction, of the electrification of light, to which I have had repeated occasion to refer, made his name familiar to the whole scientific world; but the processes of reasoning by which he arrived at them, or to which in his mind they gave rise, were ignored or not understood.[2]   Whilst

[1] Tait, in 'Recent Advances of Physical Science,' p. 302, and Clerk Maxwell, in article "Atom " (' Ency. Brit.,' 9th ed., or 'Collected Scientific Papers,' vol. ii. p. 472).

[2] See Helmholtz's 'Faraday Lecture,' delivered before the Chemical Society on April 5, 1881, reprinted in his ' Vorträge und Reden,' vol. ii. p. 275, &c.   "Since the mathematical interpretation of Faraday's theorems by Clerk Maxwell has been given, we see indeed how sharply defined the conceptions are and how consistent the reasoning which lay concealed in Faraday's words, which to his contemporaries appeared so indefinite and obscure ; and it is in the highest degree remarkable to see how a large number of comprehensive theorems, the proof of which taxes the highest powers of mathematical analysis, were found by him without the use of a single mathematical formula,

Continental philosophers, following Coulomb, tried to put into mathematical language the action at measurable distances of magnetic masses and elements of electrical circuits,[1] Faraday fastened upon the peculiar lines in which iron filings arranged themselves in the neighbour-

by a kind of intuition with instinctive certainty. I would not depreciate Faraday's contemporaries because they did not see this. I know myself too well how often I sat hopeless, gazing at one of his descriptions of lines of force with their numbers and tension, or looking for the meaning of statements where the galvanic current is regarded as an axis of force and much the like" (p. 277). Rosenberger tells us that it may be in part attributed to the displeasure and annoyance with which foreign philosophers received Faraday's theoretical views, that Poggendorff, who printed Faraday's earlier memoirs *in extenso* in his 'Annalen,' only give a short abstract of the later series. See Rosenberger, 'Die moderne Entwickelung der elektrischen Principien,' Leipzig, 1898, p. 105.

[1] These researches, of which the fourth chapter of this work gave some account, and which culminated in Weber's well-known law of electrodynamic action of electrical particles at a distance, absorbed almost exclusively the attention of natural philosophers abroad. Mathematicians of the highest rank, such as Laplace, Gauss, and Riemann, worked at the subject. It is, however, interesting to note that Gauss, with that remarkable instinct for physical adaptation of mathematical ideas which characterised also the magnetic researches which he carried on between 1830 and 1840, refrained from the development of a mathematical theory of electrodynamic action for reasons which he later explained to Weber. When

the latter prepared for publication that elaborate series of exact measurements which, irrespective of the theory attached to them, formed the foundation of modern electrical science and of the correlation of the phenomena of magnetism, of electricity at rest and in motion, of induction and of diamagnetism, Gauss wrote as follows under date 19th March 1845 : "The subject belongs to those investigations which occupied me very extensively about ten years ago (especially 1834-36). . . . Perhaps I may be able to think myself again into these matters, which have now become so foreign to me. . . . I should no doubt have long ago published my researches ; but at the time when I broke them off, that was wanting which I then considered to be the very keystone—nil actum reputans si quid superesset agendum—namely, the deduction of the additional forces (which have to be added on to the mutual action of particles of electricity at rest, if they are in relative motion) from action, not instantaneous, but (like that of light) propagated in time. With this I could not succeed at the moment, but so far as I can remember I left the subject not entirely without hope that this might later be possible ; yet, if I remember aright, with the subjective conviction that it would previously be necessary to form for oneself a workable representation (*eine construirbare Vorstellung*) of the manner in which the propagation takes place" (Gauss, 'Werke,' vol. v. p. 627, &c.)

hood of the poles of magnets ;[1] inquired into the nature and condition of the region—afterwards termed the "field " —which surrounded magnetised and electrified bodies ; invented the term " electrotonic state " and " dielectric "[2] to describe the part which the surrounding medium played in the so-called actions at a distance ; and conceived it to be in a state of tension, which he further described by filling it with so-called " lines of force." The region or " field " [3] of magnetic and electric action, filled with these curved lines of force, possessing definite direction and frequency, gave him a clear mental representation of the direction and intensity of magnetic and electric forces at any point in space in the neighbourhood of magnets or of electric currents. For Faraday, the lines of force in the magnetic field, from being originally merely a convenient geometrical device,[4] ac-

45.
" Lines of force."

[1] "By magnetic curves I mean the lines of magnetic forces, however modified by the juxtaposition of poles, which would be depicted by iron filings, or those to which a very small magnetic needle would form a tangent" (Faraday, ' Experimental Researches on Electricity,' 1st series, November 1831, No. 114 note). " When an electrical current is passed through a wire, that wire is surrounded at every part by magnetic curves, diminishing in intensity according to their distance from the wire. . . . These curves, although different in form, are perfectly analogous to those existing between two contrary magnetic poles opposed to each other " (ibid., 2nd series, January 1832, No. 232).

[2] The term "electrotonic state " was introduced in 1831 to describe the conditions of matter in the neighbourhood of electric bodies. "It is probable that what will affect a conductor will affect an insulator also, producing, perhaps, what may deserve the term of the electrotonic state " (ibid., No. 1661, 1838), "the intervening particles assuming for the time more or less of a peculiar condition, which (though with a very imperfect idea) I have several times expressed by the term electrotonic state " (ibid., No. 1729). " I use the word ' dielectric ' to express that substance through or across which the electric forces are acting " (December 1838, ibid., No. 1168, note).

[3] The term " magnetic field " seems to have been used for the first time in the year 1845 (see ' Exp. Res.,' No. 2252, vol. iii. p. 30).

[4] November 1837 : " I use the term line of inductive force merely as a temporary conventional mode of expressing the direction of the power in cases of induction. . . . The power, instead of being like

quired gradually a physical[1] significance, for he had very early convinced himself of the fact, known already

that of gravity, which causes particles to act on each other through straight lines, . . . is more analogous to that of a series of magnetic needles. . . . So that in whatever way I view it, and with great suspicion of the influence of favourite notions over myself, I cannot perceive how the ordinary theory . . . can be a correct representation of that great natural principle of electrical action" ('Exp. Res.,' No. 1231). "I have used the phrases *lines of inductive force* and *curved lines* of force in a general sense only. . . . All I am anxious about at present is, that a more particular meaning should not be attached to the expressions used than I contemplate" (ibid., No. 1304). And after having referred to the agreement of his results with those of Poisson, arrived at by starting from "a very different mode of action," and with the experimental results of Snow Harris, he concludes by saying, "I put forth my particular view with doubt and fear, lest it should not bear the test of general examination," &c. (No. 1306).

[1] It took more than ten years before the purely geometrical or conventional use of the term "lines of force" ripened into a physical conception. The latter is definitely expounded in a paper in the 'Philos. Magazine' for June 1852. We can compare this gradual development of a symbolical into a physical theory with the gradual development of the atomic theory ; atoms and molecules becoming a physical necessity to chemists long after they had been used simply as a convenient representation of the laws of equivalence and of the fixed proportions of combination (see vol. i. of this work, chap. v., p. 432, &c.) Faraday, during the

years 1840 to 1850, laboured at two great problems : the one he solved brilliantly and in the direction he anticipated ; the other remains a problem to this day. The first refers to the action of magnets on the dielectric. The dielectric, the space which Continental philosophers considered as a vacuum so far as magnetic and electrical phenomena are concerned, had been filled by Young and Fresnel with the luminiferous ether. Faraday suspected that this luminiferous ether cannot be insensible to magnetic action, and he sought in the experimental proof of the action of magnets on rays of light in the surrounding space a support for his view of the part which the dielectric plays in the transmission of electric and magnetic action. After many ineffectual attempts to prove this, he could at last (November 1845) announce his results to the Royal Society as follows : "These ineffectual exertions . . . could not remove my strong persuasion derived from philosophical considerations ; and therefore I recently resumed the inquiry by experiment in a most strict and searching manner, and have at last succeeded in *magnetising and electrifying a ray of light, and in illuminating a magnetic line of force.* . . . Employing a ray of light, we can tell, *by the eye*, the direction of the magnetic lines through a body ; and by the alteration of the ray and its optical effect on the eye, can see the course of the lines just as we can see the course of a thread of glass or any other transparent substance, rendered visible by the light" ('Exp. Res.,' vol. iii., No. 2148 and note). The second problem which Faraday attacked was to prove a similar "connection be-

to Cavendish, that in the case of electric attraction and repulsion, the nature of the intervening medium was of importance : it played a part in the electric phenomena in the same way as in the propagation of light and heat the intervening medium played a definite part. This part had been entirely overlooked by Continental philosophers, who worked on the hypothesis of an immediate action at a distance, based upon the analogy of gravitation. Their researches, carried on by methods similar to those invented by Laplace and his school for the calculation of the combined effect of gravitational forces at various points in space, entirely ignored the question how such effects were brought about. As time did not seem to enter as an appreciable factor, the investigation of the mechanism by which action at a distance was communicated was set aside as unnecessary or impossible : the astronomical view of the phenomena sufficed. For Faraday, the intervening medium, which—as in the communication of light and heat—took an active part, the question of its nature and mode of action was very important; he accordingly first of all gave it a name. As in optics the term luminiferous ether had been recently revived, and had become familiar through Young and Fresnel, so through Faraday were introduced the terms " dielectric " and " magnetic field," as the carriers of electric and magnetic action; and though for a long time used only by himself, they

tween gravity and electricity." On the failure of this attempt he fully reported in his Bakerian Lecture, November 1850 ('Exp. Res.,' vol. iii. p. 161). But the former results were sufficient to ripen gradually in his mind the idea of the physical nature of the lines of force, which he expounded with increasing precision from 1851 onward. (See 'Exp. Res.,' 28th series, vol. iii. p. 328 ; also pp. 402, 438).

have been the means of keeping before the minds of
natural philosophers the question how these actions
are mechanically communicated, a problem which lay
outside of the astronomical view of the phenomena.
To Faraday himself the analogy between the phenomena
of these actions meant also a real physical relation
or even identity, a supposition which he followed up
with unwearying patience and all the experimental
resources of his inventive mind, till he succeeded in
showing by experiment that magnets in the neighbourhood of transparent substances which have a polarising
effect on rays of light possessed the property of altering
the direction in which the polarised rays show their
laterality.   Faraday's conception of "lines of force"
filling all space and explaining electric and magnetic
action, radiation, and possibly also gravitation, was
elaborated during the years 1830 to 1850.   An opinion
then prevailed that his discoveries stood in opposition to
the views elaborated and experimentally verified by
Continental philosophers.   The first who showed the
analogy and threw out a hint how the two views could
be brought into harmony was William Thomson (Lord
Kelvin).   As early as 1842,[1] when scarcely eighteen

46.
Develop-
ment of the
conception
by Lord
Kelvin.

[1] "On the uniform motion of
Heat in homogeneous solid bodies,
and its connexion with the mathematical theory of Electricity,"
'Cambridge Mathematical Journal,' February 1842. The following
note is attached to the reprint in
the 'Philosophical Magazine' of
1854 : "The general conclusions
established show that the laws of
distribution of electric or magnetic
force in any case whatever must be
identical with the laws of distribution of the lines of motion of
heat in certain perfectly defined
circumstances. With developments
and applications contained in a
subsequent paper (1845), they constitute a full theory of the characteristics of lines of force, which
have been so admirably investigated
experimentally by Faraday, and
complete the analogy with the
theory of the conduction of heat,
of which such terms as 'conducting power of lines of force' ('Exp.
Res.,' Nos. 2797-2802) involve the
idea."

years old, but already acquainted with English experimental and French mathematical researches, he pointed
out how phenomena of flow—*i.e.*, of motion—could be
mathematically grasped by a formula quite similar to
that of the distribution of masses at rest and apparently governed by attractive forces at a distance. For
instance, the distribution of temperature at various distinct points in a space in which a flow of heat from an
origin had brought about a stationary condition (the
equilibrium being dynamical, not statical), was mathematically expressed by a formula identical with that
which, according to Poisson and others, gave the distribution of electrical or attracting masses. Now we
know that in the former case the equilibrium is maintained by a flow across the intervening space, which takes
time. This suggests, therefore, the possibility of explaining the so-called statical effects of attracting or
repelling masses kinetically by a process of flow or motion
going on in the intervening medium, a notion to which
Faraday clung tenaciously. In 1845 Thomson reverted
to this subject, and after harmonising the two views,
concluded by stating that the latter " method of establishing the mathematical theory would be even more simple
if possible than that of Coulomb." [1]

[1] " On the Mathematical Theory
of Electricity in Equilibrium,"
1845. See 'Reprint of Papers on
Electrostatics and Magnetism,' 2nd
ed., p. 29. A study of these mathematical researches of Lord Kelvin,
beginning early in the 'forties and
extending over more than twenty
years, is of special historical interest, as showing the gradual
growth of a physical out of a purely
mathematical theory : most of the
conceptions which have since become general through Maxwell's
electro-magnetic theory, as it has
been developed and popularised
by subsequent writers (notably
Prof. Poynting, Prof. Oliver Lodge,
and Mr Oliver Heaviside), being
already contained in Thomson's
papers as mathematical notions.
Thomson is throughout careful to

This suggestion was not carried out for some time, and then not by Thomson himself, but, at his instigation, by Clerk Maxwell.   In the meantime, however, Thomson added another step to the one already taken, by bringing recent discoveries of Faraday, as well as his

point out how the elementary experimental data referring to electrical charges, as well as to magnetic bodies, can be mathematically expressed equally well by the conceptions of Coulomb and Poisson and by those of conduction and flow, which are more in conformity with Faraday's physical ideas : neither of the mathematical analogies, of attraction at a distance or of conduction through an intervening medium, being sufficient for a physical theory.   These papers contain further the record of the gradual growth in the author's mind of the kinetic view of natural phenomena. Thomson was the first (1851) to introduce the terms " field " and " lines of force " into mathematical literature, adopting them from Faraday.   They have since become indispensable not only to the electrician but likewise to the mathematician ; forming, as it were, a unifying term for apparently distant regions of physical phenomena, and being introduced as fundamental notions at the beginning of dynamical treatises.   See, for instance, the article by M. Abraham entitled " Geometrische Grundbegriffe," in the second part of the fourth volume of the ' Encyclopädie der mathematischen Wissenschaften,' Leipzig, Teubner, 1901.   Independently and quite unknown to Faraday, or to each other, two eminent mathematicians, Sir W. R. Hamilton at Dublin and Herrmann Grassmann at Stettin, were elaborating, between 1835 and 1845, the geometrical conceptions and vocabulary which are required in the representation of "directed" quantities. Their expositions have since become much simplified, and now form, under the title of "vector analysis," an indispensable geometrical instrument.   The gradual evolution of the kinetic view of physical phenomena (which here concerns us most) in the memoirs of Thomson is most remarkable.   *Inter alia*, he made a communication in 1847 to the British Association at Oxford, in which he dealt with the phenomena of terrestrial magnetism, stating that "it becomes an interesting question whether mere electric currents could produce the actual phenomena observed.   Ampère's electro-magnetic theory leads us to an affirmative answer which must be regarded as merely theoretical ; for it is absolutely impossible to conceive of the currents which he describes round the molecules of matter as having a physical existence" (Reprint, 2nd ed., p. 469). On this passage he himself remarks in 1872 : "From twenty to twenty-five years ago, I had no belief in the reality of this [Ampère's] theory ; but I did not then know that motion is the very essence of what has hitherto been called matter.   At the 1847 meeting of the British Association in Oxford I learned from Joule the dynamical theory of heat, and was forced to abandon at once many, and gradually from year to year all other, statical preconceptions regarding the ultimate causes of apparently statical phenomena " (ibid., p. 423 note).

unique conception of the communication of electric and magnetic phenomena, into connection with the mathematical theory which had been founded and worked out by Poisson and Green. Without attempting to give a physical explanation of Faraday's lines of force, he showed how they could be utilised in calculating the complicated action of magnetic push-and-pull forces; suggested that the newly discovered property called diamagnetism, in virtue of which bodies in the neighbourhood of powerful magnets appeared to be repelled, not attracted, could be explained as a differential[1] effect of

[1] It was in the year 1845 that Faraday, after having discovered the "magnetisation of light," and made visible the "magnetic lines of force" ('Exp. Res.,' Nos. 2146-2242), entered upon that remarkable series of experiments and speculations which led him to the discovery of diamagnetism and to the assertion of the "magnetic condition of all matter" (ibid., Nos. 2243, &c.) In 1847 Thomson wrote : "According to Mr Faraday's recent researches it appears that there are a great many substances susceptible of magnetic induction, of such a kind that for them the value of the coefficient i is negative. These he calls diamagnetic substances, and in describing the remarkable results to which his experiments conducted him with reference to induction in diamagnetic matter, he says, 'All the phenomena resolve themselves into this, that a portion of such matter, when under magnetic action, tends to move from stronger to weaker places or points of force.' This is entirely in accordance with the result obtained above ; and it appears that the law of all the phenomena of induction discovered by Faraday with reference to diamagnetics may be expressed in the same terms as in the case of ordinary magnetic induction, by merely supposing the coefficient i to have a negative value" (Reprint, p. 502). In the Reprint (1854) of his early papers (1842) on the corresponding problems of magnetism and heat (Reprint, p. 18) he added a note to the effect that the "same demonstration is applicable to the influence of a piece of soft iron, or other paramagnetic, or to the reverse influence of a diamagnetic on the magnetic force in any locality near a magnet in which it can be placed, and shows that the lines of magnetic force will be altered by it precisely as the lines of motion of heat in corresponding thermal circumstances would be altered by introducing a body of greater or less conducting power of heat. Hence we see how strict is the foundation for an analogy on which the conducting power of a magnetic medium for lines of force may be spoken of, and we have a perfect explanation of the condensing action of a paramagnetic, and the repulsive effect of a diamagnetic upon the lines of force of a magnetic field, which have been described by Faraday" (Reprint, p. 33 note ; cf. Faraday, 'Exp. Res.,' Nos. 2807, 2808).

the magnetic actions which belong to all substances; introduced the term magnetic "permeability"[1] as descriptive of the degree in which various substances acquire magnetic properties and conduct the lines of magnetic force in the neighbourhood of powerful magnets; and finally demonstrated how, if these properties were considered as having different degrees in the different axes of crystals, in analogy with the different elasticities which they exhibited, the consequence would be a turning effect which would explain the changed optical properties of crystals under the influence of magnetic action.[2] In these investigations the ideas of

[1] This property was afterwards termed "permeability" by Thomson (Reprint, p. 489, 1872). The general rule of magnetic action can then be expressed by saying that "by virtue of differential action a body may behave paramagnetically or diamagnetically according as it is placed in a less or a more permeable medium than itself" (Chrystal in article "Magnetism," 'Ency. Brit.,' 9th ed., vol. xv. p. 248).

[2] On the Theory of Magnetic Induction in Crystalline and Non-crystalline Substances" ('Philos. Mag.,' March 1857; also Reprint, 2nd ed., p. 471, &c.) Poisson had already foreseen the mathematical possibility of what Faraday termed magne- (correctly magneto-) crystallic action, but "ce cas singulier ne s'étant pas encore présenté à l'observation, nous l'exclurons de nos recherches" ("Mémoire sur la Théorie du Magnétisme," 'Mém. de l'Institut, Paris, 1826,' quoted by Thomson, Reprint, p. 484). Stimulated by the discoveries of Faraday, Plücker at Bonn, during the extraordinary interval which separated the second from the first period of his original geometrical speculations (see vol. i. p. 242 of this work), de-

voted himself to the study of the electric and magnetic properties of gases and crystals, and in 1847 commenced that remarkable series of physical memoirs through which he became the fellow-worker, if not the rival, of Faraday. One of his first discoveries was the action of magnets on crystals, published in 1847 (Pogg. Ann., or Plücker's 'Physicalische Abhandlungen,' ed. Pockels, Leipzig, 1896, p. 6, &c.), which supplied to Thomson "the very circumstance the observation of which was wanting to induce Poisson to enter upon a full treatment of the subject, and made the working out of a mathematical theory of magnetic induction . . . independently of any hypothesis . . . upon a purely experimental foundation . . . important" (Thomson, loc. cit., p. 471). Plücker was an original thinker, and mainly a self-taught genius, imperfectly acquainted with the labours of his contemporaries or predecessors. This has been noted by his biographers as much in his geometrical as in his physical researches (see the memoirs of Clebsch and of Prof. Riecke, prefixed to the two volumes of the 'Gesammelte Abhandlungen').

Faraday are used merely for the sake of describing and calculating in the simplest manner phenomena which had been experimentally discovered : no attempt was made to explain physically how these actions come about. In fact, under the hands of Thomson the conceptions of Faraday were formulated as Dalton's atomic theory had been elaborated by chemists in the first half of the century, for the purpose of symbolically representing and calculating observed phenomena.

But the "lines of force" of Faraday were not to remain a mere symbolical representation, any more than Dalton's atoms were to remain merely counters of a chemical arithmetic. Both theories were to be raised to the rank of physical theories. What the kinetic theory of gases did for the atomic theory was done for Faraday's symbolism by the researches of Clerk Maxwell. And as the fact that the molecules of matter could be really counted, and their distances and velocities measured, gave life and actual meaning to the atomic view of natural phenomena,

47.
Clerk
Maxwell.

In his early geometrical researches he worked in ignorance of the remarkable 'Traité' of Poncelet, which had been published in 1822 (*loc. cit.*, vol. i. p. 594, &c.) : even the writings of his countryman Möbius were unknown to him. Still more extraordinary was his comparative unacquaintance with the electrical measurements and theories which dominated German research when he commenced his physical labours, and which emanated from the school of Gauss and Weber. But he was equally ignorant of the purely mathematical theories of Poisson and Thomson, which, as he himself candidly confessed, might have saved him from important errors (*loc. cit.*, vol. ii. p. 460), and which were later made more widely known in Germany by the excellent treatise of his pupil Beer ('Einleitung in die Elektrostatik,' &c., Braunschweig, 1869), posthumously edited by Plücker himself. The fact that Plücker was not influenced by the spirit of Weber's researches probably made him more appreciative of Faraday's purely physical methods. In such names as Beer, Clebsch, Klein, Fessel, Geissler, and Hittorf, Plücker counts an illustrious array of pupils and fellow-workers. See Clebsch's characteristic of Plücker, *loc. cit.*, vol. i. p. xii, &c.

so the rays of electric and magnetic force seen by Faraday in the abstraction of his intuitive mind became a reality for every experimentalist when Hertz in 1888 actually showed the wonderful action of electric waves at a distance. Atoms and lines of force have become a practical —shall I say a popular?—reality, whereas they were once only the convenient method of a single original mind for gathering together and unifying in thought a bewildering mass of observed phenomena, or at most capable of being utilised for a mathematical description and calculation of actual effects.

For a quarter of a century after Faraday had conceived the notion of looking upon electric and magnetic phenomena as depending on a property belonging to all matter, and pervading all space, like radiation and gravity, the only natural philosopher who to any extent entered into his ideas was Thomson. Even Tyndall, who came more than any other prominent physicist under Faraday's immediate and personal influence, and contributed largely to our knowledge of the new phenomena discovered by his great master, does not seem to have assimilated his scientific language and reasoning. It required a mathematical mind really to grasp and put into form Faraday's notions. Encouraged by Thomson, and soon after the publication of Thomson's mathematical theory of magnetism, Clerk Maxwell devoted himself to a theoretical study of electricity and allied subjects, a field which Thomson had then almost monopolised in this country.[1] The first of Maxwell's revolu-

[1] See Professor Glazebrook's little book on 'James Clerk Maxwell and Modern Physics,' published in the "Century Science Series," 1901. On page 42 a letter of Maxwell is quoted, in which he speaks of

48.
His series
of works
on the
theory of
electricity.

tionary series of works, 'On Faraday's Lines of Force,' was published in December 1855. The series was completed by the appearance in 1873 of his great work on 'Electricity and Magnetism,' which has formed the centre of a large literature to which all the scientific schools of Europe and America have contributed. Historically, Maxwell brought together two distinct and very fruitful lines of reasoning, due to Faraday and Thomson.[1] He was impressed with the desideratum of every physical theory bearing on any large class of phenomena—viz., that it must be mathematical and physical at the same time. His own theory had to embrace and unite all the purely arithmetical and geometrical regularities which had been discovered, and which at that time were known to describe correctly the facts of electric, mag-

"poaching upon Thomson's electrical preserves." In the preface to the treatise on electricity and magnetism, he refers to the apparent discrepancy between the views of Faraday and the mathematicians, and he states that he had arrived at "the conviction that this discrepancy did not arise from either party being wrong. I was first convinced of this," he proceeds, "by Sir William Thomson, to whose advice and assistance, as well as to his published papers, I owe most of what I have learned on the subject.

[1] In a different reference we may say that Maxwell's theory was prepared by three independent lines of research, starting respectively in France, Germany, and England : (1) The investigation of the actions at a distance of electrified and magnetised bodies, and of electric currents, which found mathematical expression in the formulæ of Coulomb and Ampère. The full significance and capabilities of the formulæ of electrostatic and magnetic action had been demonstrated by Thomson, who especially showed that these relations were not necessarily confined to the physical theory which had been elaborated on the Continent, but that, *mutatis mutandis*, they lent themselves equally well to the physical ideas of Faraday. (2) The exact measurements of magnetic, electro-dynamic, and galvanic action started by Ohm and Gauss in Germany, and much extended by Weber. (3) The idea of physical lines of force, filling space and representing action through contiguous particles, not at a distance, elaborated by Faraday. These three lines of research were brought together in the theory of Maxwell, which in the beginning professed to be only a mathematical but ended by being a physical theory.

netic, and galvanic phenomena, such as Coulomb's electrostatic and magnetic laws, Ampère's electro-dynamic and
electro-magnetic formulæ, and Ohm's and Faraday's laws
referring to galvanic currents, and many others. It
had also to give an intelligible representation of the
elementary actions of which these complicated phenomena are made up. In order to arrive at the latter, the
method usually employed is to look for analogies in
other provinces of science where the desired unification
has already been brought about. The great natural
philosophers of the French school who had so successfully accomplished the most extensive unification yet
attempted in any large branch of knowledge—the unification of physical astronomy under Newton's gravitation formula—had tried to follow up this analogy in
other realms of research, and had developed what I
called in a former chapter the astronomical view of
natural phenomena. Ampère, and notably Weber, had
extended this analogy so as to embrace electric and
magnetic phenomena. There was, however, another
analogy which was more familiar to the great experimentalists in this country, notably to Faraday—namely,
the analogy of those various phenomena which depend
on processes of emanation, of a gradual spreading out,
of a flow or conduction : those phenomena where the
factor of time comes in, and where an apparently stationary condition is brought about by a mode of motion,
or what has been termed a "dynamic equilibrium."
Thomson, starting from Fourier's mathematical analysis
of such processes, had been led to see how far-reaching
this analogy is, and had latterly (1852) extended it to

embrace the processes of the flow of heat, of electricity, magnetic and diamagnetic, and of fluid motion. "He called attention to the remarkable resemblance which the diagrams of flow bore to those which Mr Faraday had recently shown at the Royal Institution to illustrate his views regarding the action of ferro-magnetics and diamagnetics in influencing the field of force in which they are placed, and justified and illustrated the expression 'conducting power for the lines of force' by referring to rigorous mathematical analogies presented by the theory of heat."[1]

This view, which Thomson had merely shadowed forth, was more fully worked out by Maxwell in 1855 and 1861. His methods[2] were "generally those suggested by the processes of reasoning which are found in the researches of Faraday, and which, though they had been interpreted mathematically by Prof. Thomson and others, are very generally supposed to be of an indefinite and unmathematical character when compared with those employed by the professed mathematicians." The first addition which he introduced, by which he made Faraday's "lines of force" mathematically more definite, was to change them into "tubes of force," which represented not only the direction of force at every point of space, but also—according to their sectional dimensions—the intensity of the force. These tubes were supposed to be

49.
His conception of "tubes of force."

---

[1] Abstracts of two communications to the British Association at Belfast in 1852, "On certain Magnetic Curves : with Applications to Problems in the Theories of Heat, Electricity, and Fluid Motion" (Reprint of Papers, &c., p. 519, &c.)

[2] James Clerk Maxwell "On Faraday's Lines of Force," 'Transactions of the Cambridge Philosophical Society,' 1855. See 'Collected Scientific Papers,' vol. i. p. 157.

filled with a moving fluid, and the velocity of the flow—inversely proportional to the sectional area of the tubes—represented the intensity of the force at any point in space. He also showed how very much simpler the conception becomes, if the law of the acting forces is the experimentally established law of the inverse square of the distance.

This thought of "referring to the purely geometrical idea of the motion of an imaginary fluid"[1] was the beginning of the now universally adopted view of a very large class of phenomena, and it was at the same time a great step in the development of the kinetic or mechanical view of natural processes. These lines or tubes of force,[2] with which all space surrounding magnets or electrified bodies was supposed to be filled, enabled Maxwell further to give a definite representation of that peculiar state of matter of which Faraday had very early formed an indefinite conception, and which he called the "electrotonic state." Thomson had already in 1847[3] shown how the ideas of Faraday, who as early

50.
"Electro-
tonic state"
of matter.

[1] How little Maxwell originally intended to give a physical theory is seen from the concluding sentences of the introduction to his first paper (loc. cit., vol. i. p. 159) : "By referring everything to the purely geometrical idea of the motion of an imaginary fluid, I hope to attain generality and precision, and to avoid the dangers arising from a premature theory professing to explain the cause of the phenomena. If the results of mere speculation which I have collected are found to be of any use to experimental philosophers, in arranging and interpreting their results, they will have served their purpose, and a mature theory, in which physical facts will be physically explained, will be formed by those who by interrogating Nature herself can obtain the only true solution of the questions which the mathematical theory suggests."

[2] Faraday had already in 1852 spoken of shells and tubes of force, and invented the term sphondyloid to denote the portion of space enclosed between such shells of force ('Exp. Res.,' vol. iii., No. 3271).

[3] In 1847 ('Cambr. and Dubl. Math. Journal,' reprinted in 'Math. and Phys. Papers,' vol. i. p. 76) Thomson wrote that Faraday's theory of electrostatic induction

as 1831 conceived this peculiar condition of matter to
be equivalent to a state of strain, could be represented
by the mechanical analogy of the strains existing in an
elastic solid. He had distinguished three distinct forms
of this elastic strain, and had identified these three
forms severally with electrostatic, magnetic, and galvanic
forces. He had not given a physical explanation of the
origin of these forces, but had merely used the "mathematical analogies of the two problems (the electrical and
the elastic) to assist the imagination in the study of
both."[1]   Maxwell now took a further step and proceeded to give a physical or mechanical description of the
nature of this state of stress, of the electrotonic state of
matter. With this object in view he conceives of a
medium which is capable of exerting force on material
bodies by being itself strained, and exhibiting the

"suggests the idea that there may
be a problem in the theory of
elastic solids corresponding to every
problem connected with the distribution of electricity on conductors,
or with the forces of attraction and
repulsion exercised by electrified
bodies. The clue to a similar representation of magnetic and galvanic forces is afforded by Mr
Faraday's recent discovery of the
affection, with reference to polarised
light, of transparent solids subjected to magnetic or electro-
magnetic forces."

[1] Quoted from Maxwell's paper
"On Physical Lines of Force," in
the 'Philos. Mag.' 1861 (see 'Coll.
Papers,' vol. i. p. 453), in which
Maxwell applies Rankine's conception of molecular vortices to the
representation of magnetic phenomena. He refers to his earlier paper
(1855) on (geometrical) "lines of

force" in which he had "shown
the geometrical significance of the
electrotonic state," and had used
"mechanical illustrations to assist
the imagination, but not to account for the phenomena."   "I
now," he says, "propose to examine
magnetic phenomena from a mechanical point of view, and to
determine what tensions in, or
motions of, a medium are capable
of producing the mechanical phenomena observed. If by the same
hypothesis we can connect the
phenomena of magnetic attraction
with electro-magnetic phenomena,
and with those of induced currents, we shall have found a theory
which, if not true, can only be
proved to be erroneous by experiments which will greatly enlarge
our knowledge of this part of
physics" (ibid., p. 452).

phenomena of tension and pressure (magnetic action) as also of motion of its parts (electro-magnetic action). Now in a medium which is so constituted—*i.e.*, which possesses elastic mobility of its parts—we know that by a whirling or vortex motion phenomena of pressure and tension can be produced in certain parts, and the questions accordingly presented themselves to Maxwell, How by such tension and pressure in certain parts of the medium can magnetic phenomena be represented ? and How can the vortices communicate motion to, or receive motion from, the interlying movable particles of the medium ?   He succeeded in working out a very complete model of such a medium, representing by its mechanical motions both magnetic and electro-magnetic phenomena. Especially was he successful in visualising Faraday's lines or tubes of force, and endowing them with mechanically measurable forces.   Maxwell admits that " his conception . . . may appear somewhat awkward.   I do not," he says, " bring it forward as a mode of connection existing in nature. . . . It is, however, a mode of connection which is mechanically conceivable and easily investigated ; . . . so that I venture to say that any one who understands the provisional and temporary character of this hypothesis will find himself rather helped than hindered by it in his search after the true interpretation of the phenomena." [1]

[1] 'Collected Papers,' vol. i. p. 486. At the end of his paper on physical lines of force, Maxwell touches on the philosophical question, "how much evidence the explanation of phenomena lends to the credibility of a theory, or how far we ought to regard a coincidence in the mathematical expression of two sets of phenomena as an indication that these phenomena are of the same kind.   We know that partial coincidences of this kind have been discovered ; and the fact that they

The idea of a medium of extreme rarity, pervading all space and interpenetrating all matter, capable also of the elastic reactions of a solid body, was not repugnant to physicists at the time when Maxwell wrote. Though violently opposed forty years earlier when proposed by Fresnel and Young, it had gradually, through the development of optical theories, become a well-recognised instrument of scientific thought. In such a medium a disturbance or displacement is propagated with a certain velocity dependent on its elastic nature—the so-called constants of density and rigidity. Now, looking upon a charge of electricity not as a material something—an imponderable—but as a displacement of the medium, the question arose, Does the velocity with which such a displacement travels compare at all with the known velocities of other elastic disturbances, such as light is conceived to be? It was known to electricians that an amount or charge of electricity can be either stationary (called statical electricity) or in motion (called an electric current); and Weber and Kohlrausch had in 1856 actually measured the number of units of statical electricity which must flow through an electric circuit in order to produce the known mechanical effect of a unit of electric current. The quantity which they found, and which corresponded to a velocity, was of the same order as the velocity with which the elastic disturbance which we call light is known to travel. Maxwell was the first

51.
Correspondence between velocities of light and of e ectricity.

are only partial is proved by the divergence of the laws of the two sets of phenomena in other respects. We may chance to find, in the higher parts of physics, instances of more complete coincidence which may require much investigation to detect their ultimate divergence" (p. 188).

to see the physical significance of this correspondence.[1] "I have deduced the relation between the statical and dynamical measures of electricity, and have shown by a comparison of the electro-magnetic experiments of MM. Kohlrausch and Weber with the velocity of light as found by M. Fizeau, that the elasticity of the magnetic medium in air is the same as that of the luminiferous medium, if these two coexistent, coextensive, and equally elastic media are not rather one medium."[2]

After having pointed out this remarkable correspondence and other analogies between electrical and optical properties which could be verified by experiment, Maxwell seems to have felt satisfied that a dynamical or kinetic explanation of electric and magnetic phenomena based upon rotary and translational motions and elastic strains in the magnetic field was quite possible. The detailed descriptions given in his earlier papers he looked upon merely as crude mechanical devices by which some of the known effects of magnets and currents could be described. The valuable result was, that the electro-magnetic field could be looked upon as a mechanical system; that the observed actions at a distance could be conceived as communicated through this mechanical system in definite measurable time; and that certain analogies had been pointed out as existing between

52. "Elastic disturbances" of the same medium.

1 'Philos. Mag.,' January and February, 1862; 'Coll. Papers,' vol. i. p. 492.

2 Cf. 'Coll. Papers,' vol. i. p. 500: "The velocity of transverse undulations in our hypothetical medium, calculated from the electro-magnetic experiments of MM. Kohlrausch and Weber, agrees so exactly with the velocity of light calculated from the optical experiments of M. Fizeau, that we can scarcely avoid the inference that light consists in the transverse undulations of the same medium which is the cause of electric and magnetic phenomena."

optical, electrical, and magnetic phenomena, which by
carefully devised experiments might be verified and
extended.

Through Maxwell, following on Faraday and Thomson,
the treatment of electric and magnetic phenomena had
thus entered on a similar stage to that which the
treatment of optical phenomena had attained half a
century earlier through Young and Fresnel. A kinetic
or mechanical view, more or less precise and definite, had
been propounded; a considerable number of facts had
been brought into connection, into line and order; the
direction which experimental research must take had
been indicated; and finally a correspondence had been
established between two great groups of phenomena, those
of electricity and magnetism on the one side, those of
light on the other. It might have been expected that
Maxwell would now take the same course as that taken
by Fresnel about the year 1820, and perfect his views
by giving his theory of molecular vortices greater precision and definiteness—*i.e.*, by perfecting the electro-
magnetic model, as Fresnel and others perfected in their
time the system of vibrations by which they visualised
the processes of light. This is not the method which
Maxwell adopted.[1] In his later and more important

---

[1] The progress of Maxwell's reasoning is clearly marked in the three
memoirs, belonging respectively to
the years 1855, 1861, and 1864, of
which the last appeared in the
'Transactions' of the Royal Society, and which are reprinted in
the first volume of the 'Collected
Scientific Papers.' The first memoir
on "Faraday's Lines of Force" adheres strictly to the mathematical
formulation of Faraday's conception, much in the spirit of Thomson's many expositions. The second,
on "Physical Lines of Force," follows Faraday in the attempt to take
the original symbol in real earnest
as a physical arrangement, and de-
vises, or applies for that purpose,
the theory of molecular vortices.
The third memoir, which is by far
the most important and original,

writings he adopted a different and more general process
of reasoning.   If electrical and magnetic as well as
optical phenomena are produced by the motions of the
parts of a medium possessed of certain mechanical properties, this medium represents a mechanical system, and
must therefore be subject to the general laws which
regulate all mechanical systems.   These general laws are
laid down in dynamics, where it is shown that a complete
knowledge of the behaviour of such a system can be
reduced to the knowledge of the distribution in it of a
quantity called Energy.

53.
Conse-
quences
on the lines
of a theory
of Energy.

I intend in the next chapter to trace historically the

drops this somewhat crude device,
as well as the older theory of particles acting at a distance, with
forces which, according to Weber,
depend on their velocities, and starts
from "the conception of a complicated mechanism capable of a vast
variety of motion, but at the same
time so connected that the motion
of one part depends . . . on
the motion of other parts, these
motions being communicated by
forces arising from the relative displacement of the connected parts, in
virtue of their elasticity" (Papers,
vol. i. p. 533).   He further says :
"I have on a former occasion attempted to describe a particular
kind of motion and a particular
kind of strain, so arranged as to
account for the phenomena.   In
the present paper I avoid any hypothesis of this kind ; and in using
such words as electric momentum
and electric elasticity in reference
to the known phenomena of the induction of currents and the polarisation of dielectrics, I wish merely
to direct the mind of the reader to
mechanical phenomena which will
assist him in understanding the

electrical ones.   All such phrases
in the present paper are to be considered as illustrative, not as ex-
planatory.   In speaking of the
energy of the field, however, I
wish to be understood literally.   All
energy is the same as mechanical
energy, whether it exists in the
form of motion or in that of elasticity, or in any other form.   The
energy in electro-magnetic phenomena is mechanical energy.   The
only question is, Where does it
reside ?   On the old theories it
resides in the electrified bodies,
conducting circuits, and magnets,
in the form of an unknown quality
called potential energy, or the power
of producing certain effects at a
distance.   On our theory it resides
in the electro-magnetic field, in the
space surrounding the electrified
and magnetic bodies, as well as in
those bodies themselves, and is in
two different forms, which may be
described without hypothesis as
magnetic polarisation and electric
polarisation, or, according to a very
probable hypothesis, as the motion
and the strain of one and the same
medium" (p. 563).

growth of this conception as applied not only to the energy of visible and measurable mechanical motion, but to all other forces of nature which have in the course of the century not only been measured in terms of this one quantity, but also represented with more or less success as dependent on the energy of specific forms of motion, be this rotatory or vibratory or translational motion, regular and periodic or irregular and disorderly motion. It is clear that such a general abstract view as Maxwell (first among natural philosophers) took of a special problem was only possible after it had been shown how all physical and chemical actions and effects can be reduced to a common measure. The influence of the development of these views on the kinetic view of nature has been very great. The first and most natural effect of measuring all forces of nature in terms of the energy of motion is to strengthen the kinetic view of natural phenomena. This, however, is not the only view which is possible, or which has been taken, as I shall endeavour to show more fully hereafter.

The influence of Maxwell's ideas on scientific—nay, even on popular—thought has been very considerable. The main conception around which research, both mathematical and experimental, has moved during the last twenty years is the conception of light as an electromagnetic phenomenon. This view has been much supported and extended by the experiments of Heinrich Hertz, who by ingenious contrivances succeeded in actually exhibiting electro-magnetic waves, and in showing how they differ from light waves merely in length and period, and agree with them so far as reflexion and refraction and other properties are concerned. Luminous waves are now considered by many physicists to be merely electro-magnetic waves of short wave length and great frequency, such as the organ of vision is capable of perceiving in the form of light. The electric and magnetic medium is identical with the luminiferous ether, postulated by Young and Fresnel, and rays of light are merely an electric and magnetic disturbance propagated as a periodic or wave motion.

These discoveries and theories have gone a long was to destroy the older astronomical view of natural phenomena, which explained many effects by the action at a distance of particles of ponderable or imponderable matter. The firm conviction has taken hold of the modern scientific intellect or imagination that space is a *plenum* filled with a continuous medium, and that the undoubted atomic nature of ponderable matter may be owing merely to a specific and unmodifiable form of motion with such properties as Lord Kelvin has shown to belong to vortex filaments. The difficulty still remains how to explain the phenomenon of gravitation as well as the increased amount of inertia or mass which belongs to all ponderable matter as compared with that material substance which we call ether.

54. Destructive effect of the new theories on the astronomical view.

The reason why Maxwell abandoned his earlier schemes, in which he tried to construct a mechanical model of the electro-magnetic field, is not quite clear.[1] The idea has, however, been taken up by others, and elaborate descriptions have been attempted, by which the

[1] A suggestion regarding this is given by Dr J. Larmor in 'Æther and Matter,' p. 28.

processes going on in the neighbourhood of electrically charged bodies, of electric currents, of magnets and diamagnets, can be visualised.[1] For didactic purposes such elaborate models may prove to be of great value, though as a true mechanical basis of a physical theory of natural processes they have to be received with caution. None of those physicists who have expended their ingenuity in devising these contrivances seem to attach more than a symbolic or ideal value to them : they have, however, the desired effect of producing on the mind of the learner, of the practical inventor, or of a popular audience a strong conviction that all physical phenomena can be described as processes of motion, and that the ultimate solution of the problem of natural philosophy is to be found in a kinetic or mechanical view of phenomena. Physics and chemistry are, according to this

[1] Such illustrations may be found in Dr Oliver Lodge's ' Modern Views of Electricity,' a book which has had a large circulation and has helped to diffuse correct and practically useful ideas on electric and magnetic problems and phenomena. There is a danger of such mechanical illustrations becoming too rigid and of their being taken too literally; still, for the purposes of practical application and handling it is indispensable to possess some mechanical mode of representation and construction by which actual problems can be readily solved. The success of Dr Lodge's attempt both in this country and on the Continent, especially in Germany, proves sufficiently that it meets a much-felt want. See *inter alia* Prof. Rosenberger's five lectures, ' Die moderne Entwickelung der elektrischen Principien,' Leipzig, 1898, p. 133. A great authority abroad, Prof. Ludwig Boltzmann, has made use of a peculiar kind of mechanical motion, investigated by Helmholtz, to illustrate electrical phenomena. The characteristic of such motion — which is termed cyclic—is this, " that in the place of every particle which changes its position, an equal and equally moving particle enters, so that the condition of the system during the motion is nowise altered " (' Vorlesungen über Maxwell's Theorie,' Leipzig, 1891 and 1893, vol. i. p. 14). Cycles can be " coupled," &c. The general dynamical relations of such cyclic systems are investigated, and by introducing the necessary restrictions, based upon experimental facts, and suitable hypotheses— facts and hypotheses being clearly distinguished — the general equations of Maxwell are arrived at.

view, destined to become ultimately merely chapters in dynamics as the doctrine of mechanical motion.

A similar reluctance to look upon the vibrations of the luminiferous ether merely as a convenient symbolism, as a crude method of visualising molecular processes, which in reality we cannot picture to ourselves, does not seem to have troubled the minds of the great propounders of the undulatory theory of light—*i.e.*, of the elastic solid theory, as it is now termed in contradistinction to the electro-magnetic theory propounded by Maxwell. The greatest living exponent of the former view, Lord Kelvin, who in his Baltimore Lectures grappled with the difficulties which still beset that view—falling back on the principle of optical consonance and resonance, suggested by Professor Stokes to explain some of the interactions of the ether and ponderable matter ; upon the theory of free and forced vibrations, suggested by Bessel and Sellmeier ; and on his own fruitful suggestion of the vortex atom to explain some of the properties of ponderable atoms moving in the continuum which fills all space—expresses himself very definitely on this point.   " We must not listen to any suggestion that we may look upon the luminiferous ether as an ideal way of putting the thing. A real matter between us and the remoter stars I believe there is, and that light consists of real motions of that matter, motions just such as are described by Fresnel and Young, motions in the way of transverse vibrations.   If I knew what the magnetic theory of light is, I might be able to think of it in relation to the fundamental principles of the wave theory of light.   But it seems to me rather a backward step from an absolutely definite

55.
Lord Kelvin
on the
vibrations
of the ether.

mechanical notion that is put before us by Fresnel and his followers, to take up the so-called electro-magnetic theory of light in the way it has been taken up by several writers of late."

But whilst, no doubt, the train of reasoning started by Maxwell, and developed by his followers, has somewhat destroyed the simplicity and directness which the older vibratory theory of light and the kinetic theory of gases had brought into our mechanical views of natural phenomena, the subsequent experimental proof of the existence of electric waves by Hertz has done much popularly to strengthen that view. The discovery of other kinds of rays, by Lenard, Röntgen, and others, has likewise tended in the same direction, though their exact nature is still a subject of much conjecture.

Nor can it be denied that the practical usefulness also of these lately discovered forms of radiation has tended in the same direction; as has, all through the last thirty years, the enormous development of electrical industry in its many branches. Up to the beginning of the nineteenth century the principal electric and magnetic phenomena known were what we term statical; the study of these centred in the conception of electric and magnetic charges concentrated on or in conductors and acting at a distance. The practical interest was limited to mariners' compasses and light-ning-conductors. The discovery of the galvanic current, and still more its applications by Davy to the decomposition of the most refractory chemical compounds, introduced an entirely new class of phenomena. Continental science, in Coulomb, Ampère, and Weber, first developed the line of reasoning and research suggested by statical phenomena and applied this to dynamical phenomena. Faraday, following Davy, approached the subject from the point of view of the chemist. It was soon suspected, and latterly proved by actual measurements,˙ that the quantities which come into play in statical charges, and even in a violent thunderstorm, are small compared with those of a steady electrical current. The phenomena of electricity in motion became of infinitely more practical importance than those of electrical equilibrium or of static tension. The views of Faraday, Thomson, and Maxwell, which Helmholtz, educated though he was in the Continental methods, adopted and introduced into German scientific literature, lent themselves, as he recognised, more successfully and directly to the solution of the problems which applied science forced upon theorists.

Something, indeed, has been lost by this fundamental change which has come over modern reasoning in electrical matters. This has been most clearly and pointedly expressed by M. Poincaré, the eminent French mathematician, who has done so much to illumine physical and mechanical problems from the side of pure mathematics. "Maxwell," he says, "does not give a mechanical explanation of electricity and magnetism ; he confines himself to the proof that such an explanation is possible." Accordingly, those who were brought up in the traditions of the school of Laplace and Cauchy feel dismayed at the indefiniteness which adheres to the expositions of Maxwell's latest and greatest work. "A great French philosopher," M. Poincaré proceeds, "one of those

56.
Indefiniteness of the electromagnetic theory.

who have most completely fathomed Maxwell's work, said to me once, 'I understand everything in the book except what is meant by an electrically charged body.'" Professor Glazebrook tells us: "We cannot find in the 'Electricity' an answer to the question, What is an electric charge? Maxwell did not pretend to know, and the attempt to give too great definiteness to his views on this point is apt to lead to a misconception of what those views were. . . . Still, in order to grasp Maxwell's theory, this knowledge is not necessary."

Nevertheless, Maxwell's followers in this country and abroad are not satisfied to leave those points which are obscure or indefinite in his theory unilluminated. I have already referred to the valuable practical illustrations of Lodge. What has been done in a more systematic manner on the Continent and at home I shall briefly refer to at the end of the next chapter. We may call it a revival of the atomic view of electricity.

CHAPTER VII.

ON THE PHYSICAL VIEW OF NATURE.

I HAVE already remarked that none of the three great generalisations which we have so far reviewed have been creations of the philosophers of the nineteenth century. Their first enunciation belongs to antiquity, though they have only within the last three hundred years been expressed in sufficiently precise terms to permit of practical measurements and mathematical deductions. The first step towards a scientifically comprehensive employment of the familiar but vague terms of attraction, of atoms, and of undulations came, as we have seen, in each case from some solitary thinker of this country: from Newton, from Dalton, from Thomas Young. The systematic elaboration belongs to the combined scientific exertions of all the civilised nations of the world. In books on astronomy, physics, and chemistry, up to the middle of the century, we can hardly find any theoretical expositions which are not based upon one or more of these three ideas. Indeed they govern the entire science of inanimate nature during the first half of the century. None of these three principles, however, appeared suf-

1. Recapitulation.

ficient to cover the whole field. The law of gravitation embraced cosmical and some molar phenomena, but led to vagueness when applied to molecular actions. The atomic theory led to a complete systematisation of chemical compounds, but afforded no clue to the mysteries of chemical affinity. And the kinetic or mechanical theories of light, of electricity, and magnetism, led rather to a new dualism, the division of science into sciences of matter and of the ether. The unification of scientific thought which was gained by any of these three views, the astronomical, the atomic, and the mechanical, was thus only partial. A more general term had to be found under which the different terms could be comprised, which would give a still higher generalisation, a more complete unification of knowledge. One of the principal performances of the second half of the nineteenth century has been to find this more general term, and to trace its all-pervading existence on a cosmical, a molar, and a molecular scale. It will be the object of this chapter to complete the survey of those sciences which deal with lifeless nature by tracing the growth and development of this greatest of all exact generalisations—the conception of energy.

2.
Insufficiency of the astronomical, atomic, and kinetic views.

3.
The conception of energy.

The complex of ideas and the manifold courses of reasoning which are centred in this conception form such an intricate network, the interests involved are so great, the suggestions which led up to it so numerous, the consequences which resulted for science and practice so far-reaching, that the historian has no little difficulty in laying bare the many lines of thought which apparently cross and re-cross each other. Accordingly the history of this subject has been written from various points of view,[1] and angry controversies [2] as to priority

[1] The histories are mostly in German. I give the titles of the more important. Foremost stand the writings of Prof. Ernst Mach—viz., 'Die Geschichte und die Wurzel des Satzes von der Erhaltung der Arbeit' (Prag, 1872), incorporated in the author's 'Popular Scientific Lectures,' translated by Thomas J. M'Cormack, Chicago, 1894 ; and the same author's 'Die Mechanik in ihrer Entwickelung, historisch-kritisch dargestellt' (Leipzig, 1883, 2nd ed., 1889, also translated by M'Cormack, London and Chicago, 1893). The philosophical faculty of the University of Göttingen has twice (in 1869 and in 1884) made the principles of dynamics the subject of a prize competition, presumably both times at the instigation of the late celebrated Professor Wilhelm Weber. The first competition led to the publication of E. Dühring's 'Kritische Geschichte der allgemeinen Principien der Mechanik' (Leipzig, 1872 ; republished, with much controversial matter, in 1876 and 1887) ; the second to the publication of Prof. Max Planck's 'Das Princip der Erhaltung der Energie' (Leipzig, 1887). In the same year as the last book there appeared 'Die Lehre von der Energie,' by Dr Georg Helm (Leipzig, 1887), and lately his very complete work, 'Die Energetik, nach ihrer geschichtlichen Entwickelung' (Leipzig, 1898).

[2] The controversy turned mainly on the question of the claims of Dr Julius Robert Mayer of Heilbronn. The experimental work of Joule in England and the theoretical work of Helmholtz in Germany were published in ignorance of the writings of Mayer. Even the earlier important papers of William Thomson (Lord Kelvin) and Rudolph Clausius appeared before the name of Mayer was generally known. The question then arose to what extent the publications of Mayer really anticipated the discoveries and theories of Joule, Helmholtz, Thomson, and Clausius. It can hardly be held that they influenced them. The whole of the evidence as to the former point is contained in a very complete publication by Prof. Jacob J. Weyrauch, "Kleinere Schriften und Briefe von Robert Mayer" (Stuttgart, 1892), which forms a supplement to the edition by the same author of Robert Mayer's 'Schriften,' entitled "Die Mechanik der Wärme" (Stuttgart, 3rd ed., 1893). Both books contain very careful and exhaustive notes. Whoever desires to settle the question of Mayer's claims, which, however, will always depend much on individual opinion, will find all the documentary evidence collected in these interesting volumes. A further controversy arose later as to the discovery and enunciation of the second law of thermodynamics, the great doctrine of the "Dissipation of Energy." This controversy arose over the publication of the late Prof. P. G. Tait's 'Sketch of Thermodynamics' in 1868, which is an amplification of two articles by the same author in the 'North British Review' of 1864. The controversy, which referred mainly to R. Clausius's share in the enunciation of the second law, can be studied in Tait's little volume (1st ed., 1868 ; 2nd ed., 1877), in vols. 43 and 44 of the 4th series of the 'Phil. Mag.,' in his 'Recent Advances in Physical Science' (especially the preface to the 3rd edition, 1885), and in the 2nd

of discovery and as to the real points at issue have arisen. The history of thought only takes note of these in so far as they are indications of what was of real (not of personal) interest in the process, and are thus a measure of the value which was inherent in its development.

None of the different views or theories with which the earlier generations of philosophers during the century operated seemed sufficient to give an insight into the real essence, the $\phi\acute{v}\sigma\iota\varsigma$, of natural phenomena. Neither the astronomical nor the atomic nor the kinetic view was all-embracing. On the Continent, both in France and in Germany, the sciences were rigidly marked off from one another, the connecting links were few and ill-defined, and speculations as to the general forces and agencies of nature were left to metaphysicians and treated with suspicion. In England alone the name of natural philosophy still obtained, and in the absence of separate schools of science, such as existed abroad, suggested, at least to the self-taught amateur or to the practical man, the existence of a uniting bond between all natural studies. It is significant that the term under which we now comprise, and by which we measure, all natural agencies, the term Energy, was first distinctly used in this sense by Dr Thomas Young in his lectures on Natural Philosophy,[1] a course which, be it noted, also embraced

4.
The term
first used
by Young.

edition of the 2nd vol. of Clausius, 'Die mechanische Wärmetheorie' (Braunschweig, 1879), p. 324, &c. In the labyrinth of these controversies I have found Helm a fair and conscientious guide.

[1] Vol. i. p. 59 of the edition of Kelland. Young says : "The term Energy may be applied, with great propriety, to the product of the mass or weight of a body into the square of the number expressing its velocity. . . . This product has been denominated the living force (the *vis viva*), . . . and some have considered it as the true measure

Chemical Science, though for merely external reasons this was summarily handled.   It is equally significant that the first valuable suggestions as to the connection of the various sciences, and the practical or common measure of the various agencies, came from practical or professional persons who took an outside and general view of physical and chemical processes and their application in arts and medicine.   Young himself was a medical man, as were Robert Mayer and Helmholtz after him.   Practical men such as Watt felt the necessity of measuring not so much forces (in the Newtonian sense) as the action of forces, and introduced the term power, and the quantity called horse-power [1] to measure the capacity of an engine for doing work.   Newton had already measured this action [2]

5. Watt introduces the term "power."

of the quantity of motion ; but although this opinion has been very universally rejected, yet the force thus estimated well deserves a distinct denomination." See also p. 172.

[1] The quantity called horse-power was introduced by Boulton and Watt to measure the power of the engines they built and sold at Soho towards the end of the eighteenth century. They caused experiments to be made with the strong horses used in the breweries in London, and from the result of these trials they assigned 33,000 lb., raised one foot per minute, as the value of one horse-power.   Dr Young in his 'Lectures' has the following statement: "A steam-engine of the best construction, with a 30-inch cylinder, has the force of forty horses ; and since it acts without intermission, will perform the work of 120 horses or of 600 men, each square inch of the piston being nearly equivalent to a labourer" (vol. i. p. 103).

[2] See the Scholium to the "Axio-mata sive Leges Motus," p. 25 of the first edition of the 'Principia,' in which the "Agentis Actio" is measured "ex ejus vi et velocitate conjunctim." Thomson and Tait ('Natural Philosophy,' 1886, part i. p. 250 sqq., and Tait, 'Dynamics,' 1895, p. 181) have drawn attention to the fact that this passage of the 'Principia' contains implicitly the modern notion of energy, and the principle of the conservation of energy. The continental historians named above are inclined to give Huygens credit for having first made explicit use of the idea of the conservation of the quantity now termed energy, and they trace the further elucidation of it to the Bernoullis, especially John Bernoulli, who repeatedly speaks of the "conservatio virium vivarum," and "urges that where vis viva disappears, the power to do work (facultas agendi) is not lost, but is only changed into some other form" ('Opera,' 1742, vol. iii. pp. 239 and 243, quoted by Planck, loc. cit., p. 10).

of a force by the product of the force (itself measured by
the velocity of a moving mass) and the velocity or space
per unit of time through which it pushes or pulls a
moving body, and Leibniz [1] had suggested the term *vis
viva* to distinguish it from the *vis mortua*, the force
or pressure itself. But the first clear and consistent
fixing of the terminology which has since been universally
adopted is to be found—not in the 'Mécanique analytique' of Lagrange (that classical work on theoretical
mechanics), but in the 'Mécanique industrielle' of
Poncelet (1829).[2] He introduced the term "mechanical

[1] Leibniz's occupation with dynamics began with his publication of
two theses in 1672, which he dedicated respectively to the Academy
of Sciences in Paris and to the
Royal Society. In distinction from
the writings of Huygens and
Newton, where precise definitions
take the place of metaphysical
discussions, Leibniz's tracts — except in the comparatively rare cases
where he confines himself to mathematical formulæ—are vitiated, like
those of Descartes, by philosophical
speculations. Thus, though eminently suggestive, they contributed
little to the clearing up of ideas.
Influenced by Huygens and by
Newton, he opposed in 1686 the
ideas of Descartes on the measure
of force, and has the merit of
having introduced the term *vis
viva* in 1695, and of having started
the celebrated discussion on the
measure of force which was carried
on during fifty-seven years on the
Continent, and only settled by
D'Alembert in his 'Traité de Dyn-
amique' (1743) by stricter definitions. An excellent account of the
questions involved, and of the
gradual clearing up of ideas, will
be found in Prof. Mach's historical
treatise on dynamics referred to

above. See the English translation
by M'Cormack, p. 272, &c. It is
there shown that one of the great
defects of Descartes' and Leibniz's
dynamical writings was the want
of a clear definition of mass or
inertia ; also that this conception
follows more simply from Newton's
definition of force than from Huygens' conception of work (ibid.,
p. 251).
[2] By the side of, and sometimes
in opposition to the purely analytical
school headed by Lagrange, Laplace,
and later by Cauchy, there grew
up in Paris the school of practical
mathematicians which taught the
application of theory to practice,
to problems of artillery, engineering, and architecture. They created
modern geometry, and to a great
extent modern mechanics. Monge,
Coulomb, the elder Carnot, Poncelet, Coriolis, were their leaders :
Navier, Lamé, Chasles, de Saint
Venant, followed, and combined
their more synthetic methods with
the analytical methods of the
former school. Through Monge,
Carnot, Navier, and Poncelet,
geometry and dynamics were led
into those channels which have
since been so successfully followed
in all applied work. To them

work" for the definite quantity which had before him been variously designated as power, effect, action, &c., and he distinctly states that the inertia of matter transforms work into *vis viva* and *vis viva* into work. He also measures this quantity "work" quite in the modern fashion—by the "kilogrammetre," which gives the same conception as the foot-pound, only in a different measure.

6.
Poncelet
introduces
the term
"mechanical work."

Long before the terminology thus invented and fixed by Watt, Young, and Poncelet had been accepted by scientific writers, a change in the current notions on the forces of nature had been gradually brought about from quite a different quarter. Uninfluenced by the theoretical views which were developed and firmly held

mathematics was not merely the science of magnitude, but quite as much that of position, of design and perspective, of mechanical work and effect. They introduced a whole series of new and practical ideas, drawn from their own applications, and created a new vocabulary. They worked hand in hand with physicists and chemists, some of whom had little taste for the extremely abstract and analytical methods of the school of Laplace and Cauchy. Poncelet's original geometrical work, which will occupy us in a later chapter, led him into many controversies. It was, however, greatly appreciated in Germany and later in England. His influence on German applied mechanics has been quite as great as that on geometry; and the great text-books of mechanics by Weissbach, Redtenbacher, Rühlmann, and others, are as much indebted to Poncelet and other French models as the German text-books on mathematics, physics, and chemistry were for a long time to the well-known works of Biot, Pouillet, Cauchy,

Francœur, Lamé, Regnault, and others. The influence of Poncelet on practical mechanics, and especially in the fixing of an adequate terminology, can therefore be studied equally well in French and in German historical writings. Among the former I may mention especially the 'Exposé de la Situation de la Mécanique appliquée par Combes, Phillips et Collignon,' Paris, 1867, and among the latter, notably the above-mentioned writings of Helm, who traces the growth of the conception of mechanical work in French writings, and its influence on German thought ('Energetik,' p. 12, &c.) See also Dühring, *loc. cit.*, p. 471, &c. I may also refer to Heun's Report ('Jahresbericht der deutschen Mathematiker-Vereinigung,' vol. ix. part 2, 1901), where the sciences comprised in "Mechanics" are distinguished according as they are astronomical (Laplace, Poincaré), physical (English mathematical physics, Kirchhoff, Helmholtz, Hertz), geometrical (Poinsot, Chasles, Ball), or technical (Watt, Poncelet, Rankine).

by the school of which Laplace was the most distinguished representative, natural philosophers like Black,[1] Rumford, and Davy had approached the study of those phenomena where heat and chemical change are the prominent features. The phenomena which they studied experimentally can be comprehended under the head of the disappearance and appearance of heat as measured by the thermometer, or as recognisable directly by our sensation of heat. Black accounted for the disappearance of heat by the doctrine of latent heat, and measured this by the capacity[2] for heat, or the specific heat of different substances. Rumford made exact measurements of the heat generated by friction, and showed that Black's doctrine of latent heat did not account for it. Both Black and Rumford were led to science from the side of practical interests. Black, like Young after him, was a physician. Rumford was all through his life occupied with the

7.
Black,
Rumford,
and Davy.

[1] Joseph Black (1728-99), one of the founders of chemistry, and a prominent figure in that illustrious circle of philosophers who, during the second half of the eighteenth century, made the literature and science of Scotland renowned over the whole world, published very little, being mostly known through his teaching and his pupils. His name is, even to the present day, rarely to be found in French books; whereas in Germany, mainly owing to the historical writings of Herrmann Kopp, and quite recently of Prof. E. Mach, his great merit and originality have been fully recognised. See Kopp, 'Geschichte der Chemie,' vol. i. p. 226, &c.; 'Die Entwickelung der Chemie,' 1873, pp. 57, &c., 88, &c.; E. Mach, 'Die Principien der Wärmelehre,' 1896, p.

156, &c. Black, who as early as 1755 had shown that carbonic acid gas could disappear as a gas and become "fixed," showed later that heat could disappear as temperature and become "latent." By himself, indeed, the former important discovery was not interpreted against the then reigning phlogistic theory, nor was the latter used to upset the material theory of heat. Now, however, both discoveries are corner-stones in the history of science.

[2] According to Dr Young ('Lectures,' new ed., p. 499), the term "capacity" is due to Dr Irvine, who, as well as Dr Crawford, was much influenced by Black's lectures. These were first published in 1802 by Robison, three years after the author's death.

practical application of scientific knowledge. Black's experiments and measurements contributed largely to fix the difference between temperature and quantity of heat; he demonstrated clearly that heat may disappear in the form of temperature and exist as latent heat, that is, heat not discoverable by the thermometer. He, however, adhered to the view that heat was a material substance, which, though it might become latent, did not disappear as such. Rumford [1] was the first who definitely went a step further and suggested the convertibility of heat and mechanical work. It was not the disappearance of heat but its appearance when mechanical work was performed which attracted his attention. After eliminating all the sources from which the heat produced during the boring of cannon could have been derived, he comes to the conclusion that "it appears to be extremely difficult, if not quite impossible, to form any distinct idea of anything capable of being excited and communicated in the manner the heat was excited and communicated in those experiments, except it be motion." Davy, who, like Black, approached science in the interests of the medical man, comes to the conclusion in his first published papers, from experiments on the generation

---

[1] Count Rumford's "Inquiry concerning the Source of the Heat which is excited by Friction" was published in a later edition of his 'Essays.' The experiments with the boring of cannon were carried on at Munich in 1796 and 1797 ; the substance of the essay was read before the Royal Society in January 1798. The 'Essays' were republished in America and translated into several foreign languages. See Rumford's 'Works,' London, 1876, vol. i. p. 482, and vol. ii. p. 471. In 1804 Count Rumford published, in his 'Mémoires sur la Chaleur' (Paris, an. 13), a "Historical Review of the Various Experiments on Heat" ('Works,' vol. iii. pp. 138-240).

of heat by friction and percussion, that heat is not matter, but "may be defined a peculiar" motion, probably a vibration,[1] of the corpuscles of bodies tending to separate them. Rumford's and Davy's memoirs referred to belong to the last years of the eighteenth century. Dr Young, in his celebrated lectures on natural philosophy, discussing the experiments of Rumford and Davy came to the conclusion "that heat is a quality, and that this quality can only be motion." He refers to Newton's view "that heat consists in a minute vibratory motion of the particles of bodies," and to his own undulatory theory of light. This analogy with light seems to have for a long time served to unify the speculations [2] of those who were inclined to

[1] See his "Essay on Heat, Light, and the Combinations of Light," which appeared in Beddoes' 'Contributions to Physical and Medical Knowledge,' 1799. This essay Davy soon after condemned as "infant chemical speculations," from which he turned away to experimental work, remarking that chemical knowledge was yet too incomplete to allow of generalisations, and that the "first step will be the decomposition of those bodies which are at present undecompounded." This was written in 1799. In 1800 (30th March) Volta's invention of the "pile" was communicated to the Royal Society, and on the 30th April of that year the first pile was constructed in this country. See the first and second volumes of Davy's 'Collected Works,' London, 1839. Davy's first publication on voltaic electricity appeared in the September number of 'Nicholson's Journal.' Though the speculations of Davy on heat and light, in which heat is conceived to be motion and light (strangely) to be material, were discarded by him, they attracted the attention of Franklin and of Count Rumford. Davy states that his experiments on the generation of heat "were made long before the publication of Count Rumford's ingenious paper on the heat produced by friction" (loc. cit., vol. ii. p. 117). In spite of his own refusal to follow up the lines of thought suggested by them, they were probably the cause of Davy's appointment as lecturer on chemistry at the Royal Institution : see vol. i. p. 83 ; also Memoir of Count Rumford ('Works,' vol. i. 417), and Paris's 'Life of Davy,' vol. i. p. 112, &c. Tait, in 'Recent Advances,' gives a full account of Rumford's and of Davy's work.

[2] See 'Young's Lectures,' 51 and 52. In the second edition, published by Kelland forty years after the Lectures were delivered, the editor makes the following significant remark : "The theory of heat

embrace a mechanical or kinetic view of the nature of heat. Joule, as stated above,[1] was the first who emancipated himself from it.

But whilst these suggestions that heat may be re- garded as somehow connected with motion remained mostly vague and undeveloped, they tended to impress upon the scientific mind the interchangeability—or, as it was called, the correlation of the different forces of nature; and the idea seems to have forced itself in- dependently on many minds, through the study of very different groups of natural phenomena. In Germany we may look upon Liebig as the centre of a great scientific movement which tried by means of chemistry to bring the realms of organic and animated exist- ence under the treatment of exact methods. Not only were the methods of organic analysis perfected by him and his school, and many compounds inves- tigated which appeared to be specially the bearers of the living process; but he was also among the first to study the economy of living organisms, the circulation of matter, and the play of the varied processes by which life is maintained. Among these processes, the phenomenon of animal heat, its origin, and the part it plays in the living organism attracted special attention.

8. Correlation of forces.

9. Liebig.

may be said to rest where it did at the time these Lectures were written. The facts which have just been mentioned clearly point out its undulatory character" (p. 506). Between the years 1835 and 1845 theoretical ideas on the nature of heat were entirely dominated by the remarkable discoveries of Melloni, Baden-Powell, Forbes, and others referring to radiant heat, which was shown to have the same properties of reflexion, refraction, and polarisation as light possessed. The analogy of this form of heat with light threw into oblivion the beginnings of a more general mechanical theory of heat, which —as we shall see further on—had been laid by Sadi Carnot in 1824.

[1] See vol. i. of this work, p. 434.

By his work on organic chemistry, by his many controversies, such as that on fermentation, by his popular letters on chemistry, and especially by his great influence as a teacher, Liebig himself did much to bring about an alliance of the separate sciences and a connection between practical pursuits and abstract research, and to draw attention to the interdependence of the various forces of nature. Only second in influence was Johannes Müller of Berlin. Among the many expressions which took their origin in the circle of studies suggested by these influences, we may select three as giving increasingly clear emphasis to the point now under consideration—viz., the correlation of all the physical forces of nature. These expressions are those of the convertibility of forces, of the existence of a common measure of force, and of the conservation implying the perdurability of a certain quantity—now termed Energy—of which all phenomena are merely a partial exhibition. They are connected with the names of Karl Friedrich Mohr, Julius Robert Mayer, and Hermann Helmholtz.

10.
John Müller.

Were it my object merely to write the history of science, I should probably follow the example of some historians [1] and omit altogether the first of these names in the present connection. But as my object is to write the history of scientific thought, I feel bound to give a

---

[1] Mach, in his recent very lucid and valuable work, 'Die Principien der Wärmelehre,' Leipzig, 1896, does not mention Mohr. On the other side, Helm ('Die Energetik,' 1898, p. 9) mentions Mohr and likewise Planck ('Das Princip der Erhaltung der Energie,' 1887, p. 21). Tait's first edition of 'Recent Advances,' 1874, does not contain Mohr's name. The third edition gives a full account of Mohr's early papers (pp. 51 and 60, &c.) See also the appreciative article on K. F. Mohr in the 'Ency. Brit.'

foremost place to the short memoir of F. Mohr entitled
"On the Nature of Heat," which appeared in 1837 in
an obscure scientific periodical published at Vienna.
The publication of it remained unknown, even to the
author himself, and was certainly unappreciated by the
scientific world for more than thirty years.[1]

11.
F. Mohr.

[1] The story of Mohr's memoir is curious, not to say romantic. His original paper, ' Ueber die Natur der Wärme,' was offered to Poggendorf and refused, as were the later memoirs of Mayer and Helmholtz. A dread of introducing speculative matter into the ' Annalen ' prevented likewise — as I related above (p. 66, note 2)—the appreciation of much of Faraday's later work. He then sent the MS. to Baumgartner, in Vienna, who— always interested in theoretical physics—printed it in a periodical (' Zeitschrift für Physik ') of which he and von Holger were joint-editors. He did not inform the author of this. Mohr was a remarkably original thinker, in whose mind important ideas rose at times to extraordinary clearness, but who, like many original thinkers, did not always appreciate his own ideas at their true value, and accordingly treated them with neglect, and did not consistently develop them. In the present instance he contented himself with inserting an abstract in the ' Annalen der Pharmacie ' (vol. xxiv. p. 141), of which he was then joint - editor, together with Liebig and Merck. He made no further inquiries as to the fate of his larger memoir, and, in conversation with friends up to the year 1860, as also in his ' Mechanische Theorie der chemischen Affinität' (Braunschweig, 1868, p. 45), used to deplore the loss of a document which, more fully than the short paper in the ' Annalen der

Pharmacie,' would have established his priority in the clear enunciation of a remarkable principle which fifteen years later received general recognition. The matter would probably have rested there had it not been that Tyndall, in the year 1862, in a celebrated lecture before the Royal Institution, commenced that long series of historical and controversial publications in which many persons, including himself, Joule, Tait, Colding, Helmholtz, Akin, Bohn, Dühring, Zöllner, and others took part, and in which, among several claims prior to or contemporary with Mayer's, those also of Mohr received due recognition. It seems to have been especially Dr Akin who drew attention to Mohr's claims, and searched in the forgotten volumes of the Austrian periodical for the original memoir, which, unknown to the author himself, had been inscribed on p. 419 of the fifth volume. This discovery he announced to Mohr himself after having already, in November 1864 (' Phil. Mag.,' 4th series, vol. xxviii. p. 474), given several extracts, among which is the one quoted by me in the text. Mohr published, in 1869, a sequel to the above-mentioned book, entitled ' Allgemeine Theorie der Bewegung und Kraft,' in which he refers to Dr Akin's discovery, and reprints the original memoir in full. Since that time his name has figured in many historical accounts as one of the pioneers in the development of the energy - concep-

It forms, therefore, no link in the actual development of the energy-conception ; but it is a significant evidence of the direction in which the ideas of natural philosophers were then moving, and of the high degree of clearness to which they rose in individual instances. When we read the following words : "Besides the known fifty-four chemical elements there exists in nature only one agent more, and this is called 'Kraft'; it can under suitable conditions appear as motion, cohesion, electricity, light, heat, and magnetism," it seems difficult, even after the lapse of two generations, to alter anything in this clear and simple enunciation of the law of the conservation of energy. It has indeed been stated that "unless some still earlier author should be discovered, there can be no doubt that Mohr is to be recognised as the first to enunciate in its generality what we now call 'conservation of energy.'"[1] At the same time, the case shows how little, at the beginning of a scientific movement, purely abstract statements are capable of really guiding research into fruitful channels. There is with Mohr no attempt to establish or apply an actual measure[2] of the amount of energy appearing in the various instances which he mentioned. This further step was taken five years later by J. R. Mayer, who can claim to be the first[3] to have ventured on a

12.
Mayer.

tion ; his merit being variously appraised according to the purely scientific, the philosophical, or the more practical standpoint taken up by various critics. See, *inter alia*, P. G. Tait's 'Recent Advances,' 3rd ed., p. 60, &c. ; also the correspondence of Mohr and Mayer in the latter's 'Kleinere Schriften und Briefe,' ed. Weyrauch, p. 407, &c.

[1] See the article on K. F. Mohr in the 'Ency. Brit.,' 9th ed.

[2] See on this point Weyrauch, in Mayer's 'Kleinere Schriften,' p. 408.

[3] Helm ('Energetik,' p. 34) begins the list of undoubted determinations of the heat-equivalent with

numerical estimate as between mechanical energy on the one side, and the amount of one of the imponderables—*i.e.*, heat as measured by the thermometer—on the other. Although his methods were not free from objection,[1] while his arguments were mixed up with

Mayer, 1842. His determinaton is contained in his first paper, published, as was Mohr's, in Liebig's 'Annalen' (vol. xlii., May), with the title "Bemerkungen über die Kräfte der unbelebten Natur." The experiments performed by Rumford in 1798 were made the basis of a calculation of the heat equivalent, *i.e.*, of the weight which can be lifted one foot if the heat required to raise a pound of water 1° be converted into work against gravitation, and the figure turns out to be 1034 lb. as compared with 772 lb. given by Joule himself ('Phil. Trans.,' 1850; 'Joule's Papers,' vol. i. p. 299). The earlier computations of Séguin, based upon the work done by the expansion of steam, were referred to by Joule, Tyndall, and Tait in 1862 and 1864 ('Phil. Mag.,' 4th series, vols. xxiv. and xxviii.), and shown to lead to figures further off the mark than those of Mayer. In the course of this later controversy it became for the first time generally known that A. Colding, an engineer in Copenhagen, had a little later than Mayer (1843), and almost simultaneously with Joule, given a determination of the equivalent based upon friction of metals, which was lower than Mayer's. He accordingly now figures as second in Helm's list. One of Joule's earliest experiments with heat, "evolved by the passage of water through narrow tubes," gave the equivalent as 770, very near the figure, viz., 772, finally settled on as correct in 1850.

[1] The reasoning of Mayer is not completely contained in his first

paper, which subsequently, on a suggestion of Joule's appeared in translation in the 'Phil. Mag.' (4th series, vol. xxiv. pp. 123, and 371 *sqq.*) The assumption (called by Thomson in 1851 "Mayer's hypothesis," see 'Math. and Phys. Papers,' vol. i. p. 213) that "the work spent in the compression of a gas . . . is exactly the mechanical equivalent of the . . . heat evolved," which Joule did not think it right to accept without satisfying himself by experiments (see 'Phil. Mag.,' 4th series, vol. xxiv. p. 122), was based by Mayer on an almost forgotten experiment of Gay Lussac's in the year 1807, as is evident from his subsequent paper, published in 1845 (reprint in 'Mechanik der Wärme,' ed. Weyrauch, 1893, p. 53), and still more from his correspondence with Baur previous to his first publication (ibid., p. 20, and 'Mayer's Briefe,' p. 130, September 1841). The subject was exhaustively investigated by Thomson and Joule in a joint-memoir on "the thermal effects of fluids in motion," 1852 (reprinted both in Joule's and Lord Kelvin's Scientific Papers), when it was shown that for air Mayer's hypothesis was approximately, but not absolutely, correct. So long, therefore, as the history of Mayer's reasoning was not completely known, it appeared as if he had by a kind of accident hit upon an approximately correct figure. See Tait, 'Recent Advances' (3rd ed., p. 53 ; but also Helm, 'Energetik,' p. 24, and Mach, 'Wärmelehre,' p. 249).

philosophical speculations which tended to prevent their ready acceptance, it cannot be denied that, as a first approximation, "his equivalent" was sufficiently near the truth to be practically useful.

But neither the happy generalisation of Mohr, which was lost or forgotten, nor the numerical estimate of Mayer, which remained unnoticed, succeeded in impressing contemporary philosophers with the importance of the subject. This was done almost at the same date, though quite independently, by the persistent and persevering experiments and measurements of James Prescott Joule, who laboured unnoticed and practically without support from 1841 to 1847, when he had the good fortune of gaining the attention and friendship of William Thomson (Lord Kelvin).[1]

13. Joule.

<hr />

[1] Joule not only defined more clearly the different data and conditions on which the correctness of the result must depend, but had also at his command a much greater wealth of novel experimental facts, brought together by his own resourceful mind. Thus from 1843 to 1850 he published no fewer than ten series of experiments, approximating from widely differing results to the true figure. See Helm's list ('Energetik,' p. 34). After he had laboured for more than five years his work was, in 1847, at the meeting of the British Association in Oxford, still almost unknown. He himself reports as follows in 1885 ('Joint Scientific Papers,' 1887, p. 215): "It was in the year 1843 that I read a paper 'On the Calorific Effects of Magneto-Electricity and the Mechanical Value of Heat' to the Chemical Section of the British Association at Cork. With the exception of some eminent men . . . the subject did not excite much general attention ; so that when I brought it forward again at the meeting in 1847 the chairman suggested that, as the business of the section pressed, I should not read any paper, but confine myself to a short verbal description of my experiments. This I endeavoured to do, and discussion not being invited, the communication would have passed without comment if a young man had not risen in the section, and by his intelligent observations created a lively interest in the new theory. The young man was William Thomson, who had two years previously passed the University of Cambridge with the highest honour, and is now probably the foremost scientific authority of the age." See also Lord Kelvin's account of the meeting in 1847 in 'Popular Lectures and Addresses' (London, 1894, vol. ii. p. 556, &c.)

A pupil of Dalton, Joule was early drawn into the circle of ideas and investigations which are contained in Faraday's experimental researches. With much ampler means, and possibly also with a greater love for accurate quantitative measurements, than Faraday possessed, he grasped the great importance of the law of electrolytic equivalence as affording the means of accurately measuring chemical processes, and of giving definite expression to the vaguer ideas supported by Faraday and others that force was indestructible, and that the different forces of nature were mutually convertible. These ideas had received popular circulation and current expression in Grove's celebrated lectures on the "Correlation of Physical Forces" in 1842 and 1843. Joule, in whose mind they seem to have existed as axioms, set himself to devise accurate instruments and methods by which the convertibility of different forces, their "mechanical duty," could be measured, and their equivalence put into figures. The first numbers which Joule found differed considerably,[1] so that the conclusion arrived at that the mechanical duty or "value" of a degree of heat is a constant quantity could only have been drawn by one who had a strong *a priori*[2] con-

[1] For details see Helm, 'Energetik,' p. 34; also vol. i. p. 265, note, of the present work. Joule's equivalent varied from 742 to 890 foot-pounds, and was finally fixed at 772 in 1850, this figure being correct to ½ per cent (Joule's 'Scientific Papers,' p. 328).

[2] Philosophical considerations are mixed up with all the early enunciations of the principle of the indestructibility of force, or energy as it was later more clearly termed.

A predisposition to believe that some quantity besides matter could not be lost or created, but only preserved and transformed, existed in the minds of Mohr, Séguin, Mayer, Colding, Joule, Hirn, and has been traced variously back to the writings of earlier thinkers, such as Montgolfier, Faraday, Davy, Oersted, Leibniz, &c. Prof. Mach ('Wärmelehre,' p. 238, &c.) discusses this point fully. The principle gradually became firmly

viction in that direction. The experimental result did not satisfy Helmholtz, who, about the same time, was led to consider the origin of animal heat in living organisms, a problem with which Liebig[1] had been greatly occupied for several years. Without himself devising or instituting new experiments, or attempting any determination of the equivalent as others—notably Colding and Holtzmann—were doing, Helmholtz, in 1847, undertook a theoretical investigation which has since become classical—a corner-stone in the philosophy of the subject. He first of all gave the principle involved a correct mathematical expression, showed how it could be considered as an extension of the theorem known in abstract dynamics as the conservation of the *vis viva* of a mechanical system, attempted to define the nature of forces, in the Newtonian sense, which would be subject to the new principle, and brought it into logical connection with the axiom laid down and used by French philosophers, that perpetual motion is an impossibility. After clearing the ground so far as abstract dynamics is concerned and giving the necessary definitions, sharply distinguishing between acting (living) forces and mere tensions (dead forces), Helmholtz proceeds to draw all

14.
Helmholtz.

established according as strict definitions, experimental proofs and figures, and mathematical formulæ took the place of vague speculations. Joule did the experimental, Helmholtz the mathematical, part of the work ; but it is interesting to see how little the latter without the former was able to impress contemporary German writers with the value of the principle which he established. He

himself even did not for a long time develop the line of reasoning which he had begun.

[1] See Helmholtz, 'Bericht über die Theorie der physiologischen Wärmeerscheinungen,' 1845, reprinted in 'Wissenschaftliche Abhandlungen,' vol. i. No. 1, also on Joule's early experiments in 'Ueber die Erhaltung der Kraft,' ibid., vol. i. p. 33.

other forces of nature into his consideration, showing, in the case of the phenomena of heat, electricity, galvanism, and magnetic induction, how the different agencies can be brought into comparison with mechanical ones by measuring the work they perform ; refers to the attempts to fix the mechanical value of heat; concludes in each case that no observed phenomena—not even the processes in living organisms—stand in contradiction with the principle announced, and ends with the words : " I think in the foregoing I have proved that the abovementioned law does not go against any hitherto known facts of natural science, but is supported by a large number of them in a striking manner.   I have tried to enumerate as completely as possible what consequences result from the combination of other known laws of nature, and how they require to be confirmed by further experiments.   The aim of this investigation, and what must excuse me likewise for its hypothetical sections, was to explain to natural philosophers the theoretical, practical, and heuristic importance of the law, the complete verification of which may well be looked upon as one of the main problems of physical science in the near future." [1]   The reasons why this valuable document attracted little attention at the time and was set aside, as were the earlier contributions of Mohr and Mayer, by the central organ of experimental physics abroad, are interesting from a historical point of view.   The first and main reason seems to have been that none of the three original and independent expressions contained any new experimental

[1] 'Gesammelte Abhandlungen,' vol. i. p. 67.

facts,[1] and that the then reigning school of natural philosophers in Germany discouraged theoretical deductions, as possibly leading back to the fatal "philosophy of nature," out of which they had only just escaped. Men of the intellectual eminence of Liebig, through whose labours an enormous mass of new facts had been accumulated, and who desired to see the more hidden processes of organic life subjected likewise to rigorous measurements, showed indeed a certain appreciation of the attempted definitions of Mohr and Mayer, struggling as he and they alike were under the still existing confusion in the fundamental conceptions.[2]   And these were not

[1] See Mohr, 'Allgemeine Theorie der Bewegung und der Kraft,' p. 82, &c. Poggendorf did not reply to Mayer's repeated communications and did not return the MS.; the fact that he received it was first established by Zöllner, who in 1877 recovered the MS. from Poggendorf's heirs (Mayer's ' Schriften und Briefe,' ed. Weyrauch, p. 100), and gave a facsimile of it in his ' Wissenschaftliche Abhandlungen' (Leipzig, vol. iv., 1881, p. 672). Helmholtz, who in 1847 had no knowledge of Mayer's writings, did full justice to his claims in his address, ' Ueber die Wechselwirkung der Naturkräfte' (1854), and vindicated them against Tait's criticisms in a letter published by the latter in his 'Sketch of Thermodynamics' (Edinburgh, 1868); see Helmholtz, ' Wissenschaftliche Abhandlungen,' vol. i. p. 71, &c. Helmholtz closes his later comments on the subject (' Vorträge und Reden,' vol. i., 3rd ed., 1884, p. 74) with the following significant remark : " The best ideas run the risk of remaining barren, if not accompanied by that energy which lasts till the convincing proof of

their correctness has been given." This explains the neglect of Mohr and Mayer, and why in England the interest in the energy ideas only became general after Joule's, Thomson's, and Rankine's labours, as Helmholtz himself remarks in 1854 (' Vorträge,' &c., p. 39).

[2] Helmholtz ("Ueber Mayers Priorität," ' Vorträge,' vol. i. p. 69) says : " That the [*i.e.* Mayer's] dissertation contained really important ideas, that it did not belong to the wide-ranging literature of vague suggestions, such as are annually served up by badly informed amateurs, could at best only be noticed by a reader who had already turned over in his mind similar reflections, and who could recognise them under the somewhat strange vocabulary of the author. Liebig, who, in the same year in which Mayer's dissertation appeared, published his book on animal chemistry, in which he fully discussed the question as to the origin of animal heat, was perhaps such a reader, and was therefore willing to insert the article in his annals." The same remark would refer equally to Mohr's earlier essay. It is now known

sufficiently cleared up in Mohr's short *aperçu*, which does not attempt to distinguish between the two different meanings of the word force, nor in the earlier papers of Mayer, who, however, in later writings shows a clear appreciation of the difficulty. In Helmholtz's memoirs the desired clearness was only attained by mathematical reasoning, which in his age and country was accessible to but few naturalists. The second and probably the fundamental obstacle in the way of a just recognition of the new truth lay in the fatal use of the term "force" in two distinct meanings. Popularly the difficulty has only been removed by the creation of a new vocabulary, and dates from the introduction of the term "work" by Clausius in 1850, and of the term "energy" by William Thomson, who adopted it from Young in the year 1852. The confusion which had been kept up by employing the word "force" to mean not only pressure or dead force (in the Newtonian sense) but also acting force (*vis viva* in the Leibnizian sense), and with this confusion the whole meaning of the great controversies which raged for many years between the Cartesians and Leibnizians on the correct measure of force, was then removed, and a grammatical and logical founda-

15.
"Work" and "energy" introduced by Clausius and Thomson.

from Mayer's published correspondence that some remarks of Liebig himself, which appeared early in 1842, induced him to send him his first paper in order "not to lose the right of priority" (letter to Griesinger, 5th-6th December 1842, in 'Schriften und Briefe,' ed. Weyrauch, p. 190). Mayer there says: "Liebig wrote to me, *inter alia*: 'As to what force, cause, and effect are, there exist in general such confused notions that an easily understood explanation must be considered to be of real value.' One would accordingly think that he himself considers himself quite above this general confusion; that this is not so, I could see sufficiently from his 'phenomena of motion in the animal organism' (Liebig, 'Die organische Chemie, &c.,' 1842, p. 183, &c.)"

tion secured on which a new generation could enter at once into the possession of correcter dynamical and physical views. It is now being recognised more and more that the word "force" applies only to a mathematical abstraction, whereas the word "energy" or "power to perform work" applies to a real quantity; and there are not wanting suggestions that the former should be altogether banished from scientific text-books, and that the latter denotes not merely a property of matter, but that it is after matter the only real thing or substance in the material world.[1]

This radical change in the fundamental notions which underlie all physical reasoning was not brought about, however, till the vaguer views expounded by Mayer in Germany, and the exact measurements of Joule in England, had been united by the independent labours of Thomson and Clausius, whose earliest researches (also carried on independently of each other) had been suggested by the

---

[1] The late Prof. P. G. Tait has on various occasions expressed himself in this sense. See his lecture on "Force," delivered before the British Association, Glasgow, in 1876, and reprinted in 'Recent Advances,' 3rd ed., also the closing paragraphs of his article "Mechanics," in the 9th ed. of the 'Ency. Brit.,' reprinted as 'Dynamics,' 1895, where he says (p. 356): "The only other known thing in the physical universe, which is conserved in the same sense as matter is conserved, is energy. Hence we naturally consider energy as the other objective reality in the physical universe, and look to it for information as to the true nature of what we call force;" and (p. 361): "In all methods and systems which involve the idea of force, there is the leaven of artificiality. The true foundations of the subject, based entirely on experiments of the most extensive kind, are to be found in the inertia of matter, and the conservation and transformation of energy. With the help of kinematical ideas, it is easy to base the whole science of dynamics on these principles; and there is no necessity for the introduction of the word 'force,' nor of the sense-suggested ideas on which it was originally based." We must, however, in that case extend the conception of matter to embrace also the ether (see Tait, 'Properties of Matter,' p. 5, 2nd ed.)

still earlier writings of Sadi Carnot and Clapeyron in
France. Thomson's interest in the subject dates from
the middle of the 'forties. He was then occupied with
finding a method for measuring heat on the absolute
scale. Mohr, Mayer, and Helmholtz all approached the
thermo-dynamical problem in the medical or physiological
interest. Trained in the school of Liebig and Johannes
Müller, they were led to study the economics of organic
processes and the mechanism of the physiological phenomena of animal heat, of motion, and of nutrition. Sadi
Carnot, as after him Clapeyron in France and Joule in
Manchester, approached the thermo-dynamical problem
from the side of practical interests, created by the introduction and universal application of steam in the useful
arts. The great change worked by the steam-engine,
especially in England, the utilisation of coal and iron-
stone, the foundation of England's growing industrial
wealth, seemed to Sadi Carnot to be concentrated in the
problem of the motive power of heat; as to Liebig, the
key which would unlock the mysteries of vegetable
growth, of animal nutrition, and of human labour, with
their economic, industrial, and political aspects, lay in
the problem of combustion. As in the domain of electrical science, so in that of thermotics, the first thing to
do was to arrive at a correct method of measuring heat
as distinguished from temperature. It was a problem of
applied mathematics. About the same time Gauss had
established the system of absolute measurement from a
universal point of view, and he and Weber had applied
it to magnetic and electrical phenomena. Thomson
set himself to do the same thing in thermotics, and

he found in the ideas expounded by Poncelet, Sadi
Carnot, and Clapeyron, the means of accomplishing the
object.   We now see how there lay, in the fundamental
problem of thermo-dynamics, the unifying idea of sciences
hitherto far apart and working on independent lines and
with independent standards of measurement, speaking, as
it were, separate languages.   And what was the new idea
which lay concealed in Sadi Carnot's forgotten pamphlet ? [1]
In Carnot's original memoir it appears as an axiom at
the beginning of his reflections.   " The production of
motion," he says, " in steam-engines is always accompanied
by a circumstance on which we must fix our attention.
This circumstance is the re-establishment of equilibrium,
or level, in the caloric—that is to say, its passage from
one body where the temperature is more or less elevated,

[1] The story of Sadi Carnot's
memoir is not less curious than that
of Mohr's first paper.   It was first
given by Lord Kelvin in his earliest
article, " On an Absolute Thermo-
metric Scale" (1848), reprinted in
' Math. and Phys. Papers,' vol. i.
p. 100), and "An Account of Carnot's Theory " (1849, ibid., p. 113).
He had in 1845 searched in vain for
the ' Puissance motrice du Feu ' in
all the bookshops of Paris.   In 1848
he obtained a copy from Lewis
Gordon in Glasgow.   It was known
to him before through Clapeyron's
memoir in the 14th vol. of the
' Journal de l'École polytechnique '
(1834).   Sadi Carnot published his
memoir as a pamphlet in 1824.   It
has since been republished by his
brother, Hippolyte Carnot (' Réflexions sur la Puissance motrice du
Feu et sur les Machines propres à
développer cette Puissance,' Paris,
Gauthier-Villars, 1878), with important posthumous papers, from
which, inter alia, it is evident that

Carnot, before he died, had abandoned the material theory of heat,
and actually, by an unknown process, calculated the mechanical
equivalent of heat as 360 kilogram-
mètres.   As in several other cases,
so also in that of Sadi Carnot, the
line of reasoning initiated by Laplace, and brilliantly developed by
his school, militated against the
acceptance of the dynamical as
opposed to the material conception
of the phenomena of heat ; and
M. Bertin, in his "Rapport sur le
Progrès de la Thermodynamique en
France " (' Recueil de Rapports,'
&c., p. 5) could write in 1867 : "Il
faut bien l'avouer, pareeque c'est la
vérité : nous sommes restés longtemps, je ne dis pas rebelles, mais
étrangers aux nouvelles idées : elles
nous sont restées trop longtemps
inconnues, et encore aujourd'hui,
on peut regretter qu'elles n'occupent
pas une place plus considérable dans
notre enseignement scientifique."

to another where it is lower. . . . The production of moving force is therefore due in steam-engines, not to a real consumption of caloric, but to a transference from a hot body to a cold body." [1]

If it is the object of physical science to describe the processes of nature completely and in the simplest language, we have here an instance of a description of a very general property in very simple language, and in terms which reduce it to a measurable quantity. Without this, progress is impossible. It is not likely, however, that Carnot saw the full significance of his simple statement, how in it he had introduced into physical and mathematical science the great question of the availability of the forces of nature, as Mohr and Mayer in Germany, and Faraday and Grove in England, somewhat later, dwelt on the correlation or interchangeability of those forces. The two ideas were separately developed. When they came together in one mind, when Thomson fully realised the importance and meaning of both —as he undoubtedly did earlier than any other natural philosopher—he at once established the great doctrine of the dissipation, also called degradation or depreciation, of energy. But it required some modification of Carnot's enunciation of this general property before it could be put into its modern form. This modification was preparing itself in Carnot's own mind, as his papers, posthumously published, have revealed to us.[2] What required to be modified was the word

17.
Carnot introduces the idea of "avail-ability."

18.
Thomson introduces the idea of "dis-sipation."

---

[1] Carnot, 'Puissance motrice,' ed. 1878, pp. 5 and 6.

[2] His notebook contained the following entry ('Puissance motrice,' ed. 1878, p. 90) : "Lorsqu'une hypothèse ne suffit plus à l'explication des phénomènes, elle doit être abandonnée. C'est le cas où se

caloric. Carnot was brought up under the influence of
the school that looked upon heat as an imponderable
substance which might hide itself—might become latent
—but could not be created or destroyed. This was
the view of Black, of Laplace, of Fourier; it was not the
view of Cavendish, of Davy, of Rumford. The views
of the former were embodied in great treatises, and consistently worked out with much collateral extension of
physical and mathematical knowledge; the views of the
latter were expressed in detached experiments and .in

19.
Fourier.

casual reflections. Fourier[1] had just (1822) given to
the world his epoch-making work, the 'Théorie analytique de la Chaleur,' in which he had stated that " the
properties of heat form a special order of phenomena
which are not to be explained by principles of motion
and equilibrium;"[2] and again, "There exists a very

trouve l'hypothèse par laquelle on
considère le calorique comme une
matière, comme un fluide subtil."
Again (p. 92) : "La chaleur est le résultat d'un mouvement. Alors il est
tout simple qu'elle puisse se produire
par la consommation de puissance
motrice et qu'elle puisse produire
cette puissance. Tous les autres
phénomènes . . . pourraient s'expliquer dans cette hypothèse : mais il
serait difficile de dire pourquoi, dans
le développement de la puissance
motrice par la chaleur, un corps
froid est nécessaire, pourquoi, en
consommant la chaleur d'un corps
échauffé, on ne peut pas produire
du mouvement." And (pp. 93 and
94) : " Lorsque l'on fait naître de la
puissance motrice, par le passage de
la chaleur du corps A au corps B, la
quantité de cette chaleur qui arrive
à B, cette quantité est - elle la
même, quel que soit le corps em-

ployé à réaliser la puissance motrice ?
Y aurait-il moyen de consommer
plus de chaleur à la production de
la puissance motrice et d'en faire
arriver moins au corps B ? Pourrait-
on même la consommer tout entière
sans en faire arriver au corps B ?
Si cela était possible, on pourrait
créer de la puissance motrice sans
consommation de combustible et
par simple destruction de la chaleur
des corps." And (p. 94) : "La
chaleur n'est autre chose que la
puissance motrice, ou plutôt que le
mouvement qui a changé de forme.
C'est un movement dans les particules des corps."

[1] On the tardy reception and
recognition of Fourier's work see
vol. i. p. 241, note, of this work.

[2] 'Théorie analytique de la
Chaleur,' 1822 : 'Discours préliminaire,' p. iii.

extensive class of phenomena which are not produced by mechanical forces, but which result solely from the presence and accumulation of heat. This part of natural philosophy cannot be brought under dynamical theories; it has principles peculiar to itself, and is based upon a method similar to that of the other exact sciences.[1] . . . The dilatations, indeed, caused by the repulsive force of heat, the observation of which dilatations serves as a measure of temperature, are dynamical effects; but it is not these dilatations which we calculate when we investigate the laws of the propagation of heat."[2] He proceeds to build up this new science "upon a very small number of simple facts, of which the causes are unknown, but which are gathered by observation and confirmed by experiments,"[3] and he thus arrives at certain general relations, expressed in the form of equations, which are different from, though analogous to, and not less rigorous than, the general equations of dynamics.

One of the great experimental facts upon which Fourier bases his theory of the propagation (i.e., the conduction and radiation) of heat is this, that all motion of heat depends on differences of temperature. He examines how differences of temperature are equalised and deduces the law of the flow of heat.[4] Although he does

[1] Fourier, 'Théorie analytique,' p. 13.   [2] Ibid., p. 14.
[3] Ibid., pp. xi, 18, 39.
[4] I cannot here omit to point out how elegantly Prof. Mach has translated into the language of common-sense the whole process of Fourier for establishing the fundamental equation of the theory. See his 'Principien der Wärmelehre' (Leipzig, 1896), pp. 78, &c., 116 sqq. Every student of physics should read the chapters referring to this subject. The mathematical formulæ will thus become living to him; but he will also see how necessary the abstract mathematical expression of common-sense conceptions is in order to avoid false reasoning.

not find it necessary to enter upon any theory of the nature of heat, the analogy with the flow of water from higher to lower levels would naturally present itself. For his purpose this analogy had no importance. For the purposes of Sadi Carnot, who noticed that upon the difference of temperature depended not only the flow of heat, but also the work it might eventually do, the same analogy seemed all-important. "We may," he says, "justly compare the motive power of heat with that of a fall of water: both have a maximum which cannot be exceeded. The motive power of a fall of water depends upon its height and the quantity of the liquid; the motive power of heat likewise depends on the quantity of caloric employed and on what we will take the liberty of calling the height of its drop—that is, the difference of temperature of the bodies between which the exchange of caloric has taken place."[1] In this analogy two further assumptions seem to be implied: First, that the work capable of being done is in direct proportion to the difference of levels of height or of temperature; secondly, that the quantities with which we operate, of water or of caloric, remain the same, before and after the fall. Neither of these inferences is necessary; neither is permissible. Carnot does not adopt the first inference,[2] but he does adopt the second,[3] though he significantly remarks that the

20.
His influence on Carnot.

[1] 'Puissance motrice du feu,' ed. 1878, p. 15.

[2] "Dans la chute d'eau, la puissance motrice est rigoureusement proportionelle à la différence de niveau entre le réservoir supérieur et le réservoir inférieur. Dans la chute du calorique, la puissance motrice augmente sans doute avec la différence de température entre le corps chaud et le corps froid ; mais nous ignorons si elle est proportionelle à cette différence" (ibid., p. 15 ; compare also pp. 38, 39).

[3] " La production de la puissance

foundations on which the theory of heat rests require careful examination.[1] Further thought evidently led him to doubt the correctness of the second assumption. It is the first point to which Thomson, more than twenty years after, directs his attention. He conceives the idea of measuring temperature by such a scale that for an equal drop in the scale—*i.e.*, by letting down heat by an equal number of degrees on the new scale—equal amounts of work shall be done.[2] The speculations of Sadi Carnot remained unnoticed for a long time. Ten years later Clapeyron[3] reverted to the subject, and put the reflections of Carnot into graphical form and into mathematical language. He introduced the conception, based on Carnot's theory, of the ratio of heat transferred from a higher to a lower level of temperature to the maximum of work obtainable,—a quantity independent of the substance employed,—and he called this fixed ratio Carnot's function. It was through his paper that

21.
Clapeyron's graphical method.

motrice est . . . due . . . non à une consommation réelle du calorique, mais à son transport d'un corps chaud à un corps froid, c'est-à-dire à son rétablissement d'équilibre" (ibid., p. 6).

[1] "Au reste, pour le dire en passant, les principaux fondements sur lesquelles repose la théorie de la chaleur auraient besoin de l'examen le plus attentif. Plusieurs faits d'expérience paraissent à peu près inexplicables dans l'état actuel de cette théorie" (ibid., p. 20, note). "La loi fondamentale que nous avions en vue . . . est assise sur la théorie de la chaleur telle qu'on la conçoit aujourd'hui, et il faut l'avouer, cette base ne nous parait pas d'une solidité inébranlable" (p. 50). As stated above (p. 118, note), Carnot emancipated himself from the conventional or material view of the nature of heat. See the appendix to the edition of 1878.

[2] See 'Cambridge Philosophical Society Proceedings,' June 1848 ; reprinted in Thomson's (Lord Kelvin's) 'Math. and Phys. Papers,' vol. i. p. 100.

[3] Benoît Pierre Émile Clapeyron was an engineer. In 1834 he published, in the fourteenth cahier of the 'Journal de l'École Polytechnique,' his "Mémoire sur la Puissance motrice de la Chaleur." It was through a translation of this paper in 'Taylor's Scientific Memoirs' that Thomson heard about Carnot's earlier work, and through a translation in Poggendorf's 'Annalen' (1843) that Helmholtz became acquainted with the subject.

Helmholtz in Germany, and Thomson in England, heard about Sadi Carnot himself. Sadi Carnot, so much earlier and so unlike Mayer, had nevertheless one point in common with him. This point seems to have given a common anchorage to all those thinkers who, in the course of a generation, gradually lifted the theory of heat and energy out of twilight into clear thought. Sadi Carnot, Mayer, Joule, Helmholtz, Thomson, all express or imply the same idea — viz., the impossibility of a perpetual motion.[1] In one form or other this seems

22.
Perpetual
motion
impossible.

[1] The conception of a "perpetual motion," or, as it is termed abroad, of a "perpetuum mobile," and that of its impossibility, have been changed and more clearly defined in the course of the hundred years which followed the decision of the Paris Academy of Sciences in 1775 not to receive in future any scheme of perpetual motion. Into the same class of axiomatic impossibilities were also thrown the "squaring of the circle" and the "trisection of the angle." Helmholtz (appendix to his Lecture on 'Die Wechselwirkung der Naturkräfte,' 1853, dated 1883) remarks that the proof of the impossibility did not then exist, and that the resolution was therefore based merely on the experience of past failures. The doctrine of Energy, the arithmetical discoveries of Gauss, and the elegant researches of Hermite and Lindemann, have thrown much light on these celebrated problems. In the last chapter of this volume I shall revert to the two latter; as to the first, the "perpetual motion," what follows may tend to clear the popular conceptions. Tait has correctly remarked that "perpetual motion is simply a statement of Newton's first law of Motion" ('Recent Advances,' 3rd ed., p. 74). He might have added that it took probably as much ingenuity on the part of Galileo to arrive at the principle of inertia—viz., that "all motion is perpetual until force interferes to alter and modify it"—as it took to formulate correctly the other principle that such a perpetual motion is of no use, because you cannot do any work with it, except by using it up or annihilating it. In the beginning of the nineteenth century the impossibility of a mechanical device for the so-called perpetual motion was universally admitted, though —as Rosenberger ('Geschichte der Physik,' vol. iii. p. 229, note) remarks — this was not also extended to physical processes, it being taught that the processes of nature represented a "perpetual cycle which uninterruptedly renewed itself." In fact, the truth was beginning to dawn that if motive power or energy could not be obtained out of nothing neither could it be destroyed. Carnot in 1824, and Mayer in 1842, both take it as an axiom that power cannot be created; Mohr in 1837, and Joule in 1843 and 1845, are equally convinced that power cannot be

to be an axiom with them, but even this apparently simple article of faith in natural philosophy meant something different to different thinkers according to the greater or less clearness of their physical conceptions. Helmholtz, in his celebrated memoir of 1847, conceives all natural processes to be ultimately reducible to purely mechanical processes, and in doing so he sees that a well-known law in mechanics, the conservation of the *vis viva*, must have a meaning for all natural forces. This he proceeds to develop. Others, like Faraday, Mohr, Grove, have a silent conviction that besides ponderable matter there is some other quantity in nature which is indestructible and cannot be created, but only changed and transferred ; they frequently call it force, and thus entangle themselves or their readers in

destroyed. Under the influence of Oersted's philosophy Colding expresses similar ideas in 1843 (see 'Phil. Mag.'), 4th series, vol. xxvii. p. 58). In fact, during the fifth decade of the century the three conceptions of the impossibility of creating power, its indestructibility, and the convertibility of its different forms, were more and more clearly enunciated. They were at last expressed in the formula of the " conservation of energy." It was Thomson (Lord Kelvin) who then—in 1852—first clearly recognised that the old phantom of a perpetual motion was turning up again in a new form. (See his Essay on " Dissipation of Energy " in the 'Fortnightly Review,' March 1892, reprinted in ' Popular Lectures and Addresses,' vol. ii. p. 452.) Ever since Thomson's essay of 1852 naturalists and philosophers may be said to be trying to formulate in the simplest terms the great principle of nature, that though energy is never lost, it becomes — for our practical purposes — unavailable. Prof. Ostwald has expressed this by reviving the terminology of the perpetual motion. " It is not generally recognised that the principle of perpetual motion has two sides. On the one side . . . perpetual motion could be realised if one could create energy. . . . The expression of the impossibility of doing this is the first law of Energetics. . . . A perpetual motion could, however, on the other side be attained if it were possible to induce the large store of energy at rest to enter into transformations. . . . This might be termed a perpetual motion of the second kind." The impossibility of this Ostwald terms the second principle of Energetics (' Allgemeine Chemie,' vol. ii. part 1, p. 472 ; cf. Helm ' Energetik,' p. 304).

that confusion which the indefinite use of the word had caused, especially among Continental writers. One of the first practical applications of this idea as referred to the motive power of heat in Carnot's sense was made by William and James Thomson in 1849. They had both fully realised that lowering of temperature might be accompanied by the doing of work by heat, and that elevation of heat to a higher temperature meant expense of work. If, therefore, work could be done by heat without lowering the temperature, there was an apparent gain of motive power without corresponding expenditure. It was known that water at freezing temperature expanded in becoming ice : it was capable of doing work, frequently very destructive work, without a lowering of temperature. In order to convert water into ice of the same temperature, heat must be abstracted. Here, then, was a case of a possible transference of heat without fall of temperature, and the creation or gain of great power to do work; but, according to Carnot's principle, equality of temperature implied an absence of expenditure of work. So here was a case of gain without expenditure of power simply by a transference of heat at freezing-point. James Thomson [1] saw the solution of the paradox. If water

23.
Application by William and James Thomson.

[1] The reasoning of James Thomson, based again upon the impossibility of a perpetual motion, is given in the following passage of his communication to the Royal Society of Edinburgh, dated January 2, 1849 (reprinted in his brother, Lord Kelvin's, 'Math. and Phys. Papers,' vol. i. p. 156) : "Some time ago my brother, Prof. William Thomson, pointed out to me a curious conclusion to which he had been led by reasoning on principles similar to those developed by Carnot with reference to the motive power of heat. It was that water at the freezing-point may be converted into ice by a process solely mechanical, and yet without the final expenditure of any mechanical work. This at first appeared to me to involve an impossibility, because water expands while

in expanding by freezing is made to do work, it over-comes pressure; it has to freeze under pressure. The temperature of water freezing under pressure must be lower than that of water freezing under ordinary conditions.[1] Knowing the mechanical duty of a degree of temperature and the work of the expansion of ice, he could calculate how much the freezing-point of water must be lowered by pressure. In 1850 his brother William Thomson verified this theoretical prediction by actual experiment.[2] It is well known how Helmholtz in 1865 made use of this theoretically predicted and practically verified phenomenon in his celebrated glacier theory.[3] Both James and William Thomson, when they drew the conclusions from Carnot's theory, still adhered to the doctrine of the entire conservation of heat.[4] But William Thomson, who was equally ac-

freezing; and therefore it seemed to follow that if a quantity of it were merely enclosed in a vessel with a movable piston and frozen, the motion of the piston consequent on the expansion being resisted by pressure, mechanical work would be given out without any corresponding expenditure; or, in other words, a perpetual source of mechanical work, commonly called a perpetual motion, would be possible. . . . To avoid the absurdity of supposing that mechanical work could be got out of nothing, it occurred to me that it is necessary further to conclude that the freezing-point becomes lower as the pressure to which the water is subjected is increased."

[1] "The mechanical pressure promotes—as is generally the case with the alternate action of different forces in nature — such a change, viz., melting of ice, as is favourable

to the effect of its own action" (Helmholtz, 'Vorträge und Reden,' vol. i. p. 217).

[2] 'Proceedings of the Roy. Soc. of Edinburgh,' January 1850, reprinted in 'Math. and Phys. Papers,' vol. i. p. 165.

[3] Helmholtz, *loc. cit.*, p. 215 *sqq.*, where also the phenomenon discovered and called "regelation of ice," by Faraday, is similarly explained.

[4] It is important to notice this, as the formula with which we are now familiar, that the mechanical work gained meant consumption of heat, was not available at that time. This is significantly pointed out by Helm ('Energetik,' p. 69). The reasoning was accordingly more difficult and refined. James Thomson, however, had at the time some misgivings on the then prevalent view, and in a footnote he refers to the "possibility of the absolute

quainted with Carnot's ideas and with Joule's work, increasingly felt the necessity of reconciling both views in one consistent view. So did Clausius independently at Zürich. The result was the doctrine of the "conservation of energy,"—not of heat, as Carnot had it,—and the embodiment of the two correct ideas contained independently in Carnot's and Joule's work in the two well-known laws of thermo-dynamics [1] — viz., the conservation, equivalence, and convertibility of energy, as

24.
The two
laws of
thermo-
dynamics.

formation or destruction of heat as an equivalent for the destruction or formation of other agencies, such as mechanical work" ('Math. and Phys. Papers' vol. i. p. 161, note). The acceptance of the doctrine of the convertibility of heat and mechanical work — implying the conservation of energy in place of the conservation of heat, as Carnot had it—seems to have taken place in Lord Kelvin's mind immediately after his paper referred to above in consequence of a paper by Rankine "On the Mechanical Action of Heat" (Roy. Soc. Edinburgh, Feb. 1850), as is shown by his letter to Joule, dated October 1850 (loc. cit., vol. i. p. 170). He there refers also to a memoir by Clausius in Poggendorf's 'Annalen' of April and May of the same year as adopting "Joule's axiom instead of Carnot's" (ibid., p. 173).

[1] The reconciliation of Joule's dynamical theory of heat with Carnot's doctrine, and the necessary modification of the latter, is contained in Lord Kelvin's classical memoir, "On the Dynamical Theory of Heat," in the 'Trans. of the Roy. Soc. of Edinburgh,' March 1851 ('Math. and Phys. Papers,' vol. i. p. 173 sqq.) In the introduction, Davy, Mayer, Joule, and notably Liebig, are mentioned as earlier supporters of the doctrine

of the convertibility of heat into mechanical effect, Rankine and Clausius as the latest contributors (p. 176). The first and celebrated enunciation of the second law by Thomson is given at the very beginning (p. 179), and in the sequel the denial of it is shown to mean the possibility of a perpetual motion. A little farther on Thomson refers to Clausius in the words : "The merit of first establishing the proposition upon correct principles is entirely due to Clausius, who published his demonstration of it in the month of May last year" (1850). It has on the other side been admitted by Clausius ('Die mechanische Wärmetheorie,' 2te Aufl., 1876, vol. i. p. 358) that Thomson's independent development of the second law, though published later, is conducted from a more general point of view, whereas his own treatment was purely mathematical and confined to special cases. The most general and philosophical expression of the new principle was given by Thomson in his celebrated communication to the Royal Society of Edinburgh, April 19, 1852, "On a Universal Tendency in Nature to the Dissipation of Mechanical Energy" (reprinted in 'Math. and Phys. Papers,' vol. i. p. 511).

expressed in the first law, and the doctrine of the availability of energy as expressed in the second law.   It was Thomson who first clearly saw that the axiom of the impossibility of a perpetual motion would be infringed if the first law of thermo-dynamics—the indestructibility of energy—was accepted without the second.   For practical use, for doing work, it is not sufficient that energy be not lost ; it must be available—get-at-able.   Energy may be in a condition in which it is useless—hidden away— and to bring it forth again may either be for us impossible (if it be dissipated), or may require an expenditure of work—*i.e.,* of energy—to do so.   The second law puts into mathematical language another very important and very striking property of the processes in nature.   Let us dwell on this a moment.

The doctrine of the preservation of energy, of the equivalence of the different forms of energy, tended to put all the forms of energy on the same level.   If they be convertible, they appear to be of the same value. If in doing work, energy was not consumed but only changed, it stood to reason that it might be changed back again, so that the work could be done over again. In other words, if all processes are purely mechanical processes—modes of motion—a supposition which very early forced itself with more or less clearness on the pioneers of the science of energy, they must be reversible : it must be possible to turn them round again, to undo what has been done, or to do what has been undone. Now the common-sense view of nature tells us at once that this is impossible ; but it does not seem to have struck the earlier propounders of the doctrine of the equivalence and correlation of forces, such as Faraday, Mohr, Mayer, Grove—not even Joule and Helmholtz— that if neither matter nor power is lost, the phenomena of loss and waste in nature and in human life remain unexplained. The only mind to whom this problem presented itself was Sadi Carnot, and it presented itself to him in an extreme form; for he started with the idea that even heat itself in doing work was not lost or destroyed, but handed over from the hotter body (the boiler of the steam-engine) to the colder body (the condenser of the steam-engine). We now know that this view was not correct—that the whole heat is not handed over, but always only a portion of the heat. But, with this exaggerated view in his mind, he tried to explain the phenomena of loss and waste, and he conceived that the explanation lay in the lowering of the temperature. " It would be difficult to say why " — though he had assumed it as an axiom that—" in the development of motive power by heat, a cold body should be necessary, why in consuming the heat of a heated body we cannot produce motion." [1]   Heat at high temperature is of more value for doing work than the same amount of heat at

---

[1] The words quoted are taken from one of the fragments published in the year 1878 by H. Carnot from the posthumous MSS. of his brother, Sadi Carnot. In this fragment he approaches the modern conception that heat is the result of motion : he sees that all other phenomena can be explained by this hypothesis ; but he pauses after having stated the difficulty quoted above in the text, and reverts, after some further queries, to the same diffi- culty in the words, "Can one con- sume the heat entirely without letting any arrive at the body B [viz., from a body A]? If this were possible, one could create motive power without consumption of fuel, and simply by the destruction of the heat of bodies " (' Puissance motrice, &c.,' ed. 1878, pp. 92 and 94). It is interesting to see how nearly these reflections approach to those made more than twenty years later by Thomson.

low temperature.   By doing work, as also by conduction, and radiation with absorption, this inequality of temperature is spent, *i.e.*, lost.   Clausius and Thomson alone seem to have grasped the value of this conception.   The difficulty was to put it into mathematical language—into calculable terms.   Each did this independently. Thomson, more than any other thinker, put the problem into common-sense language, brought the subject home to the practical reason ; at the same time he put it into mathematical language, allowing the conceptions of waste [1] and of value and of availability (or usefulness) of energy to be scientifically—that is, measurably—defined.   In 1851 he put the axiom upon which Carnot's reasoning is based (without knowing the words of Carnot quoted above) into the following words : [2]   " It is impossible by means of inanimate material agency to derive mechanical effect from any portion of matter by cooling it below the temperature of the coldest of the surrounding objects." He saw at once, when adopting Joule's doctrine of the convertibility of heat and mechanical work, that, if all processes in the world be reduced to those of a perfect

---

[1] The term "wasted," as distinguished from "annihilated," is first introduced in Part 1 of the "Dynamical Theory of Heat," 1851, p. 189 of 'Math. and Phys. Papers,' vol. i. ; and in the following year, in a paper read before the Royal Society of Edinburgh on the 19th of April, entitled, "On a Universal Tendency in Nature to the Dissipation of Mechanical Energy," the subject is brought home to the general understanding by a succession of short theses referring to the dissipation and possible limited restoration of energy ('Papers,' vol. i. p. 511, &c.)

[2] 'Math. and Phys. Papers,' vol. i. pp. 179, 511.   Helmholtz ('Vorträge und Reden,' vol. i. p. 43) said in 1854 : "In any case we must admire the acumen of Thomson, who could read between the letters of a mathematical equation, for some time known, which spoke only of heat, volume, and pressure of bodies, conclusions which threaten the universe, though indeed only in infinite time, with eternal death."

mechanism, they will have this property of a perfect
machine, namely, that it can work backward as well as
forward.   It is against all reason and common-sense
to carry out this idea in its integrity and completeness.
" The essence of Joule's discovery is the subjection of
physical phenomena to dynamical law.   If, then, the
motion of every particle of matter in the universe were
precisely reversed at any instant, the course of nature
would be simply reversed for ever after.   The bursting
bubble of foam at the foot of a waterfall would reunite
and descend into the water; the thermal motions would
reconcentrate their energy and throw the mass up the
fall in drops, re-forming into a close column of ascending
water.   Heat which had been generated by the friction
of solids and dissipated by conduction and radiation with
absorption, would come again to the place of contact and
throw the moving body back against the force to which
it had previously yielded.   Boulders would recover from
the mud the materials required to rebuild them into
their previous jagged forms, and would become re-united
to the mountain-peak from which they had formerly
broken away.   And also, if the materialistic hypothesis
of life were true, living creatures would grow backwards
with conscious knowledge of the future, but with no
memory of the past, and would become again unborn.
But the real phenomena of life infinitely transcend
human science; and speculation regarding consequences
of their imagined reversal is utterly unprofitable.   Far
otherwise, however, is it in respect to the reversal of the
motions of matter uninfluenced by life, a very elementary
consideration of which leads to the full explanation of

25.
Summary
statement
of Thomson
(Lord
Kelvin).

the theory of dissipation of energy." [1] Whilst Clausius in Germany and Thomson in England were busy reconciling the truths contained in Carnot's older researches with the new conceptions firmly established by Joule's classical measurements, putting both into mathematical and into popular language, correcting our mathematical formulæ as well as our vocabulary, other applications of the new ideas assisted in procuring for them general recognition and acceptance. Rankine [2] in England, Zeuner [3] in Ger-

26.
Rankine, Zeuner, and Hirn.

[1] Lord Kelvin, in a paper read before the Royal Society of Edinburgh, 2nd February 1874, on "The Kinetic Theory of the Dissipation of Energy" ('Proceedings,' vol. viii. p. 325 *sqq.*) See also his article in the 'Fortnightly Review' for March 1892, reprinted in 'Popular Lectures and Addresses,' vol. ii. p. 449 *sqq.*

[2] The earliest formal treatise on thermo-dynamics was Macquorn Rankine's article on "The Mechanical Action of Heat" in Nichol's 'Cyclopædia' for the year 1855. The part he took in the development of the new science was practical and at the same time highly speculative. His papers on temperature and elasticity of steam and other vapours, on the expansion of liquids by heat, and on the mechanical action of heat, of dates 1849 and 1850 (see 'Miscellaneous Scientific Papers,' ed. Millar, 1881, pp. 1, 16, 234), entitle him to be considered as one of the first—if not the first (see his claim to priority in a letter in Poggendorf's 'Annalen,' p. 81, 1850)—to reconcile Carnot's discovery with the mechanical view. His investigations were peculiar, combining practical applications of great value and important predictions (see Tait's memoir prefaced to Rankine's 'Papers,' p. xxix) with daring

speculation ; his deductions being founded on his theory of molecular vortices. Though he exerted in this country a great influence on the early workers in thermo-dynamics, his theories were scarcely relished in Germany (see Helmholtz's criticism of Rankine's methods in 1853, quoted by Helm, 'Energetik,' p. 114), where Clausius's independent and simultaneous researches on the same subject had meanwhile usurped attention. But Rankine's 'Manual of Applied Mechanics' (1857), his 'Manual of the Steam-engine and other Prime Motors' (1859), were the first books of practical application in which, through a happy nomenclature and an extensive use of graphical methods (Watt's indicator diagram and Carnot's cycle), the new ideas were introduced to a wider circle. See Helm's estimate of Rankine's work in 'Energetik,' p. 116 *sqq.*

[3] Somewhat later than Rankine in this country, Zeuner in Switzerland and Germany, following upon Clausius's theoretical memoirs, introduced the mechanical treatment of practical heat-problems. His 'Grundzüge der mechanischen Wärmetheorie' (1860) was to many a revelation. Appearing about the time when the German mechanical and chemical industries were starting upon a new development,

many, and Hirn [1] in France, studied the most important of all machines then in use, the steam-engine, in the light of the new discoveries. It became possible to define clearly what was meant by the efficiency of an engine, and to distinguish between those losses of the energy of heat or temperature which were dependent on the use of steam as the working substance, and therefore inherent and unavoidable, and those losses which depended upon the mechanism and upon the carrying out of the process employed. The older teachings contained in treatises written before a knowledge, or even an idea, of the

largely based upon the scientific training afforded in the excellent chemical laboratories and polytechnic schools of Germany, it assisted in giving to German industrial enterprise that scientific character which was at first ridiculed and has latterly been extolled in unbounded measure, and which—combined with the organising ability inherited from English ancestry—seems to be one of the distinctive features of the great industrial progress of America. First among writers on the Continent Zeuner gave such a connected exposition of the principles developed by Clausius, Thomson, and Rankine as met the requirements of practical engineers; attached to them applications referring to the steam-engine; criticised the views adopted by Watt and later writers, notably de Pambour, with reference to the behaviour of saturated vapour in the steam-cylinder during expansion and compression; and largely prepared the way for the great improvements in steam, air, and refrigerating engines which have been brought out on the Continent by those trained in his school. Through Clausius, Zeuner,

and others, Dingler's ' Polytechnic Journal' became the organ by which the many discussions on the new mechanical theory, and notably the second law of thermo-dynamics, gradually forced themselves upon the attention of practical men.

[1] Equally important were the labours of Adolph Hirn (1815-90). He was a self-made man who had grown up in the midst of the important textile industry of Alsace. With a naturally inquiring disposition he combined the scientific and artistic accomplishments for the manifestation of which the chemical and mechanical products of that country have long been renowned. He approached some of the great theoretical problems connected with practical engineering, such as those of heat, steam, lubrication, and superheating, by a long series of carefully planned experiments. A very interesting account by several authors is given in a publication by Faudel and Schwoerer (' G. A. Hirn, sa Vie, sa Famille, ses Travaux,' Paris, 1893). Hirn, like Rankine, was not only an engineer, but also an artist and a philosopher.

mechanical value and the availability of heat existed, had to be largely altered, and corrected notions laid down, frequently as a result of prolonged discussion.[1] As an example, I may refer to the controversy between Hirn and Zeuner as to the cause of the great discrepancy between the theoretical and practical figures referring to the work in the steam-cylinder, the so-called " Water or Iron " controversy.[2]

But whilst it must be admitted that the corrected views regarding the nature of heat—the preservation

---

[1] The best account of the practical bearings of the mechanical theories of Rankine and Clausius is to be found in Prof. Unwin's " Forrest Lecture," delivered 2nd May 1895, before the Institute of Civil Engineers, and published in the 'Electrician,' vol. xxxv. p. 46 *sqq.* and p. 77 *sqq.* He there refers to the great discrepancy between the "rational" and the "experimental" theories, and to Hirn's experiments and practical results, notably with the "steam-jacket," and his introduction of "superheating"· in 1855. "No doubt the rational theory altogether underrated the enormous facility of heat-exchange, which arises out of the contact between a conducting cylinder-wall and a vapour in a condition of the greatest instability, and liable to condense or evaporate on the slightest change of thermal condition" (p. 50). The several controversies through which Clausius defended and gradually elucidated the somewhat obscure statement which he gave of the so-called second law of thermo-dynamics may be studied with advantage in the 2nd edition of his collected Memoirs ('Die mechanische Wärmetheorie,' Braunschweig, vol. i., 1876), where his replies to criticisms of Holtz-

mann, Decher, Zeuner, Rankine, Wand, and Tait are most instructive. A good account is also given in Baynes's 'Lessons on Thermodynamics,' Oxford, 1878, p. 103 *sqq.*

[2] See Prof. Unwin, *loc. cit.*, p. 79. " On the appearance of Isherwood's researches in 1863, the discrepancy between the rational theory and the results of experiment were recognised by Rankine and others. But the conditions of the steam-cylinder condensation are so complex that for a long time the more theoretical writers practically ignored both Hirn's and Isherwood's results. Zeuner perhaps had pushed the rational theory to the furthest limit of detail, and with the greatest insight into practical conditions. But it was not till 1881 that he began to explicitly admit the largeness and importance of the condensing action of the cylinder. Zeuner then was disposed to attribute initial condensation to the presence of a permanent and not inconsiderable mass of water in the clearance space of the engine. . . . In opening a discussion with Hirn in 1881, Zeuner wrote that if the presence of water in the clearance space was conceded, the Alsatian calculations would be

and waste (degradation) of energy, have hardly resulted in those practical achievements and improvements[1] which in other departments of applied science, notably in chemistry and electricity, have followed upon new discoveries, the influence of these new conceptions on scientific thought and method themselves has been enormous. Next to the conceptions introduced by Darwin into the descriptive sciences, no scientific ideas have reacted so powerfully on general thought as the ideas of energy. A new vocabulary had to be created; the older text-books, even where they dealt with known subjects in perfectly correct ways, had to be rewritten; well-known and approved theories had to be revised and restated in correcter terms, and problems which had lain dormant for ages to be attacked by newly invented methods. I propose in the rest of this chapter

greatly shaken. . . . There thus arose a rather angry controversy which has been summed up in the question, ' Is it water or iron?' I do not know that this controversy has been as yet completely decided." See also Peabody, ' Thermodynamics of the Steam - Engine,' 4th ed., New York, 1900, p. 301 *sqq.*

[1] This explains how it comes about that theoretical thermodynamics is still regarded with suspicion, not to say aversion, by many engineers of the old school, whose knowledge is principally based upon experience derived from the steam-engine. The first theoretical treatment of the steam-engine by Rankine in England, and Zeuner in Germany, exhibited such enormous discrepancies between theory and practice; the simplifying assumptions which were introduced in order to make the behaviour of steam in the cylinder at all calculable were so far wide of the mark, — that a general consensus seems to prevail among theoretical engineers that progress depends less upon an immediate application of thermodynamic principles, than upon a careful analysis—guided by theory —of elaborate tests upon the various types of engines now in use. Such experiments are accordingly—following the example of Hirn—being carried out in many scientific establishments in this country, on the Continent of Europe, and notably in the United States of America, and are elaborately recorded in many modern publications. See Peabody, ' Thermo - dynamics of the Steam - Engine,' 4th ed., preface, and chaps. xiii. and xiv. ; Ewing, ' The Steam-Engine,' 1894, p. 31.

to glance summarily at these revolutions in the domain of scientific thought which the physical view, by regarding nature as the playground of the transformations of energy, has brought about. What I have just indicated will suffice to bring some order into the account I propose to give. There are four distinct directions in which we have to look. *Firstly*, there is the clearer definition of the new ideas laid down in the new vocabulary of scientific and popular language during the second half of the century. *Secondly*, there is the revision and recasting of the whole body of physical and chemical knowledge in the light of the new insight which had been attained. *Thirdly*, there is the criticism of existing theories from the new points of view; and *lastly*, there are the fresh departures which these novel ideas have suggested.

27. Revolutions brought about by idea of energy.

The first definite use of the new conceptions of power and work, and of a scale of mechanical value, were contained in the writings of Poncelet and Sadi Carnot in France during the first quarter of the century. The first philosophical generalisations were given by Mohr and Mayer; the first mathematical treatment was given by Helmholtz; the first satisfactory experimental verification by Joule, during the second quarter of the century. The practical elaboration of the whole system following upon Joule's and Regnault's experiments belongs, through Thomson and Rankine in this country, and through Clausius in Germany, to the third quarter of the century. Students in our age entering on the study of mechanical, physical, chemical, and even physiological processes, reap the benefit of these labours by at once grasping the

underlying unity and correspondence of all natural phenomena, inasmuch as they all depend on the transformation of a quantity, termed energy, which is in
many cases measurable in its best-known form—*i.e.*, as
energy of motion—and, where this is not possible, in
the form of heat.

Helmholtz had already, in 1847, summarily reviewed
the whole field, beginning with a restatement of the
fundamental formulæ of dynamics in the light of the
new principle, and ending with a reference to the transformation of energy in living vegetable and animal
organisms. The key to his explanations is to be found
in the introduction of a term to denote what becomes
of energy if it ceases to exist as energy of motion or as
a velocity, when it is changed to energy of mere position.
To this end he introduces the idea of stress or tension.
The conception is already contained in older books on
mechanics as latent force (Carnot),[1] and the purely
mathematical treatment of dynamics by Lagrange and
Hamilton had prepared the ground by showing how all
dynamical problems could be reduced to the knowledge
of two quantities, the *vis viva* and the force function.

28.
Helm-
holtz on
"tension."

[1] L. N. M. Carnot (1753-1823),
usually termed the great Carnot,
father of Sadi Carnot, member of the
Directory, War Minister, and one
of the most celebrated generals of
France, has a name in science
through his 'Essai sur les Machines
en général' (Dijon, 1784), his 'Principes fondamentaux de l'Équilibre
et du Mouvement' (Paris, 1803), as
well as through his 'Réflexions sur
la Métaphysique du Calcul infinitésimal' (Paris, 1797) and his
'Théorie des Transversales' (Paris,
1806), by which he became, together with Monge, one of the
founders of modern geometry, of
which more in a subsequent chapter.
He introduced the principle of the
'Corrélation des Figures de Géométrie' (Paris, 1801). His books
were translated in Germany, where
they had a great influence. On his
connection with the history of the
conception of energy, see Bohn in
'Phil. Mag.,' iv. 300, vol. xxix. ;
also Helm, 'Energetik,' p. 13 ; and
the Éloge by Arago of the year
1837.

The exposition of Helmholtz, however, does not seem to have been understood or accepted. The general recognition of the relation of active and latent forces dates rather from Thomson's and Rankine's writings in 1851 and the following years. Thomson uses the term "mechanical energy" (later, from 1851, intrinsic energy, or simply energy), and considers this quantity to be a measure of the store of power to do work which a material system possesses;[1] and Rankine,[2] early in 1853, introduces and defines the terms actual (or sensible) energy and potential (or latent) energy, which are at once adopted by Thomson[3] in the place of the terms dynamical and statical energy, which he

[1] The memoir of Thomson in which he introduces the physical conception of the quantity "energy" in the place of a merely mathematical symbol used by Clausius, and inaugurates the terminology of modern physics, is contained in the 'Transactions of the Royal Society of Edinburgh,' vol. xx., Part 3 (read December 15, 1851, and reprinted in 'Math. and Phys. Papers,' vol. i. p. 222), as an appendix to the great paper "On the Dynamical Theory of Heat, with Numerical Results deduced from Mr Joule's Equivalent of a Thermal Unit, and M. Regnault's Observations on Steam" (Trans. Edinb. Soc., March 1851 : reprinted in 'Phil. Mag.,' 1852, and 'Math. and Phys. Papers,' vol. i. p. 174 sqq. ; see especially p. 186, note). The term energy had indeed been used by Thomson already in 1849 as a synonym for mechanical effect, but he had not then accepted the dynamical theory. He merely puts the question in a footnote to his exposition of Carnot's theory : "When thermal agency is . . .

spent, what becomes of the mechanical effect which it might produce? Nothing can be lost in the operations of nature—no energy can be destroyed" ('Papers,' vol. i. p. 118, 1849).

[2] In a paper read before the Philosophical Society of Glasgow, January 5, 1853, reprinted in 'Miscellaneous Scientific Papers,' ed. Millar, p. 203 sqq. See also Rankine's note, dated 1864, in the 28th vol. of the 4th series of the 'Phil. Mag.,' p. 404.

[3] See the Proceedings of the Glasgow Philos. Soc., January 1853, reprinted with additions from Nichol's 'Cyclopædia' (1860) in 'Math. and Phys. Papers,' vol. i. p. 521. In this paper Thomson also introduces the term "electrical capacity" of a conductor. Thomson subsequently introduced the word "kinetic" in place of "actual" energy. See also Thomson's Lecture before the Royal Institution, February 29, 1856, reprinted in 'Math. and Phys. Papers,' vol. ii. p. 182, and 'Popular Lectures,' vol. ii. p. 418, especially the note to p.

had employed before. How little these ideas, which
have now been introduced into elementary text-books
as the very alphabet of physical knowledge, commended
themselves in that age, except to a few intellects that
had been occupied for many years trying to fix precise
terms which should be capable of mathematical definition, and at the same time correspond to common-sense
experience, is evident, *inter multa alia*, from the criticism by Sir John Herschel in 1866.[1] Here it is
maintained that the use of the term " potential energy "
" is unfortunate, inasmuch as it goes to substitute a

425. A very complete and careful
historical account of the gradual
invention and crystallisation of the
vocabulary of the energy conception is given by Helm, 'Die Lehre
von der Energie,' Leipzig, 1887, p.
36 *sqq.*

[1] The passage quoted appears in
an article "On the Origin of Force,"
by Sir John Herschel, in the first
volume of the 'Fortnightly Review,' 1865, p. 439. The article is
well worth reading for those who
wish to realise the enormous benefit
which has been rendered to science
by banishing the indefinite use of
the word force and by introducing
the term energy, restricting the use
of force to the meaning attached to
it by Newton. Sir John Herschel
still speaks of the "conservation of
force " (as did likewise Helmholtz,
who, however, very early introduces
the term *Arbeitskraft*, power to do
work, thus removing all ambiguity).
Rankine replied to Herschel's criticism in a paper read before the
Glasgow Philosophical Society, 23rd
January 1867 (reprinted in 'Miscell. Scient. Papers,' p. 229 *sqq.*)
He there states that the quantity
itself occurs as a mathematical symbol in Newton's 'Principia' (prop.
39), but till recently had received

no appropriate name. He closes his
remarks by the still more important reflection : "One of the chief
objects of mathematical physics is
to ascertain, by the help of experiment and observation, what physical quantities or functions are
'conserved.'" As such he enumerates mass, resultant momentum,
resultant angular momentum,
total energy, thermo-dynamic function. Whilst this physical problem
was being defined by Rankine,
Cayley, Sylvester, and Hermite
were working at the corresponding
problem in pure mathematics to
decide what properties or quantities remain unaltered (*i.e.*, invariant), if an arrangement of
several algebraical symbols is subjected to algebraical operations.
It is the modern doctrine of "invariants." This doctrine has led to
an enormous extension and simplification of the theory of mathematical forms or quantics. It is the
key to all mathematical tactics, and
prepares a useful instrument for
the application of mathematics to
physical problems. See Major Mac-
Mahon's Address to the Mathematical Section of the British Association, Glasgow, 1891.

truism for a great dynamical fact"; an admission which would mean that it brings common-sense and precise mathematical expression into close proximity and harmony, or describes a very general phenomenon completely and in the simplest way.

In order to become generally recognised as the simple alphabet of scientific language, the new ideas had to be made the foundation of the whole structure of physical and chemical knowledge, theoretical as well as experimental; the elements and axioms had to be restated so as at once to express the new view and to open out the enlarged aspect which had been prepared. The different departments of mechanics, physics, and chemistry had to be elaborated and co-ordinated according to a uniform design. Helmholtz had indeed, as early as 1847, roughly sketched the plan of the work, but occupied as he was during the twenty following years mainly with another much-neglected field, the analysis of the phenomena of sensation, he did not return to his original thesis till many years later, when he made an application of fundamental importance.

Meanwhile the important task of rebuilding the edifice of the physical sciences, and establishing on a large scale that which I term the physical view of nature, fell almost exclusively into the hands of what we may call the Scotch school of natural philosophy—James and William Thomson, Macquorn Rankine, James Clerk Maxwell, P. G. Tait, and Balfour Stewart, in this country; whilst Clausius abroad worked almost alone. Rankine and James Thomson very early (1855) conceived the idea of a general science called "Energetics" or "the

30.
The Scotch school.

abstract theory of physical phenomena in general." [1]
It is only in our day, after the lapse of a quarter of
a century, that these ideas have been taken up by
others, and that the plan begins to be realised. The
reasons why at the time it was abandoned were
manifold.

To begin with, it was soon found, notably by Joule,
Helmholtz, and William Thomson, that the new principle of the conservation of energy, if applied to various
other phenomena outside of the narrower field of thermotics, led to a co - ordination and comprehension of
them which was then quite unexpected : opening out
new aspects, disclosing unknown properties, and suggesting innumerable experiments. As instances I may
refer to the thermo-elastic and thermo-electric phenomena of bodies, which very early occupied the attention of the founders of the theory of energy. The
discharge of the Leyden-jar, the generation of electric
currents in the voltaic cell, the heat of electrolysis,
the actions of permanent magnets and those between

[1] In a paper read before the
Philosophical Society of Glasgow,
May 1855, entitled "Outlines of
the Science of Energetics," and reprinted in 'Miscellaneous Papers,'
ed. Millar, p. 209 *sqq.* See for the
above definition p. 228. James
Thomson's contribution is to be
found in a paper on "Crystalliza-
tion and Liquefaction," read before
the Royal Society, December 5,
1861, in which he establishes and
gives examples of the application
of "a general physico-mechanical
principle or axiom," which indicates when a "substance or system
will pass into the changed state."
As Helm says, it is a first attempt
to find a general rule for the transformation of energy ('Lehre von
der Energie,' 1887, p. 63). That
such a general rule can in the
present state of our knowledge
be established on purely energetic
principles is upheld by some (Ostwald, Helm) and disputed by
others (see especially Planck,
'Thermodynamik,' 1897, p. 71
sqq.), who state their conviction
that the "energy-principle clearly
does not suffice for the definition
of natural processes." The whole
discussion merges into a philosophical question, of which more
later on.

electric currents and magnets, the phenomena of diamagnetism, Ampère's theory and Weber's basis of
electric measurement, Seebeck's production of electric
currents by heating in a non-homogeneous conductor,
the remarkable phenomena known by the name of
Peltier, the electro-dynamic properties of metals, the
thermo-elastic properties of matter, were all studied
in the light of the new principle, the conservation
and transformation of energy. Another very important problem presented itself, viz., the introduction of
the new ideas into the higher educational literature,
the re - writing of the text - books of science on the
basis of the principle of energy, and especially the
development of the fundamental notions in mechanics
in conformity with the more modern views. Here,
then, it became evident that the physical view of
natural phenomena, according to which they are all
instances of the transformation of energy, could be
considered and expounded as a further development of
the laws of motion as laid down in Newton's ' Principia.' It was especially the third law of motion, in
which Newton stated the equality of action and reaction, that lent itself to such an interpretation as
would at once lead to the wider grasp and deeper
insight into natural processes which the principle of
energy afforded. Accordingly about the year 1860,
when the new ideas on energy had, in the minds of
the great pioneers, acquired that importance which
has enabled them to become the basis of a more
and more comprehensive view—-the physical view—of
natural phenomena, the necessity was experienced of

bringing them into harmony and continuity with the older Newtonian ideas. These had been only imperfectly transmitted by the many commentaries and textbooks of the Cambridge school. The same was the case in the system of Lagrange, in which the whole of mechanics had been reduced to a mathematical expression, the physical and experimental foundations being pushed aside. The 'Principia' of Newton was again studied, and re-edited in the unabridged form, and an interpretation and amplification of the third law of Motion—so as to embrace the principle of energy—was made the key to the science of dynamics. Dynamics was not taught after but before statics. Statics was treated as a special case of the theory of motion. To make the new position still more marked, it was proposed to make the term dynamics the general term which embraces kinetics and statics as subdivisions, and to reserve the word "mechanics" for the science of machines. The change which then took place in the didactic methods can be seen by comparing the first and second editions of the well-known treatise by Tait and Steele on 'The Dynamics of a Particle.' The real compendium of the new doctrine is the treatise on Natural Philosophy by

31.
Thomson
and Tait.

Thomson and Tait, which has probably done more than any other book in this country to lead the mathematical studies at the foremost universities and colleges into paths more useful for physical and experimental research. The greatest exponent of the new ideas was James Clerk Maxwell, to whom is also due the merit of having applied them for the purpose of testing and

confirming the worth of the treasure which lay hidden
in the experimental researches of Faraday. Next to the
handbook of Thomson and Tait, no writings probably
have done more—especially outside of England, on the
Continent and in America—than those of Maxwell to
revolutionise the teaching of natural philosophy.

I must now revert to what I said in the last chapter regarding Maxwell's attempt to put the ideas of
Faraday on the communication of electric and magnetic
phenomena through space into mathematical language—
i.e., into measurable terms. I there related how Maxwell's earliest treatment of the subject was an attempt
to construct a mechanical model of the dielectric that
would be capable of exhibiting and transmitting the properties of stress—*i.e.*, of tension and pressure—which
the experimental researches of Faraday had partly demonstrated and partly suggested. In the sequel, as
was said, he desisted from this attempt, which has
since been taken up and further elaborated by others,
and resorted to a different train of reasoning. This
line had been suggested by the introduction of the
doctrine of energy into all physical research. As the
work of scientific chemists was for a long time exclusively governed by the application of the principle
of the constancy of weight or conservation of matter,
so, when once the mathematical expression of the
various forms of energy had been correctly established,
it became possible to arrive at a multitude of relations
of physical quantities merely by applying the principle
of the constancy of the quantity of energy. In this
way the principle of energy is a kind of regulative

32.
Clerk
Maxwell.

principle, one which allows us to deal with the grand total or outcome—mathematically called the integral—of physical processes and changes without necessarily possessing a detailed knowledge of the minute elements or factors—mathematically called differentials—out of which they are compounded. Inasmuch as what we actually observe are always integral effects—*i.e.*, summations or aggregates of great numbers of individual and unobservable processes — this line of reasoning is not infrequently very useful, and has been in many cases applied to arrive at important conclusions. In fact, it is the analogue in science of the method according to which practical men very often succeed in carrying on extensive business transactions, of which they possess a merely external though accurate knowledge; or of the balance-sheet of an industrial undertaking which exhibits and guarantees the correct result, though only the profit and loss account and the ledgers would show how this result has been arrived at.

33.
Faraday.

Faraday had taught us how to look upon any given portion of space in which electric, magnetic, chemical, and thermal changes were going on as a connected system, which he termed the electro-magnetic field. He and others—notably Oersted, Ohm, Weber, Lenz, and Joule —had shown how the different occurrences in such a system could be reduced to a common measure, and how they were observably connected. Maxwell brought all these phenomena together under the term "energy of the electro-magnetic field," and set himself to study the possible forms and changes of this quantity under the law of the conservation of energy—*i.e.*, as the preservation of the sum-total of the energy.   This energy could exist as motion (actual or kinetic energy), being either motion of electricity as in the current controlled by the law of Ohm, or motion of ponderable masses, such as magnets or electric conductors ; or it might be dissipated energy—*i.e.*, energy apparently lost in the form of heat—controlled by the law of Joule, or, to complete the summation, it might be stored-up energy—potential energy.   Faraday's researches had suggested where this store was : it was in the surrounding space, which must be considered as capable of being strained or put into a condition of stress, as elastic bodies are capable of being strained.   Thomson and Tait had shortly before shown how to submit the properties of elastic systems to calculation in the most general manner, by studying the modes in which energy, actual and potential, was distributed in them, whether at rest or in motion.   The way seemed then paved for Maxwell to consider with the greatest generality the properties of the electro-magnetic field, reducing them all to mechanical measures.   This he did by introducing the generalised conception of a displacement or strain which exists in the field, and which is communicated as a periodic or vibratory motion with a velocity dependent on the properties or so-called constants of the medium.   It is known how he succeeded in identifying very completely all the various experimentally ascertained electric and magnetic phenomena, fixing their nature and quantities in conformity with experience, and arriving finally at the suggestion that the velocity of the transmission of the electro-magnetic displacement in air must be the same as that of light, the latter being, in fact, an electro-magnetic disturbance of very short wave length. I also mentioned above how this suggestion received a brilliant confirmation from Hertz when he succeeded in exhibiting electro-magnetic waves, which in travelling through space, though not luminous, showed all the properties peculiar to light waves, such as reflexion, refraction, polarisation, &c.

Whilst in this country, during the period from 1850 to 1870, the Scotch school of natural philosophy was thus occupied in rebuilding the whole edifice of physical science on the new basis afforded by the energy ideas, Clausius in Germany worked at the further elaboration of the dynamical theory of heat, and, as I stated above, at the kinetic theory of gases, without abandoning the astronomical view of natural phenomena, which, with its supposition of forces acting at a distance, still almost exclusively governed theoretical physics and chemistry abroad. No one did more to emphasise the difference between this and Faraday's views than Clerk Maxwell, who had welded the latter into a consistent scheme by means of the conception of energy. About the year 1870 Helmholtz again appeared as a leader of scientific thought in this domain, and placed himself at the head of a movement which by degrees almost completely swept away the older ideas. It was by him or at his suggestion that many of the more modern English works of science were translated [1] and intro-

[1] Notably Thomson and Tait's 'Natural Philosophy,' and several of Tyndall's well-known more popular works on 'Sound,' 'Heat,' and 'Fragments of Science.' Helmholtz was also one of the first natural philosophers of eminent rank abroad who broke with the older habit of exclusiveness which clung to academic teachers in Germany, and who followed the English example set by the "Addresses" of

duced in Germany, and that especially the ideas of Faraday and Maxwell were popularised, expounded, and submitted to elaborate tests. These culminated in the brilliant discoveries of Hertz already referred to.

As in his earlier researches into the connection of the phenomena of heat and mechanical work, so in these later ones concerning the electro-dynamic laws, Helmholtz seems to have approached his subject primarily in the interest of physiological[1] science.   At that time

34.
Helmholtz
on electro-
dynamics.

the British Association and the still older "Lectures" of the Royal Institution. Before his time there were only rare instances—notably those of Bessel, Liebig, and Humboldt—where scientific thinkers of the first rank condescended to influence general opinion and polite literature by stepping down from the university chair into the arena of a popular audience. No other German scientific thinker has left a collection equal to Helmholtz's 'Vorträge und Reden,' not even Bessel, whose 'Populäre Vorlesungen über wissenschaftliche Gegenstände' (ed. Schumacher, Hamburg, 1848) are too little known. Du Bois-Reymond's 'Reden' are a mine of information on the history of science, and von Baer's 'Reden' (Braunschweig, 1886) contain some excellent and original discourses.

[1] Emil du Bois - Reymond, in many passages of his remarkable addresses, and latterly in his appreciative Éloge of Helmholtz (Leipzig, 1897), has preserved the historical data for a genetic history of Helmholtz's electrical researches, which, beginning in 1851, and culminating in Hertz's brilliant experiments on the "rays of electric energy" in 1888, completely changed the aspect of electrical science in Germany and to a less degree in France. The older view,

based upon a mathematical development of the fundamental conception of Ampère and mainly associated with the brilliant name of Wilhelm Weber, whose very extensive and accurate measurements largely supplied the material for the modern theory, is practically unknown to electricians in this country. No English text-book contains even a reference to a view which was once dominant abroad, and which for this reason forms a very interesting episode in the history of thought. In the fourth chapter I have referred to this view as, beside the theory of Boscovich, presenting one of the most remarkable applications of the astronomical view of nature, which originated in this country but was mainly cultivated by the French school. I must now briefly refer to the counter-movement, which in Germany is mainly identified with the name of Helmholtz. He may be said to have left the mark of his genius on the scientific history of his country as Lord Kelvin has done on that of England. His collected papers show us —and du Bois-Reymond tells us— how Helmholtz's interest in electrical problems was connected with the remarkable phenomena of animal electricity, to the exploration of which the former devoted his

there existed three different theories which aimed at finding a general formula or law that should embrace all known electro-dynamic phenomena. The two earlier ones were propounded independently and about the same

life. Du Bois-Reymond was a pupil of Johannes Müller. One of the merits of Müller's school was to have made the discoveries of physics useful for physiology and medicine as the school of Liebig made those of chemistry. Helmholtz was trained in the school of Müller, but he also came largely under the influence of Franz Neumann of Königsberg, the great teacher of mathematical physics, and of Gauss and Weber, the originators in Germany of the system of absolute measurements. It is known that the interest in electrical phenomena received a great impetus through Galvani's and Volta's discoveries. But as du Bois-Reymond ('Reden,' vol. ii. p. 389) tells us, the galvanic pile constructed by Volta withdrew attention from the phenomena of animal electricity to the much more powerful actions of artificial arrangements of metals and solutions. The study of animal electricity was for a time continued only by Italian professors, and beyond the seas by Alexander von Humboldt in his observations on the torpedo ; and had to wait till the school of Müller, and notably du Bois-Reymond, approached the subject methodically with the methods and ideas of modern science. This was in the fifth decade of the century. Modern science in Germany had, however, studied the properties of the galvanic current exhaustively only in linear (one dimensional) and in closed circuits or conductors. The phenomena of nervous and muscular electric currents demanded the study of sudden and repeated electrical impulses, and of the behaviour of currents in two and three dimensional conductors, and in unclosed conductors or circuits. Incited by du Bois-Reymond, Helmholtz undertook to deduce from the formulæ of Ampère, Neumann, and Weber the action of electric currents in these modified conditions. It was then found that these formulæ gave indefinite results and required to be modified or amplified. After many years of thought and research Helmholtz arrived at a generalisation which comprehended all the different existing theories as special cases. He then—in addition to a masterly mathematical discussion —betook himself to devise special experiments to decide which of the three possible expressions of the general formula came nearest the truth. A perusal of the memoirs contained in the first volume of his 'Wissenschaftliche Abhandlungen' (pp. 429 - 820) shows how by gradual and strictly logical steps he convinced himself of the intrinsic correctness of Faraday's conception, which, in addition to the phenomena in linear conductors or wires, constantly took notice also of those of the surrounding medium or space — i.e., of the electromagnetic field. Looking back from our present position on the development of the ideas concerning electricity in motion, we can say that Continental thinkers tried to gain a correcter and more complete understanding by a mathematical, English science by a physical, extension of the then existing notions. Helmholtz in his Faraday Lecture (1881) showed how both courses, consistently pursued, lead to the same result.

time by Franz Neumann and Wilhelm Weber; the later one was the theory of Maxwell based upon the totally different view which was maintained and gradually unfolded in the experimental researches of Faraday. The two former looked to the effects of the action of electricity at measurable distances, and has been called the telescopic view; the latter reduced these to the action which takes place in contiguous portions of matter or of space, and has been called the microscopic view. Helmholtz first of all, by an independent line of reasoning, brought the three mathematical formulæ in which these different views found expression under one common formula, of which each appears as a special case, and then proceeded by theory and experiment to decide which of the three possible special forms is to be adopted. As a theoretical test he applied the principle of the conservation of energy in a manner in which it had at that time hardly been used by Continental thinkers. His reasoning, which was largely discussed and criticised by eminent philosophers, gave to this principle the prominence and importance which it has ever since maintained in all Continental treatises. It meant the introduction of the physical view of natural phenomena.[1]

[1] In England the publication of Thomson and Tait's 'Natural Philosophy' formed, as stated above (p. 144), an epoch in the teaching of the physical sciences, notably through the prominence given to the principle of the conservation of energy. A similar epoch was created in Germany, not so much by Helmholtz's enunciation of the principle in 1847 as by the use he made of it, in one remarkable instance, in reviewing and criticising the existing and apparently conflicting theories. As Lavoisier introduced the chemical balance—based upon the conservation of matter—as a test for the correctness of chemical statements, so Helmholtz used the principle of the conservation of energy in two distinct forms, as a test of the validity of electrical

In the mean time this view had gained great support
by the efforts of quite a different section of scientific
workers, whose labours had opened out a new and
promising field of research. The new field for a considerable period belonged almost as exclusively to foreign
science as the energy-conception had for twenty years
belonged to this country. Early and for the most
part isolated labourers were Kopp and Hess in Germany,
Regnault and Berthelot in France, Julius Thomsen in
Copenhagen.[1] They (with many younger men) can be

statements. These two forms were
the impossibility of a perpetual
motion and the equality of action
and reaction. See his Faraday
Lecture, 1881. Both in the positions of Thomson and Tait and of
Helmholtz the principle of energy
is, however, like Lavoisier's principle, purely a regulative, not a
constructive, principle of scientific
research. It exerts a control and
enables us to check the correctness
of results. Both in chemistry and
physics other principles or methods
are required for extending — not
merely correcting—our knowledge.
Such principles are in the abstract
sciences the formula of gravitation,
the atomic theory, the ether; in the
natural sciences the morphological
and genetic theories. The whole
domain of physics and chemistry
has been reviewed for teaching purposes from this point of view by
Hans Januschke, 'Das Princip der
Erhaltung der Energie,' Leipzig,
1897. See p. 14 *sqq.*
[1] Although the history of thought
has more to do with theories than
with the mere discovery of facts,
and with the latter mainly when,
as in exceptional instances, they
change the scientific aspect of phenomena, I think it important to
mention specially the great merit

of Victor Regnault's experimental
researches. How much the progress
of physical and chemical theory is
indebted to his elaborate and extremely accurate measurements of
many physical constants may be
seen by the perusal of Lord Kelvin's early memoirs on the dynamical theory of heat. The several
(so-called) laws of Boyle, Dulong,
and others were subjected by Regnault to exhaustive tests ; the behaviour of steam in the steam-
engine formed a subject of
elaborate investigation ; the proof
that chlorine could be substituted
for hydrogen in hydrocarbons supplied a prominent support to the
chemical theories of Laurent. In
general Regnault's work is a model
of accuracy supported by great ingenuity in the construction of
apparatus and the surmounting
of difficulties. Like Liebig, he was
the master of many pupils who subsequently became eminent. Besides
being professor of chemistry and
physics in Paris, Regnault was
actively connected with the celebrated porcelain works of Sèvres.
Similar remarks might be made
with reference to the labours of
Hermann Kopp, who was for many
years probably the only professor
of physical chemistry in Germany.

considered as the founders of the modern science of
physical chemistry, which has received an elaborate exposition in the great work of Professor Ostwald.   This
work is probably quite as epoch-making in the domain
of chemistry as Thomson and Tait's ' Natural Philosophy '
has been in that of physics.

35.
Ostwald's
physical
chemistry.

I have already explained how in the development of
chemistry the attention of its great representatives was
almost entirely absorbed in gaining a knowledge of the
different substances with which they had to deal, and
how through preoccupation with the natural history of
matter, its decomposition, analysis and synthesis, and
appropriate classification, the other more scientific questions regarding the physical agencies which were at
work in chemical processes—constituting the doctrine
of chemical affinity—were almost completely neglected.
This I traced largely to the influence of that powerful
instrument of exact research, the atomic view, which
had been introduced into chemical science through
Lavoisier and Dalton.[1]   The pursuit of physical chem-

[1] It is not an unusual experience
to find that the change from one
theory to another, though an advance from disproved to more correct views, is also accompanied by
some loss either in definiteness or
in actual knowledge of facts. The
undulatory theory lost the definite
notion of a rectilinear ray of light,
which was only regained by prolonged and difficult analysis ; the
electro-magnetic theory of Maxwell
has not as yet given a clear representation of those electrical charges
which the older theory of Coulomb
and Weber introduced in the form
of stationary or moving electrical
masses. Something similar happened when the older phlogiston
theory was dispelled by the atomic
theory, and all attention was concentrated upon change of weight.
The older theory maintained that
when a metal is calcined it loses
something — viz., phlogiston ; the
new theory had proved that it gains
something—i.e., weight in the form
of combined oxygen. More recent
knowledge has shown that both
theories are right. It gains weight
and loses potential energy, or power
to do work—i.e., to combine, giving rise to molecular motion or
heat. The phlogiston theory contained the correct idea that besides
matter there is something else—

istry, the consideration of chemical as related to other physical forces, such as gravitation, heat, or electricity, though it very greatly occupied the pioneers of chemical science in the early years of the century,— notably Berthollet and Gay-Lussac in France, Dalton and Davy in England, Berzelius in Sweden,—fell gradually into popular disfavour, so much so that even Faraday's electrolytic law had hardly any influence on the development of chemistry.[1] This one-sided direction of chemical reasoning and observation was still further promoted by the great practical and technical results which followed from the atomic conception, the ease with which processes worked out in the laboratory could be imitated on a large scale in the factory and the workshop. It was the increased power over matter and its manifold transformations which followed immediately in the wake of atomic chemistry that gave it its interest, notably when through the study of the carbon compounds — incorrectly termed organic chemistry—new industries of undreamt-of magnitude and importance were created, and when through chemical knowledge the older methods of metallurgy were rapidly superseded. To the popular mind the result is always more interesting than the process of research or of reasoning which leads up to it; the possession of the product than the knowledge of the procedure. The

viz., energy. That the correct idea contained in the phlogistic conception was not at once given up, but only gradually lost sight of, is seen from the fact that Lavoisier's first table of elements contained 'caloric' as one of the simple bodies. See Kopp, 'Entwickelung der Chemie,' p. 209.

[1] On the causes of this see Helmholtz's Faraday Lecture ('Wissenschaftliche Abhandlungen,' vol. iii.) and Ostwald, 'Allgemeine Chemie,' 2nd ed., vol. ii. part 1, p. 530.

new substance with startling properties—be they useful or only curious and rare — has almost immediately a value, whereas the manifold transformations by which it was discovered, invented, or produced escape general notice, and are accordingly of secondary interest. This interest grows in proportion as another factor of equal commercial importance gradually and slowly asserts itself, namely, the factor of cost of production, the property through which not only the material itself, but also the labour bestowed upon it, and the most intricate transmutations and secret manipulations, gain a place and definite figure in the ledger of the accountant. Those of us who entered into practical life about the beginning of the last generation of the century know well by experience how then for the first time was being established the great system of statistics, of cost of production, which now governs every well-conducted industry and manufactory, though in general this department is still but little understood. Now, in proportion, as with progressing civilisation we come more and more to use artificially prepared products in the place of natural ones, the cost-figures become more complex : there is not only the raw material and the labour of getting it, not only the general economy of arrangement and administration by which we save labour and avoid waste—there is the whole aggregate of changes and processes, manual, mechanical, and chemical, through which the raw material has to pass. These must all have a common measure by which they possess a figure of value in the ledger of the book - keeper, otherwise the latter could not produce a statement of cost. Watt,

36.
The factor
of "cost"
in industry.

when supplanting manual labour on a large scale by the
introduction of his perfected steam-engine, had suggested
the term " horse-power " as the common measure of both ;
and the French mathematicians, who treated mechanics
with a view to practical application, had introduced the
term " work." In the general industries, however,—
outside of special branches, notably marine engineering,—
these measures were very crudely applied ; they became
unintelligible and meaningless where other agencies—
notably those of chemistry and electricity—had to be
employed. It is only since the terms " power " and
" work " have been enlarged and the more general conception of energy introduced that it has become possible
to measure the new forces or agencies in terms applicable to all alike. Practically as well as theoretically
the system of measurement remained imperfect so long
as the energy of chemical combination could not be
measured in the same way as Watt measured the
energy of heat, and as Joule and others taught us
how to measure the energy of an electric current. The
term " energy " has thus become as important a conception for practical as it has been long recognised to
be for purely scientific purposes. If the only power
we use is manual labour or steam power, there exists
a crude way of measuring both by the hands employed
and the weight of coal burnt ; but electrical power is
not so exclusively dependent on a personal or material
item, and thus it can only be measured by a system in
which the several items of cost are reduced to a common
term. It is through the wholesale introduction of the
electric current as a practical agent that the thing called

" energy " has become a commercial commodity as it had before become a scientific measure.

That chemical reactions are connected with mechanical, gravitational, optical, caloric, and electric phenomena has been known for a long time. Each of these manifestations has therefore been studied as affording a measure of the energy of chemical reactions, and these have in turn been looked upon as results of attractions, or of mass actions, or of thermal conditions, or of electrical polarities. We have thus mechanical, thermo - chemical, electro - chemical theories of affinity. Valuable discoveries and important suggestions have also been arrived at by these special researches: we have the laws of mass-action suggested by Berthollet and revived in modern times by Guldberg and Waage; the all-important electrolytic law of Faraday and the so-called third law of Berthelot in thermo-chemistry; further, the important researches of Kopp and Hess. None of these discoveries, however, seemed really to grasp the whole subject of chemical reaction, and accordingly they remained for a long time unknown, or fell, after a short life, into oblivion and disrepute. It has been one of the greatest performances of the last twenty years of the century to have approached the all-important question, " What is chemical affinity, and how is it to be measured ? " in a comprehensive spirit, and to have brought it to the verge of solution. The merit of having done this belongs the more incontestably to Prof. Wilhelm Ostwald,[1] because no one

37.
Berthelot
and Ost-
wald.

---

[1] Prof. Ostwald's principal work is the 'Lehrbuch der allgemeinen | Chemie,' of which the first edition appeared in two volumes (Leipzig,

has taken such pains as he to gauge the value of
many single and isolated steps that had been taken
before him, and to combine them all through his own
researches into a comprehensive doctrine. The practical importance of these labours—so long insufficiently
understood—will doubtless in the near future be realised in proportion as the increasing competition of industry shall emphasise the necessity of studying the
economics of production : this economy consisting not only
in the absence of waste of matter, but likewise in the
saving of work—*i.e.*, in the absence of waste of energy.[1]

1885-87); the second edition, of
which the first volume appeared
in 1891, is in progress, and will
comprise three volumes. It is
divided into three parts : *Stöchio-
metrie, Chemische Energie*, and *Ver-
wandtschaftslehre*. Nothing can give
a better idea of the enormous
development of chemical science
in the nineteenth century than a
glance at those two monuments of
learning and research, Beilstein's
' Organische Chemie ' (Leipzig,
1893-1900, 5 vols., 3rd ed.) and
Ostwald's 'Allgemeine Chemie.'
They form the basis for future
development, as did Leopold
Gmelin's ' Handbuch der Chemie '
for the greater part of the past
century. The first edition of
Gmelin appeared in 1817. See
Kopp's ' Geschichte der Chemie '
(vol. ii. p. 100). Since the publication of his great text-book, Prof.
Ostwald has done enormous service to science by the foundation
jointly with Prof. van't Hoff of the
' Journal für physicalische Chemie,'
in 1889, and still more by the opening of the first laboratory specially
designed for physical chemistry, in
Leipzig, in the year 1887. But
perhaps the most original and
suggestive work o   Ostwald is

his work on the scientific foundations of Analytical Chemistry
(Leipzig, 3rd ed., 1901. Transl.
by G. M'Gowan).

[1] How recent is the systematic
treatment and general recognition
of physical, theoretical, or general
chemistry can be seen from the
historical sketches which had been
published prior to Ostwald's great
work. Kopp, in his excellent account of the development of chemistry, published in the Munich collection, and frequently referred to
in the fifth chapter of this work
(vol. i. pp. 382, &c.), has hardly any
occasion to refer to physical chemistry up to the year 1870. This
is the more remarkable, as Kopp
himself was a solitary ingenious
worker in this isolated province.
A good account of his labours
is contained in Thorpe's ' Essays
in Historical Chemistry,' 1894,
p. 299. A later and brilliant
writer on the historical growth
of chemical knowledge, Dr A.
Ladenburg, in his ' Vorträge über
die Entwicklungsgeschichte der
Chemie ' (2nd ed., Braunschweig,
1887), condenses all he has to say
regarding this subject into a
few pages in his last lecture. If
German science is destined to

The ideas through which unity and coherence have been introduced into the many different trains of reasoning which were bent upon unravelling the mysteries of chemical affinity came from an unexpected quarter —from the country which, in the early part of our century, had become, through Berzelius, the centre of a great school of chemical research. Prof. Ostwald, in his recent historical sketch of the doctrines of chemical affinity, dates the latest period from the year 1886,[1] when Svante Arrhenius published his theory of the chemical solutions decomposed by the galvanic current, the so-called electrolytes. That the reader may understand what importance belongs to this latest development of physical chemistry, I must go further

38.
Arrhenius.

distinguish herself in the wider sphere of general or physical chemistry as much as she has done in the past by the extreme and one-sided culture of organic or structural chemistry, it will be largely owing to the influence of the school of Ostwald and that of the industrial factor mentioned in the text, which nowadays emphasises as much the economical control of chemical reactions as it did formerly the discovery and preparation of new compounds. The ultimate success in the industrial preparation of artificial indigo, which was theoretically long known, is an example well worth careful attention.

[1] Prof. Ostwald had himself about the same time made an attempt in the second volume of the first edition of his great work to unite the *disjecta membra* of physical chemistry, notably of the theory of affinity, into a systematic whole. This first attempt may have contributed quite as much as the special labours of others, among whom he mentions specially Helmholtz, Van't Hoff, Duhem, Planck, and Arrhenius, to create an era in chemistry. It may also be noted that, like every other important step in chemistry, this latest theoretical phase is characterised by violent controversies. These became more pronounced as Prof. Ostwald introduced into the second edition of his work the idea of "energetics" as a general and sufficient basis for the whole of physics and chemistry; making a very emphatic protest against the older physical theories, based upon attractions, atomism, or kinetics, which he stigmatises as mechanical. On this important controversy I shall have to report at the end of the present chapter, where I shall also give the full literature of the subject. In the meantime, see also Ostwald, 'Allgemeine Chemie,' vol. ii. part 1, preface, and part 2, p. 182 *sqq.*

back in the history of the subject and draw attention
to the gradual change which the nineteenth century
has brought about in our ideas regarding the different
states in which matter is supposed to exist, be it
in motion or in rest: the solid, the liquid, and the
gaseous states.

Not very long ago the impressions of common-sense,
according to which a fundamental difference separates
solid from liquid and liquid from aeriform bodies, permeated scientific treatises also. Rigid demarcations
were maintained between hydrostatics and pneumatics,
and likewise between the doctrines of bodies at rest
and such as are in a state of perceptible motion.
One of the most marked changes which the century
has witnessed, has been the breaking down of these
older landmarks of science. The state of rest—once
supposed actually to exist—has had to give way to a
state of concealed yet measurable motion, as in the
case of the kinetic theory of gases, which explains dead
pressure by the bombardment of innumerable particles
darting about.   The idea of dynamical equilibrium—*i.e.*,
the maintenance of a state of uniform motion—has
in many cases taken the place of static equilibrium or
rest, as in the doctrine of the flow of heat, the theory
of exchanges of radiation, and the conception that the
rigidity of solids depends upon a peculiar form of whirling motion—the vortex. Similarly the intermediate or
transition states which lie between the solid and fluid,
the properties of viscosity and of colloidal substances,
and of vapours as marking the transition between
liquids and gases, have attracted more attention in pro-

portion as experimental science has taken the place of that purely mathematical treatment which obtained at the beginning of the century, notably in the Continental schools, and which thought it could exhaust the infinite variety of natural phenomena by a few easily defined properties measured by constants. The narrowness of this view has been gradually overcome by the influence of the great experimental philosophers in this country, and the independent development of chemical research abroad. Beside Faraday must be especially named Thomas Graham [1] and Thomas Andrews, whose original experiments did so much to extend and deepen our knowledge of the less obvious properties of matter. Graham carried on, between 1825 and 1850, extensive experiments on the diffusion of liquids and gases, on absorption, and on the phenomena of osmosis or gradual filtering of substances through porous partitions, showing how in liquids motion and pressure exist similar to that which is now

39.
Graham and
Andrews.

[1] Thomas Graham (1804 - 69), for many years professor at University College, London, then Master of the Mint, cultivated the unexplored regions of physics and chemistry in an original spirit and yet with very simple apparatus, some of which is still used under his name. His ingenious labours attracted the attention of Liebig, through whose influence was brought about the translation of 'The Elements of Chemistry' into German by Otto. This work in its subsequent enlarged editions has formed for sixty years, next to Gmelin's 'Handbook,' a cornerstone of chemical literature in Germany, where Graham's name is a household word. The discoveries of Graham on the movement and "miscibility" of gases led to the well-known law, "that the diffusion rate of gases is inversely as the square root of their density." From gases he advanced to the more complicated study of liquids, divided bodies into two classes, "crystalloids" and "colloids," studied the "transpiration" of gases through fine tubes, and their "osmosis" or gradual filtering through porous (and many apparently non-porous) partitions. In many directions he anticipated later discoveries and collected invaluable materials for subsequent theories. *Inter alia*, he established the existence of "alcoholates," compounds analogous to "hydrates," and maintained the metallic nature of hydrogen.

generally attributed to gases. Andrews [1] in the 'sixties carried on his important experiments on the transition of bodies from the liquid to the gaseous state, and came to the conclusion " that the gaseous and liquid states are only remote stages of the same condition of matter, and are capable of passing into one another by a process of continuous change." [2]   He also referred to the " possible continuity of the liquid and solid states of matter."

Another important step by which our conceptions of the nature of the liquid condition of matter were considerably enlarged and altered—motion being introduced where a former view had seen only rest—was taken by Clausius, who, following Joule and Krönig, had about the same time given its modern form to the kinetic theory of gases. What suggested this step was the phenomenon of electrolysis. The older view looked upon the action of the electric current, which, passing through substances in a state of fusion or solution, liberated the constituents out of which they were composed, as an exertion of a force contrary to the forces of chemical affinity, by which the chemical constituents were supposed to be held together. In this case energy would have to be spent in doing work against chemical forces. It was, however, very soon found that the decomposition, or—as Sainte Claire Deville first called it [3]—the

[1] See vol. i. p. 316, note, of this History.

[2] See 'The Scientific Papers of Thomas Andrews,' with a Memoir by Tait and Crum Brown, London, 1889, p. 316.

[3] Sainte Claire Deville (1818-81) approached chemical research from the side of medicine, and after a series of original investigations, first in organic then in metallurgical chemistry, entered upon his remarkable work in thermal chemistry at the time when Clausius in Germany was being led from an entirely different point of view to the same subject. He introduced the term dissociation to denote the

dissociation of the electrolyte, was not the consequence, but the accompanying feature or condition, of the existence of an electric current in a solution. Clausius first expressed this distinctly in 1857, and Helmholtz repeated it in 1880. The conception was thus introduced that in certain (not in all) solutions of chemical compounds dissociation might exist independently of an electric current, and that the latter, if introduced, only directed the already dissociated and wandering molecules (ions), freeing them at the same time of their electric charges.[1] This conception, though at first violently

breaking-up of chemical compounds not so much through the presence of other chemical agencies as through altered physical conditions, such, notably, as heat, evaporation, and condensation. "Deville's observations on dissociation . . . have a very direct bearing on the kinetic theory of gases, and it is a fact of interest in the history of science that Deville did not recognise the validity of that theory. Our estimate of the ingenuity, skill, and patience shown in his experimental work, and of the genius and sound judgment which directed his theoretical conclusions, is perhaps raised when we recollect that he was neither led in the first nor biassed in the second by ideas derived from the kinetic theory, and his hostile, or at least neutral, attitude towards it gives perhaps greater value to the evidence that his work has contributed to its soundness" (A. Crum Brown, 'Ency. Brit.,' 9th ed., article "Sainte Claire Deville").

[1] I have already mentioned (vol. i. p. 435, note) that Clausius, when introducing his kinetic theory and distinguishing between molecules and atoms, could refer to several eminent chemists who had inde-

pendently arrived at similar ideas by quite different trains of reasoning. Again, when introducing, in 1857, his theory of dissociation by solution, he could refer to similar anticipations. Williamson had said already, in 1850 (Liebig's 'Annalen,' vol. lxxvii. p. 37), at the meeting of the British Association in Edinburgh : "We are led to the conclusion that in an aggregate of molecules of every compound there exists a continual exchange of the elements contained in it. Suppose, for instance, that a vessel with hydrochloric acid were filled with a great number of molecules of the compound ClH, then the view at which we have arrived would lead us to the supposition that every atom of hydrogen does not remain in quiet juxtaposition with an atom of chlorine, with which it is combined, but that there is a continual exchange of places with other hydrogen atoms" (Clausius, ' Mechanische Wärmetheorie,' vol. ii. p. 167, Braunschweig, 1879). For an illustration of the theory of Clausius modified to meet more recent conceptions, see O. Lodge's 'Modern Views of Electricity,' 1892, p. 83, &c.

attacked by chemists, became gradually better understood and gained ground. The merit of having finally introduced into our modern notions the idea of the free mobility of the constituents of electrolytic compounds belongs to W. Hittorf and F. Kohlrausch. The name of the latter will be connected in the history of science with the phenomenon of the "migration of the ions," which he has expressed, after ten years of research (1869-79), in his well-known law. The question was put and answered, "What becomes of the energy of the electric current?" It was found that electrolytic conduction increased with dilution and temperature—two agents which would favour dissociation. The phenomena of dissociation had, moreover, been studied independently of the galvanic current. Following in the track of Graham and Andrews, a number of physicists abroad—notably van der Waals, Raoult, and Van't Hoff—had confirmed and extended the view that bodies in solution resembled gases, that the osmotic pressure of a liquid resembled ordinary gas pressure, that the law of Avogadro regarding the number of molecules in a gas could be transferred to matter in a state of solution, and that the magnitude of the osmotic pressure in a liquid could be used as a measure of the number of dissociated—wandering—molecules which are contained in a given volume of a solution, just as the pressure of a gas would increase if the number of molecules in a given space were increased through the splitting up of compounds. Apparent anomalies in the behaviour of gases approaching condensation were explained by the aggregation, and similar ones in dilute solutions by the dissociation, of molecules.

41.
Hittorf and
Kohlrausch.

The decisive step was taken in 1887 by Arrhenius,[1] who has the merit of having brought together the two independent courses of research and reasoning, and made them fruitful for each other.   He shows [2] " that the difference between active and inert molecules consists in this, that the former are split into their ions, the latter not.   Only the free ions take part in the conduction of electricity and in chemical reactions : this is the reason for the proportionality of the two (Faraday's law).   The ions behave in solution like independent molecules : this is the reason of the deviation which electrolytic solutions show from the extended gaseous laws (Van't Hoff's discovery)."   "What a change has come over our conceptions," exclaims Victor Meyer,[3] " if we have to accustom ourselves to see in a dilute solution of common salt, no longer the undecomposed molecules of a salt, but separate atoms of chlorine and sodium.   For these revolutionary innovations we are indebted to the labours of Van't Hoff, Arrhenius, Ostwald, Planck, Pfeffer, de Vries, but, so far as experiments go, notably to the splendid researches of Raoult, which for years have been preparing the way for this mighty theoretical advance."

The year 1887, which brought together these two fruitful lines of reasoning and research, can also be considered as the epoch when the new science of physical chemistry was fairly launched into existence.   The year

42.
Victor
Meyer on
change of
chemical
views.

[1] In a communication to the Academy of Stockholm of 8th June and 9th November 1887.

[2] Quoted from Ostwald's ' Allgemeine Chemie,' 2nd ed., vol. ii. part 1, p. 656.

[3] See the highly interesting Address by Victor Meyer before the German " Naturforscherversammlung" at Heidelberg in 1889, entitled " Chemische Probleme der Gegenwart" (Heidelberg, 1890), p. 32.

1826 marks the revival of mathematical studies in Germany through the appearance of Crelle's journal; so the year 1887 saw the first number of Ostwald and Van't Hoff's 'Zeitschrift für physicalische Chemie.' From that period the physical properties of chemical substances, so long neglected, or only studied by isolated students, have received systematic, mathematical, and exact treatment, guaranteeing something like continuity and completeness, and leading on to the solution of the great remaining question, What is chemical affinity?

The eminent natural philosophers to whom is mainly due the foundation of this modern science, claim also to be gradually realising the idea which was suggested by the early representatives of the theory of energy—notably by Rankine and James Thomson—that of a general doctrine of energy, termed energetics; and they hold that this suggestion is only realisable by breaking with the conventional ideas which the older physical theories—the astronomical, atomistic, and kinetic views—have imposed upon our reasoning. They further hold that the gradual development of chemistry into an exact science necessarily requires the introduction of this broader view which they embrace, and that the older views—useful in their way—only suffice to comprehend certain restricted groups of natural phenomena, whereas in chemical changes, where all imaginable natural processes seem to come together, a larger and more independent theory is indispensable. It is interesting to note how very generally they trace this larger view to the long unnoticed labours of a natural philosopher in the New World, Professor Willard Gibbs of Yale.

The train of thought methodically and comprehen- ^{44.} Willard sively followed out in Gibbs's various memoirs had its Gibbs. origin in the early speculations of William Thomson (Lord Kelvin) and Clausius, to which I referred above. Thomson was the first who, in adopting (after much hesitation) the mechanical view of the phenomena of heat, the doctrine of the convertibility and equivalence of the different forms of energy, recognised that, in order to describe natural phenomena correctly, this view required a qualification. The change of the different forms of energy into each other can for the most part take place only in one direction; there is a general tendency in nature towards a degradation or dissipation of energy. Energy, though not lost, becomes less useful, less avail- able. The least available form of energy is heat; and it is in that form that in all natural changes a por- tion of energy becomes lost, dissipated, or hidden away. Thus we have to recognise the difference between available and unavailable, between useful and useless, energy. In the sequel Thomson showed in definite instances [1] how to calculate the available and the un-

[1] See 'Math. and Phys. Papers,' vol. i. No. LIX., 1852, "On a Uni- versal Tendency in Nature to the Dissipation of Mechanical Energy"; and No. LXIII., 1853, "On the Restoration of Mechanical Energy from an unequally heated Space." In Tait's 'Sketch of Thermodynam- ics' (1868), we read (p. 100): "It is very desirable to have a word to express the *availability* for work of the heat in a given magazine, a term for that possession the waste of which is called *Dissipation.* Un- fortunately the excellent word *en- tropy,* which Clausius has introduced in this connection, is applied by him to the negative of the idea we most naturally wish to express. It would only confuse the student if we were to endeavour to invent another term for our purpose." He then proceeds to use the term entropy in an altered sense, in which it measures the available instead of the unavailable energy, creating for some time a great confusion and some unnecessary irritation. See on this the early editions of Clerk Maxwell's excellent 'Theory of Heat,' and the footnote to p. 189, 8th ed., and Clausius 'Die

available energy : he introduced the word " motivity," the conception of a quantity of a " possession the waste of which is called dissipation." Whilst Thomson was thus putting into scientific language and calculating an important and obvious property of nature—namely this, that her processes mainly proceed in a certain definable direction—Rankine and Clausius were labouring independently at the mathematical wording, the analytical expression, of this remarkable discovery. Wherever a change in a system of various elements, factors, or quantities takes place mainly in a definite sense or direction, it is presumable that there exists a definite quantity which is always growing or always decreasing. This quantity may not be directly observable or measurable, as in mechanical motion velocity or distance is directly measurable; it may be hidden—we may have no special sense with which we can perceive it, as we possess a pressure sense, a heat sense, a sound and light sense; nevertheless, it may be indirectly discoverable, being made up (a function) of definite observable quantities and factors (such as heat, temperature, mass, volume, pressure, &c.) Now Rankine and Clausius found that in all thermal changes

mechanische Wärmetheorie,' vol. i. p. 387, and vol. ii. p. 324 *sqq.* A great deal of this confusion would have been avoided had Tait in 1868 introduced a really new term—viz., that suggested later (1876) by Thomson in a communication to the Royal Society of Edinburgh, and more fully explained in a paper in the ' Phil. Mag.,' May 1879, the term "Thermo-dynamic Motivity." We should then have two terms, inasmuch as the "con-sideration of the *energy* and *motivity*, as two functions of all the independent variables specifying the condition of a body completely in respect to temperature, elasticity, capillary attraction, electricity, and magnetism, leads in the simplest and most direct way to demonstrations of the theorems regarding the thermo-dynamic properties of matter" (*loc. cit.*, ' Papers,' vol. i. p. 459).

or heat processes—and this practically means in all
natural processes—there is such a quantity which is
always on the increase, and which thus measures in
mathematical language the growing loss of available
or useful energy in the world.   Rankine simply called it
the "thermo-dynamic function"; Clausius thought it
important to give it a name which would co-ordinate it
with energy, and he called it entropy:[1] energy which
is turned inside, becomes hidden or locked up.   Clausius
thus gave a different wording of Thomson's doctrine of

45.
Entropy.

[1] Clausius had already in 1854
(Pogg. 'Ann.,' vol. xciii. p. 481) arrived at the principal consequences
and the final enunciation of what
he termed "the second law of
thermo - dynamics," a law which
refers to the transformation, as the
first refers to the conservation, of
energy. He there arrives at similar
conclusions to those put forth by
Thomson two years earlier.   The
word entropy, however, was not introduced by him till 1865 (Pogg.
'Ann.,' vol. cxxv. p. 390), when he
introduced it with the following
remarks : " I have intentionally
formed the word entropy as much
as possible on the model of that
of energy, for the two quantities
which are to be designated by these
two words are in their physical
meaning so intimately related that
a similarity in the terms seemed to
me to be justified." As stated
above (p. 167, note), Lord Kelvin, who
worked simultaneously and independently at the same subject, laid
more stress upon the direct statement, that in all transformations
of energy we have to distinguish
between the available and the total
intrinsic energy, and introduced
the terms energy and motivity as
two functions of all the variables
specifying the conditions of a
system. In his article on Heat,
contributed to the 'Ency. Brit.,'
9th ed., he gives the mathematical
relation of motivity to entropy
('Papers,' vol. iii. p. 167). The term
motivity has not become current in
thermo - dynamical treatises, but
the need has been very generally
felt of reserving the word energy in
a restricted sense for available
energy, such energy as can be put
to mechanical use.   Wald, in a
very interesting dissertation, 'Die
Energie und ihre Entwerthung'
(Leipzig, 1889), deplores (pp. 43
and 44) the fact that the word
energy has not been reserved to
denote useful, available energy.
"Had the word energy," he says,
"been introduced before the discovery of the first law of thermo-
dynamics, then certainly only mechanical energy would have been
termed simply energy." In the
use of the word Kraft in some
writers, such as Mayer, there
seems occasionally a confusion between available and total or intrinsic energy.   See Le Chatelier
in 'Journal de Physique,' 1894.

the universal tendency in nature towards a dissipation of energy, by saying, "The entropy of the world is always on the increase."

For about twenty years after these conceptions had been introduced into scientific language and reasoning, mathematicians and physicists were mainly occupied in defining more clearly this hidden quantity, and in defending what was called the second law of thermo-dynamics against misconceptions and attacks. In 1875 Lord Rayleigh could still say,[1] "The second law of thermo-dynamics and the theory of dissipation founded upon it has been for some years a favourite subject with mathe-matical physicists, but has not hitherto received full recognition from engineers and chemists, nor from the scientific public. And yet the question under what circumstances it is possible to obtain work from heat is of the first importance. Merely to know that when work is done by means of heat, a so-called equivalent of heat disappears, is a very small part of what it concerns us to recognise."

Whilst these words correctly describe the general attitude of the scientific public towards this important discovery, two men had already made a beginning in

46.
Horstmann.

the direction indicated—Horstmann[2] in Germany, and

[1] 'Proceedings of the Royal Institution,' vol. vii. p. 386.

[2] Prof. Ostwald in the historical section of his 'Verwandtschafts-lehre' ('Allg. Chemie,' 2nd ed., vol. ii. part 2, p. 111, &c.), Helm in 'Energetik' (p. 141, &c.), and Duhem in his 'Traité de Mécanique chimique' (1897, vol. i. p. 84, &c.) all do full justice to the long-un-recognised labours of Horstmann,

which began in the year 1869 and were continued in Liebig's 'An-nalen' in various communications during the early 'seventies, not without undergoing violent attacks from representatives of the older conceptions. Ever since James Thomson's celebrated prediction (see above, p. 126), physicists had recognised the importance of thermo - dynamical considerations,

Willard Gibbs [1] in America. They seem to have been the first to approach the question of chemical equilibrium, the result of the action of various conflicting chemical forces, termed affinities, from a general comprehensive point of view; recognising that the theory then commonly adopted on the Continent—the thermo-chemical theory of affinity—was incorrect or incomplete. This theory, which had been principally elaborated by Julius Thomsen in Copenhagen and by Berthelot in France, was supported by the large amount of valuable experimental research for which we are indebted to these two eminent men and their numerous followers.

whilst chemists persisted in the exclusive use of atomistic conceptions, which, as Horstmann pointed out, are of no avail in problems of that nature (see Helm, 'Energetik,' p. 143).

[1] More fundamental than the labours of Horstmann were those of Gibbs, which began with the year 1874, and were for a long time buried in the 'Transactions of the Connecticut Academy.' They were known to Maxwell, but remained generally unknown, partly owing to their abstract nature, partly to the fact that the majority of Continental chemists were not prepared to appreciate the mathematical form in which his expositions were clothed. Previous to the study of questions of chemical equilibrium, Gibbs had successfully developed an idea of James Thomson's—viz., the graphical representation of the different thermodynamic quantities in three instead of merely in two dimensions. Thomson had represented the properties of a body or system by referring them to volume, pressure, and temperature. Gibbs refers them to volume, energy, and entropy, the former quantities being always definable by the latter, but not *vice versâ*. The advantages of this representation were demonstrated to English students in Maxwell's 'Theory of Heat.' In Germany it was Prof. Ostwald who, by collecting and translating the memoirs of Gibbs, first made them accessible to students ('Thermodynamische Studien,' von Willard Gibbs, Leipzig, 1892). Subsequently both Ostwald and Helm have done much to promote an understanding of Gibbs's methods. See Ostwald, 'Allg. Chemie,' vol. ii. part 2, p. 114, &c.; Helm, 'Grundzüge der mathematischen Chemie' (Leipzig, 1894), and 'Energetik,' *passim*. Subsequently Gibbs also introduced the very general and useful term "phase" to denote the different states in which a substance can exist. This term denotes not only such differences as were formerly called in German *Aggregatzustände*, but likewise conditions of dissociation, allotropic and isomeric modifications.

It measured chemical reactions by what is termed their heat - toning, *i.e.*, by the amount of heat developed, and culminated in the celebrated third law of thermo-chemistry—viz., that such reactions take place as are accompanied by the greatest amount of energy liberated in the form of heat. Now, although this contains an adequate description of a very large number of reactions that take place at the temperatures at which we operate in our laboratories, the rule is by no means universal, and it required a great amount of ingenuity to explain away the many exceptions which presented themselves. The rule needed to be modified or amplified. The measurement of the energy of a chemical process by the heat-toning was not the only instance in which the thermal side of a phenomenon had been considered a sufficient means of measuring. In an allied department, that of electrolysis, Helmholtz had suggested, as early as 1847, that the electro-motive force of a galvanic cell may be measured by the heat-toning of the chemical processes which produce the current, and for a long time this was considered to be a correct expression of facts. In consequence, however, of some discrepancies which had presented themselves, Helmholtz himself was induced, about 1881, to examine the subject more thoroughly. He arrived at the conclusion that the heat-toning is not always a correct measure; and at the same time he introduced a more adequate and generally applicable method of measurement. In fact, he arrived at the conception of available or useful energy for processes which take place at constant temperature. To this quantity, which decides in which direction a reaction takes place (temperature remaining constant), he gave the name of free energy. He showed that in a state of equilibrium the free or available energy must be a minimum. He also showed the connection in which the available or free energy stands to the quantity introduced by Rankine and Clausius, the entropy which measures the unavailable or hidden energy. By making chemical changes depend on the increase or decrease of a definite measurable quantity a parallel was established between chemical and mechanical processes, the latter always taking place in the direction of a decrease of potential energy. Free energy has thus been appropriately termed by M. Duhem the thermo-dynamic potential.

Helmholtz did not apply this fruitful view to chemical processes on any extensive scale, but his explanations have done much to establish that correcter and more comprehensive way of treating such questions which has since become general. Horstmann had indeed led up to this view, Willard Gibbs had applied it before, and Lord Rayleigh had suggested it.[1] The conception of

---

[1] The general use of the conception of useful or free energy must be dated from the remarkably lucid expositions of Helmholtz, though it is now recognised by all who have studied the history of this fertile conception that the physical notion of available energy goes back to Thomson (see Tait, 'Thermodynamics,' 1868, p. 100) and Maxwell ('Heat,' p. 187, 8th ed. ; Duhem, 'Mécanique chimique,' vol. i. p. 92; Le Chatelier in 'Journal de Physique,' 1894, p. 291); that the mathematical formulæ were given by Massieu (quoted by Duhem, 'Le Potential Thermodynamique,' 1886, pp. v. and 11), and more definitely explained and applied to the physical phenomena of dissociation by Gibbs ('Thermodynamische Studien,' ed. Ostwald, p. 66, &c. ; 'Amer. Journ. of Sciences and Arts,' 1879) ; and that it is especially owing to the labours of Duhem that the subject has received the attention of chemists. M. Duhem, in the introduction to the work of 1886, gives a very valuable and lucid historical exposition, and subsequently in his large work in four volumes ('Mécanique chimique,' 1897-1900) a vast number of applications. For the history of thought the import-

available energy as distinguished from total energy had been introduced by Lord Kelvin and by Maxwell. This free energy is measured not only by the heat liberated, but depends on all the other factors, such as volume and pressure, the number of chemical substances engaged, and their physical conditions. The doctrine of energy and the conception of free energy pointed out a method of co-ordinating all these different factors and reducing them to a common measure. As Rankine, by the introduction of the term potential energy, did much to clear the ideas and guide the reasoning in dynamical science, so Helmholtz, by introducing the term free energy, did a great deal to introduce into chemical science the fruitful conceptions which had been elaborated and applied in physical research. The term free or available energy seems to describe more naturally the characteristic property of all energy which is useful for doing work, whilst the opposite term entropy—which measures the unavailable or hidden energy—refers to a quantity for which we have no immediate means of perception.[1]

ance of these somewhat abstruse expositions lies mainly in two directions: First, in the recognition of the fact that for the correct description of natural phenomena and changes the knowledge of the total energy is as little sufficient as that of the total weight or mass, but that it is necessary to introduce the conception of useful energy, of energy which is free or available for doing work; secondly, in the recognition that the course of chemical changes or reactions cannot be measured by attending to one special property, such as weight, or temperature, or entropy, but that it requires the measurement of a quantity which comprises all the different agencies in nature, this quantity being the energy of the system or substances in question and its availability. A third point, which is of more or less importance according to the general view adopted, is this, that the mathematical formulæ involved have exhibited the analogy between chemical and mechanical processes, the latter being those which were earliest and are most easily grasped by the mind.

[1] As Prof. Ostwald has remarked, it is to a great extent a matter of taste what particular form one adopts out of the many in which the

It was about this time—after experimental research had been carried on for many years by Julius Thomsen and Berthelot, after Horstmann had made a beginning of

second law of thermo-dynamics can be expressed ('Allg. Chemie,' vol. ii. part 2, p. 150). In every case it is simply a question how most conveniently to express and apply the general principle that heat cannot of itself pass from a colder to a hotter body, the principle on which Fourier built his "Théorie de la Chaleur," and which revealed itself as the rationale of the expositions of Carnot when in the middle of the century their hidden truth emerged from the criticisms of William Thomson (Lord Kelvin) and Clausius. Thus already in the different treatment of the same subject there showed itself the twofold tendency which reasoning on physical matters so frequently exhibits — viz., towards physical directness and mathematical elegance ; the former leading to practical application, the latter to analytical refinement. Maxwell, in a review of Tait's 'Thermodynamics,' written in 1877 ('Scientific Papers,' vol. ii. p. 666), contrasts the methods of Clausius and Thomson, and Prof. Mach ('Wärmelehre,' 1896, p. 300) has made similar remarks. Of Thomson the former says, "that he does not even consecrate a symbol to denote the entropy, but he was the first to clearly define the intrinsic energy of a body, and to him alone are due the ideas and the definitions of the available energy and the dissipation of energy. . . . He avoids the introduction of quantities which are not capable of experimental measurement." Since these criticisms a great deal has been written to make the second law of thermo-dynamics and the

conception of entropy more intelligible. The object here again has been twofold : first, to make the conceptions useful for the practical purpose of perfecting the heat engines (Rankine, Zeuner and his school) and of investigating the conditions of chemical equilibrium (Gibbs, Helmholtz, Duhem) ; next, to place the second law, which deals with the transformation of energy, on an equally firm foundation with the first law, which deals with the conservation of energy. There is no doubt that the principle of the conservation of energy owes a very large part of its intelligibility to the fact that for purely mechanical systems it follows from such well-known dynamical axioms as the laws of motion. When heat was conceived to have a mechanical equivalent in mechanical work, the more general principle of the conservation of energy seemed intelligible by mechanical conceptions. The second law, however, introduced a property of natural processes which is not so easily understood mechanically— viz., that they are not reversible —and this property was shown to be connected with a special physical quantity, for which we have a special sense—viz., temperature. The problem of making the second law mechanically intelligible thus coincides with the problem of giving a mechanical definition of temperature. It is not sufficient to call heat a mode (or, more correctly, the energy) of motion ; we must express temperature, on the difference of which the usefulness of heat depends, in some way by motion, we must arrive at a

introducing thermo - dynamics into chemistry, after W.
Gibbs had shown how to look at chemical energy as a
sum of many forms of energy, and after Helmholtz had
more clearly defined the useful conception of free or
available energy as the measure of chemical reaction—
that Prof. Ostwald at length ventured after the lapse of
eighty years to unite in a comprehensive doctrine the
scattered fragments of our existing knowledge regarding chemical affinity.   This he did as a restorer of the
forgotten labours and fame of Berthollet.[1]   By the

49.
Ostwald's
' Allgemeine
Chemie.'

kinetic definition of temperature.
The two principal founders of
thermo - dynamics, Clausius and
Lord Kelvin, did not resort to
kinetic conceptions when establishing the two laws which deal
with the conservation and transformation of energy : Rankine,
however, connected the subject
with his theory of molecular vortices ; and Clausius, who was one
of the founders of the kinetic
theory of gases, very early attempted to interpret the laws of
the transference of heat by the
help of that theory.   So likewise did Maxwell, Helmholtz,
Boltzmann, and many others.
Mr Bryan, in a very valuable
report on the "Researches relating to the Connection of the
Second Law with Dynamical
Principles," has given a critical
summary of these various attempts (see Brit. Assoc. Reports,
1891, p. 85).   The three peculiar
forms of motion referred to in
our last chapter — periodic, rotational, and rapid translational (disorderly) motion—have been used to
suggest manifold means of translating thermo-dynamical processes
into kinetic models, explaining,
as Mr Bryan says, "the second
law, about which we know some-

thing, by means of molecules
about which we know much less"
(p. 121).   It does not seem that
much more has been gained than
a general presumption that a
mechanical illustration is possible.
To the statistical ideas elaborated
mainly by Maxwell and Boltzmann I shall revert when treating generally of the statistical view
of nature.

[1] Prof. Ostwald has himself, in
the Inaugural Lecture which he
delivered on the occasion of his
accession to the chair of physical
chemistry at Leipzig, 23rd November 1887, given a very lucid
statement of the principles involved.   He goes back to the two
theories of chemical action represented at the beginning of the
century by Bergmann on the one
side and Berthollet on the other.
In place of the conflict of chemical
forces, in which the stronger obtains a complete victory (complete
reactions)—the view of Bergmann—
Berthollet introduces the "manifold play of forces acting to and fro,
the result being that every one gets
its due.   The more powerful substance gets more, the weaker less.
Only in cases where one of the
possible compounds in consequence
of its properties entirely leaves

publication of the second volume of his 'Lehrbuch der allgemeinen Chemie' a great impetus was given to physical chemistry. The large addition to our knowledge in this branch, and the consolidation and criticism of research which it brought about, and to which the second edition, now appearing, gives ample testimony, mark this publication as an epoch in modern scientific thought. To this development is attached the growth of the special view of natural phenomena which Ostwald and some other Continental thinkers embrace, and which they are inclined to place in opposition to the older views as a more comprehensive one. The older views they somewhat contemptuously term the materialistic views of nature — the views, in fact, which I have presented under the headings astronomical, atomic, and mechanical. As this most recent outcome of what I termed the physical view of nature refers to fundamental conceptions and has furnished much matter for discussion

the field of contest, either by falling down as insoluble or escaping as gas, can that complete decomposition take place which Bergmann held to be the normal result" ('Die Energie und ihre Wandlungen,' Leipzig, 1888, p. 20). That complete reactions were for a long time studied with predilection was most natural, especially as they are the most useful for practical purposes; but the study of moving chemical equilibrium, depending on what is now termed mass action and involving the question of the velocity of reactions, has in recent times again asserted itself. Ostwald dates the revival of this long-neglected branch of research from the year 1867, when "two Norwegian chemists, Guldberg and Waage, put the ideas of Berthollet into precise mathematical form and subjected the resulting equations to the test of observation and verification" (ibid., p. 21). Ostwald then shows further how Bergmann's theory was simultaneously revived in M. Berthelot's famous third law derived from thermo-chemistry. This in turn had to yield to the correcter views which date from Gibbs's studies "on the equilibria of heterogeneous substances" (see 'Thermodynamische Studien,' p. 66, 1875; also Ostwald, 'Allg. Chemie,' vol. ii. part 2, p. 163, on the reconciliation of Bergmann's and Berthollet's views; and further, Berthelot in 'Comptes Rendus,' 1894, 118).

abroad, I will try to sum up finally the principal points
in it which are of importance for the history of contemporary thought.

Ever since the conception of energy as a quantity
which, like matter, is preserved in all natural processes,
forced itself with more or less clearness upon natural
philosophers, the question has been insistent as to the
number of different forms in which this quantity can
manifest itself; and some of the earliest propounders of
the doctrine attempted an enumeration of the different
forms, mechanical energy of motion and of attraction
usually heading the list. When that form of energy
which we call heat was subjected to examination, and the
remarkable property formerly called latent heat defined
in the new terminology, the want arose of bringing about
some kind of connection between our ideas of motion and
those of heat, which were shown to be mutually convertible quantities in nature. Before that time sound
and light had already yielded to the kinetic view, and an
enormous increase of our knowledge in acoustics and
optics had followed. Thus we find some of the pioneers
of the physical or energy view of nature—notably Rankine
and Joule in this country, Redtenbacher and subsequently
Clausius abroad—engaged in translating the properties
of heat into mechanical analogies.[1]   It was not thought

[1] Rosenberger, in his 'Geschichte
der Physik' (vol. iii. p. 550, &c.),
gives a number of references to
theories mostly forgotten which
were published before and after
the year 1850. Clausius, who
keeps his mechanical theory of
heat quite separate from his kinetic
theory of gases (see the three
volumes on 'Die mechanische
Wärmetheorie,' 2nd ed., 1876, &c.),
admits, nevertheless, in a paper
published in 1857 (Pogg. 'Ann.,'
vol. c., and 'Mechan. Wärmetheor.,'
vol. iii. p. 1, &c.), that "from the
beginning of his researches referring to heat he had attempted to
account to himself for the internal

essential, but it was found to be convenient—mainly for
didactic purposes—to elaborate such analogies, explaining
or describing the less known by that which is more
familiar. Regarding the value of such attempts there
have always existed two opinions. I have had occasion
to refer to them when explaining the atomic theory.
There were those who looked upon that theory merely
as a convenient symbolism, and there were those who
looked upon atoms and molecules as really existing
things. The latter view has gained force and importance
through the necessity of more and more elaborating the
atomic hypothesis in order to represent not merely the
chemical constitution of compounds, but likewise their
manifold physical differences, some of which, in fact,
could only be described by geometrical conceptions. I
need only refer to what I said above on the kinetic
theory of gases, and on the property termed chirality
manifested by some chemical substances in solution, as
well as on the phenomena of isomerism. In the last

state of motion of a hot body, and
that he had arrived at a conception
which he had already before his
first publication (in 1850) used for
various investigations and calculations." He further states that
hearing through William Siemens
that Joule had expressed a similar
idea (Manchester Phil. Soc., 1848
and 1857), and more especially after
the publication of Krönig (1856),
he resolved to publish his views.
It is interesting for our present
purpose to see how Clausius, like
Maxwell in a different domain of
research, was originally guided by
definite mechanical representations.
It is equally noteworthy that Lord
Kelvin's original researches on the
subject of heat were quite free
from this element, though we
owe to him in other departments
some of the most suggestive kinetic illustrations ; and that he has
quite recently offered valuable
criticisms on the attempted mechanical interpretation of the
second law of thermo-dynamics (see
p. 112 of Bryan's Report, quoted
above, p. 176, note). Also the
first English treatise on thermo-
dynamics written for didactic purposes (Tait's Sketch, 1868) contains
no reference to molecular theory,
and Hirn, one of the most active
workers in the region of experimental proofs, kept clear of it.

chapter, while dealing specially with the kinetic view
of natural phenomena, I had again occasion to refer to
the opinion which has latterly crept into mechanical
explanations—namely, that they are to be looked upon
merely as symbolical, an opinion which did not enter the
minds of the original propounders of the vibratory theory
of sound and light, and which some eminent natural
philosophers to-day strongly oppose. An opposite fate
seems to have befallen the mechanical hypothesis in
chemistry and in physics. Whilst Dalton's atoms were
accepted with hesitation, the further elaboration of the
atomic view has made it almost impossible to resist it
as a physical reality; whereas the necessary complications introduced into Young's undulatory theory in
order to make it cover electro - magnetic phenomena
have given it the appearance of unnaturalness and artificiality—so much so that Maxwell himself abandoned
the line of reasoning which led him originally to his
fundamental formulæ, and contented himself with more
general considerations derived from the conception of
energy.

50.
"Kinetics"
and "ener-
getics."
The conceptions which are expressive of the view dealt
with in this chapter—the energy ideas—have had a
similar fate. There have been those who have interpreted this view to mean that all phenomena in nature
can be translated into the language of mechanics: they
have accordingly been stimulated to invent all manner
of kinetic contrivances by which light, heat, electricity,
and chemical action can be represented. Others have
interpreted the equivalence of all forms of energy to
mean that kinetic energy is only one of the forms in

which this quantity can appear : they have thus exerted themselves to find such general properties as belong to all the forms in which energy presents itself to us. They look upon energy as a much more general conception than motion, and they think it a mistake to try to narrow the conception so that it can only mean the energy of attraction and repulsion (the astronomical view), that between the ultimate particles of matter (the atomic view), or the energy of various forms of motion (the kinetic view).

On the purely scientific side the mechanical view has much to say for itself, and can point to achievements which recommend it as a fruitful method of progress and research, and as even more fruitful for the purposes of instruction. It can claim to give in many instances an apparently easy account of the common-sense or obvious properties of bodies, and it gives this account in terms which lend themselves to strict definition, to measurement, calculation, and prediction of phenomena ; it destroys all vagueness, and adopts, as it also stimulates, mathematical, which is the most cogent kind of reasoning. The kinetic theory of gases and the vibratory theory of light are notable examples. The ideas of energy and the remarkable properties of the lowest form of energy— i.e., of heat — became gradually clearer and lost their strangeness as potential energy came to be defined as energy of position, available (or free) energy as the kinetic energy of regular or orderly, unavailable (or bound) energy as that of irregular or disorderly motion, and when the strange quantity termed entropy, which Clausius and Rankine strove in vain to bring home to

the general scientific intelligence, revealed itself as the
measure of the disorder which prevails in the motion of
the ultimate material elements of a system.[1] Faraday's
lines of force and the whole elaborate imagery invented
and afterwards discarded by Maxwell to describe the
interaction of magnets, electric currents, and charged
bodies, have proved to be most valuable instruments of
thought—a useful scientific shorthand—in the hands of
the teacher, as in those of the practical electrician. And
although the illustrious propounder of the vortex-atom
theory of matter seems latterly to have discouraged the
use of this kinetic contrivance as not likely to lead
to any great revelations regarding the ultimate constitution of matter or the nature of the imponderable,[2] the

[1] Helmholtz, in his first memoir
on the thermo-dynamics of chemical processes ('Sitzungsberichte der
Akademie zu Berlin,' 2nd February
1882), after having established the
formulæ for the free energy in iso-
thermal processes without reference
to kinetic hypothesis, concludes his
exposition with the following remarks : "We require, finally, an
expression in order to be able to
distinguish clearly what in theoretical mechanics is termed *vis viva* or
actual energy from the work equiva-
lents of heat, which are indeed
mostly to be regarded likewise as
vis viva of invisible molecular motion. I would suggest that the
former should be called the *vis
viva* of orderly motion. I call
orderly all motion in which the
compounds of velocity of the
moving masses are differentiable
functions of the space co-ordinates.
Disorderly motion would then mean
all motion in which the motion of
each particle has no similarity to
that of its neighbours. We have

every reason to believe that heat-
motion is of the latter kind, and one
might in this sense regard entropy
as the measure of disorder. For
our means, which compared with
molecular structure are coarse, only
orderly motion can be freely converted again into other forms of
mechanical work" ('Wissenschaftl.
Abhandl.,' vol. ii. p. 972).

[2] "I am afraid it is not possible
to explain all the properties of
matter by the vortex-atom theory
alone—that is to say, merely by
motion of an incompressible fluid ;
and I have not found it helpful in
respect to crystalline configurations,
or electrical, chemical, or gravitational forces. . . . We may expect
that the time will come when we
shall understand the nature of an
atom. With great regret I abandon
the idea that a mere configuration
of motion suffices" (Lord Kelvin,
quoted by Prof. S. W. Holman in
'Matter, Energy, Force, and Work,'
New York, 1898, p. 226).

foremost intellects are still busy in working this to them promising vein of reasoning.[1]

The opponents of the kinetic, mechanical, or material views of natural phenomena have always existed: in the early years of the century they described their view by the word " dynamic." At that time it was the atomic theory they principally objected to. But their criticisms, though not without use in exposing the limited nature of all mechanical explanations, failed to yield any fruits, inasmuch as they moved in vague expressions and did not lend themselves to that powerful method by which alone the conquest of nature has been effected, viz., mathematical reasoning, combined with observation.

The more recent critics of the mechanical interpretation of physical phenomena, among whom I will only mention Prof. Ostwald of Leipzig, Prof. G. Helm of Dresden, and Prof. Ernst Mach of Vienna,[2] are fully

51.
Criticism of mechanical view.

[1] " With reference to the vortex-atom theory, I do not know of any phenomenon which is manifestly incapable of being explained by it ; and personally I generally endeavour (often without success) to picture to myself some kind of vortex-ring mechanism to account for the phenomenon with which I am dealing. . . . I regard the vortex-atom explanation as the gaol at which to aim," &c. (Prof. J. J. Thomson, quoted ibid.)

[2] Prof. Ernst Mach is the earliest of these writers and had worked on quite independent lines before the other two names began to figure in scientific literature. His criticisms refer both to metaphysical and mechanical theories. His position is original and unique, and his writings, which are a splendid example of critical and historical analysis, have been invaluable to me. His earliest important essays date from the year 1872 (' Die Geschichte und die Wurzel des Satzes von der Erhaltung der Arbeit,' and ' Die Gestalten der Flüssigkeiten,' Prag). They are now generally accessible, having been collected and translated (under the title ' Scientific Lectures,' Chicago, 1895) by Prof. T. J. M'Cormack. His ' Science of Mechanics ' (translated by the same author from the second German edition, London and Chicago, 1893) has, ever since its first appearance in 1883, had a great influence in Germany ; and latterly also in this country, as may be seen from such works as Prof. Karl Pearson's ' Grammar of Science ' (1st ed., 1892, p. 387), and notably from Prof. Love's ' Dynamics ' (p. 85).

aware of the importance of mathematical presentation of their doctrine, and the two former have in fact done more than any one else to introduce mathematics into chemistry. But they maintain that their exact treatment is not arrived at by introducing hypothetical quantities such as the atomic and other theories are founded upon, but by contenting themselves with measuring such quantities as are presented directly in observation, such as energy, mass, pressure, volume, temperature, heat, electric potential, &c., without reducing them to imaginary mechanical or kinetic quantities.[1] To what extent they

A great many aspects of physical science which have been more prominently brought forward by the modern school of "Energetics" are to be found discussed in Mach's much earlier writings. To his valuable 'Principien der Wärmelehre' (Leipzig, 1896) I have frequently had occasion to refer in this chapter.

[1] In recent discussions and treatises two distinct tendencies must be distinguished. First we have the very useful effort to bring about a correlation of the different departments of physics and chemistry, including their applications in industry and in physiology, by the introduction of the conception of energy and the principles of its conservation and transformation. This dates practically from the publication of Thomson and Tait's 'Natural Philosophy.' The theoretical foundations of this undertaking have been very fully discussed, notably in Germany. I mention only the valuable series of writings of Prof. Max Planck, a list of which is contained at the end of his 'Thermodynamik' (Leipzig, 1897). They begin with his prize essay ('Das Princip der Erhaltung der Energie,' 1887) and his earlier dissertation (Munich, 1879) "On the Second Law." Out of this another endeavour has grown. The aim is to make the conception of energy the fundamental notion, and by following its physical appearance in its different forms, to arrive at certain fundamental relations expressed in equations, which are to serve as the basis for calculation, as in conventional physics the dynamical equations formed the starting-point for the various physical theories. In this more radical scheme the quantity "energy" was to play a part similar to that which the quantity "force" played in Newtonian dynamics. This method was probably suggested by the novel mode of treatment invented originally for heat - problems by Lord Kelvin and by Clausius, and most strictly adhered to by the former. The isolated character of this classical thermo-dynamics can be got over either by introducing a kinetic hypothesis on the nature of heat or by extending the method of thermo-dynamics to other physical provinces. The former was the most plausible view; it has its origin in the writings of Rankine

may succeed in doing this consistently seems at present uncertain. It has been maintained that the very elements of all physical measurement, the independence of the three dimensions in space, necessitates us to supplement the energy-conception—which by itself includes no more reference to direction than the conception of mass—by an assumption of a purely mechanical nature such as the number of degrees of freedom, and that the much-discussed correlation of all forms of energy, as it is suggested by W. Gibbs's formulæ, cannot be usefully carried farther. This correlation [1] has been

and Clausius. The latter method grew out of the gradual application of thermo-dynamics to chemical phenomena, where the mechanical treatment had turned out to be powerless. This more ambitious scheme of remodelling the whole of physics, chemistry, and mechanics on the model of the classical thermo-dynamics dates from the year 1887, when Prof. Georg Helm published his first treatise ('Die Lehre von der Energie,' Leipzig) and revived the word "energetics" invented by Rankine. Subsequently he published his application to chemistry ('Grundzüge der mathematischen Chemie,' Leipzig, 1894), very much under the influence of Willard Gibbs's studies of chemical equilibria and Duhem's elaboration of Helmholtz's conception of free energy. His last work ('Die Energetik,' Leipzig, 1898) gives a history of the gradual purification of the energy conception from mechanical admixtures, into which all earlier writers on the subject except Lord Kelvin are shown to have lapsed, and attempts a reconstruction of mechanics on "energetic" principles, defending the author's position

against various criticisms which had meantime been made.

[1] The great generalisation of the science of energetics referred to in the text was first explicitly put forth by Helm in his treatise of 1887. He himself holds that he there finally brought together suggestions made in various ways by Zeuner (1866), Mach (1871), Gibbs (1875), Maxwell (1875), Von Oettingen (1885), and Popper (1884), and expressed them in the form of a general principle. The two factors into which all energy can be separated are called by various subsequent writers intensity, potential level on the one side; extensity, capacity, weight, on the other. In spite of further expositions of Helm in 1890 the subject did not attract much attention till Prof. Ostwald introduced it in a slightly modified form in the second edition of his great work on physical chemistry (1893), making it the foundation of the doctrine of affinity. He had evidently, between the first and second editions, given up the mechanical for the "energetic" treatment of the subject (see, *inter alia*, note 2, p. 114, of the 2nd edition; vol. ii. p. 12). At the meeting of the German

placed at the summit of the modern theory of energetics
by Helm and Ostwald, after earlier writers, such as
Zeuner and Mach, had already used it or drawn atten-

"Naturforscherversammlung," held at Vienna in 1894, a committee was appointed to report in 1895 at Lübeck on the "actual position of energetics," and the introduction of the subject was put into the hands of Dr Helm. His address and the discussion which followed have been given in extract in the published 'Verhandlungen' (vol. ii. part 1, p. 28, &c.), and since continued in 'Wiedemann's Annalen,' vols. lvii. et seqq. Simultaneously, however, the subject received a much more fundamental or philosophical development through Prof. Ostwald's general address at Lübeck with the somewhat polemical title "Die Ueberwindung des wissenschaftlichen Materialismus." From that moment the mechanical view of nature bore the stigma of materialism, to which the other side replied by attaching to the new or energetic view the stigma of "metaphysical" (see Planck, 'Wied. Ann.,' vol. lvii. p. 77) as being scientifically vague and useless. It cannot be said that the whole matter has yet been fully discussed or fathomed. Prof. Boltzmann, Prof. Carl Neumann, and Dr Helm have treated the questions at stake with much patience, and have made valuable approaches to a mutual understanding. The various contributions are most fully discussed in Helm's latest work, 'Die Energetik' (Leipzig, 1898). Some of those who originally assisted in introducing the energetic treatment have since refused to go the length of Helm's and Ostwald's final generalisations, though they prefer —for the purpose of the treatment of thermo-dynamical and chemical problems — the phenomenological method, admitting at the same time the usefulness of the atomic and mechanical hypotheses, though some do not look upon them as indispensable. This phenomenological view, which deals only with observable and measurable quantities, in contradistinction to the atomic and kinetic views, is largely represented by Prof. Nernst (see his 'Theoretical Chemistry,' translated by Palmer, London, 1895, p. 22), and by Prof. Planck (see his 'Thermodynamik,' Leipzig, 1897), though the latter considers it merely provisional, a stepping-stone in the direction of a mechanical view (p. v, preface). Prof. Boltzmann has summed up the position from a general point of view in his address at Munich in 1899. He there very lucidly defines the mechanical, energetic, and phenomenological positions, admitting the usefulness of all three, but also points out the fundamental difficulties into which a one-sided and exclusive development of any of them unavoidably leads us. Having himself done so much in applying atomic theories, he concludes by saying that "the numerous conquests of the atomic doctrine cannot be won by phenomenology or energetics," and maintains "that a theory which yields something that is independent and not to be got in any other way, for which, moreover, so many physical, chemical, and crystallographic facts speak, must not be combated but further developed" ('Verhandlungen der Versammlung zu München,' 1899, p. 121).

tion to it. It can be set out in the statement that wherever energy shows itself it appears as composed of two factors — the intensity and the capacity factors. These terms, borrowed from the older theories of heat and electricity, measure the quantity of energy as well as the direction in which changes of energy take place : the general law being that energy, in whatever form it may appear, tends to go from places of higher to places of lower potential or intensity.

The characteristic feature of this most recent outcome of the physical view of natural phenomena is that it takes in real earnest the suggestion at which many natural philosophers have independently arrived, that energy is a substance quite as much as matter. This granted, it seems at least reasonable to some thinkers to see how far they can get by employing the two conceptions of matter and energy alone without adopting a third something, the ether, which was introduced at a time when the idea of the conservation of energy had not yet been formulated.[1]

52.
The out-
come.

[1] For an indication of the further development of this point of view I must refer the reader to the chapter on Photo - chemistry in Prof. Ostwald's great work ('Allg. Chemie,' 2nd ed., vol. ii. part 1, p. 1014, &c.) "In the interest," he says, "of a conception of nature which is free from hypotheses, we must ask whether the assumption of that medium, the ether, is unavoidable. To me it does not seem to be so. If we ask for the cause of all displacements of energy in space which we can singly observe, we find that it always consists in differences of intensity. . . . The main point is that, having conceived energy to be a real thing, indeed the only real thing in the so-called outer world, there is no need to inquire for a carrier of it when we find it anywhere. This enables us to look upon radiant energy as independently existing in space. We have found in the general law of intensity — i.e., in the empirical fact that energy tends to equalise forced changes of its density in space — the principle according to which transmission of energy in space necessarily takes place when there appears anywhere an excess." From this and other passages of Prof. Ostwald's writings it seems as if mass likewise was to be given

53.
Recent
triumphs of
atomic view. But whilst the question as to the true method of physical research is still being ventilated abroad, as it has recently begun to be in this country also,[1] the mechanical conceptions of atoms and ether have quietly gained new victories. At the end of the last chapter I related how, in the hands of Maxwell and his followers, the word "electricity" gradually lost its substantial meaning, so that there remained only the conception of a state of motion or stress in the electromagnetic field, it being difficult to assign a definite sense to the term, an electric charge. That those who were brought up under the ideas of Coulomb and Weber would naturally regard this as a defect has also been noted. Still more had the substantial nature of electricity been forced upon those who studied the electrolytic action of solutions and currents, the wandering of

up as a secondary phenomenon of energy. See Boltzmann, *loc. cit.*, last note, p. 114, &c. ; also, *inter alia*, Dr R. Pauli, 'Der erste und zweite Hauptsatz,' Berlin, 1896, preface.

[1] The discussions which began in Germany in the year 1895 at the meeting at Lübeck, and have, after being continued at subsequent meetings, and in the volumes of the 'Annalen der Physik und Chemie,' come to a kind of standstill by the exhaustive treatise of Helm on the one side and by Boltzmann's summing up on the other, do not seem to have attracted much attention in this country. Interest in the subject was, however, latterly aroused by two criticisms of the principles of scientific method coming from entirely different quarters. The first, which was of a purely philosophical character, was con-

tained in Prof. James Ward's 'Gifford Lectures' (1896-98), published in two volumes with the title 'Naturalism and Agnosticism.' The other was an Address delivered by M. Poincaré at the Congress of Physicists in Paris in 1900. In consequence, the subject of the legitimacy of the various physical principles, such as action at a distance, atomism, kinetic and ether theories, the use of mechanical models, and many kindred questions, have been discussed in the Addresses of Poynting (1899), Larmor (1900), and Rücker (1901), before the British Association, with a very emphatic attestation of the usefulness and indispensableness of the atomistic theory regarding the constitution of matter, and the view that a continuous ether is the carrier of all physical actions through space.

the ions, and how, during the process, wandering atoms gave up or lost a definite something—viz., their electrical charges.   It seemed impossible in this case to do without an atomic or molecular view of electricity.   Accordingly, Helmholtz, in his celebrated Faraday Lecture (1881), after having traced the gradual displacement of the Weberian theory of electrical particles acting at a distance by that of Faraday, feels himself constrained to say : " I see very well that the assumption of two imponderable fluids of opposite qualities is a rather complicated and artificial machinery, and that the mathematical language of Clerk Maxwell's theory expresses the laws of the phenomena very simply and very truly ; . . . but I confess I should really be at a loss to explain . . . what he considers as a quantity of electricity, and why such a quantity is constant, like that of a substance."   And further on he says : " If we accept the hypothesis that the elementary substances are composed of atoms, we cannot avoid concluding that electricity also . . . is divided into definite elementary portions, which behave like atoms of electricity."

Besides the phenomena of chemical decomposition, there was another very large and important class of phenomena which gradually led up to the conception of the substantial and atomic nature of electricity. This province of independent, and for a long time isolated, research was opened out by the combined genius of Plücker and Geissler.   It was in the year 1857, two years before the announcement of the discovery of spectrum analysis, that Plücker, with the

54.
Modern electrical researches.

aid of the now well-known vacuum tubes of Geissler,[1] of Bonn, began that long series of experiments on the discharge of electricity in rarefied gases, on the influence of magnets upon the course of the luminous rays, and on the spectra of incandescent gases, which subsequently, in the hands of Sir William Crookes [2] in this country, of Hittorf, Goldstein, Elster and Geitel, and of Giese in Germany, and of a great number of other natural phil-

[1] See the Memoir of Plücker in the 'Annalen der Physik und Chemie' (1857); "Ueber die Einwirkung des Magneten auf die elektrischen Entladungen in verdünnten Gasen" (reprinted in 'Gesammelte wissenschaftliche Abhandlungen,' vol. ii. p. 475, &c.) Before Plücker took up the investigation with improved means of exhaustion (later perfected by the well-known Sprengel pump), several French experimentalists — notably Quet, Gassiot, and Abria—had independently marked the difference of the light near the positive and negative poles, mostly in ignorance of the observations recorded by Faraday in his early "Experimental Researches," as far back as 1838, referring to the "dark discharge." Lord Kelvin, in his Presidential Address before the Royal Society (November 1893), refers to the researches of Faraday, and to a long list of contributions to the same subject contained in the Proceedings and Transactions of the Royal Society. Except those of Faraday, they are all later than Plücker's earliest papers. Lord Kelvin himself says : " Fifty years ago it became strongly impressed on my mind that the difference of quality between vitreous and resinous electricity, . . . essentially ignored as it is in the mathematical theories . . . with which I was then much occupied

(and in the whole science of magnetic waves as we have it now), must be studied if we are to learn anything of the nature of electricity and its place among the properties of matter." Cf. the words of Hittorf (Pogg. 'Ann.,' vol. cxxxvi. p. 1), quoted by Rosenberger, 'Geschichte der Physik,' vol. iii. p. 778.

[2] The experiments and discoveries of Sir W. Crookes on "Radiant Matter," beginning with his paper in the 'Transactions' in December 1878, and continued in many subsequent communications, as also in his Address before the Brit. Assoc. in 1879, especially his theoretical explanations based upon conceptions taken from the kinetic theory of gases, made a great sensation and led to much discussion in this country and abroad. The term Radiant Matter was adopted from Faraday (see Rosenberger, loc. cit., vol. iii. p. 779). The corpuscular theory of light was not indeed revived ; but in general, after much criticism, Crookes's views have to a large extent been adopted ; and if not the corpuscular theory of light, certainly that of electricity has been greatly supported by these brilliant experiments. See J. J. Thomson in the Princeton Lectures (1898), p. 189 sqq., and Prof. Kaufmann's Address, delivered at the Hamburg meeting in September 1901 (translated in the 'Electrician' of November 8, 1901).

osophers, revealed a large array of strange and startling
phenomena, which have latterly been brought somewhat
into line and order by the researches of Prof. J. J. Thomson,[1] of Cambridge. A great many half-forgotten facts
and experiments, which did not fit into the regular programme of electrical science or practice as it had been
elaborated by the older doctrine of Coulomb and Weber
on the one side, or by the more modern of Faraday and
Maxwell on the other, were collected and shown to
throw quite a new light on the processes of radiation
and electrification, and on the relations of the atoms of
ponderable matter to the vacuum, now looked upon as
filled with a continuous substance, viz., the ether. The
older views of the two electricities, brought before
the eye by the celebrated figures of Lichtenberg;[2]
many isolated facts connected with the electric spark
and statical electricity, such as were collected by Riess
seventy years ago, or demonstrated in the hydro-electric
machine of Armstrong; theories, many times abandoned

---

[1] Impressed with the importance
which attaches to the phenomena in
question for a further development
of the theory of electricity founded
by Faraday and Maxwell, Prof. J. J.
Thomson, in his 'Researches,' published in 1893 as a sequel to Maxwell's great treatise, devoted a
long chapter to "The Passage of
Electricity through Gases." His
own celebrated contributions to
this subject, after having been
published in the 'Philosophical
Magazine,' and brought before the
Dover meeting of the British Association in 1899, are now summarised in his lectures on "The Discharge of Electricity through Gases"
(1898). A very interesting earlier
summary of the researches of

others as well as of their own by
Elster and Geitel, will be found in
the 'Annalen der Physik' (1889),
vol. xxxvii. p. 315 *sqq.*

[2] Whilst the differences between
the discharges from the positive and
negative terminals, after having
for a long time been looked upon
as isolated curiosities of electrical
science, were being taken up and
studied in connection with the
subject here referred to (see J. J.
Thomson, 'Researches,' p. 172 *sqq.*),
Lord Armstrong, during the past
ten years of his long and eventful
life, carried on a series of experiments on a large scale, and with
very powerful specially designed
apparatus, on 'Electrical Discharge
in Air and Water' (1895).

and as often revived, like that of Prout,[1] on the constitution of matter; the fanciful speculations of Zöllner,
based upon the views of Wilhelm Weber,—all these
scattered fragments or glimpses of knowledge promise
at the end of the century to come together into a consistent theory of the nature of electricity as an atomi-
cally-constituted substance which is associated with
particles of ponderable matter, or may even be the
ultimate constituent of such matter itself. When a
large mass of experimental facts and many lines of
special reasoning gradually converge towards a common
view, two things are indispensable in order to weld them
into a consistent whole, viz., a new name or vocabulary and an hypothesis as to the elementary processes
which will allow of a simple construction and subsequent
mathematical calculation of the more complicated phenomena of actual experience.   In the case before us, both

[1] See the concluding chapter of
Prof. J. J. Thomson's 'Discharge of
Electricity through Gases' (especially p. 197, &c.), where, after discussing Goldstein's "ether" theory
and Crookes's "corpuscular" theory
of the nature of the celebrated
cathode rays, he, mainly on the
strength of his own and Lenard's observations and calculations, inclines
towards the latter theory, concluding that the carriers of the negative
charges of electricity "are small
compared with ordinary atoms or
molecules, . . . this assumption
being consistent with all we know
about the behaviour of these rays."
"It may," he continues, "appear
at first sight a somewhat startling
assumption in a state more sub-
divided than the ordinary atom;
but a hypothesis which would involve somewhat similar assumptions
—namely, that the so-called elements are compounds of some
primordial element—has been put
forward from time to time by
various chemists. Thus Prout believed that the elements were all
made up of the atoms of hydrogen,
while Sir Norman Lockyer has advanced weighty arguments founded
on spectroscopic considerations in
favour of the composite nature
of the so-called elements. With
reference to Prout's hypothesis,
if we are to explain the cathode
rays as due to the motion of small
bodies, these bodies must be very
small compared with an atom of
hydrogen, so that on this view the
primordial element cannot be hydrogen." See also Sir W. Crookes's
protyle theory referred to, vol. i.
p. 402, note 2.

requisites were supplied before the close of the century. Here and abroad, the term electron, introduced by Dr Johnstone Stoney [1] about ten years ago, has been generally accepted to denote the ultimate particle of electricity, the atom of electricity—positive or negative—of Helmholtz. Mathematical theories have been worked out independently abroad by Prof. H. A. Lorentz [2] of Leyden, and in this country by Dr Joseph Larmor [3] of Cambridge. [4]

55.
The term "electron."

[1] See 'British Association Report,' 1891, p. 574, "On the Cause of Double Lines in Spectra," by G. Johnstone Stoney : "The lines of the spectrum of a gas are due to some events which occur within the molecules, and which are able to affect the ether. These events may be Hertzian discharges between molecules that are differently electrified, or they may be the moving about of those irremovable electric charges, the supposition of which offers the simplest explanation of Faraday's law of electrolysis. . . . Several considerations suggest that the source of the spectral lines is to be sought not in the Hertzian discharges, but in the carrying about of the fixed electric charges, which, for convenience, may be called the electrons."

[2] Prof. Lorentz's principal writings are the two memoirs, "La Théorie électromagnétique de Maxwell et son Application aux Corps mouvants" (Leyden, 1892), and "Versuch einer Theorie der elektrischen und optischen Erscheinungen in bewegten Körpern" (Leyden, 1895). His first labours, indeed, go back to the year 1880.

[3] Dr Larmor's principal publications are, "A Dynamical Theory of the Electric and Luminiferous Medium" ('Philos. Transactions,' 1894);

Part ii., "Theory of Electrons," 1895 ; Part iii., "Relations with Material Media," 1898 ; and his Adams Prize Essay, " Æther and Matter, a Development of the Dynamical Relations of the Æther to Material Systems on the Basis of the Atomic Constitution of Matter" (Cambridge, 1900). Dr Larmor's several shorter papers and addresses, to which I shall refer, are very helpful as introducing one into this novel domain of science.

[4] A little later than Lorentz and Larmor, Dr Wiechert of Königsberg began (in 1896) a series of publications on the same subject, with the aim of making the Maxwellian conceptions more definite. With him, also, the problem narrows itself down to a reconciliation of the continuity of the ether with the atomic nature of ponderable matter, and of the electrical charges attached to it. His views, together with a historical analysis of the labours of his great predecessors, Coulomb, Ampère, Biot and Savart, Neumann, Faraday, Maxwell (including the formal simplifications introduced into Maxwell's scheme by O. Heaviside, Hertz, and Poynting), Von Helmholtz, and H. A. Lorentz, are very concisely set out in a memorial essay entitled ' Grund-

The theory of Maxwell had not only failed to give a definite meaning to the conception of a charge of electricity ; it had also, in the general term " dielectric," somewhat obliterated the clear distinction between empty space and space filled with insulating matter, such as air. Empty space, *i.e.*, space devoid of matter, was supposed to be filled with some continuous substance, the ether, which was the seat or bearer of electric and magnetic actions, the electro-magnetic field. When the only clearly known property of this ether, the fact that it was the carrier of radiation or the luminiferous medium, was identified with its electro-magnetic nature—light being conceived to be an electro-magnetic disturbance— the new theory had to attack the great question of the relation and interaction of ether and matter, in which all the remaining problems of physical optics seemed centred.[1]   How was the electro-magnetic theory of light,

lagen der Elektrodynamik,' published on the occasion of the unveiling at Göttingen, in 1899, of the monument erected in honour of Gauss and Wilhelm Weber. It is interesting to see how, from apparently quite independent beginnings, and in centres far removed from each other, the ideas of the atomic nature of electricity have almost simultaneously become crystallised, and have united themselves with the great experimental labours emanating from Plücker and Crookes to give rise, at the end of the century, to the modern theory of electrons.

[1] One of the most important of these problems is the question to what extent the ether takes part in the motion of ponderable matter through it.   Astronomical aberration, discovered by Bradley, and easily explained by the then current projectile theory of light (see above, chap. vi. p. 10, note), has caused great difficulty to the undulatory theory, and even Sir George Stokes, whose ideas on the subject have been very generally quoted and accepted, would, in his Burnett Lectures on Light (1883), say no more than that "according to the theory of undulations . . . it is not inexplicable" (ed. of 1887, p. 25).   That the electro-dynamic view of the ether should take up the problem was most natural, and the discussion of it is accordingly placed at the opening of Lorentz's memoir of 1895 ; the effect of the motion of the earth on optical phenomena having already been treated by him in 1887.   Dr Larmor treats very fully of this subject in the first section of his

or the wave theory of electricity, to deal with the problem of ether and matter? In this combined scheme what and where were the electric charges or units?

57.
What are electric charges?

On the Continent the labours of Prof. H. A. Lorentz of Leyden, and the almost simultaneous memoir of Von Helmholtz, approached this subject from the side of certain optical problems, notably the vexed question whether the luminiferous ether is stagnant, or participates in the movements of ponderable matter through it, and the phenomena of dispersion. These writings have formed the beginning of a long series of theoretical and experimental researches, which are by no means concluded. In this country we must chiefly consult the many and highly interesting writings of Dr Larmor for a fundamental discussion of the numerous problems involved. At the same time we find there a very thorough criticism, appreciation, and embodiment of the many scattered suggestions and contributions of English and Continental thinkers. Dr Larmor starts from a beginning which is peculiar to him. He finds among the older theoretical discussions of the nature of the luminiferous ether one[1] which will permit of such an

58.
Dr Larmor's position.

essay "On Æther and Matter," and W. Wien has quite recently introduced it for discussion at the "Deutsche Naturforscherversammlung" (Düsseldorf, 1898, Bericht i. p. 49). On the occasion of this discussion, Prof. Lorentz said: "Ether, ponderable matter, and, we may say, electricity, are the building stones out of which we compound the material world, and if we only knew whether matter, in its motion, carries the ether with it or not, a way would have opened by which we could penetrate a little deeper into the nature of those building stones and their mutual action" (loc. cit., p. 56).

[1] The historical traditions of Dr Larmor's theory seem to lie in what may be called the Dublin school of mathematical physics, with the great names of Rowan Hamilton (vector analysis), Mac-Cullagh, and, in recent times, the much lamented G. F. Fitzgerald. "The form under which the atomic electric theory is introduced in Dr Larmor's latest essay

elaboration as admits on the one side the Maxwellian definitions of the propagation of electro-magnetic waves, and on the other the definition of electrons as permanent but movable states of twist or strain, which form the atoms of electricity, and possibly, in their aggregate, ponderable matter itself. The history of thought is mainly interested in this latest and most comprehensive " theory of the electric and luminiferous medium," because it is almost entirely based upon that great advance in physical theory which we owe to Helmholtz and Lord Kelvin, "the discovery of the types of permanent motion, which could combine and interact with each other without losing their individuality, though each of them pervaded the whole field." This has rendered possible an entirely new mode of treatment,[1] and at least made thinkable the reconciliation of the two apparently contradictory notions of modern physics, the continuity and uniformity of the all-pervading ether and the discontinuity of the embedded particles of matter and electricity. The history of thought also takes further note that these latest and yet unfinished theories revert, after the interval of thirty

originally presented itself . . . in the course of an inquiry into the competence of the æther devised by MacCullagh to serve for electrical purposes as well as optical ones " ('Æther and Matter,' p. vi.) " No attempt was made to ascertain whether MacCullagh's *plenum* could, in addition to its vibratory functions, take up such a state of permanent strain as would represent the electrostatic actions between charged conductors, or such state of motion as would represent the electro-dynamic action between currents. The first hint on this side of the matter was Fitzgerald's passing remark in 1880 ('Phil. Trans.,' "On the Electro-magnetic Theory of Light"), that Mac-Cullagh's optical equations 'are identical with those of the electro-dynamical theory of optics developed by Maxwell'" (p. 78).

[1] See Larmor's Address to the British Association at Bradford ('Report,' p. 624).

years, to the older and apparently abandoned views contained in the writings of Wilhelm Weber, who dealt with electric particles and their actions at a distance. The chasm has been bridged over by such theories as those of Lorentz and Larmor, and the missing link supplied which prevented Gauss [1] from accepting that theory when it was first communicated to him by its author.[2]

[1] See above, p. 67, note, where Gauss's letter is quoted; also Larmor, *loc. cit.*, and 'Æther and Matter,' pp. 22, 72 ; ' Philos. Transactions,' vol. clxxxvi. (1895), p. 726 ; H. A. Lorentz, 'La Théorie électromagnétique de Maxwell,' 1892, p. 71 : " On voit donc que, dans la nouvelle forme, la théorie de Maxwell se rapproche des anciennes idées.   On peut même, après avoir établi les formules assez simples . . . regarder ces formules comme exprimant une loi fondamentale comparable à celles de Weber et de Clausius. Cependant, ces équations conservent toujours l'empreinte des principes de Maxwell." Further : Lorentz, 'Versuch einer Theorie,' &c. (1895), p. 8 : " In general there lies in the assumptions which I make in a certain sense a return to the older electric theory. The kernel of Maxwell's views is hereby not lost, but it cannot be denied that with the assumption of ions we are not very far removed from the electrical particles with which one operated formerly." Wiechert (' Grundlagen der Electrodynamik,' p. 108) expresses himself similarly. Lastly, I may refer to Prof. Kauffmann's very interesting Address delivered at Hamburg, September 1891, translated in the ' Electrician ' (November 1901, p. 95 *sqq.*) So we may perhaps say that as Larmor attaches himself to the traditions of the Dublin school, Lorentz and other continental representatives of the atomic view attach themselves to the school of Gauss and Weber.   In proof that Weber's ideas never died out in the Göttingen school, see Rieck's Eloge of Weber, Göttingen, 1897, p. 27, and a very significant remark in the verdict of the philosophical faculty on Planck's Prize Essay ('Die Erhaltung der Energie,' 1887, p. 10).

[2] It would be unjust to dismiss this subject, the overwhelming importance of which becomes evident if we glance at the many contributions which fill the third volume of the ' Rapports présentés au Congrès International de Physique ' (Paris, 1900), without stating that the atomic theory of electricity not only furnishes the very keystone which Gauss was looking for seventy years ago, but that it has also stood the test of experimental verification in the observation by Zeemann of the effect of magnetism on the rays of light, an effect which Faraday sought for in vain about the time when Gauss was in search of the keystone of electrodynamics.   A very concise and interesting account of Zeemann's phenomenon will be found in M. A. Cotton's monograph " Le Phénomène de Zeemann " ("Scientia," Phys. Mathem., Paris, 1899) : " Comment M. Zeemann a-t-il eu l'idée d'étudier avec un appareil de polarisation la lumière émise

59.
Objections
raised by
atomists.

The propounders of this atomic view of electricity
very naturally look with little favour on those other
theories which, under the name of energetics or phenomenology, would restrict the method of science to the use
of only such quantities and data as can be actually seen
and directly measured, and which condemn the introduction of such useful conceptions as the atom, the electron,
and the ether, which cannot be directly seen and can
only be measured by indirect processes; and there is
no doubt that the century ends with a very emphatic
assertion of the rights and the legitimacy of the atomic
and mechanical views of nature, regarding the energy
principle as a regulative but not, by itself, a constructive
method of research and progress; for, as Dr Larmor says,
"If a molecular constitution of matter is fundamental,
energy cannot also be so."[1] Nevertheless though in
many ways opposed, the two views of nature meet at
least in one important point. Both theories have been

dans le champ magnétique ? Ici
encore, la théorie vint aider l'expérience ; cette fois, c'est à H. A.
Lorentz que l'on est redevable du
résultat obtenu. Il est juste de
dire que d'autres considérations,
par exemple celle de Lord Kelvin"
(see Tait, Proc. Royal Soc., Edinburgh, 1875-76, p. 118) "auraient
pu, elles aussi, probablement conduire à cette découverte de la
polarisation des raies. Mais en
fait, cette découverte a été faite
grâce à l'intervention de la théorie
des 'ions' de H. A. Lorentz. Dans
cette théorie, dit M. Zeemann, on
admet qu'il existe dans tous les
corps de petites masses électrisées,
ou 'ions,' dont les mouvements
constituent tous les phénomènes
électriques ; les vibrations lumineuses seraient des vibrations de
ces ions. L'état de l'éther est

déterminé entièrement par la
charge, la position et le mouvement de ces ions. . . . M. Lorentz
fit remarquer que les bords des
raies élargies devaient être pol-
arisés. L'expérience permit à
Zeemann de vérifier cette conclusion de Lorentz" (p. 37).
[1] 'Æther and Matter,' p. 286 :
"One effect of admitting a molecular synthesis of dynamical principles . . . is to depose the conception of energy from the fundamental
or absolute status that is sometimes
assigned to it. . . . We can know
nothing about the aggregate or total
energy of the molecules of a material system, except that its numerical value is diminished in a definite
manner when the system does mechanical work or loses heat. The
definite amount of energy that plays
so prominent a part in mechanical

forced to consider anew the ultimate principles of all physical reasoning, notably the scope and validity of the Newtonian laws of motion and of the conceptions of force and action, of absolute and relative motion, as defined or implied in the mechanical scheme which is based upon them.   Also with their increasing complexity[1] modern dynamical explanations have undoubtedly, to every impartial observer, acquired a certain character of artificiality which suggests the question to what extent all such mechanical schemes are an expression of actual truths or merely useful illustrations.   For the pursuit of scientific research this question is perhaps of little importance : a method is a correct one if it leads to correct results verified by observation.   Philosophically, as bearing upon the processes, powers, and limits of human reasoning, the question is all-important. We are thus led beyond the province of scientific into that of philosophic thought.   In future chapters we shall frequently have occasion to note this tendency of the purely scientific thought of the century to lead up to philosophical problems.   Wherever this is the case a history of scientific thought may legitimately close one of its chapters.

60.
Artificial character of modern dynamical explanations.

61.
The philosophic problem raised.

and physical theory is really the mechanically available energy. . . . This energy is definite, but is not, like matter itself, an entity that is conserved in unchanging amount. . . . It may and usually does diminish, in the course of gradual physical changes."

[1] The three volumes of the 'Rapports,' &c., mentioned above, have been significantly prefaced by a discourse of M. Poincaré on the relations of experimental and mathematical physics, in which he insists upon the unity and simplicity of nature as the two conditions which make generalisations possible and useful.   With special reference to modern electrical theories, such as those of Lorentz and Larmor, which he had already criticised in his course on 'Electricité et Optique' (2nd ed., 1901, p. 577, &c.), he discusses the possibility of ultimate mechanical explanations.   Of these, according to his view, an "infinity" is always possible.   He asks what is the aim we are following—"Ce n'est pas le mécanisme, le vrai, le seul but, c'est l'unité."

CHAPTER VIII.

ON THE MORPHOLOGICAL VIEW OF NATURE.

1.
The abstract
sciences.

THE different aspects of nature which I have reviewed in the foregoing chapters, and the various sciences which have been elaborated by their aid, comprise what may appropriately be termed the abstract study of natural objects and phenomena. Though all the methods of reasoning with which we have so far become acquainted originated primarily through observation and in the reflection over things natural, they have this in common, that they—for the purpose of examination—remove their objects out of the position and surroundings which nature has assigned to them : that they *abstract* them. This process of abstraction is either literally a process of removal from one place to another, from the great work- and store-house of nature herself, to the small workroom, the laboratory of the experimenter ; or—where such removal is not possible—the process is carried on merely in the realm of contemplation : one or two special properties are noted and described, whilst a number of collateral data are for the moment disregarded. In the former case, it is by a process of actual or physical, in the latter by one of purely mental, abstraction that our study begins and is prosecuted. One very powerful instrument of research, where through size and distance—be they very great or very small—objects of nature are beyond our actual reach, is given us in the diagram and the model. There we, for the sake of study, picture or imitate on a reduced or an enlarged scale the movements of the heavenly bodies which are too large or of the atoms which are too small for our actual grip. Now and again the natural philosopher who thus uses the abstract methods of experiment, registration, and calculation, is forcibly reminded that he is in danger of dealing not with natural, but with artificial, things. Instances are plentiful where, through the elaboration of fanciful theories, the connection with the real world has been lost and scientific reasoning has been led astray, to be recalled to a more fruitful path only by the effort of some original genius living in immediate communion with the actual world.

There is, moreover, in addition to the aspect of convenience, one very powerful inducement for scientific workers to persevere in their process of abstraction, in the study of such things and phenomena as can be handled in the laboratory and the workshop, and studied by diagram and by model. This is the practical usefulness of such researches in the arts and industries. In these we do actually abstract the possessions of nature from their proper hiding-places; we drag the minerals from the bowels of the earth; we cut up the timber of exotic growth into artificial fragments; we break up that natural equilibrium in which electrical and

2.
Convenience and usefulness of the process of abstraction.

chemical agencies have, for thousands of years, evaded our discovery and our regard. Having done so, we create an artificial world of our own making which ministers to our wants, comforts, pleasures, and supplies that most inestimable of all commodities of civilisation, varied and stimulating work for ready hands and active brains. The wants and creations of artificial life have thus proved the greatest incentives to that abstract and artificial treatment of natural objects and processes for which the chemical and electrical laboratories with the calculating room of the mathematician on the one side, and the workshop and factory on the other, have in the course of the century become so renowned. All this great activity is—as I have abundantly shown—more and more governed by the scientific, the exact, or the mathematical spirit.

3. Interest opposed to the spirit of abstraction. There is, however, in the human mind an opposite interest which fortunately counteracts to a considerable extent the one-sided working of the spirit of abstraction in science and the growing tendency towards artificiality in our practical life. This is the genuine love of nature, the consciousness that we lose all power if, to any great extent, we sever or weaken that connection which ties us to the world as it is—to things real and natural: it finds its expression in the ancient legend of the mighty giant who derived all his strength from his mother earth and collapsed if severed from her. In its extreme and purest form this interest probably lies at the root of all poetry and all art, and it accordingly governs a great part of the literature and thought of the century. It will occupy us later on in our historical

survey.   At present it interests us only as far as it asserts itself also in science.   In the study of natural objects we meet with a class of students who are attracted by things as they are : not so much by those which we artificially prepare in our laboratories, as by the infinite variety of real forms ; not so much by the geometrical types which allow us to bring them together under some abstract formula, as by the apparent disorder and divine confusion in which real things are scattered about in the heavens and on our globe.   It is not the general equation which in its complete solution contains all real and many unreal instances merely as special cases that interests them, but the individual examples themselves.   The general laws of motion admit of an infinity of special cases which may never occur in nature ; organic chemistry adds daily to the already enormous array of compounds which do not present themselves in living organisms.   Clearly, besides the abstract sciences, which profess to introduce us to the general relations or laws which govern everything that is or can be real, there must be those sciences which study the actually existing forms as distinguished from the possible ones, the " here " and " there," the " where " and " how," of things and processes ; which look upon real things not as examples of the general and universal, but as alone possessed of that mysterious something which distinguishes the real and actual from the possible and artificial.   These sciences are the truly descriptive sciences, in opposition to the abstract ones.   They are indeed older than the abstract sciences, and they have, in the course of the period under review in this work,

4.
The descriptive sciences.

made quite as much progress as the purely abstract sciences. In a manner, though perhaps hardly as powerful in their influence on practical pursuits, they are more popular; they occupy a larger number of students; and inasmuch as they also comprise the study of man himself, they have a very profound influence on our latest opinions, interests, and beliefs—*i.e.*, on our inner life. It is the object of this and some of the following chapters to trace concisely the altered ways and means by which, in the course of the last hundred years, the study of the actual things and events of nature has been prosecuted. For those who wrote the history of the descriptive sciences in the middle of our century, the arrangement of this vast subject presented little difficulty. It had been in the main accomplished by the great naturalists who, during the seventeenth and eighteenth centuries, laboured to bring the large and ever increasing number of natural objects into some supposed system and some professed order, to enumerate them in catalogues or marshal them in museums. The familiar division of natural things into animals, vegetables, and minerals had received a general sanction. Separate sciences, with separate chairs at the universities, which still survive, attended to the separate treatment of these subjects. One of the greatest changes which the present age has witnessed has been the breaking down of the old landmarks and of the stereotyped divisions which existed in the beginning and all through the first half of the century.[1]

5.
The breaking down of old landmarks.

[1] This change has also very much lessened the interest with which we now regard the solution of a problem which, down to recent times, was much discussed—the classification of the sciences. It will be seen that of the many principles of division which have been

If we try to specify a little more closely the agencies and interests that were at work in bringing about this very marked change, which, like every change of the kind, has been reflected by the altered vocabulary of our languages, we come upon two distinct influences—

adopted, the present work only retains that one principle which, in some form or other, appears in every attempt towards classification—the difference between the abstract and the concrete or actual. The two original philosophical systems which France and England in the course of the century have produced, the positivist philosophy of Comte and the philosophy of evolution of Herbert Spencer, have both dealt elaborately with the problem of the classification of the sciences. In this they betray their descent from the philosophy of Bacon and their practical tendencies. It is mainly in the interests of teaching that the division of the sciences is of importance ; and so here it has proved to be indispensable, but also, not unfrequently, narrowing and harmful. German philosophers, who have generally been more influenced by the traditions of Descartes, Spinoza, and Leibniz, have attached less importance to the rigid divisions. The result has been that in Germany, more than in any other country, those modern sciences have grown up which cultivate the borderland that separates the existing well-marked provinces which are artificially kept up by the older chairs at the universities. Examples of this are the new sciences of physiological psychology and of physical chemistry, both brilliantly and for the first time represented at the university of Leipzig. The two great conceptions, however, which have probably done more than any others to break down the old conventional landmarks that kept

the sciences asunder, the conception of energy and the idea of descent, were first prominently put forward in this country. The classical treatise on the division of the sciences in the widest sense is the ' De Augmentis Scientiarum ' of Lord Bacon. An important and original work on the subject is André Marie Ampère's ' Essai sur la Philosophie des Sciences, ou Exposition analytique d'une Classification naturelle de toutes les Connaissances humaines ' (1834). An analysis of the book is given in Whewell's ' Philosophy of the Inductive Sciences,' vol. ii., Book 12. Ampère's classification, on the model of that in botany, is symmetrical and dichotomous. Aug. Comte's classification, contained in the second "Leçon" of the ' Cours de Philosophie positive ' (1830, vol. i.), is termed by its author "une échelle" or "une hiérarchie encyclopédique." Mr Herbert Spencer, in an essay ' On the Genesis of Science ' (1854), republished with additions in the third volume of his ' Essays ' (1874), criticised Comte's attempt to classify the sciences "serially." He more than any other thinker has assisted in breaking down the older idea, which was very prominent in many classifications of the great French naturalists, the idea of the subordination of things in nature, of the " échelle des êtres," and the corresponding conception of an hierarchy of the sciences. In the place of this serial arrangement, a genealogical arrangement, under the specific term of evolution, was introduced, and the sciences were co-ordinated according to their

one of which has tended enormously to broaden our view of natural objects and events; the other to narrow it down and make it more definite, scientifically accurate, and precise. The former has tended to sweep away the older landmarks and divisions as inadequate to afford us a correct view of nature; the latter has tended to create new divisions and definitions, more in harmony with the lines on which the abstract sciences of physics and chemistry have been developed, and has thus brought the actual objects and events of nature more within the grasp of those exact and mathematical methods which those sciences have perfected. The former

6.
The spirit of exploration.

has been carried on in the vast workshop of nature herself by those daring and far-seeing travellers who, with Alexander von Humboldt at their head, have attempted to gain a view of nature on an extensive scale. For the sake of the increase of natural knowledge alone, they visited distant countries where the elemental forces of nature, undisturbed by the inroads of civilisation, have battled and co-operated to produce the magnificent floras and faunas of the tropics, or where, as in Siberia, the eternal cold has preserved intact the remains of bygone periods. Equipped with the instruments and methods of modern science, they recognised the necessity of studying the actual formation and stratification of rocks, the geographical distribution of organic life on the surface of the

genesis, the three great divisions being the abstract, abstract - concrete, and concrete sciences. My readers will readily see the similarities and the differences which exist between this classification and the more general distinctions which I have adopted; and I remind them again that I am not writing a history of Science but of Thought, and that all divisions of this great subject are, more or less, arbitrary.

globe, or in the depths of the ocean; of visiting the real dwelling-places, the habitat of living beings: thus counteracting and enlarging the narrow and pedantic views which the older, purely systematic, and lifeless treatment of natural objects was in danger of fostering.   We know how the germs of two of the greatest generalisations of science were laid in the minds of Mayer and of Darwin during their visits to distant countries, and how fertile in natural knowledge of all kinds have been the voyage of the Challenger and many other similar expeditions, and with what interest and curiosity scientific and popular audiences listen to the narrative of such daring explorers as Fridjof Nansen.

The other and much more concentrated influence, which from the opposite side co-operated with the labours of the great explorers in remodelling the descriptive sciences and infusing new life and vigour into them, has been not less marked.   There has always existed one great interest, in which nearly all the descriptive branches of natural knowledge have found a common rallying ground and a uniting purpose — namely, the art of healing, the alleviation of human suffering and the curing of disease.   During long ages, when the purely scientific interest was almost dead, physical and chemical research was created or kept alive by the physician, the alchemist, and the apothecary; medical works like those of Celsus and Galenus in antiquity [1] have been the ency-

7.
The medical interest.

---

[1] It may also be pointed out that Aristotle was descended from a family of doctors, that—according to Zeller ('Philosophie der Griechen,' vol. ii., part 2) — the assumption is warranted " that the medical art of his father Nicomachus, who was the medical adviser and friend of the Macedonian king, Amyntas, had a prominent influence on the mental development of his son."

clopedias of the existing knowledge of nature, and celeb-
rities like Boerhaave, Linnæus, and Haller in more modern
times have been the living centres of all the natural
sciences. The same uniting bond has not been wanting in our century, when it has again, as many times
before, manifested its powerful influence, has brought
together researches which were on the point of falling asunder, and infused new life and interest into the
driest of studies. As I have had occasion to remark
above, the modern school of medicine originated in the
attempt—begun by Lavoisier in France, but carried out
on the largest scale in the chemical and physiological
laboratories of Germany—of making the new discoveries
in physical science and chemistry fruitful for medical
purposes and the treatment of pathological cases. The
discovery of galvanism gave probably the earliest impetus, and was, to the discredit of an exacter treatment,
largely misused in the earlier part of the century, till
Du Bois Reymond, in the middle of the period, based his
elaborate researches on more correct methods, and created
nearly all the knowledge we now possess of the electrical
currents in the nervous system. Somewhat earlier, Liebig
led the study of the phenomena of animal heat and of
the food relations of the animal and vegetable kingdom;
the brothers Weber had introduced dynamics into the
theory of the motion of the heart and the limbs; whilst
Johannes Müller and his numerous school about the same
time laid the foundations of physiological and pathological
acoustics and optics. Quite independently of these applications of the mechanical and physical sciences, which led
some over-hastily to imagine that in the doctrine of the

8.
Physical
science
applied to
medicine.

organism as a pure machine lay an answer to the great problems of life and consciousness, Theodor Schwann proclaimed about 1840, on the basis of minute microscopic observation, the essential identity of animal and vegetable—*i.e.*, of all living—structure, thus taking probably the greatest step in uniting researches which had so far been carried on in a disconnected fashion. Here is the beginning of the modern theory of the organic cell—of cellular pathology, and the actual inauguration of modern biology. Twenty years later, the appearance of Darwin's 'Origin of Species' urged still further the study of the whole of organic life from a comprehensive point of view. In addition it led to a closer union with the sciences of inorganic nature, an appeal being now made to palæontological and geological records in proof of the gradual development of all forms of living as well as of inanimate reality. The studies of the geologist, which up to then had been prosecuted on independent lines, joined hands not only with those of the zoologist and botanist, but likewise with the theory of cosmological genesis of the planetary system, as proclaimed at the end of the former century by Laplace in his 'Exposition du Système du Monde,' and fifty years earlier by Kant in his 'Natural History of the Heavens.' If in the course of our century, through the combined influence of travel on the one side and medicine on the other, the history of natural objects has been united in the larger conception of biology, this itself at the close of the century promises to be united with geology and astro-physics (a science almost entirely founded on the invention and on the revelations of the

9.
Schwann.

10.
Darwin.

spectroscope), into the still wider conception of a general science of evolution, as enunciated already forty years ago in the writings of Herbert Spencer, and in a more shadowy form by Herder in the eighteenth century, and by Leibniz in the seventeenth.

11.
Herbert
Spencer.

Seeing, then, that the treatment of the descriptive sciences of nature has been so radically changed during the course of the century, and that the change has been accompanied by a complete revolution in our modes of thinking and reasoning on these subjects, the historian of Thought cannot be content with merely chronicling the progress of the methods in use in the separate sciences, such as mineralogy, geology, botany, and zoology, even with the addition of the more recent sciences of palæ-ontology, physiology, and comparative anatomy. He might in doing so fairly grasp the history of the descriptive sciences up to the year 1850. It is exactly in this manner that Whewell, in his 'History of the Inductive Sciences,' treated this part of his subject. Beyond that period the old landmarks designated by those names have disappeared or become of secondary importance. On the other side, whilst a history of Evolution in Science might seize on the great characteristic feature of the more modern research which belongs to the second half of the century, it would hardly suffice to sum up the leading ideas of the descriptive branches of science as they were carried on on independent lines during the earlier years of our period. Evolu-tion had then no definite meaning, and Biology was a disregarded term. We must thus look out for some more general aspects which belong alike to the earlier

12.
Whewell's
divisions
abandoned.

and later periods, and which will enable us to see how that great change has gradually come about.

All studies that deal with the actual things and events by which, on a large and on a minute scale, we are surrounded in nature, are comprised under the term Natural History.   In opposition to Natural Philosophy, which comprises our abstract knowledge of the possible forms of motion and the possible combinations of the elements into which we have so far been able to decompose matter, Natural History deals only with such forms and combinations as actually exist around us, only with such processes of change as actually take place in nature.   Some of these forms and changes we may be able to collect in our museums or imitate in our laboratories, but the forms of nature cannot in this way be exhausted, nor her processes understood.   Her forms or things do not exist in isolation, but always in a certain environment, having a definite plan, a position in time and space.   These surrounding features are as important as the things themselves.   Besides this, the processes of nature draw on the great factor of time with a much more liberal hand than we can permit ourselves to do.   Nevertheless, as in the abstract sciences we deal with things at rest and with things in motion, so we can appropriately divide our study of the real and the actual into the attempt to give some account of the forms and things which actually exist and continually recur, and the study of the changes which things undergo.   In abstract science the terms statics and dynamics, the doctrines of rest and of motion, have been generally introduced, to distinguish the two great aims of study; some cor-

13.
Divisions of natural history.

responding terms may appropriately define the twofold
interest which we take in natural objects.   The term
morphology [1] was introduced early in the century by

[1] The term morphology was introduced by Goethe to define a series
of researches and studies to which
he was led by his equal interest in
art, nature, and human society.
Returning from Italy, which he describes as "rich in forms," to Germany, which he terms in contrast
"gestaltlos," he reports that three
distinct problems had presented
themselves.   "Wie die begünstigte
griechische Nation verfahren um die
höchste Kunst im eigenen National-
kreise zu entwickeln. . . . Wie die
Natur gesetzlich zu Werke gehe,
um lebendiges Gebild, als Muster
alles künstlichen, hervorzubringen.
. . . Wie aus dem Zusammen-
treffen von Nothwendigkeit und
Willkür, von Antrieb und Wollen,
von Bewegung und Widerstand ein
drittes hervorgeht . . . die menschliche Gesellschaft."   For the purpose of finding an answer to the
second of these questions, Goethe
collected and observed, read and
speculated, and formed the conception of a general science of organised beings, termed morphology,
which was not to treat merely of
external figure, but to comprise also
physiology and the study of development.   It is the first great attempt
to think of nature as a whole, and
to break down the rigid lines which
divided the several natural sciences.
He thus inaugurated the modern
view of nature by introducing the
general science of morphology.   His
first literary attempt in this direction was the now celebrated
pamphlet on the ' Metamorphosis
of Plants,' in which he represents
the leaf as the typical formation
from which the other parts of the
plant can be derived.   Whether
this derivation is a real process in
the sense of modern evolution, or a
merely ideal one in the sense of the
earlier archetypal view, Goethe does
not clearly say.   This uncertainty
Goethe shares with the whole school
of the "Naturphilosophie," as Julius
Sachs points out in his ' History of
Botany'   (German edition, 1875,
p. 170).   This is not the point to
which I want to draw attention at
present.   More important is the
remark which Goethe makes in the
further historical account of the
gradual development of his morphological ideas.   Wolf, the philologist,
pointed out to him that his own
namesake, Caspar Friedrich Wolf,
had anticipated Goethe in the attempt to demonstrate the fundamental identity of the different
parts of a plant.   In the sequel of
his most appreciative analysis of
Wolf's expositions, Goethe characteristically notes that Wolf does
not include in his conception the
"metamorphosis of animals," or introduces it only as something entirely different.   That Goethe's idea
of morphology as a general science
of the forms and change of forms in
nature is applicable likewise to inanimate forms—to geological, geographical, and many other formations, nay, even to rigid things like
crystals, and to such unstable formations as the parts of speech and
language—has in the course of the
century been abundantly recognised.   It is known how, guided by
the same general interest, Goethe
studied the formations and transformations of animals, rocks, and
clouds, though, according to Zittel
('Gesch, der Geologie,' 1899, p. 275),
C. F. Naumann first used the expression, "morphology of the surface of the earth," in 1850.   Goethe's

one who loved above all things to watch the works of nature in their proper abodes—who combined the poetical with the scientific interest,—by Goethe.   The term genesis [1] has long been employed to describe the processes by which the actual world has come to be what it is.   To the statical and dynamical aspects of the abstract sciences correspond accordingly to some extent the morphological and genetic aspects of the natural sciences.   To some extent only, for in nature, where everything is subject to continual flow, we never come upon a realisation of absolute rest, a pure form, a rigid type.   Rather would I put it in this way : In the perpetual variety of change the morphological view tries to define those recurring forms or types which present themselves again and again, towards which all changes seem to revert; thus bringing some order into

14.
Morphology
and genetics.

morphological writings have been for the first time completely edited and annotated in the three volumes (6 to 8) of the second division of his works now being published by the Goethe-Gesellschaft at Weimar. The authority whom I approach nearest in the use I make of the term morphology is probably Haeckel. See the first book of his ' Generelle Morphologie der Organischen Wesen' (1866, vol. i. pp. 1-108).

[1] Goethe's morphological studies were equally directed towards the formation and the transformation of living things : morphology was to him the science of "Bildung und Umbildung." In the course of the century the terms morphology and morphological school have come to mean more and more that complex of comparative researches which historically prepared the genetic, developmental, or evolutionist school of thought, but which

were mainly dominated by the conception of fixed types and forms, and, though searching for the laws of modification, did not rise to a clear enunciation of a theory of evolution and descent. Goethe himself hovered all his life long between an artistic predilection for the perfect form or model and a deeper philosophical conviction of the continual flow of things. See a remark of his (' Werke,' II., vol. vi. p. 304) in an aphorism on "genetic treatment": "Erst bin ich geneigt mir gewisse Stufen zu denken; weil aber die Natur keinen Sprung macht, bin ich zuletzt genöthigt mir die Folge einer ununterbrochenen Thätigkeit als ein Ganzes anzuschauen, indem ich das Einzelne aufhebe, ohne den Eindruck zu zerstören." See also a remark on Goethe's undefined position in Carus, 'Geschichte der Zoologie' (1872), p. 590.

what would otherwise be disorder and confusion. On the other side, the genetic view deals with the transition from one form to another in the course of time; takes more interest in movement and in the process and function; and seeks for their probable laws and regularities. Without wishing to limit these remarks to merely organic or living things, the difference between the morphological and genetic views can be brought home to the mind by referring to the different objects of anatomy and physiology.[1] This twofold and very general aim—the desire to know what is, and how it has come to be—has existed at all times, though frequently obscured by artificial and temporary restrictions. From this point of view I propose to survey the mental attitude of the century towards the real things and events of nature, as distinguished from the artificial or mathematical forms and processes of our studies and our laboratories, our calculating and measuring rooms. The

[1] Genetic theories have everywhere been prepared and ushered in by morphological studies. So in Goethe's time; so later on, after Darwin had given a definite law of descent, and Herbert Spencer had fixed the vocabulary and ideas of evolution, this relation is manifested by two great works, the 'Generelle Morphologie der Organischen Wesen,' by Prof. Ernst Haeckel in Germany (1866), and Francis M. Balfour's 'Elements of Embryology' (1874) in England. It is characteristic that Prof. Haeckel, in the further development of his literary activity, dropped the term morphology, and published the desired new editions of his great work under two different titles, 'Natürliche Schöpfungsgeschichte' (1868, 2 vols.), and 'Systematische Phylogenie' (1896, 3 vols.) The division of the great modern biological doctrine into morphology and genetics is in conformity with Mr Herbert Spencer's treatment in the 'Principles of Biology,' vol. ii., published in 1865, and with the two divisions of Haeckel's 'Generelle Morphologie,' which treated respectively of the "science of developed forms" and the "science of developing forms"— i.e., of structure and process. I have chosen such expressions in the text as will permit of a comprehension of inanimate as well as of animated nature. In 1875 there were founded simultaneously in Germany two periodicals, representing respectively the morphological and genetic sides of animal biology.

present chapter will deal with the morphological, the following with the genetic, views of nature.[1]

Were the real world only one out of many possible worlds which the mathematical mind can imagine, though through its complication and intricacy it might still far surpass its powers of analysis; were the actual forms of nature only some of the infinitely possible states of equilibrium, the events and changes surrounding us in space and time only a few of the countless combinations of motion taught in dynamics; were the actual course of things—as mathematicians since Laplace have fancifully put it—only one particular solution of the general differential equations of the world-motion, — then the two great domains of morphology and genesis would exhaust the subject and satisfy all the interests by which natural history has been created.   Unfortunately for the pure mathematician, but fortunately for the rest of mankind, notably the poet and the artist, it is not so.   An enormous gulf separates the creations of nature from the most perfect machine; and the fact that, with all the most delicate methods at her command, her most perfect machines, like the human eye, do not come up to the demands of the optician,[2] shows us that other agencies

15. Other aspects.

[1] As in abstract mechanics, the study of the conditions of equilibrium, *i.e.*, statics, preceded in time the study of the phenomena of motion, *i.e.*, dynamics, so in the study of nature the apparently finished or developed forms attracted attention before their genesis was inquired into; and as the key to statics has in the course of time been discovered to lie in dynamics, so the key to an understanding of form and structure has been found to lie in the dynamical theory of descent or evolution.   In animal biology a separate influence —the medical interest—led, however, very early to a study of function and of the processes in the living organism.

[2] This refers to a well-known remark of Helmholtz in his popular lectures on the 'Theory of Light' (1868), where he enlarges on the remarkable imperfections of the eye as an optical instrument.   His real

and other interests are at work than we have as yet been able to grasp. So long as astronomy was content to observe the orbits and motions of the heavenly bodies from a distance, it indeed appeared possible to define that science as merely "une question d'analyse"; but in astronomy even, spectroscopy has brought distant objects near to us and opened out endless vistas into a purely descriptive branch of the science, a natural history of the heavens. Still more so is this the case when we fix our gaze on the world immediately surrounding us—on the things and events in which we ourselves take an active part. Here two phenomena attract our attention

16.
Life and
mind.

—the problem of life, and the problem of consciousness or mind. The knowledge which we possess, or imagine we possess, of the latter, which is gained from a purely introspective point of view, the psychological aspect, I leave at present quite out of the question. As external observation through our senses would never have given it; as in the map of reality which we call nature, we have not even succeeded in accurately locating consciousness,—I relegate this large department of Thought to a different place in this work. At present we have to do only with the study of nature, the first condition of

object was to dispel the popular conception that the accuracy and variety of the performances of the human eye could be explained by the precision and complexity of its structure, as if it were an optical instrument of a degree of perfection which could not be equalled by any optician. In the sequel Helmholtz shows how this admiration of a wrongly supposed mechanical perfection must make room for an admiration of a different kind, as

"every work of the organic formative power of nature is for us inimitable"; a remark which really supports the argument in the text ('Vorträge und Reden,' 3. Aufl. 1884, vol. i. p. 240, &c.) It is also important to note how Helmholtz traces the imperfections of the eye to its genesis—i.e., its development in the embryo. The genetic supplements the purely structural examination (ibid., p. 255).

which is that her phenomena have, or have at some time had, a definite place and position in space.   Here, then, the phenomena of lower and higher life and the new creations of human culture, art and industry, open out a great department of reality which is accessible to external observation and study.   Without committing ourselves to any theory on the subject, we have in this department to deal with the phenomena of apparent or real design and purpose.   How has the century dealt with these phenomena ?   The answer to this question, the history of nineteenth century thought as directed towards the phenomena of life and of mind as natural phenomena, will be dealt with in two further chapters, which will respectively deal with the vitalistic [1] and the psycho-

---

[1] It would have been in some respects preferable to use the word "biological" instead of vitalistic.   In fact, in the original draft of this passage I used the former term.   The reasons which made me alter it are the following : The term biology was first used in 1801 by Lamarck in his ' Hydrogéologie.' " About the same time it occurred to Treviranus that all those sciences which deal with living matter are essentially and fundamentally one, and ought to be treated as a whole ; and in the year 1802 he published the first volume of what he also called ' Biologie.'   Treviranus's great merit lies in this, that he worked out his idea, and wrote the very remarkable book to which I refer. It consists of six volumes, and occupied its author for twenty years —from 1802 to 1822.   That is the origin of the term ' biology ' ; and that is how it has come about that all clear thinkers and lovers of consistent nomenclature have substituted for the old confusing name of ' natural history,' which has conveyed so many meanings, the term ' biology,' which denotes the whole of the sciences which deal with living things, whether they be animals or whether they be plants." This extract from Huxley's "Lecture on the Study of Biology" (South Kensington, Dec. 1876, reprinted in ' American Addresses,' &c., 1886, p. 129, &c.), has induced me to adopt the term "vitalistic" to denote those doctrines and chapters in biology which deal specially with the principle and phenomena of life.   A very large portion of biology deals with such phenomena of living things as can be studied without any reference to a doctrine or theory of life in particular, they being either mere facts of distribution or that very large and increasing class of biological processes which admit of purely mechanical, physical, or chemical description and explanation.   The very fact, however, that the question whether the principle of life is purely mechanical

physical views of nature. Thus four distinct chapters, dealing severally with the morphological, the genetic,

17.
Vitalistic
and psycho-
physical
aspects.

the vitalistic, and the psycho-physical aspects of nature, will together attempt to describe the manifold and changing methods of reasoning by which our century has approached the actual things and events which surround us.

" Nature does not employ all figures, but only certain ones of those which are possible : and of these, the determination is not to be fetched from the brain, or proved *a priori*, but obtained by experiments and observations." These words, set down nearly two centuries ago by a now forgotten natural philosopher,[1] express clearly the object of a study which, towards the end of the eighteenth century had received definite expression in vari-

---

or not is not yet decided, makes it necessary to retain in a history of Thought a special term comprising all speculations which deal with the purely scientific solution of that problem. In fact, the question what is life is still unanswered. *A fortiori*, these remarks refer also to the question, What is mind or consciousness ? But the two chapters referring to these problems will limit themselves to an historical exposition of what has been done to solve them by purely scientific, *i.e.*, exact, methods. The full name of the author of the ' Biologie ' was Gottfried Reinhold Treviranus (1776-1837) of Bremen. Though introducing the larger conception of biology, his own original labours were mainly in the domain of zoology. His brother, Ludolf Christian Treviranus (1779-1864), devoted himself mainly to botanical

science, and was largely influenced by the doctrines of the " Naturphilosophie." On the former, see Carus, ' Geschichte der Zoologie ' (München, 1872), *passim ;* on the latter, Sachs, ' Geschichte der Botanik ' (ibid., 1875, p. 291).

[1] They are quoted by Whewell (' Hist. Induc. Sciences,' 3rd ed., vol. iii. p. 165), from a work entitled ' Dissertatio de Salibus ' (1707), by the Italian Professor at Padua, Dominico Gulielmini (1655-1710). He was a practical physician as well as a natural philosopher. He was the forerunner of Romé de Lisle and Haüy, inasmuch as he established the principle, not then sufficiently appreciated, that the constancy of the angles is characteristic of all crystals. See Kopp's ' Geschichte der Chemie,' vol. ii. pp. 83-404.

ous branches of natural science, and which can be best characterised by the term morphology.[1]   The word was first applied only to plants, then also to animals, and later still to crystals and minerals.   The words quoted above refer to the forms of inanimate nature, to crystals. In all these cases we have to do with definite individual objects, which can be removed from their surroundings and examined in the laboratory.   There is, however, no reason why a study of the actual forms of nature on a large scale, such as the physiognomy of landscape, the configuration of mountains and valleys, the shapes of glaciers, the actual distribution of land and water on our globe, the stratification of rocks, the formation of clouds, and many other things, should not all be comprised under the term, the morphological view of nature.   And conceived in this larger sense, the study of nature as a whole and in its separate parts had at the end of the eighteenth century already made very important progress.   In fact, natural history had, in the course of that century, gradually emerged from the previous epoch, that of the purely systematic and classificatory attempts, which aimed at giving inventories, collecting specimens, and classifying natural objects, naming, describing, and identifying them. The interest of the latter was a practical one, frequently

18.
Morphology
defined.

[1] In the 'Leçons sur les Phénomènes de la Vie communs aux Animaux et aux Végétaux,' a work which did so much to break down the older division of the sciences which deal with animals and vegetables separately, Claude Bernard says (p. 333 of vol. i., 1885): "Dans un autre équilibre cosmique, la morphologie vitale serait autre. Je pense, en un mot, qu'il existe virtuellement dans la nature un nombre infini de formes vivantes que nous ne connaissons pas. Ces formes vivantes seraient en quelque sorte dormantes ou expectantes. . . . Il en est ainsi des corps nouveaux que forment les chimistes ; ils ne créent pas, ils étaient virtuellement possibles dans les lois de la nature."

prompted by the needs of the medical profession, which studied animals as affording an insight into the analogous structure and functions of the human body;[1] and plants, because they largely furnished the materials for the preparation of medicines. To this must further be added the practical interests of agriculture, of gardening, and of the artificial culture of flowers and exotic plants, and the breeding of domestic animals. All these interests, however stimulating they may have been and still are, introduce an element of artificiality into the study of nature. They have all a greater concern for natural objects, be they beautiful or useful, than they have for nature itself. From this artificial position the true sciences of nature had to emancipate themselves by slow degrees and with many efforts. Ever since the time of Linnæus, through whose labours the systematic attempts received a kind of finality, and even in his own writings, great discussions were carried on as to

19.
Artificial and natural systems.

the difference between a natural and an artificial order of plants and animals. " The natural orders,"[2] says Linnæus, " teach us the nature of plants, the artificial orders enable us to recognise plants. The natural orders, without a key, do not constitute a method; the method ought to be available without a master. . . . The habit of a plant must be secretly consulted. A practised botanist will

[1] Referring to Albrecht von Haller, Victor .Carus ('Gesch. d. Zoologie,' p. 567) says, " Through the leap which physiology took, thanks to his labours, zootomical researches developed in a direction which brought them into complete subjection to physiology, with a neglect of the independent importance which belongs to them. . . .

It diverted attention from the immediate object of zoology, the explanation of animal forms and their variety, to the more remote problem —the explanation of the phenomena of life."

[2] Quoted by Whewell ('Hist.,' vol. iii. p. 268) from the ' Genera Plantarum' (1764).

distinguish at the first glance the plants of different quarters of the globe, and yet will be at a loss to tell by what mark he detects them. There is, I know not what look—sinister, obscure, in African plants; superb and elevated in the Asiatic; smooth and cheerful in the American; stunted and indurated in the Alpines." [1] The inventor of the sexual system of plants, which proved to be such a good "finder" in the hands of the botanist and herbalist, speaks of the difficulty of the task of discovering the natural orders. "Yet," he says, "I, too, have laboured at this—have done something, have much still to do, and shall labour at the object as long as I live." [2]

Linnæus's artificial system met with little acceptance in France, where, under the opposite influence of Buffon,[3]

20.
Linnæus and
Buffon.

[1] Quoted by Whewell ('Hist.,' vol. iii. p. 268) from the 'Philosophia Botanica' (1751).

[2] Ibid., quoted from the 'Classes Plantarum' (1738). Julius Sachs, in his excellent 'History of Botany' (Munich, 1875, transl. from the German by H. E. Garnsey, 1890), says of Linnæus, that in his morphological as well as in his systematic labours, there existed two unreconciled conceptions—a superficial one, meant only for practical use, which found expression in his artificial sexual system, and a deeper, scientifically valuable one. "For practical purposes of description he elaborated his nomenclature of the parts which, however useful, appears nevertheless flat and superficial, as any deeper foundation through a comparative study of forms is wanting. But alongside of this, there appears in various passages of his writings the desire for a more profound conception of plant-forms. What he had to say on this subject he brought together under the term 'metamorphosis plantarum'" (p. 110 of the German edition).

[3] Buffon's great name has a place in the history of the genetic as well as of the morphological view of nature, inasmuch as he looked at the things of nature as much from the side of their individual speciality as from that of their connection and orderly arrangement in time and space. And inasmuch as he "does not only consider the form, but tries to maintain an interest in the general economy of the whole of nature by picturing to us the homes, the habits and customs, the instincts, &c., of living things, so he strove in general to represent the single phenomena of nature as existing in intimate connection" (Carus, 'Gesch. der Zoologie,' p. 523). "As Buffon opposed the extreme systematisers, who seemed to think it the end of science, not so much to know about an object as to be able to name it, and fit it into their system, so Daubenton (the collaborator of Buffon in France)

the great botanists, from Jussieu to De Candolle, and the great zoologists, notably Cuvier, made an attempt towards a freer and more generous and more sympathetic conception of the objects as well as the totality of nature. These attempts were continued much on the same lines till well on into the nineteenth century. Buffon's comprehensive scheme was premature, but it had a very great and beneficial influence in popularising and enlivening the frequently dry and uninteresting pursuits of the collector and systematiser. Cook's voyages during the last third of the eighteenth, and Humboldt's travels at the turn of the two centuries, did much to further a comprehensive view; but the great task of the morphologist, like every other scientific work, had to be solved by special studies in separate departments. It grew from small beginnings and detached contributions.

One of the most notable of these, and one also which has all along exerted a great influence on all morphological studies, is the theory of crystals, both natural and artificial. I have already had occasion to refer to the labours of Haüy [1] and his successors. They have led to a complete mastery of the geometrical forms which minerals occasionally present in nature, and which substances assume if allowed to solidify out of the liquid condition. The science of crystallography, now appropriately termed the "morphology of crystals," [2] has had

21.
Morphology
of crystals.

insisted on the study of each animal as an individual whole. . . . He occupied himself, therefore, with the production of a series of admirable monographs appended to the descriptions of Buffon in the 'Histoire Naturelle'" (Huxley in the chapter on Owen's position, &c., in 'Life of Richard Owen,' 1894, vol. ii. p. 280).

[1] See vol. i. p. 116, &c., of this history.

[2] See 'The Morphology of Crystals,' by N. Story Maskelyne, 1895.

a peculiar fascination as forming the transition from the abstract science of geometrical forms and statical equilibrium to the study of the actual forms of real things. Here, if anywhere, it seemed as if we might discover the link that connects the theoretically calculable with the actually existing, the possible with the real. Accordingly, we find a very general and recurring tendency to carry over the notions of crystallography into other sciences — into the morphology of plants and animals. The planes and axes of geometry, and the forces of attraction between particles of matter, have formed a theme which has been endlessly repeated and varied in explaining the elements and the forms of living matter. But whilst these fanciful analogies [1] of organic crystals, of polar distribution, and the network of tissues, to which are also allied the spiral theories of leaves and branches in plants and other geometrical arrangements, have at times attracted much attention,[2] and have served to give at least the

[1] " Ces comparaisons entre les formes minérales et les formes vivantes ne constituent certainement que des analogies fort lointaines, et il serait imprudent de les exagérer. Il suffit de les signaler. Elles doivent simplement nous faire mieux concevoir la séparation théorique de ces deux temps de la création vitale : la création ou synthèse *chimique*, la création ou synthèse *morphologique*, qui en fait sont confondues par leur simultanéité, mais qui n'en sont pas moins essentiellement distinctes dans leur nature " (Claude Bernard, ' Leçons sur les Phénomènes de la Vie,' &c., vol. i. p. 296). See also on the extravagances of such search for analogies, .Jul. Sachs, ' Gesch. d. Botanik,' p. 173, &c.

[2] I shall revert to this subject when speaking of the elder De Candolle. Here only a passing remark on the " spiral theory," which was mainly developed by K. F. Schimper and Alexander Braun, after the regular geometrical arrangement of leaves around their stalks had already been noticed in the eighteenth century by Charles Bonnet, following Cæsalpinus. For about thirty years, from 1830 onward, the spiral theory was very popular in Germany. In France, the somewhat related theories of symmetry of De Candolle, of metamorphosis of Goethe and of spiral

semblance [1] of an explanation of organic structures and
forms, they have in reality done as little as Boscovich's
centres of force and curves of attraction and repulsion
in mathematical physics to establish a firm basis for
actual research; for nowhere have they been capable of
exact determination such as has been applied to the
angles and figures of crystals.

Simultaneously with the science of crystallography
there came into being the science of minerals on a
larger scale of study, through actual observation in
definite localities of the formation and stratification
of rocks; of the traces of the influence of the great

22.
Morphology
on a large
scale.

arrangements of Schimper, became
known under the term "Morphologie végétale," through Auguste
de Saint Hilaire in his 'Leçons de
Botanique' (1840). To the spiral
theory, although strongly opposed
in course of time by Wilhelm Hof-
meister, one of the founders of the
genetic conception of plant life,
Sachs, the historian of botany,
nevertheless assigns an important
historical influence, "as through
Schimper's theory the morphologically so important relative position
of the plant organs was for the first
time placed in the foreground of
morphology" (loc. cit., p. 180). See,
however, on this subject the paper
by A. H. Church on "Phyllotaxis"
in vol. i. p. 49 of 'The New
Phytologist,' 1902.

[1] The early propounders of the
cellular theory of organic structures
adopted the view that cells were
formed in a surrounding liquid in
the manner of crystals in a mother-
liquor. When it was established
that organic structures grow by
intussusception, not by juxtaposition
and accretion, like crystals, and that
cells multiply by division, the discoveries of Graham, who divided

bodies into crystalloids and colloids,
were utilised for the purpose of
explaining or illustrating organic
processes. On this distinction is
based the celebrated "micellar
theory" of Nägeli, who, in his
'Mechanisch-physiologische Theorie
der Abstammungslehre' (München
und Leipzig, 1884), works out a
complete mechanical doctrine of the
constitution and formation of organic structures. The ideas contained in this elaborate treatise
have been much used in Germany
by various writers, but mostly only
as convenient illustrations. See
O. Hertwig, 'The Cell' (transl. by
Campbell, 1895), p. 58, &c. The
micellar theory does not seem to
have found much favour in France
or in this country, where a general
opinion prevails which is probably
best represented in the words
of Claude Bernard: "Les phénomènes physico-chimiques des êtres
vivants, quoique soumis aux lois
de la physique et de la chimie
générales, ont leurs conditions par-
ticulières qui ne sont réalisées que là,
et dont la chimie pure ne peut offrir
qu'une image plus ou moins inexacte"
('Phén. de la Vie,' &c., vol. ii. p. 487).

agencies of nature,—of water, atmosphere, and of ice and heat. Last came the study of the fossil remains of organic life as the means of fixing the age and the order of succession of various geological formations. Werner[1] in Germany, Cuvier[2] in France, Hutton[3] in Scotland, William Smith[4] in England, led the way, from different points of view, towards an actual knowledge and a possible theory of the existing forms and structures in and on the crust of our globe. The study of these subjects, morphology on the largest scale, necessitated distant travels, the examination of formations *in situ* and under diametrically opposite conditions. Its greatest and unequalled representative was Alexander von Humboldt,[5] who also brought the observations of geographical, geological, and mineralogical facts and details into connection with the study of climate, of the weather, of the distribution of plants and animals.[6]

23. Humboldt.

[1] See *supra*, vol. i. p. 283.
[2] Ibid., p. 125.
[3] Ibid., p. 283.
[4] Ibid., p. 291.
[5] A good account of the gradual development of the plan of "Cosmos" will be found in Bruhns's 'Life of A. von Humboldt' (transl. by Lassell, 1873), vol. ii., *passim*. It is clear that two great influences co-operated to ripen in Humboldt's mind the conception of unrolling a great tableau of the physical world in its purely material and in its ideal or poetical aspects : the influence of the great scientific movement then emanating from Paris, and the not less important influence of the ideal movement represented by the names of Herder, Goethe, and Schelling, which emanated from the centre of Germany.

"But, however greatly Humboldt may be indebted to the inspiring influence of his contemporaries, the great merit of the work lies in what he alone has accomplished— the attempt by means of a comprehensive collation of details, and the institution of the most searching comparisons, to give a scientific foundation to the ideal cosmology of Herder, Goethe, Schelling, and their disciples . . . In him may be said to be united the two schools of philosophy, so brilliantly represented during the closing years of the former century. On this account he was at the same time exposed to the censure of the representatives of either system " (vol. ii. p. 312).
[6] The third volume of the ' Life of Humboldt,' in the original German edition, gives an account

He may be called the morphologist of nature on the largest scale : the representation of the grand aspect of things as exhibited in his ' Cosmos,' and in his earlier ' Ansichten der Natur,' was the leading idea of his life and work. Through him and his friend Karl Ritter " comparative geography received a treatment worthy of the subject, showing its connection with the history of the human race and the advancement of civilisation, inasmuch as the configuration of the earth is proved to have been an important element in the dispersion of nations." [1]

But morphology, or the study of forms and structures, has to be carried on not only on the large, the gigantic scale, as by Humboldt; it is quite as important, and has probably been even more influential, when directed towards the minute, the imperceptibly small, which ordinarily quite escapes our notice. If

by various specialists of Humboldt's labours in the sciences of astronomy, geology, geography, the distribution of animal and plant life, meteorology, and other provinces of research, some of which largely owe their existence to his initiative. The study written by Ewald on his geological work, and that of Griesbach, on what is termed in German animal and plant geography, are specially interesting. Unfortunately this most fascinating volume has not been brought out in the English edition. As illustrating the comprehensiveness of Humboldt's view it is well to note how, before beginning to put together his materials in the great tableau which the ' Kosmos ' was intended to be, he drew two entirely different pictures of nature on our globe ; first in the large

work on the New Continent (' Voyage aux Régions équinoxiales du Nouveau Continent,' in six parts, published in Paris, 1805 to 1834), and then from an entirely opposite aspect in his works on Central Asia (' Asie Centrale : Recherches sur les Chaînes et Montagnes et la Climatologie comparée,' 3 vols., Paris, 1843). " To Humboldt the importance of the Asiatic expedition consisted in its elevating him above the one-sided effect of having contemplated nature exclusively in the New World, and leading him, so to speak, to feel experimentally that the earth, in common with every other object, is possessed of opposite sides " (' Life of Humboldt,' vol. ii. p. 212).

[1] See ' Kosmos,' vol. i. p. 60 (German edition, 1845).

the great revolution of ideas which the seventeenth century witnessed was much assisted by the invention of the telescope and founded upon its revelations, the change of thought during the nineteenth century has been connected more with the revelations of the microscope. The great movement of ideas started by Galileo, and continued through Kepler, Newton, and Laplace, was accompanied by the perfection of the telescope. The invention of the microscope enabled Nehemiah Grew and Malpighi to begin half a century later their embryological studies, and to inaugurate a line of research which, in our days, through a long series of observations [1] from Amici to Strasburger on the pro-

24.
Morphology
on a minute
scale.

[1] These observations begin with the year 1830, when Amici, to whom great improvements in the microscope are due, "traced the pollen grain from its lighting on the carpel tip down into the recesses of the ovule" (Geddes and Thomson, 'The Evolution of Sex,' p. 140), and removed all doubts and uncertainty by his observations on orchids in 1845 and 1846. "Here he demonstrated the whole series of processes, from the pollen dust on the stigma to the formation of the embryo" (Sachs, 'Gesch. d. Botanik,' p. 469). About the same time (1843) Martin Barry "observed the presence of the sperm within the ovum in the rabbit ovum" (Geddes and Thomson, *loc. cit.*, p. 142). It took, however, a quarter of a century, from the first discovery of Amici, before the process of fertilisation described by him was accepted by embryologists as typical for both plants and animals. Bischoff, the great authority in Germany, after confirming the entrance of the sperm-cell into the ovum, maintained by Barry in 1843, and by Newport (with frogs) in 1851 and 1853, expresses his "infinite astonishment," adding that "Dr Barry is certainly the first who has seen a spermatozoon in the interior of any ovum, and notably in the ovum of a mammal, and that to him belongs the glory of this discovery" (Theod. Bischoff, ' Bestätigung des von Dr Newport bei den Batrachiern und Dr Barry bei den Kaninchen behaupteten Eindringens der Spermatozoiden in das Ei,' 1854, p. 9). For the history of scientific thought it is significant to see how little, even in the middle of the century, discoveries referring to the phenomena of plant life or structure were known or utilised by students of animal life. A mutually fructifying influence seems to date like so many other advances from the publication, in 1859, of the ' Origin of Species.' "The distinctively modern era in the history of fertilisation dates from about 1875, when the brilliant researches of Auerbach, Van Beneden, Bütschli,

cess of fecundation in plants, and from Martin Barry to Hertwig and Fol on that in animals, has been brought to a temporary climax. The combination of telescope and microscope in the spectroscope has opened out a field of research in astronomy of which Laplace had no conception.

So much has depended, during our century, on the unravelling and disentangling of the imperceptibly small (once considered an unworthy occupation), that a short reference to the history of that optical instrument to which we are so greatly indebted may not be out of place.

25.
The Micro-
scope.

The gradual perfection of the microscope is as much indebted to the problems and labours of anatomical workers during the seventeenth and the nineteenth centuries, as anatomy itself reciprocally has been indebted to the microscope. Robert Hooke, in 1660, first gave a useful form to the compound instrument. Leuwenhoek perfected the simple microscope ; and during the earlier part of our century no one did more than Amici in Modena and Lister in England [1] to start that great suc-

Fol, O. Hertwig, and others, showed that one of the essential phenomena in fertilisation is the intimate and orderly association of the sperm-nucleus, of paternal origin, with the ovum - nucleus, of maternal origin, the result being the cleavage or segmentation-nucleus. The researches of Strasburger, De Bary, and others, established the same result in regard to plants" (J. A. Thomson, 'The Science of Life,' p. 127, 1899).

[1] The improvements of Amici seem to go back to the year 1812, those of Lister to 1826. The former is usually considered the inventor of the "immersion" system, —that of placing a drop of water between the object or its covering glass and the objective lens. This system has lately been improved by Abbe, who discovered a liquid with the same refractive index as the glass of the objective possesses. According to Hogg ('The Microscope,' 15th ed., 1898, p. 10), the immersion system was suggested by Pritchard in London before Amici hit upon it. The necessary modifications required where the immersion system is used, seem, however, to have been first worked out by the celebrated Paris opticians, MM. Hartnack and Nachet.

cession of improvements by which errors due to colour and indistinctness—the chromatic and spherical aberrations—were removed. In the middle of the century the influence of some eminent botanists, notably of Hugo von Mohl and Nägeli, in perfecting micrometric processes was considerable; whilst the last twenty years have witnessed quite a new departure in the theory of optical images, in that of microscopic vision, in the improvement of optical glass, and in the investigation of the possible limit of the magnifying powers. The most eminent physical authorities—such as Stokes and Lord Rayleigh in England, Helmholtz in Germany — have taken up one or more of these points; but the whole subject is associated with the name of Prof. Ernst Abbe[1] of Jena, who, through his connection with the well-known firm of Carl Zeiss, has been able to put into actual practice many of the suggestions which resulted from his theoretical investigations. As the historians of zoology

[1] The labours of Abbe go back to the year 1873. Simultaneously and independently, Helmholtz attacked the theory of microscopical vision and the question of "resolution"—i.e., of the possible limit to the resolving power of any optical arrangement. Airy had attacked the same subject on purely dioptrical lines. Helmholtz and Abbe went a step farther, taking into account the physical nature of light as a wave-motion, subject to interference phenomena, notably those caused by inflection, where objects with very fine markings are concerned. Abbe's methods were for a long time only imperfectly known. The publication, however, of his theories by Czapski ('Theorie der optischen Instrumente nach Abbe,' Breslau, 1893) made the whole subject better known, and has been followed by two masterly papers by Lord Rayleigh and Prof. Johnstone Stoney in the 42nd vol. of the ' Philos. Mag.' (1896). The latter paper especially gives several interesting examples of the use of recent microscopic appliances and the means of avoiding errors in handling very delicate and minute objects. It seems that the instrument cannot any longer be used without a theoretical knowledge of its optical construction, which enables the observer not only to see, but also to criticise and to interpret.

and botany tell us, the use of the microscope had made little or no progress [1] during the eighteenth century : the study of structures and tissues had lost interest in comparison with the study of the physiological functions of the parts of plants and the organs of animals, which had been respectively furthered by Hales in England and by Haller in Germany.[2] Our century thus found the morphological studies of the imperceptibly small in a very backward state : it had to improve the instrument for its research *pari passu* with this research itself.[3] But it has been truly remarked that the increased use of the microscope necessitated likewise a mental training in the interpretations and delineations of what was observed through it. "By fortifying the eye with the micro-

26.
Its improvement.

[1] "So long as, in consequence of the imperfections of optical instruments, deceptive images existed, and, for instance, all microscopical structures appeared as composed of rows of beads, the explanation of what was seen stood under the influence of deceptions, which were only gradually recognised as such" (Carus, 'Gesch. d. Zool.,' p. 629). Compare also what Sachs says (Gesch. d. Bot., p. 241).

[2] "The characteristic feature of that period lay in this, that the examination of the finer structure is always mixed up with reflections on the functions of elementary organs, so that anatomy and physiology always support each other, but also, in consequence of their imperfect state, do each other injury" (Sachs, *loc. cit.*, p. 240). Similarly Carus (*loc. cit.*, p. 567), "Through the progress which physiology made, thanks to Haller's activity, zootomical investigations took a direction which brought them into complete dependence on physiology, . . . and retarded the progress of zoology by diverting attention from its primary object— the exposition of animal forms and their differences."

[3] As late as 1827 Aug. Pyrame de Candolle could still write ('Organographie végétale,' vol. i. p. 7), "De nos jours, MM. Mirbel, Link, Treviranus, Sprengel, Rudolphi, Kieser, Dutrochet, et Amici ont publié des recherches très délicates sur le tissu végétal, et les ont accompagnées de figures nombreuses et soignées ; mais la nécessité d'employer continuellement dans ces recherches un instrument aussi difficile à bien manier que l'est le microscope composé, fait que malgré l'habileté de ces observateurs, l'anatomie délicate des végétaux est encore . . . d'une incertitude désespérante pour les amis de la vérité."

scope, it became itself a scientific instrument which no longer hurried over its objects in flighty motion, but is disciplined by the intellect of the observer and forced into methodical work."[1]   Similarly, no doubt, the increasing devotion to the pastime of sketching from life and nature in our days must have the effect of obliging the eyes of many persons to look stedfastly and carefully at the forms and outlines of things, and of thus training the artistic faculty.

It is, however, a remarkable fact that one of the greatest leaders in the morphological study of natural objects, Bichat, the great observer of membranes and tissues, despised the microscope, the instrument by which the sciences he founded were to benefit so enormously.

The object of morphology, as distinct from that of classification, can be defined as the attempt to describe, and if possible to comprehend and explain, the relative similarity as well as the graduated differences of form and structure which natural objects present to our gaze. Although the study can be conducted on a large as well as on a small scale, these similarities and differences sooner made themselves felt in the comparatively smaller objects of living nature.   These can, without apparent loss of their characteristic appearance and individuality, be collected and brought together, whereas a collection of minerals, with the exception of crystals and gems, always presents only fragments, and forces upon us the conviction that they can really be studied only in their habitation, *in situ*.   The same conviction has indeed gradually

27.
Morphology
and classifi-
cation.

<hr />

[1] Sachs, *loc. cit.*, p. 237.

made its way into botany; and last of all into zoology.
The herbarium or collection of dead plants was much
sooner superseded by the "jardin des plantes" than the
zoological museum with its skeletons, stuffed animals, and
specimens in alcohol has been supplanted by any scientific
collection of living animals. Marine stations, which study
plant and animal life *in situ*, are quite a recent invention.[1]
The study of the forms of nature or morphology in the
earlier or more limited sense, referred thus more exclu-

[1] M. Yves Delage distinguishes
four great periods in the study
of living things. The first, culminating in Linnæus and Buffon,
studies living objects in the great
outlines of their external forms, of
the habits of plants and the customs of animals. Detailed examination by dissection is resorted to,
but only as a secondary method and
in order to supplement the intuitive
discovery of natural affinities. Then
comes the second period, that of
Cuvier and his followers, relying
mainly on anatomical dissection.
The third period begins with the
marine stations. "Je ne crains
pas de dire que la fondation des
laboratoires maritimes a marqué
une troisième période et constitué
une nouvelle méthode aussi importante que les précédentes. Si
l'on songe que plus des trois
quarts des types d'invertébrés
appartiennent au monde de la
mer, que le plus grand nombre ne
pouvaient parvenir dans les centres scientifiques dans un état
convenable pour l'examen micro-
scopique, si l'on songe que tout
ce qui concerne leurs mœurs et leur
embryogénie ne peut s' étudier loin
de la mer, on comprend l'importance
de ces créations. Faut-il rappeler
que l'introduction de cette méthode
est due à H. de Lacaze-Duthiers ?
. . . Aussi la fondation du laboratoire de Roscoff a-t-elle été le signal
de la création d'une multitude
d'établissements plus ou moins
similaires sur les côtes de tous les
pays " ('L'Hérédité et les grands
problèmes de la Biologie,' p. 3).
The fourth period is marked by
microscopic anatomy, and this—
according to M. Delage—has its
home mainly in Germany. "The
study of marine zoology has, since
the publication of the 'Origin of
Species,' been found to require
more complete arrangements in the
form of laboratories and aquaria
than the isolated vacation student
could bring with him to the seaside.
Seaside laboratories have come into
existence : the first was founded in
France by Coste (1859) at Concar-
neau (Brittany) with a practical end
in view—viz., the study of food-
fishes, with an aim to pisciculture.
. . . The largest and best-supported
pecuniarily is that founded at Naples
by Anton Dohrn in 1872 ; others
exist at Trieste, Villefranche, Cette,
and at New Haven and Beaufort in
the United States ; whilst a large
laboratory, on a scale to compare
with that at Naples, has been (1888)
opened at Plymouth by the Marine
Biological Association of the United
Kingdom" (Ray Lankester, art.
"Zoology" in 'Encyclop. Brit.,' vol.
xxiv. p. 814).

sively to plants and animals, and here the term was first applied. In order to bring some kind of method into the perplexing study of living forms, two ways presented themselves; and they were consciously or unconsciously followed by morphologists with more or less success. As I mentioned above, one of the chief interests which led to zoological and also to botanical studies was the medical interest. Animals were dissected and observed, as affording by analogy an insight into the structure and processes of the human body. Physiology, the science which deals with the actions of the different parts of the animal or human frame, termed from an early period the functions of the different organs, had made considerable progress during the eighteenth century. It was then found convenient to study the whole organism as an assemblage of different organs or machines, each of which performs a certain function. Thus we have the mechanism on which voluntary motion depends, the mechanism of respiration and of the circulation of the blood through the body, the mechanism of digestion, the mechanism of reproduction, and finally, the mechanism of the nervous system with its specified and localised optical, auditory, and other organs of sense. All these parts or organs could to a great extent be separately studied and described in their mechanical, chemical, and electrical actions. These studies had, since the time of Harvey in England and Haller in Germany, made great progress. The application of chemistry to the processes of respiration and digestion, and finally, the discovery of the galvanic current by Galvani, had given a great impetus to the physiological study of the different

28.
Study of separate organs.

organs in living beings, and their functions. In plants, these organs and functions seemed to be much simpler and more easily observed than in animals, and Linnæus had selected the sexual organs, since they were the most easily distinguishable, as a primary character for his classification of the vegetable kingdom. Somewhat later [1] he classifies the animal kingdom according to the internal structure, and characterises animals for the purpose of division according to the heart and the blood. The celebrated dictum, that "minerals grow, plants grow and live, animals grow, live, and feel," which appeared in the last edition of the 'Systema Naturæ,' places a physiological distinction at the base of the classification. This conception, which has been somewhat modified since Linnæus's time to meet our altered views, is an obvious first step towards a description of natural objects. Yet this no more than the second step, which fastens upon the organs of reproduction in plants, on the heart and blood in animals, gives any clue to the comprehension of the great variety and apparent fixity of forms which the living world presents to our observation. In fact, purely morphological considerations were subordinated to physiological ones, and were brought in only to assist in the further subdivision of the two great kingdoms. Linnæus felt the artificiality of his classification—the arbitrariness of the characters he selected for the purpose of division. But a more natural system could only be arrived at by an intimate knowledge of and intercourse with living nature, as well as by a careful comparison of its hidden forms and organisation—i.e., by a more de-

29.
Outdoor
studies.

[1] See Carus, 'Geschichte der Zoologie,' p. 503, &c.

tailed external and internal morphology.   Both lines of study, with their respective methods of observation, research, and reasoning, were equally wanted.   The former was more easily attained with plants, the latter promised more immediate fruit in dealing with animals.   In following the former, Bernard de Jussieu became the founder of modern descriptive botany; in taking up the latter, in founding comparative anatomy, Georges Cuvier became for a long time the leader in zoology.

Bernard de Jussieu was led to his natural system of classification, not by any theoretical considerations, but by the practical task of arranging the plants in the garden of Trianon, confided to his care by Louis XV., who was a great lover of botany.   He had with him as assistant his nephew, Ant. Laurent de Jussieu, who in 1789 published his ' Genera Plantarum,' which is, so far as method goes, the work of his uncle.   " This work produced a veritable revolution in botany, for only since its publication have plants been studied according to the relations which they exhibit and according to the totality of their organisation." [1]   It was not one special character or side of their existence, arbitrarily selected by a first superficial observation, which served as a means of description; their different parts or organs were conceived to be correlated—i.e., dependent on each other and united to form the totality of their organisation—their various characters were all taken into account, and looked upon as subordinated one to the other.[2]   From the time of

30.
Jussieu.

[1] See ' Histoire des Sciences Naturelles,' par Geo. Cuvier, complétée par T. M. de Saint Agy, Paris, 1845, vol. v. p. 298.

[2] Aug. Pyrame de Candolle (' Théorie élémentaire de la Botanique,' Paris, 1819, 2nd ed., p. 69) gives the following account of

Jussieu we find introduced into natural science, mainly for the purposes of classification, the ideas of the correlation of the different parts and the subordination of the various characters of a plant or an animal.   Physiology and anatomy, hitherto mainly occupied with the study of the different organs, were henceforth to be occupied with the problem of organisation, the problem of the unity of the various characters and organs.   Inspired by Jussieu, De Blainville looked upon the whole development of the natural sciences as the history of our knowledge of organisation,[1] and De Candolle, Jussieu's great successor in botany—the name that in systematic botany ruled the nineteenth century—wrote an ' Organographie végétale,' a rational description of the organs of plants.[2]

31.
Problem of
organisa-
tion.

the method of the two Jussieus : " Ce qui charactérise la méthode des Jussieu, c'est qu'elle est fondée sur la subordination des caractères. Sentant le vague des simples méthodes de tâtonnement, l'exagération du principe de comparaison uniforme et générale des organes, ils ont les premiers remarqué avec soin, que tous les organes, tous les points de vue sous lesquels on peut les considérer, n'ont pas un égal degré d'importance, ni de permanence, que quelques-uns semblent, pour ainsi dire, dominer les autres ; de sorte qu'en établissant la classification d'abord sur ces organes prédominans, puis les divisions secondaires sur ceux qui ont un moindre degré d'intérêt, on est conduit à imiter le plus possible l'ordre de la nature dans celui de la classification.   Ce principe simple et peu contestable a été fécond en conséquences importantes ; et c'est sous ce point de vue, que l'un des hommes qui a le plus profondé-

ment réfléchi sur la marche des sciences et sur le plan général de la nature, a proclamé, dans une occasion solennelle, le livre de M. de Jussieu, ' comme un ouvrage fondamental, qui fait, dans les sciences d'observation, une époque peut-être aussi importante que la chimie de Lavoisier dans les sciences d'expérience.' " (See Cuvier, ' Rapport historique sur les progrès des sciences naturelles,' Paris, 1810, p. 305.)

[1] See the ' Étude sur la vie et les travaux de M. Ducrotay de Blainville,' par Pol. Nicard, Paris, 1890, p. 157 sq.

[2] See A. Pyr. de Candolle, ' Organographie végétale ou Description raisonnée des Organes des Plantes,' Paris, 1827, 2 vols., especially vol. ii. p. 245, &c. " The classifications of the scientific taxonomist are of two kinds.   Those of the one sort are merely handy reference catalogues.   Such are the ' artificial ' systems, useful in their day and for their particular pur-

The problem of organisation was much easier in dealing with plants than with animals. In the former there seems to be only one organ or system of organs definitely developed and marked off—namely, the organs of fructification; and these had accordingly served Linnæus and his successors as the leading character for their descriptive classification. In animals there are, or seem to be at least, four or five well-defined and separated systems of organs. The selection, for the purposes of classification and morphology, was much more difficult. Accordingly we find Cuvier, who between the years 1795 and 1817 devoted himself to the morphological and anatomical study of the animal kingdom, hesitating in the selection of the leading character according to which he should classify and arrange it. As I have had occasion to remark above,[1] he finally in 1812 settled on the nervous system as the leading character governing the figure of an animal organism.[2]   Before

32.
Cuvier.

pose, but of no other value. The others, known as 'natural' classifications, are arrangements of objects according to the sum of their likenesses and unlikenesses, in respect of certain characters ; in morphology, therefore, such classifications must have regard only to matters of form, external and internal. And natural classification is of perennial importance, because the construction of it is the same thing as the accurate generalisation of the facts of form, or the establishment of the empirical laws of the correlation of structure" (Huxley in ' Life of Owen,' vol. ii. p. 283).

[1] See vol. i. p. 130 of this history.

[2] On the gradual development of Cuvier's classification see Carus, ' Geschichte der Zoologie,' pp. 602,

612, 614. " It did not escape Cuvier that the idea of subordination is artificial, and that the importance of an organ can only be fixed by experience — namely, through the proof of its constancy. Nevertheless he follows this principle, but naturally becomes vacillating. Thus in 1795 he names the organs of reproduction, to the action of which the animal owes its existence, and the organs of circulation, on which depends the individual preservation of the animal, as the most important, whilst in 1812, following the example of Virey, he declares the nervous system to be that system for the maintenance of which the other systems solely exist" (loc. cit., p. 602).

that, he had already adopted from Lamarck,[1] whose many-sided genius has made a lasting impress on the history of natural science in quite a different direction, the broad morphological division of the animal kingdom into animals with or without backbone, uniting under the former designation the four first classes of Linnæus. The more we follow Cuvier in the development of his classifying attempts, the more we find the form, the figure, the external and internal structure, urged as the aspect from which the organisation of living creatures is to be considered. To him fixity of form is the ever-recurring character of organised beings as distinguished from inorganic structures which depend on fixity of matter.[2] The clearer enunciation of this fixity of form is accompanied in Cuvier's view by the rejection of an idea which, before him, had very largely governed the speculations of naturalists. This idea, by which Charles Bonnet has been immortalised in natural history, is the conception of a graduated scale according to which living creatures can be arranged—viz., the celebrated Échelle des Êtres, coupled with the axiom, " Natura non facit saltus." This idea Cuvier rejects as untenable, and introduces in the place of it the conception of distinct plans called later " types," [3] according to which living beings are

33.
"Types."

[1] " An indirect inducement for a more pointed enunciation of the types of the various classes was given by Lamarck in 1797 when he placed the animals with white blood as 'invertebrates' in opposition to those with vertebræ which expressions (à vertèbres and sans vertèbres) come from him " (ibid., p. 612).

[2] See Cuvier's ' Éloge of Haüy '

(El. iii. p. 156, &c.) and the extracts from it and from the ' Règne animal,' given in the first volume of this History, p. 129 and notes passim.

[3] According to Carus ('Gesch. d. Zool.,' p. 615), the term "type," which became current later, was introduced by De Blainville, a philosophical naturalist who held a kind of middle position between

modelled, and which have always existed. These types or archetectonic models are capable of certain modifications, which, however, do not affect the main features of the plan. The different classes of these main types, called "embranchements," and designated as backboned, molluscous, articulate, and radiated animals, stand near each other in independence and form no scale.[1]

The morphological view of nature took a somewhat different turn in De Candolle, the successor of Jussieu in botany, who, while greatly indebted to Cuvier, acknow-

34.
De Candolle.

Cuvier and his opponent, Geoffroy St Hilaire. In 1816 Blainville gave the "principles of a new classification of the animal kingdom, in which, for the first time, the totality of structure of animals was used to characterise larger divisions." He divides animals first of all into three sub-kingdoms—symmetrical, radiate, and those without regular form. De Blainville seems to have been an inspiring teacher, whose ideas became suggestive and fruitful in many other minds. Nearly the whole of the third volume of Comte's 'Philosophie Positive' is written under a sense of obligation to De Blainville, whose 'Cours de physiologie générale et comparée' (1829-32) Comte considers "comme le type le plus parfait de l'état le plus avancé de la biologie actuelle" (vol. iii. p. 269, Paris, 1838). The 'Philosophie Positive' was dedicated to Fourier and De Blainville. How the latter also anticipated the modern conceptions of "Stoffwechsel" and "Metabolism" see Claude Bernard, 'Phénomènes de la vie communs aux animaux et aux végétaux' (1885, vol. i. p. 36).

[1] It is historically interesting to note that about the time when Cuvier was gradually defining more

rigidly his four classes, Lamarck was working at his 'Histoire naturelle des Animaux sans vertèbres,' of which the 'Système,' &c. (Paris, 1801), can be considered the first edition, the larger work appearing from 1816 to 1822. With him there is no mention of a plan or a type. His classes form a progressive series, and he was the first to follow the path from the simple to the more complex. In opposition to Cuvier, he thus wrote : " La nature, dans toutes ses opérations, ne pouvant procéder que graduellement, n'a pu produire tous les animaux à la fois : elle n'a d'abord formé que les plus simples, et passant de ceux-ci jusques aux plus composés, elle a établi successivement en eux différents systèmes d'organes particuliers, les a multipliés, en a augmenté de plus en plus l'énergie, et les cumulant dans les plus parfaits, elle a fait exister tous les animaux connus, avec l'organisation et les facultés que nous leur observons. Or, elle n'a rien fait absolument, ou elle a fait ainsi." (' Hist. des Animaux sans vertèbres,' 2nd ed., par Deshayes et Milne Edwards, Bruxelles, 1837, vol. i. p. 42.   Cf. also Carus, loc. cit., p. 615.)

ledges yet another prominent influence in the formation of his ideas. Cuvier, the zoologist, contemplating
the existing forms of nature from one of the two main
points of view, was impressed with the contrast between the lifeless and the living, seeing in the latter
stability of form, not of substance,—what we should
now term dynamical equilibrium. To him the vortex is the symbol of life. De Candolle in studying
plants is struck with the underlying regularity and
symmetry of their formation. His views were formed
after very extensive practical occupation with descriptive
botany, which was followed by a lengthy residence in
Paris, where, next to Cuvier, he came greatly under
the influence of the Abbé Haüy, the founder of
crystallography.[1] From the Jussieus he learnt the importance of looking at the "ensemble," the "port et
aspect" (facies, habitus);[2] from them and Cuvier the
value of the principle of the subordination of characters,
and the correlation of parts in the organisation of the
whole.[3] But he fastens mostly upon the underlying

[1] De Candolle, 'Théorie élémentaire de la Botanique,' 2nd ed.,
Paris, 1819, p. 72 : "Je dois encore
compter, au nombre des causes qui
ont influé sur l'amélioration des
méthodes botaniques, d'un côté les
perfectionnemens importans que la
classification zoologique a reçus,
principalement par les travaux
philosophiques de M. Cuvier, travaux qui ont réagi sur quelques
parties de la Botanique elle-même,
et dont je m'honore d'avoir profité ;
de l'autre, les importans travaux de
M. Haüy sur les lois de la crystallisation, et notamment sur les décroissemens des rangées de molécules des
cristaux, lois par lesquelles j'ai été

conduit à quelques-unes des idées
que j'exposerai dans le livre suivant." Cf. also 'Organographie
végétale,' Paris, 1827, vol. ii. p.
237.
[2] 'Théorie élémentaire,' p. 89 ;
also, p. 216.
[3] This principle is stated very
clearly by Cuvier in many places—
e.g., in the celebrated "Discours"
prefaced to the 'Recherches sur
les Ossemens Fossiles' (3rd ed.,
4to, 1825, vol. i. p. 47) : "Tout
être organisé forme un ensemble,
un système unique et clos, dont les
parties se correspondent mutuellement, et concourent à la même
action definitive par une réaction

regularity and symmetry, and studies the causes which in the actual visible specimens of plant life veil and cover up this symmetry; as Haüy [1] had taught us in crystallography to recognise the primitive forms which appear changed by the phenomena of decrescence.[2] De Candolle accordingly enters very fully into the theory of abortive, degenerate, and coalesced forms, recurring again and again to the statement that the " *ensemble* " of nature tends to make one think " that all organised beings are regular in their most intimate structure, and that various and differently combined abortive efforts produce all the irregularities which strike our glance and embarrass our combinations." [3] And the morpho-

35.
Regularity
and
symmetry.

réciproque. Aucune de ces parties ne peut changer sans que les autres changent aussi ; et par conséquent chacune d'elles, prise séparément, indique et donne toutes les autres."

[1] Cf. 'Théor. élem.,' p. 116, where he draws a parallel between the two methods in crystallography represented by Romé de l'Isle and Haüy and similar methods in botany. He reverts to this frequently — *e.g.*, 'Organographie,' vol. ii. p. 237, where he says : " Le premier raisonnait comme ceux les botanistes qui voyaient une feuille ou une corolle comme un tout unique, entaillé sur ses bords par une cause inconnue ; le second m'a servi de guide lorsque j'ai tenté de montrer que les découpures diverses des organes végétaux terraient essentiellement aux modes variés et aux degrés divers de leur agrégation."

[2] 'Théorie élémentaire,' p. 186 : " Les avortemens, les soudures des parties, leurs dégénérescences, ne sont pas plus des suppositions de désordre ou d'imperfection dans les êtres organisés, que les décroissemens des molécules ne sont des désordres dans la cristallisation."

[3] 'Théorie élémentaire,' p. 97, &c. ; also p. 236 : " La vraie science de l'histoire naturelle générale consiste dans l'étude de la symétrie propre à chaque famille, et des rapports de ces familles entr'elles ; toute la reste n'est qu'un échafaudage plus ou moins industrieux pour parvenir à ce but." And 'Organographie végétale, vol. i. p. x. : " L'organographie est la base commune de toutes les parties de la science des êtres organisés ; considérée en ce qui tient à la symétrie des êtres, elle est le fondement de toute la théorie des classifications, &c." And again, ibid., vol. ii. 239 : " Plus le nombre des êtres connus a augmenté, plus on les a étudiés avec soin, plus ou s'est convaincu de ce principe que j'ai été le premier, ou l'un des premiers à énoncer dans sa généralité, qu'il est presque certain que les êtres organisés sont symétriques ou réguliers lors qu'on les considère dans leur type, et que les irrégularités apparentes des végétaux tiennent à des phénomènes constans entre certaines limites, et susceptibles d'exister, soit séparément, soit réunis, tels

logical view is still more clearly expressed in the
further analysis of their regularity and symmetry. The
character of the structure is to be found in the existence or absence, in the relative or absolute position,
number, size, and shape of the different organs,[1] whereas
the use or functions of the organs, as well as their
other sensible properties,[2] are considered to be, not
the cause, but the consequence, of their structure, and
hence of little importance in the anatomy, and of
none in the classification, of plants, whatever may be
their value from a physiological point of view. " But
symmetry supposes a primitive plan or archetype, and
the proofs of symmetry are those of a general order."[3]
"The natural classification of organised beings consists
in appreciating the modifying circumstances, and in ab-
stracting them so as to discover the real symmetrical
type of each group."[4]   Here again De Candolle refers[5] to
the examples of the crystallographer and the astronomer,
who both make abstraction of the disturbing secondary
influences in order to arrive at the primitive form and

que l'avortement ou la dégénér-
escence de certains organes, leur
soudures entre eux ou avec d'autres,
et leur multiplication d'après des
lois régulières."
    [1] 'Théorie élém.,' p. 147: "La
symétrie organique se compose d'un
certain nombre d'élémens dont les
principaux sont : l'existence ; la
position relative ou absolue ; le
nombre relatif ou absolu ; la grandeur relative ou absolue ; la forme ;
l'usage ; la durée ; . . . les qualités
sensibles," &c.
    [2] Ibid., p. 170 : "L'usage des
organes est une conséquence de
leur structure, et n'en est nullement la cause, comme certains

écrivains irréfléchis semblent l'indiquer ; l'usage, quelle que soit son
importance dans l'étude physiologique des êtres, n'a donc eu lui-
même qu'une médiocre importance
dans l'anatomie, et ne peut en
avoir aucune dans la taxonomie."
. . . "Ce que je viens de dire de
l'usage des organes, s'applique à
bien plus forte raison encore à leurs
qualités sensibles, qui ne sont que
des conséquences plus ou moins
directes de leur structure," &c.
    [3] Ibid., p. 185.   [4] Ibid., p. 188.
    [5] See especially the chapter "De
la Symétrie végétale" at the end
of the 'Organographie,' vol. ii. p.
236 sqq.

the true orbit. It follows that "we must study the different species as constant things," [1] and that this is a more "dignified" occupation for a "naturalist than the accumulation of doubtful cases in favour of the non-permanence of species." [2]   He agrees with Cuvier in rejecting the older idea of the "échelle des êtres," [3] and he praises the sagacity of Linnæus, who suggests that the vegetable kingdom resembles a geographical chart, [4] —an idea which, in the hands of several French and German botanists, has become a fruitful conception.

In De Candolle we meet with a repeated accentuation of the recurring symmetry of form, of the existence of definite primitive types, in the vegetable kingdom. Simultaneously with him there was labouring another thinker and keen observer of nature, who was primarily struck by the resemblance exhibited in the different parts or organs of one and the same plant, and searched for the type or plan on which they were modelled.   He introduced into the vocabulary of scientific language the expression "metamorphosis of plants."   It was Goethe the poet who, in 1790, published under this title his first contribution to morphological science.   In subsequent publications and essays, covering the last forty

36.
Goethe's
metamor-
phosis.

---

[1] "Théorie élémentaire," p. 195.
[2] Ibid.   [3] Ibid., p. 230.
[4] "Linné a le premier, avec sa sagacité ordinaire, comparé le règne végétal à une carte géographique ; cette métaphore, indiquée dans son livre par un seul mot, a été développée ensuite par Giseke, Batsch, Bernardin de Saint-Pierre, L'Héritier, Petit - Thouars, &c. Et quoi qu'on ne doive la prendre que pour une simple image, cette image

est tellement juste, tellement féconde en conséquences utiles, qu'il est peut - être convenable d'entrer dans quelques détails ultérieurs.   Je suppose pour un moment cette carte exécutée ; les classes répondent aux parties du monde, les familles aux royaumes, les tribus aux provinces, les genres aux cantons et les espéces aux villes ou villages," &c. (Théor. élém., p. 231).

years of his extraordinary life, he again and again reverts to the subject, which with him is only one chapter in the extensive science of morphology, of which he was indeed the first to form a general conception. Goethe's ideas hardly influenced the course of science, but in the history of thought they form a remarkable anticipation of later views, and have accordingly been frequently referred to by contemporary writers, notably by Haeckel and Huxley in their important works on Morphology and Evolution. Of the foremost scientific writers, De Candolle was almost the only one [1] who, during Goethe's lifetime, referred to his views with approbation; seeing in his theory of the metamorphosis of the leaf a truly admirable divination [2] of vegetable organisation. Saint - Hilaire's honourable mention of Goethe's morphological contributions to zoology came only just in time to be seen by Goethe himself.[3]

---

[1] See 'Organographie,' vol. i. p. 551 : "Les parties de chaque rangée ou de chaque verticille sont susceptibles de se transformer dans la nature de la rangée qui la touche immédiatement. Ainsi l'on trouve des sépales changés en nature pétaloide (*Primula calcycanthema*), des pétales changés en étamines (*Capsella Bursa - pastoris*), des étamines changées en carpelles (*Magnolia fuscata*), ou bien l'inverse, savoir : des carpelles changées en étamines (*Euphorbia palustris*), des étamines changées en pétales (toutes les fleurs doubles), ou les pétales transformés en nature de calice (*Ranunculus abortivus*). M. Goethe a très-heureusement désigné la première de ces séries de transformations sous le nom de *Métamorphose ascendante* ou *directe*, et la seconde sous celle de *Métamorphose descendante* ou *inverse*."

[2] Ibid. vol. ii. p. 243 : "C'est ainsi qu'en voyant la manière véritablement admirable dont M. Goethe, quoiqu' habituellement occupé d'idées si différentes, a comme deviné l'organisation végétale, on est bien tenté de croire qu'il l'a moins inventé qu'il n'a généralisé avec génie quelques faits partiels heureusement choisis." This was written in 1827.

[3] See Goethe's ' Werke' (Weimar edition, Abth. II. Bd. vii.), the review of "Principes de Philosophie Zoologique. Discutés en Mars 1830 au sein de l'académie royale des sciences par M. Geoffroy Saint-Hilaire, Paris, 1830," especially p. 181, and dated Sept. 1830. In 1831 Geoffroy says of the unity of organisation : "Elle est présentement acquise au domaine de l'esprit humain ; et l'honneur d'un succès aussi mémorable appartient à Goethe." Quoted by Huxley in 'Life of Owen,' vol. ii. p. 291.

What did great harm to Goethe's correct anticipations was the fact that in optics he had unsuccessfully combated the generally accepted Newtonian theory of colours,[1] and that his morphological glimpses were taken up by Schelling and his school and incorporated in the fantastic speculations of the philosophy of nature. They shared the fate of this and passed into temporary oblivion.

The idea of the fixity of certain forms in nature, of the archetectonic modelling of her objects according to certain archetypes, which Cuvier had put forth as the result of extensive observation and inductive examination of living and fossil forms, which in De Candolle was connected with the conception of geometrical order, regularity, and symmetry, found in Goethe's mind an artistic sanction.   "It is," as the historian of botany has remarked, "the idealistic conception of nature which looks upon the organic forms as continually recurring

37.
The ideal type.

[1] A full discussion of Goethe's theory of colours will be found in two addresses of Helmholtz: the first, from the year 1853, was reprinted in the first volume of his often-quoted 'Vorträge und Reden'; the second was delivered nearly forty years later at the meeting of the Goethe Society at Weimar, in June 1892. In the latter Helmholtz significantly refers to the great revolution which in the interval had come over scientific thought through the general recognition of the principles of energy and of evolution. By the light of these we are better able to understand the shadowy but nevertheless truthful anticipations contained in Goethe's poetical and scientific writings. Helmholtz traces the errors of Goethe's colour-theory largely to the fact that he worked with imperfect apparatus and impure colours; that "he never had before his eyes perfectly purified homogeneous-coloured light, and hence would not believe in its existence.   On this difficulty," Helmholtz continues, "of complete purification of the simple spectral colours, a man like Sir D. Brewster foundered, who was much more experienced and clever in optical experimenting than Goethe, and was equipped with the best instruments" (Goethe's 'Vorahnung kommender naturwissenshaftlicher Ideen,' by H. von Helmholtz, Berlin, 1892, p. 30). Cf. also Helmholtz's Memoir on Brewster's Analysis of Sunlight, 1852. Reprinted in Wissenschaftl. Abhandl., vol. ii.

imitations of eternal ideas in the sense of Plato, and which confounds these abstractions of the mind with the objective nature of real things."[1] Nevertheless, we must recognise that through the vague and poetical expositions of Goethe's writings there is to be seen the fruitful idea of the change, the instability, of forms, as an equally important side of reality.[2] In fact, Goethe oscillates in his half-formed theories between the ideal archetypes of Plato and the more recent conceptions of Darwin and Spencer, as is proved by the vivid, even passionate, interest which he took in the celebrated controversy of Cuvier and Saint-Hilaire in the French Academy of Sciences in the year 1830,—an incident which carries us into the midst of the ideas with which the following chapter will be occupied.

Before we take up those entirely different lines of observation and reasoning, we must note a great expansion and development of the study of the form of natural objects—of morphology—in two independent directions. One of these carried the study of forms into the larger dimensions of time and space, the past

[1] Sachs, 'Geschichte der Botanik,' p. 181.

[2] Of Goethe Huxley says ('Life of Owen,' vol. ii. p. 290): "On the face of the matter it is not obvious that the brilliant poet had less chance of doing good service in natural science than the dullest of dissectors and nomenclators. Indeed there was considerable reason, a hundred years ago, for thinking that an infusion of the artistic way of looking at things might tend to revivify the somewhat mummified body of technical zoology and botany. Great ideas were floating about; the artistic apprehension was needed to give these airy nothings a local habitation and a name; to convert vague suppositions into definite hypotheses. And I apprehend that it was just this service which Goethe rendered by writing his essays on the intermaxillary bone, on osteology generally, and on the metamorphosis of plants." A very full appreciation of Goethe's merit will be found in all the principal writings of Ernst Haeckel, notably in the fourth chapter of the first volume of the 'Natürliche Schöpfungsgeschichte,' 9th ed., Berlin, 1898.

of history and the morphological changes of the earth; the other carried it into those small dimensions where the unaided eye sees only sameness and repetition, but where the microscope reveals the hidden structure, the internal and minute forms, of which living matter is made up.

I have already pointed out how the great travellers of the second half of the eighteenth century—Banks, Pallas, and Humboldt — carried the study of nature beyond the narrow limits of the museum and the work-room into the larger area of nature, of the present and the past world.   Camper in Holland, Hunter and Monro in this country, Blumenbach and Soemmering in Germany, Saussure in Geneva, towards the end of the eighteenth and the beginning of the nineteenth century had begun to unite these scattered discoveries and records into something like order and system.   It was again the great merit of Cuvier [1] to publish a monumental

38.
Palæon-
tology.

[1] Of the labours of other naturalists who preceded Cuvier, a very full account will be found in a posthumous work of Ducrotay de Blainville, edited by M. Pol Nicard and entitled 'Cuvier et Geoffroy Saint-Hilaire' (1890).   The author, as is well known, was for some time a colleague and collaborator of Cuvier, with whom he fell out, partly from personal reasons, partly owing to the whole bent of his scientific researches, which was much more philosophical than that of Cuvier. He had a very great appreciation of Lamarck at a time when that speculative naturalist was unknown or treated with neglect, not to say with ridicule. The criticisms of De Blainville on Cuvier must be taken with caution; nevertheless his works and lectures had a great influence on the development of the more philosophical side of natural science in France, as many allusions of Auguste Comte, Flourens, Claude Bernard, &c., sufficiently prove. In the chapter on Palæontology in the work on Cuvier (p. 380, &c.), De Blainville does full justice to Camper, Blumenbach, Soemmering, and other Continental naturalists, with whose labours Cuvier, through his German education, was better acquainted than his French colleagues. There is also a significant remark of his on the fact that Cuvier was essentially a collector and dissector, a man of the museum and the library, not an outdoor naturalist (p. 241).

work on the subject and to found the science of
palæontology. His researches in this subject were
based upon the collection of fossil remains which had
been begun by Daubenton for the natural history of
Buffon, and which he arranged and largely increased ; on
the collection which Camper had made at Amsterdam ;
on descriptions which he procured from all the collectors
of Europe ; notably from Blumenbach ; on his excavations
together with Brogniart in the environs of Paris. As
early as 1798 he announced his intention of collecting
everything that was known on fossil remains in a great
tableau—a plan which was not realised till 1812, when
his many separate publications were united in the great
work on the " Ossements fossiles," and was only completed
by the greatly revised and augmented edition of 1821.
This work is important in morphological science, not
only because it contains many accurate and still highly
valued descriptions of " extinct species," but also because,
in its celebrated introduction [1] on the revolutions on the
surface of our globe, it takes a comprehensive view of the
changing aspects which succeeding ages, divided by great
catastrophes characterised by distinct geological formations

[1] In this introduction (p. 52 of
vol. i.) there is also to be found the
celebrated passage in which Cuvier
says that by the application of his
principle of the "correlation of
parts" he could, if he only possessed one well-preserved fragment
of a bone, determine everything as
certainly as if he possessed the whole
animal—a statement on which De
Blainville (loc. cit., p. 417) has some
very pertinent remarks : "Ce ne
sont pas des anatomistes véritables
comme l'étaient Hunter, Camper,
Pallas, Vicq-d'Azyr, Blumenbach,
Soemmering et Meckel qui se
seraient ainsi avancés, et M. G.
Cuvier aurait été bien embarassé
lui-même, si on l'avait pris au mot,
et cependant c'est cette assertion
qui restera formulée dans la bouche
des ignorants," &c. Cuvier by this
method determined and classed
more than 150 mammals (loc. cit.,
p. 53). A more favourable view of
Cuvier's work on fossil remains is
taken by Huxley, 'Life of Owen,'
vol. ii. p. 297.

and by the fossil remains of extinct organic creations, presented on the surface of our earth. "What is certain," says Cuvier at the close [1] of this celebrated discourse, "is that we are now at least in the middle of a fourth succession of terrestrial animals, and that after the age of reptiles, after that of the palæotheria, after that of the mastodons, the megatheria, there has come the age when the human race, supported by some domestic animals, peaceably rules and cultivates the earth, and that it is only in the countries formed since this epoch in the recent alluvial deposits, peat-bogs, and concretions, that we find in a fossil condition those bones which belong to animals known and now living." Such is the *résumé* of the ideas which had followed — nay, even tormented [2] — Cuvier during his researches into fossil remains, and which led him to the conclusion [3] "that it required great events to bring about the important differences which he recognised"—differences which the slow "influence of weather, or of climate, or of domestication," could not explain, but which required the violent action of sudden "catastrophes," [4] which frequently "disturbed the life on this planet by frightful events,"[5] "broke off the thread of operations," [6] "none of the present agencies of nature sufficing to produce her bygone works."[7]

[1] "Discours sur les révolutions de la surface du globe et sur les changemens qu'elles ont produits dans le règne animal," reprinted in the 3rd ed. of the ' Recherches sur les ossemens fossiles,' 1825, vol. i. p. 172.

[2] "Ces idées m'ont poursuivi, je dirai presque tourmenté, pendant que j'ai fait les recherches sur les os fossiles, dont j'ai donné depuis peu au public la collection, recherches qui n'embrassent qu'une si petite partie de ces phénomènes de l'avant-dernier âge de la terre, et qui cependant se lient à tous les autres d'une manière intime" (' Discours,' &c., p. 140).

[3] Ibid., p. 3.   [4] Ibid., p. 8.

[5] Ibid., p. 9.   [6] Ibid., p. 14.

[7] "Ainsi, nous le répétons, c'est en vain que l'on cherche, dans les

39.
Cuvier's
catastro-
phism.

These words, which embody a conception since appro-priately termed "catastrophism," and which picture to the mind's eye a succession of morphological changes of the entire aspect of our globe, were written at a time when, in this country especially, through the labours of Hutton, an entirely opposite view was gradually pre-paring. With this we shall deal in another chapter. The Cuvierian conception of epochs in geology harmon-ised with that of distinct types of organic creation. These exhibit in space, as those do in time, certain definite and distinct morphological characters—*i.e.*, certain typical forms and structures on a vast or a small scale, around which the features of events and individuals seem to oscillate, and which permit us scientifically to classify, describe, and comprehend them. This conception gave the tone to a long line of researches on the Continent and in this country in geology as well as in natural history.

40.
Study of
analogies.

In the study of these typical forms and structures in which nature repeats herself, reverting again and again to them, but in every single case departing more or less from them; in the study of this order without monotony, this change without confusion, this variety of forms in which leading features are always recognisable,—the dis-covery of analogies played a very prominent part. Goethe's metamorphosis of plants is based upon the analogy of their different organs: before he published

forces qui agissent maintenant à la surface de la terre, des causes suf-fisantes pour produire les révolu-tions et les catastrophes dont son enveloppe nous montre les traces ; et si l'on veut recourir aux forces ex-térieures constantes connues jusqu'à présent, l'on n'y trouve pas plus de ressources" (*ibid.*, p. 20).

this first morphological fragment he had already—led by analogy—discovered the intermaxillary bone in the upper human jaw. Later he and Oken independently traced the analogy between the skull and the vertebral column in vertebrate animals, a view which was taken up by eminent anatomists, such as Meckel, Spix, and Geoffroy Saint-Hilaire.[1] The tendency which lay in these attempts, of which the metamorphosis of plants and the vertebral theory of the skull are only prominent examples, is one which was naturally provoked by the opposite tendency which anatomical studies had received through Linnæus and Cuvier. Goethe himself gives a clear explanation of its origin. In a remarkable passage in the history[2] of his botanical studies, he mentions Shakespeare, Spinoza, and Linnæus as the three masters who had led him to reflect on the great problems of art, of life, and of nature. Now, he says, the influence of Linnæus lay principally in the opposition which he provoked.

[1] A good account of the part which the vertebral theory of the skull played in comparative anatomy will be found in Whewell's History, vol. iii. p. 369, &c. But see against this Huxley in 'Life of Owen' (vol. ii. p. 304): "The hypothesis that the skull consists of modified vertebræ, advocated by Goethe and Oken, and the subject of many elaborate works, was so little reconcilable with the mode of its development that, as early as 1842, Vogt threw well-founded doubts upon it. 'All efforts to interpret the skull in this way,' said he, 'are vain.'"

[2] See the Weimar edition of his Scientific Works, vol. ii. The passage given in the text is from an earlier account contained in two numbers of the 'Morphologische Hefte' (1817), reprinted loc. cit., p. 389, &c. How Goethe continually hovered between the theory of types and that of development is seen in the following passage (1831, W. W., vol. vi. p. 120): "Das Wechselhafte der Pflanzengestalten, dem ich längst auf seinem eigenthümlichen Gange gefolgt, erweckte nun bei mir immermehr die Vorstellung: die uns umgebenden Pflanzenformen seien nicht ursprünglich determinirt und festgestellt, ihnen sei viehmehr, bei einer eigensinnigen, generischen und specifischen Hartnäckigkeit, eine glückliche Mobilität und Biegsamkeit verliehen, um in so viele Bedingungen, die über dem Erdkreis auf sie einwirken, sich zu fügen und darnach bilden und umbilden zu können."

"For as I tried to take up his sharp and suggestive
distinctions, his expressive, useful, but frequently arbitrary laws, there arose in me an inner conflict: what
he tried forcibly to hold asunder, tended according to
the innermost demands of my nature to be united." And
as the process of dividing, classifying, and keeping apart
went on among the successors of Linnæus, so it must
have produced in many genuine observers of nature a
tendency similar to that which Goethe describes. They
would emphasise the resemblances and analogies of
natural objects and their organs in proportion as the
classifiers had separated and distinguished them. And
it was just as likely that the artistic mind of Goethe
might succeed in "lifting the veil of nature," as Humboldt [1] put it, when he transmitted to Goethe his
suggestive work on the geography of plants, and as
Huxley [2] repeated in 1894. Indeed it was the former
who, on the largest scale, had traced those analogies and
correspondences in nature which are so much dearer

[1] See Goethe's own account (in Werke, 2 Abth., vol. vi. p. 163): "Sollte jedoch meine Eitelkeit einigermassen gekränkt sein, dass man weder bei Blumen, Minern, noch Knöchelchen meiner weiter gedenken mag, so kann ich mich an der wohlthätigen Theilnahme eines höchst geschätzten Freundes genugsam erholen. Die deutsche Uebersetzung seiner Ideen zu einer Geographie der Pflanzen nebst einem Naturgemälde der Tropen-länder sendet mir Alexander von Humboldt mit einem schmeichel-haften Bilde, wodurch er andeutet, dass es der Poesie wohl auch gelingen könne den Schleier der Natur aufzuheben; und wenn er es zugesteht, wer wird es leugnen?"

[2] See quotation *supra*, p. 246 note; also ('Life of Owen, vol. ii. p. 288): "The cultivator of botany, who went beyond the classification of 'hay,' became familiar with facts of the same order. Indeed, flower-ing plants fairly thrust morpho-logical ideas upon the observer. Flowers are the primers of the morphologist; those who run may read in them uniformity of type amidst endless diversity, single-ness of plan with complex multi-plicity of detail. As a musician might say, every natural group of flowering plants is a sort of visible fugue wandering about a central theme which is never forsaken, however it may, momentarily, cease to be apparent."

to the poetical mind of Goethe, and all other artists, than the separations and classifications of the men of science. "It is one of Humboldt's uncontested merits that he, in order to prove the unity which rules in the formation of the earth, searched for analogies in the geological constitution of distant countries. As we see him pointing out numerous novel coincidences between the formations of Mexico and Hungary, so likewise we owe to him suggestive hints for other similar comparisons."[1]   But the man in whose labours the tendency of thought which was uncritically followed by Goethe, and magnificently represented in Humboldt, found the clearest scientific expression, so far as animated nature is concerned, was Étienne Geoffroy Saint-Hilaire, the friend and colleague and then the great rival of Cuvier.[2]   No one recognised more clearly the deeper significance of the great outburst of the two conflicting ways of viewing nature in the Paris Academy of Sciences in 1830 than Goethe himself, who in the eighty-first year of his life was deeply stirred by seeing his favourite ideas espoused by a scientific authority of the first order.[3]

41.
Geoffroy
Saint-
Hilaire.

[1] See Julius Ewald in the third volume of the 'Leben Humboldt's' by Bruhns (German edition), p. 184.

[2] See Huxley in 'Life of Owen,' vol. ii. p. 293.

[3] Eckermann in the 'Conversations with Goethe' gives the following remarkable account, under date 2nd August 1830: "The news of the outbreak of the French Revolution arrived to-day, and created excitement everywhere.   In the course of the afternoon I went to Goethe.   'Well,' he called out to me, 'what do you think of this great event?   The volcano has come to an eruption, everything is in flames, and it is no longer a discussion with closed doors.'   'A dreadful affair,' I replied.   'But what else could one expect under the well-known circumstances and with such a ministry, but that it would end with the expulsion of the Royal Family?'   'We do not seem to understand each other, my friend,' retorted Goethe.   'I am in nowise speaking of those people; I am concerned with quite different things.   I speak of that most important conflict which has come

Similarly the aged Gauss, twenty-four years later, listened with emotion when Riemann, in his celebrated dissertation, touched a string that had been vibrating in the master's soul for fifty years, unheard or unheeded by any other thinker.[1] We can best understand the two ways of reasoning in natural objects, which found an expression in the controversy between Cuvier and Saint-Hilaire, if we read the account which Goethe himself subsequently published in a Berlin periodical: " Cuvier labours untiringly as a distinguisher, describing accurately what lies before him, ånd thus attains a command over a great breadth of facts. Geoffroy Saint-Hilaire, on the contrary, is silently exercised about the analogies of living creatures and their mysterious relations."[2] The two men had worked as colleagues for thirty-eight years, Cuvier continuing and defining more clearly the classifying work of Linnæus, who, for example, had thrown all non-vertebrate animals into one class. This led him

to pass in the Academy between Cuvier and Geoffroy Saint-Hilaire, and which is of such importance to science.' This utterance of Goethe was so unexpected to me that I did not know what to say, and that for some minutes I experienced a complete cessation of my thoughts. 'The matter is of the greatest importance,' continued Goethe, 'and you have no idea what I feel concerning the news of the 19th July. We now have a mighty ally permanently in Geoffroy. But I also see from it how great is the interest of the scientific world in France in this matter, as, in spite of the frightful political excitement, the meeting took place in a crowded house. What is best is, that the synthetic treatment of nature, introduced by Geoffroy in France, cannot again go back. . . . I have for fifty years laboured in this cause; first alone, then supported, and at last, to my great delight, excelled by congenial minds. . . . This event is for me of incredible value, and I rejoice rightly over the ultimate general victory of the cause to which I have dedicated my life, and which also is essentially my own.' "

[1] On this incident see the prefatory notice in Riemann's 'Mathematische Werke,' ed. Weber, Leipzig, 1875, p. 517; also the 13th chapter of this volume.

[2] Goethe in the ' Berliner Jahrbücher für Wissenschaftliche Kritik,' vol. ii., 1830, September, reprinted in Werke II. vol. vii. p. 167 sqq.

finally in 1817 to establish the four great classes—the vertebrate, the molluscous, the articulate, and radiated types—in the animal kingdom.   His colleague had contributed much to Cuvier's work, but had been increasingly struck by what he termed the "unity of organic composition," which he evermore looked upon as a key[1] to the comprehension of nature: he searched for one plan or type where Cuvier saw four types.   In 1818 he published his principle in a celebrated work with the title, 'Théorie des Analogies, ou de Philosophie Anatomique.'[2]   It has been correctly stated that he only gives more precise expression to a truth known to Aristotle and proclaimed by Buffon, that the mystery of organisation consists in "unity of plan combined with variety of composition."   Cuvier emphasised and studied the latter, his colleague the former.   For an intimate knowledge and description of natural objects the work of distinguishing is all important; for a comprehension of nature the connection of things, the unity of plan, the filiation and relations of beings, the mutability of species, will ever be the more important and fascinating. The former was a purely scientific, the latter a philo-

42.
Cuvier and
Geoffroy.

[1] See Goethe's detailed Report, *loc. cit.*, Werke II. vol. vii. p. 173. A very full account of this celebrated controversy is also given in the posthumous work of Ducrotay de Blainville, 'Cuvier et Geoffroy Saint-Hilaire, Biographies scientifiques,' ed. Nicard, Paris, 1890, pp. 357-378, which is specially interesting, because Geoffroy's ideas were there traced to Lamarck (p. 351), of whom Goethe takes no notice.

[2] See the "Éloge Historique d'Etienne Geoffroy Saint-Hilaire," par P. Flourens, in the third volume of his 'Recueil des Éloges,' &c., Paris, 1862, pp. 229-281. He quotes, *inter alia*, a passage from Vicq-d'Azyr: "La nature semble opérer toujours d'après un modèle primitif et général dont elle ne s'écarte qu' à regret, et dont on rencontre partout des traces. . . . On observe partout ces deux charactères que la nature semble avoir imprimés à tous les êtres, celui de la constance dans le type et celui de la variété dans les modifications," &c. (p. 276).

sophical, task. Both thinkers were right, but only partially right, as Huxley has clearly shown;[1] but it was
natural that Cuvier's position should for a long time be
regarded as the stronger; since he had shown how, by
detailed research, to increase enormously the stock of
actual knowledge about the things of nature; whereas
the uncritical and only half practical suggestions of
Goethe had undergone in the wild speculations of
Schelling, Steffens, and Oken a development that fright-
ened off men of exact thought. Cuvier saw the necessity
of crying halt to these vague dreams which he had the
merit of opposing, for the lasting benefit of true science,
with the full force of his great authority.[2]

As in France and Germany so also in England, the
tendency to distinguish minutely, to describe, to classify,
and in doing so to fill the museums with new specimens,

[1] 'Life of Owen,' vol. ii. p. 296 :
"The irony of history is nowhere
more apparent than in science.
Here we see the men over whose
minds the coming events of the
world of biology cast their shadows,
doing their best to spoil their case
in stating it ; while the man who
represented sound scientific method
is doing his best to stay the inevitable progress of thought and bolster
up antiquated traditions. The progress of knowledge during the last
seventy years enables us to see that
neither Geoffroy nor Cuvier was
altogether right nor altogether
wrong ; and that they were meant
to hunt in couples instead of pulling against one another."
[2] As to Cuvier's own wavering on
the great question of the fixity of
species, see Huxley, *loc. cit.*, p. 294 :
"During the earlier part of his
career, I doubt if Cuvier would
have categorically denied any of

Geoffroy's fundamental theses. And
even in his later years Sir Charles
Lyell, many years ago, gave me
reasons for the opinion that Cuvier
was by no means confident about
the fixity of species. There was
never any lack of the scientific imagination about the great anatomist ; and the charge of indifference
to general ideas, sometimes brought
against him, is stupidly unjust."
And further, p. 295 : "In later life,
however, Cuvier seems to have become so much disgusted by the
vagaries of the *Naturphilosophie*
school, and to have been so strongly
impressed by the evil which was
accruing to science from their example, that he was provoked into
forsaking his former wise and
judicious critical attitude ; and in
his turn he advocated hypotheses
which were none the better than
those of his opponents."

and to discover and arrange systematically unknown and extinct species, got the upper hand for a long time. No one has done better work in this large field than Richard Owen, who has been termed with some propriety the British Cuvier. But in following the lines and filling up the schedules which Cuvier had prepared, Owen and other [1] contemporary workers in the same field have also had the great merit of bringing the Cuvierian view to the point where it clearly leads on to another and more comprehensive view of nature. In the first place, it happened that in finding and describing the remains of extinct animals, increasing difficulty was experienced [2] in deciding to which of the great existing groups of animals they should be assigned. There arose the necessity of interpolating species between groups which we now look upon as widely separated. The necessity arose of forming the conception of what is now termed the "inter-

43.
Richard
Owen.

[1] Huxley, *loc. cit.*, p. 310 : "Unless it be in the 'Ossements fossiles,' I do not know where one is to look for contributions to palæontology more varied, more numerous, and, on the whole, more accurate, than those which Owen poured forth in rapid succession between 1837 and 1888. Yet there was no lack of strong contemporaries at work in the same field. De Blainville's 'Ostéographie'; Louis Agassiz's monumental work on fossil fishes, achieved under the pressure of great obstacles and full of brilliant suggestions; Von Meyer's long series of wonderfully accurate memoirs, with their admirable illustrations executed by his own hands, all belong to Owen's generation."

[2] See on this Carus, 'Geschichte der Zoologie,' p. 648, and Huxley, *loc. cit.*, p. 309, where reference is made to Owen's memoir " on an extinct mammal discovered in South America by Darwin in 1833, which Owen named *Taxodon Platensis*. It is worthy of notice that in the title of this memoir there follow, after the name of the species, the words 'referable by its dentition to the Rodentia, but with affinities to the Pachydermata and the herbivorous Cetacea'; indicating the importance in the mind of the writer of the fact that, like Cuvier's *Anoplotherium* and *Palæotherium*, *Taxodon* occupied a position between groups which, in existing nature, are now widely separated. The existence of one more 'intercalary' type was established."

calary type." Especially through palæontological finds,
the landmarks were gradually removed which separated
the distinct species and groups of organised beings.
It had happened to Cuvier only in single instances
that he had to record resemblances between widely
separated groups. Such resemblances became more and
more frequent and perplexing. In the second place,
Owen had the great merit of giving more definite expression to the conception of analogies, as developed
principally by the school which Cuvier opposed. In
fact, he revised and brought into general use the term
" homology," which had already been used by French and
German anatomists before him.[1] This term signified

[1] Great importance has been attached to the term "homology,"
which, to a reader uninitiated in
the complicated and changing vocabulary of the natural sciences,
presents not a little difficulty.
It is a good example of the
classical saying of Goethe, "dass
wo Begriffe fehlen, da stellt ein
Wort zu guter Zeit sich ein." In
the attempt to define the current
term "homology," in seeking for
numerous examples of homologies
as distinguished from analogies, naturalists were led to the recognition
of real, not only of verbal or logical
distinctions. In this respect it is
most instructive to read Owen's
treatise ' On the Archetype and
Homologies of the Vertebrate
Skeleton' (1848), the enlarged reprint of a Report to the British
Association in 1846. In it he gives
a pretty full history of the term
homology, which in the first half of
the nineteenth century became current with special meanings in three
independent sciences. With the
precision of the usage, both in
geometry and chemistry, the vagueness of the term as used by naturalists stands in characteristic contrast. "The corresponding parts,"
Sir R. Owen there says (p. 5),
"in different animals being made
namesakes, are called technically
'homologues.' The term is used
by logicians as synonymous with
'homonyms,' and by geometricians
as signifying 'the sides of similar
figures which are opposite to equal
and corresponding angles,' or to
parts having the same proportions : it appears to have been
first applied in anatomy by ⸜the
philosophical cultivators of that
science in Germany. Geoffroy
Saint - Hilaire says, 'Les organes
des sens sont *homologues*, comme
s'exprimerait la philosophie Allemande ; c'est - à - dire qu'ils sont
analogues dans leur mode de
développement, s'il existe véritablement en eux un même principe de
formation, une tendance uniforme
à se répéter, à se reproduire de la
même façon.'" After remarking
on the looseness of this definition,
Owen proceeds to give his own,
taken from the "Glossary" ap-

correspondence of parts or organs based not so much on external likeness as on similarity of origin. By admitting the latter conception, the idea of origin, the rigidity of the purely structural classification was lost. Morphology became the science, not of fixed, but of flowing forms and structures. It is remarkable that Owen, in following up this line of reasoning, was pre-eminently attracted to the oracular writings of Oken, whose influence his great forerunner Cuvier had combated with all his

pended to the first volume of his 'Hunterian Lectures,' as follows : "'Analogue'—A part or organ in one animal which has the same function as another part or organ in a different animal." "'Homologue'—The same organ in different animals under every variety of form and function." He then goes on to distinguish "special," "general," and "serial" homology. For a history of thought the important point in all these discussions is that, besides the similarity of structure and the sameness of function, relations and points of comparison of a different kind were introduced ; that these were, with more or less clearness, traced to development ; and that through this the genetic view, the doctrine of descent, was prepared by those who, like Owen, were least ready to accept it when it appeared in a definite form. In the light of this new view, of which the next chapter will treat, the whole vocabulary of the older morphologists required recasting. These older views, which traced homology to the existence of definite types, models, or patterns possessing a purely ideal existence, have been termed Platonic, inasmuch as in the philosophy of Plato the existence of a world of ideal forms or archetypes served to explain whatever of order is found in the real world of separate things. "The term 'homology,'" says Prof. Ray Lankester, "belongs to the Platonic school, but is nevertheless used without hesitation by those who reject the views of that school. Prof. Owen . . . would understand by 'homologue' the same organ in different animals under every variety of form and function. . . . But how can the sameness of an organ under every variety of form and function be established or investigated ? This is, and always has been, the stumbling-block in the study of homologies without the light of Evolutionism ; for, to settle this question of sameness, an ideal 'type' of a group of organisms under study had to be evolved from the human mind, after study of the component members of the group ; and then it could be asserted that organs might be said to be the 'same' in two animals which had a common representation in the ideal type" ('Annals and Mag. of Natural History,' 4th series, vol. vi., 1870, p. 34, &c.) See also Huxley in 'Life of Owen,' vol. ii. p. 303, &c. ; and J. Arthur Thomson, 'The Science of Life,' p. 32 (1899).

might, and who "provided him with the subject-matter of his severest as well as of his most justifiable sarcasms."[1]

The great extension of the morphological or structural view of nature into distant time and space—into palæontology by Cuvier and Owen, into geography by Humboldt, Ritter, and others—*i.e.*, morphology on an extensive scale—led to an appreciation of the labours of a different class of students of nature, namely, those who—also on a large or a smaller scale—investigated the agencies which bring about and the laws which govern the change of forms. I have now to mention the last great contribution to the purely morphological view, I mean the cellular theory, which tended ultimately in a similar direction.

45.
The cellular
theory.

The earlier researches into the minute microscopic structure of organised beings—such as those of Malpighi and Grew in the seventeenth century—were conducted by persons who took an equal interest in animal and plant life.[2] But this class of research soon fell into the hands of specialists, with the result that anatomy, the science of animal structure, and phytotomy, that of vegetable structure, were conducted on different lines

[1] Huxley, 'Life of Owen,' vol. ii. p. 315.

[2] Carus ('Gesch. der Zoologie,' p. 395) mentions especially Malpighi (1628-1694) as an exception, inasmuch as he conducted his researches from a purely scientific interest, keeping them free from extraneous practical considerations. "In his anatomy of plants there are laid, moreover, the first foundations, more firmly established by all subsequent researches, of the doctrine of the composition of all organised bodies out of cells, which has given to the whole conception of the living creation a definite starting-point, and in the sequel a firm basis for the genetic view." See also on the same subject, and on the relation of structural and physiological researches in the seventeenth and eighteenth centuries, Sachs, 'Gesch. d. Botanik,' p. 351, &c.

and for different purposes. The fact that the organisation of the higher animals, which, for medical reasons, is more interesting, can be roughly divided into a variety of separate organs or systems of organs, each of which can be, to some extent, studied by itself as we study the parts and workings of a machine, and that for the physician greater interest attaches to the functions of these organs, placed anatomy for a long time under the influence of physiology, which is the science of the performance, not of the structure, of the parts of living creatures. Phytotomy, on the other side, was for a long time neglected, awaiting the greater perfection of the microscope. Thus it came about that down to nearly the middle of the century the morphological study of animals and that of plants were pursued without much mutual benefit or regard. The phytotomists of the seventeenth century had established the fact that plants are built up of minute parts called variously utricles, bladders, vesicles, but mostly cells, and which were compared with the structure of the foam of beer or the cells of a honeycomb.[1] Different forms were assigned to these cavities,

[1] Aug. Pyr. de Candolle begins his 'Organographie' (1827) with the words : " La nature intime des végétaux, vue aux plus forts microscopes, offre peu de diversités. Les plantes les plus disparates par leurs formes extérieures, se ressemblent à l'intérieur à un degré vraiment extraordinaire," &c. ; and after going back to the observations of Malpighi and Grew, and referring to the recent ones of Mirbel, Link, Treviranus, Sprengel, Rudolphi Kieser, Dutrochet, and Amici, mentions Kieser's 'Mémoire sur l'Organisation des Plantes' (Harlem, 1812) as the only French book which contains an account of the phytotomic researches carried on by the Germans, who, after the lapse of a century, were the first to take up these studies again. In the second chapter De Candolle says : " Le tissu cellulaire, considéré en masse, est un tissu membraneux formé par un grand nombre de cellules ou de cavités closes de toutes parts ; l'écume de la bière ou un rayon de miel en donnent une idée grossière mais assez exacte " (p. 11).

and it was also recognised that they were frequently elongated into tubes or joined so as to form larger vessels. In all these researches and descriptions paramount importance was attached to the form and composition of the framework of this cellular arrangement, and only little to its contents. In fact, the historian of botany[1] characterises the period from 1800 to 1840 as that of the study of the cellular framework of plants. The skeleton, as it were, of plant structure received primarily the greater attention. In the course of these researches, which, with a few important exceptions, were all carried out in Germany, one point was permanently settled, namely, that "the cell is the one fundamental element of all vegetable structure."[2] No one did more to establish this important fact than Hugo von Mohl, whose name has been somewhat cast into the shade by the more attractive writings of Schleiden. It was Schleiden who first brought the new cellular theory into popular recognition, not without an admixture of errors, which had to be gradually eliminated in the various controversies with which his name is connected.

46.
Hugo von Mohl.

[1] See Sachs, *loc. cit.*, p. 276, &c. This period finds its consummation in the researches of Hugo von Mohl. It begins with those of Brisseau Mirbel, the first French author who took up this line. His labours were continued and criticised by a long list of German naturalists. Sachs also refers to the erroneous habit these earlier phytotomists had of getting their diagrams of what they saw by the microscope made by other persons who were supposed to be impartial—a custom fortunately abandoned by Mohl, who in his drawings did not give "undigested copies of the objects but his own impressions of them" (p. 281).

[2] Sachs assigns the final establishment of this principle to the year 1831, and considers it as one of Mohl's achievements, since, although it had been already announced by Sprengel and Mirbel, it had not been sufficiently supported by observations. Even the curious but antiquated idea, according to which the spiral fibre formed a fundamental part of plant structure, survived up to 1830 (p. 323).

But the highest value for a history of Thought attaches to this point for a different reason. In it the long-separated lines [1] of botanical and zoological study met again. Immediately after the appearance of Schleiden's epoch-making publication—and partly in consequence of it—Theodor Schwann was induced to collect, in 1839, all the known observations, coming principally from the school of Johannes Müller, which referred to the existence and formation of animal cells, and to utilise them in the enunciation of his great generalisation, "that there is one universal principle of development for the elementary parts of organisms however different, and that this principle is the formation of cells." [2]

47. Schleiden and Schwann.

[1] The fourth decade of the century was also the period in which physical and chemical methods and ideas were—notably in France and Germany — made useful for anatomical and physiological research in zoology and botany. Sachs, however, significantly warns us against the view, which has since been frequently put forward in an exaggerated form, that the physiology of plants consists in nothing but applied physics and chemistry (loc. cit., p. 393, &c.) That Schwann himself attached the greatest importance to this point can be seen from the preface to his principal work. This appeared in 1839, and was translated into English by Henry Smith, and published by the Sydenham Society in 1847 with the significant title, ' Microscopical Researches into the Accordance in the Structure and Growth of Animals and Plants.' The translator has also attached a rendering of Schleiden's ' Contributions to Phytogenesis,' which appeared first in Part II. of Müller's ' Archiv für Anatomie und Physiologie' in 1838, and was also translated in ' Taylor's Scientific Memoirs,' vol. ii. part 6.

[2] Schwann, loc. cit., p. 165. A little farther on he adds the following generalisation, which it is well to read in the light of more recent researches : " A structureless substance is present in the first instance, which lies either around or in the interior of cells already existing ; and cells are formed in it in accordance with certain laws, which cells become developed in various ways into the elementary parts of organisms. " It is clear that the discovery of what may be called the morphological element or unit of organised structures in this view meant the end of pure morphology. The problem of the explanation of existing forms was handed over to the student of development, to the genetic view and conception of nature. The cellular theory, thus enunciated in its greatest generality by Schwann, has formed a kind of provisional resting - place in the study of the forms and changes of living nature ; as Newton's gravitation formula has served as a provi-

Morphologically the microscopic examination of animal and vegetable tissues had thus led not to a clearer definition of the great differences which exist in the forms and structures of the larger and the full-grown organisms, but rather to a conviction of their intrinsic and essential sameness. These differences could not be explained in the purely morphological manner in which Haüy had shown how to trace the difference of crystalline forms to the shapes and configuration of the "molécules intégrantes." The diversity of forms had to be traced to processes of growth or development — *i.e.*, the purely morphological examination led on to the developmental or genetic study of organic forms. And this was made still more evident when the microscopic examination revealed yet other and more important elements in the composition of organic structures, elements which were seemingly quite shapeless or amorphous. The skeleton, which had so long seemed to contain the key to the understanding of organic forms, the framework of the plant structure, the cell-walls and partitions, with all their geometric figures and arrangements, turned out to be of quite secondary importance compared with the cell contents, the substance called in animals by Dujardin sarcode, and in vegetables by Von Mohl protoplasm, and with the nucleus or cell-kernel, which had been discovered by Robert Brown.[1]   Accordingly great interest attached

48.
Transition
to the study
of develop-
ment.

sional basis for physical astronomy. Both generalisations involve unsolved problems, with the difference that the formulation of the cellular theory is not as precise as that of gravitation.

[1] Both the discovery of the nucleus by Robert Brown and that of the cell contents by Dujardin preceded the enunciation of the cellular theory. Brown's discovery was referred to both by Schleiden and Schwann.   In fact, Brown's researches were much better known and followed up in Germany than in England.   His papers were trans-

to these amorphous [1] constituents, and chemical investigations as to their composition were added to the previous microscopic dissection.   The purely morphological view

lated into German by a number of botanists, and edited in five volumes between 1825 and 1834 by Nees von Essenbeck.   He did not collect his original ideas into any great work or propound a new system of classification as did Jussieu and De Candolle, whom he equals in scientific importance; his valuable generalisations were given occasionally in his numerous monographs. Sachs considers him more advanced than the two great rivals just named, inasmuch as he had an appreciation of questions of development which they lacked ('Gesch. d. Botanik,' p. 121).   Humboldt called him "botanicorum facile princeps," and succeeded in procuring for him, through his influence with Sir Robert Peel, a pension of £200 per annum.

[1] The definition of a cell—*i.e.*, of the morphological or form-element of organised matter, as consisting of a membrane, a cell content, a nucleus, and a nucleolus—stood in contrast with Felix Dujardin's description, in 1835, of a living substance which he met with in his researches in lower animal life, and which he had called "sarcode."   In the place of this name—the observation of Dujardin being little noticed —Von Mohl, after having for a time accepted the erroneous theory of Schleiden and Schwann as to cell-formation, introduced the term "protoplasma," which has been retained in science as the name of the elementary constituent of all living matter with very varying definitions, according to the different observations of animal or vegetable organisms and the increasing powers of the microscope; this having revealed structures where before only

formless, amorphous substance had been observed.   The history of these fluctuations of opinions and definitions can be read both in the older histories (Sachs, Carus) and the more recent accounts.   Among these numerous expositions, see especially Yves Delage, 'L'Hérédité et les grands problèmes de la Biologie,' 1895, p. 19, &c.; O. Hertwig, 'The Cell,' translated from the German by H. J. Campbell, 1895; and the most recent work by Dr Val. Häcker, 'Praxis und Theorie der Zellen und Befruchtungslehre,' Jena, 1899, p. 10, &c.   The cellular theory has gained enormously in importance and in popular esteem, as has also the study of all microorganisms, through its application to medicine and hygiene.   In 1847 Rudolph Virchow founded his celebrated "cellular pathology," combining the many beginnings of the cellular theory which had been laid by others, in his famous axiom "omnis cellula e cellula."   He gave up the theory of the free formation of cells, proclaimed the doctrine of the genesis of cells—even pathological ones—by cell-division, and adopted Goodsir's theory of the uninterrupted filiation of the elements of all living matter, of the autonomous cells.   As in general biology, so also in cellular pathology, the last fifty years have witnessed great controversies and many special theories, one of the chief difficulties having been to combine the doctrine of the autonomy or individuality of the cells with a correct view of their filiation and connected life.   In spite of these many changes and modifications, the name of Schwann still stands at the opening of every treatise on funda-

had exhausted itself. The fundamental unity of the organisation of living beings had been proved; how was their actual diversity to be explained? This evidently required considerations of a very different kind. What they were we shall see in the next chapter. The position of the morphologist in the middle of the century had thus become one of considerable perplexity.[1] It may be compared to that of the organic chemist about the same time. The older ideas, around which, under the great influence of Cuvier and De Candolle in zoology and botany, of Werner and Humboldt in geology, the morphological classification and description of natural objects had clustered on the Continent, had become obsolete. The doctrine of definite types, of architectonic models, or of distinct ages of creation, separated by catastrophic changes, was becoming untenable; floras and faunas of entirely different appearance had been revealed in other countries and climates in the distant past,[2] or in the great newly-discovered realm of living

mental biology, and that of Virchow at the origin of modern pathology, as the greatest practical application of the cellular theory. An exceedingly good record of the different and changing views referring to the cell will be found in the chapter on "Cell and Protoplasm" in J. A. Thomson's 'Science of Life,' pp. 101-117.

[1] "On comprend aisément le découragement de Robin renonçant à édifier son 'Traité d'Anatomie générale,' après avoir tenté inutilement, dans sa 'Chimie anatomique,' de pénétrer le mécanisme des phénomènes moléculaires s'accomplissant dans les corps organisés. La morphologie, pourtant, n'avait pas dit son dernier mot, et la barrière bio-chimique était moins rapprochée que le ne croyaient les disciples de Comte et de De Blainville" (Herrmann, article "Cellule" in 'La Grande Encyclopédie,' vol. ix. p. 1060).

[2] Owen, in the very instructive "General Conclusions" to the third volume of the 'Anatomy of Vertebrates' (1868), clearly points out how the position of Cuvier has been made untenable by these discoveries: "As my observations and comparisons accumulated, with *pari passu* tests of observed phenomena of osteogeny, they enforced a reconsideration of Cuvier's conclusions to which I had previously yielded assent" (p. 188). "Accordingly these results of extensive,

forms only accessible to the microscope. The metamorphosis of the different organs in the plant had been suggested by Wolf, and more fully demonstrated by Goethe.
Unity of organisation had been proclaimed by Saint-
Hilaire and De Blainville, and the ultimate identity of
the elementary structure of animals and plants had been
demonstrated by Schleiden and Schwann. How was the
evident relationship of the different types of living beings
to be explained ? It is interesting to note how the very
terms which were then used implied the explanation,
though this was only apparent to one or two natural
philosophers who were then secretly at work. The
word "affinity," which in chemistry has for ages been
used to denote, without explaining, the mystery of combinations and separations of different substances, had
been imported into philosophical anatomy to denote the
deeper structural likeness between animals which at the
first glance appeared to belong to different classes. This
word ordinarily implies blood-relationship, and might have

49.
Affinity.

patient, and unbiassed inductive
research—or, if there were a bias,
it was towards Cuvier—swayed with
me in rejecting the principle of
direct or miraculous creation, and
in recognising a 'natural law or
secondary cause as operative in
the production of species in orderly
succession and progression' (1849)"
(p. 789).... "Each successive parcel
of geological truth has tended to
dissipate the belief in the un-
usually sudden and violent nature
of the changes recognisable in the
earth's surface. In specially directing my attention to this moot
point, whilst engaged in investigations of fossil remains, and in the
reconstruction of the species to
which they belonged, I was at
length led to recognise one cause
of extinction as being due to defeat 'in the contest which, as a
living organised whole, the individual of each species had to
maintain against the surrounding
agencies which might militate
against its existence'" (p. 797).
Through this passage, quoted by
Owen from the preface (1866) of
the same work, a controversy arose,
it being taken by a reviewer to
prove the admission of the Darwinian theory. There followed an
explanation by Owen, rejecting
natural selection and the admitted
contest as explanations of the origin
of species.

suggested the theory of descent: it was used by those who most strongly repudiated such a doctrine.[1]

In the absence of any satisfactory explanation of the continual recurrence of certain definite forms in nature, and the presence of an evident relationship and a clear indication of metamorphosis in single instances, it was natural that morphologists of the first order, such as Owen, and other authorities in science, such as Whewell in England and Alexander Braun in Germany, should have recourse to older views and vague philosophical theories. Owen in 1848 spoke of a specific organising principle which "moulds in subserviency to the exigencies of the resulting specific forms," argues that the knowledge of such a being as man must "have existed before man appeared, for the divine mind which planned the archetype also foreknew all its modifications," and concludes that we learn from the past history of our globe that "nature has advanced with slow and stately steps, guided by the archetypal light, amidst the wreck of worlds, from the first embodiment of the vertebrate idea under its old ichthyic vestment until it became arrayed in the glorious garb of the human form."[2]

[1] Huxley in 'Life of R. Owen,' vol. ii. p. 302.

[2] See Owen's treatise 'On the Nature of Limbs,' 1849, pp. 85, 86. In the essay 'On the Archetype and Homologies of the Vertebrate Skeleton,' he concludes with the following remarks: "Now, besides the ἰδέα, organising principle, vital property, or force, which produces the diversity of form belonging to living bodies of the same materials, which diversity cannot be explained by any known properties of matter, there appears also to be in counter-operation during the building up of such bodies the polarising force pervading all space, and to the operation of which force, or mode of force, the similarity of forms, the repetition of parts, the signs of the unity of organisation may be mainly ascribed. The Platonic ἰδέα or specific organising principle or force would seem to be in antagonism with the general polarising force, and to subdue and

Whewell, in various passages of his ' History ' and of his ' Philosophy of the Inductive Sciences,' argues that the explanation of organic forms is to be found in the study of the functions which each organ is destined to perform, and brings morphology back under the guidance of physiology, from which De Candolle and others had only recently liberated it.[1] Alexander Braun, the great German botanist, wrote about the same time: " Although the organism in its growth is subject to physical conditions, the real causes of its morphological and biological speciality lie, nevertheless, not in these conditions: its laws belong to a higher grade of development of reality, to a sphere in which the capacity for spontaneous self-determination becomes evident."[2] Even Johannes Müller,

mould it in subserviency to the exigencies of the resulting specific form " (p. 172). Huxley attributes these theoretical views of Owen to the influence of Lorenz Oken, the principal scientific representative of the school of the " Naturphilosophie." In this respect Owen left the direction of study initiated and so successfully followed by Cuvier. In fact, though opposed to Darwinism, Owen did not, like Cuvier, believe in special creation, as is clearly shown in a passage frequently quoted, taken from the conclusion to the third volume of Owen's great work ' On the Anatomy of Vertebrates' (1868), p. 807 : " So, being unable to accept the volitional hypothesis, or that of impulse from within, or the selective force exerted by outward circumstances, I deem an innate tendency to deviate from parental type, operating through periods of adequate duration, to be the most probable nature, or way of operation, of the secondary law, whereby

species have been derived one from another."

[1] De Candolle is very clear on this point ; he says ('Théorie élémentaire,' p. 170) : " L'usage des organes est une conséquence de leur structure, et n'en est nullement la cause, comme certains écrivains irré-fléchis semblent l'indiquer ; l'usage, quelque soit son importance dans l'étude physiologique des êtres, n'a donc en lui-même qu'une médiocre importance dans l'anatomie, et ne peut en avoir aucune dans la taxonomie ; quelquefois seulement on peut s'en servir comme d'un indice de certaines structures à nous encore inconnues ; ainsi lorsque je vois la surface unie d'un pétale suinter une liqueur, j'en conclus que cette partie est glandulaire, et je l'assimile aux nectaires ; mais cette assimilation, bien que reconnue par l'identité de l'usage, est réellement établie sur l'identité présumée de la structure."

[2] Quoted by Sachs ('Gesch. d. Botanik,' p. 188).

who did more than any other naturalist to base zoology, anatomy, and physiology on the foundation of the exact sciences, physics and chemistry, "assumed the existence of a vital force which, differing from physical and chemical forces, enters into conflict with them, and which in organisms acts the part of a supreme regulator of all phenomena according to a definite plan."[1]

50.
Insufficiency
of the mor-
phological
view.

The insufficiency of a purely morphological description of living beings, the unsuccessful search for the morphological elements out of which organisms are built up, as crystals are formed out of the *molécules intégrantes* of Haüy, led thinkers (up to the middle of the century) to have recourse to older and vaguer conceptions, which, under the name of archetypes, formative influences, vital forces, &c., were destined to help where the purely mechanical view would not suffice. This dilemma was appropriately described somewhat later by one who had—earlier, perhaps, than any other thinker—emancipated himself from the influence of these fanciful conceptions. Herbert Spencer in his 'Principles of Biology,' published in 1863, expresses it in the following words:[2]—

"If we accept the word 'polarity' as a name for the force by which inorganic units are aggregated into

[1] See Du Bois-Reymond, "Gedächtnissrede auf Johannes Müller" ('Reden,' vol. ii. p. 217).

[2] The 'Principles of Biology,' from which this extract is quoted, appeared in successive instalments, beginning in January 1863. It is well to note that this was before the appearance of Haeckel's 'Generelle Morphologie,' which bears the date 1866. It does not appear that Spencer has had any influence on German science, though no doubt many of the conceptions put forward in the numerous treatises of German biologists are anticipated in Spencer's 'Biology,' notably in his conception of the physiological units as intermediate between compound chemical molecules and crystals on the one side, and cells on the other. In the exhaustive

a form peculiar to them, we may apply this word to the analogous force displayed by organic units. But polarity is but a name for something of which we are ignorant. Nevertheless, in default of another word we must employ this. . . . It will be well to ask what these units are which possess the property of arranging

review of these theories, given by M. Yves Delage, a very prominent position is accordingly assigned to Herbert Spencer's biological writings. In fact, he says (' L'Hérédité,' p. 424 note) : "Ici"—*i.e.*, in the 'Principles of Biology' — "est montrée, pour la première fois et avec une lucidité (parfaite, l'utilité de concevoir des particules spéciales, éléments primitifs de la substance vivante, intermédiaries aux molécules et aux cellules. Les très nombreux auteurs qui ont utilisé la même idée n'en ont créé que des variantes. Spencer est le vrai père de la conception initiale, si féconde comme on le verra." And again (ibid., p. 836) : "Brusquement, avec H. Spencer, on tombe en plein moderne. Ici plus de théories vieillottes, plus de procédés surannés. . . . Les phénomènes sont décomposés en leurs éléments avec une puissance d'abstraction qu'aucun philosophe n'a dépassée, des principes généraux sont déduits qui servent à leur tour à juger, à interpréter les phénomènes, à les ramener à leurs causes vraies. Comme résultat de ses méditations, Spencer nous offre les 'Unités physiologiques,' particules matérielles toutes identiques dans une même espèce d'êtres avec lesquelles il croit que l'organisme doit pouvoir se construire de lui-même, par le seul jeu de leurs forces moléculaires. . . . Il a . . . ouvert une voie : sa théorie est un des bras principaux du Delta de ce fleuve

qui nous servait de terme de comparaison." The other great arm of the Delta is Darwin's theory of Pangenesis, on which see *infra*, chapter xii. of this volume. Of others, such as Erlsberg, Haeckel, His, Haacke, M. Delage says : "Ils ont réussi seulement à montrer qu'en substituant aux forces polaires des 'Unités physiologiques,' des formes de mouvement ou des propriétés géométriques, on n'arrive pas à un meilleur résultat." Prof. Haeckel in his 'Generelle Morphologie' (1866) has interpolated a special investigation, as it were, between the morphology of living things and the corresponding science of inorganic or purely physical (such as crystalline and chemical) structures and arrangement under the name "Promorphology," investigating with much ingenuity all manner of symmetrical, axial, radial, &c., configurations. J. Arthur Thomson ('Science of Life,' p. 34) remarks that little attention has been paid to this subject since, but, as stated above (p. 223 note), the systematic treatment of crystallography has all through the century appeared to biologists as an enticing and seductive model, and M. Yves Delage's great work gives many examples of this tendency—see, *e.g.*, his remarks on the theories of Haacke, Cope, Nägeli, Erlsberg, and many others, pp. 304, 315, 424, 441, 451, 459, 475, 495, 502, 593, 743, &c.

themselves into the special structures of the organism
to which they belong. . . . On the one hand, it cannot
be in these proximate chemical compounds composing
organic bodies that this specific polarity dwells; . . .
the occurrence of such endlessly varied forms would be
inexplicable. On the other hand, this property cannot
reside in what may be roughly distinguished as the
morphological units. The germ of every organism is
a microscopic cell, or a structureless blastema which
nevertheless exhibits vital activities. . . . If, then, this
organic polarity can be possessed neither by the chemical
units nor the morphological units, we must conceive it as
possessed by certain intermediate units which we may
term *physiological*. . . . We must conclude that in each
case some slight difference of composition in these units
. . . produces a difference in the form which the aggregate of them assumes."

51.
Herbert
Spencer's
"physio-
logical
units."

Now, there are only two ways open to the purely
scientific thinker by which he can reach these intermediate structures lying between the mathematical forms
of crystals or the molecular arrangement of atoms, and
the visible but apparently structureless forms of cells and
protoplasm. One of these is the still more advanced
analysis of these microscopic structures by still greater
powers of magnifying instruments; the other is the
mathematical method of calculating from simple beginnings the complex forms of equilibrium which atoms or
molecules are capable of assuming under the action of
known forces. It appears unlikely that the powers of
the microscope can be much further extended; and the
mathematical calculation of even the simplest configur-

ations of attracting and repelling centres, or of linked vortex rings, is already so formidable that much cannot be expected in that direction. These intermediate units, vastly more complex than the most complex chemical molecules, and vastly more minute than the smallest visible grain of protoplasm, must therefore for a long time to come lie in the region of hypothesis, unattainable for the eye or the calculus; an indication rather than a real guide for our scientific researches. Seeing, then, that the study of forms — the morphological view of natural objects in the case of organic beings, where to the naïve contemplation of things these forms seemed full of so much significance, indicative of so much meaning, possessed of so much beauty and striking suggestiveness —has led to no comprehension of the essence of vital phenomena, and hardly even afforded a safe criterion for classification, it is intelligible how the scientific interest has moved away from the consideration of the fixed forms and structures to that of the variation and continued change of these forms. This alteration in the scientific way of looking at the actual forms of nature, goes hand in hand with the tendency we had occasion to notice when dealing with the abstract sciences. Many things which once seemed at rest, or possessed of very simple rectilinear motion, have revealed themselves to the mind's eye as complex states of motion. Colours are exceedingly minute and rapid but well defined vibrations; the dead pressure of gases is the impact of numberless quickly-moving particles; and the wonderful properties of the whirling vortex ring have made us familiar with what has been termed the dynamical or moving equilibrium, the

52.
Change of
scientific
interests.

semblance of apparent rest produced by very rapid rotary motion. Rest and fixity of form seem only to exist apparently or for transient moments in the history of natural events ; and even the finished and recurring structures of living beings, which appear to our eyes to be possessed of so much finality and sometimes of so much finish, owe these qualities only to the comparatively short space of time during which we are permitted to gaze at them, and to our ignorance of the slow but endless changes to which they are nevertheless subject.

53.
The morphological period.

The period from 1800 to 1860 can be termed the morphological period of natural science. It succeeded the period of the simpler natural history, which had been mainly occupied with classification and description of specimens. During the morphological period the knowledge of the existing things and forms of nature was not only largely extended by excursions into distant lands and periods of history, but forms were also studied *in situ*, and the living things visited in their habitats. A deeper knowledge of the connection and interdependence of natural things and events was thus gained, and the relations and resemblances, the analogies and homologies, of the various forms were impressed on the observer. Besides all this, the microscope revealed the innermost composition and the ultimate structural sameness of living matter, adding moreover the knowledge of an enormous creation which remains hidden to the unarmed eye of the ordinary observer. The morphological view also took note of the relatedness and apparent recurrence of definite forms called types, of the so-called fixity of species and the succeeding characteristic periods of creation, and sought to explain these morphologically : *i.e.,* it sought in the abstract study of forms—sometimes geometrical, sometimes artistic—the key to an understanding of the recurrence as well as the continued variation of definite types. The relationship was mostly looked upon as ideal, not real. How a gradual change came over this view of nature, how the study of development led on to the modern phase of natural science which is governed by the genetic view, I shall try to show in the next chapter.

CHAPTER IX.

ON THE GENETIC VIEW OF NATURE.

1.
Statics
and dyna-
mics of liv-
ing forms.

WHILST the great influence of such leaders in scientific thought as Cuvier, De Candolle, and Humboldt on the Continent, and of Richard Owen in this country, was mainly exerted in spreading the morphological view of nature, describing on a large scale or in minuter detail the typical recurring forms which natural objects or natural scenery present to the eye of the unbiassed observer, another school of naturalists was secretly busy in following up the changes to which all the things of nature seem continually subjected. They were as much impressed with this restless movement of everything as the others were with the continual recurrence of certain definite forms—be they geometrical or artistic. The general ideas which underlay their researches were not new,—they were probably older and more familiar [1] than

[1] Cosmogonies of all sorts abound in almost every literature, ancient or modern, whereas Cosmography, accurate, painstaking, and reliable, is of comparatively recent date. The first attempt to give a purely descriptive picture of nature as a whole, beginning with the larger features of the universe and ascending through terrestrial, inanimate and animate, phenomena to the central and crowning phenomenon of human life, was A. von Humboldt's ' Kosmos ' ; and it is interesting to note how averse the author was to introduce genetic expositions. In fact, it has been truly remarked that Humboldt's influence went to

the types and epochs of the other and dominant school ; but they were difficult to grasp, being not unfrequently fantastic compromises between the legends of religious tradition and the beginnings of scientific thought.   For a long time they evaded the endeavour to put them into

encourage purely morphological and to discourage genetic considerations.   Accordingly the many beginnings of a scientific account of the origin and historical development of the things around us, of which Lyell gave the first fairly accurate summary in the first volume of his ' Principles of Geology' (1st ed., 1830), were hardly noticed in the ' Kosmos' (vol. i., 1845, vol. ii., 1847).   None of the celebrated cosmogonical hypotheses, which we shall deal with in this chapter,—neither the ' Protogæa' of Leibniz nor the ' Époques de la Nature' of Buffon, neither Kant's nor Laplace's nebular theory, nor even the brilliant introduction to the ' Ossemens fossiles' of Cuvier, though the latter, and still more Laplace, must have had a great personal influence on him, — receive any adequate attention in the pages of ' Kosmos.'   They are rarely referred to, and then only as works of imaginative value, for which the true scientific groundwork, extensive observation, and especially the experiences and results of travel, are wanting. Humboldt, whose mind was stored with these riches in an abundance and variety unequalled before or since, limited himself to a portraiture, to a panoramic and morphological, to a structural and architectonic view of things, with which he combined a deep sense of the reaction which the contemplation of nature must have on the artistic faculty.   (See the Introduction to the second, the most brilliant, volume of ' Kosmos.')

Genetic theories were to his mind premature and foreign to his purpose.   " The mysterious and unsolved problems of development do not belong to the empirical region of objective observation, to the description of the developed, the actual state of our planet.   The description of the universe, soberly confined to reality, remains averse to the obscure beginnings of a history of organic life, not from modesty, but from the nature of its objects and its limits " (' Kosmos,' vol. i. p. 367).   " The world of forms, I repeat, can in the enumeration of space relations only be pictured as something actual, as something existing in nature ; not as a subject of an intellectual process of reasoning on already known causal connections. . . . They are facts of nature, resulting from the conflict of many, to us, unknown conditions of active push - and - pull forces. With unsatisfied curiosity we approach here the dark region of development.   We have here to do, in the proper sense of the frequently misused word, with world-events, with cosmical processes of immeasurable periods. . . . The present form of things and the precise numerical determination of relations has not hitherto succeeded in leading us to a knowledge of states traversed, to a clear insight into the conditions under which they originated.   These conditions are not therefore to. be termed accidental, as man calls everything that he cannot explain genetically " (vol. iii. p. 431).

exact language. It is only in the second half of the
nineteenth century that the many independent lines of
reasoning, the fragments of the great doctrine of development, have been united together, that the search after the
principles or laws which govern the restless change has
been rewarded by a certain number of definite results,
and that what was once vague, fanciful, and legendary
has become a leading idea in all the natural sciences.
As in other instances which we have had occasion to
notice, so also in this case, the appearance of clearer and
more definite ideas has been heralded and helped by a
novel mode of expression, by a new vocabulary. The

2.
"Evolu-
tion."

word "evolution" has in this country done much to
popularise this way of regarding natural objects and
events : abroad, the word has not met with the same
popular acceptance. It was known there and used in
science and literature when it was yet unknown in this
country, and has in consequence not been monopolised in
the same way as in the English language, to denote the
continuous and orderly development of states and forms
of existence.[1] Moreover, it has been identified in this

[1] On the older and modern use
of the word "evolution" in the
English language see Huxley's
article in the 9th ed. of the
'Ency. Brit.' It is reprinted in
his collected essays with the title
"Evolution in Biology." According to Huxley, the term "evolution" was introduced in the former
half of the eighteenth century in
opposition to "epigenesis." The two
terms denoted the two theories of
the generation of living things, by
development of pre-formed germs
(pre-formation) or by successive
differentiation of a relatively homogeneous rudiment (after-formation).
Harvey, the expounder of the latter
theory against Malpighi, who embraced the former, calls the first
"metamorphosis." Leibniz, Bonnet, and latterly Haller, were "evolutionists" in the older sense of the
word ; Harvey, C. F. Wolf, and
the modern school of embryologists,
with von Baer as its most eminent
representative, were adherents of
the originally Aristotelian theory
of "epigenesis." "Nevertheless," as
Huxley says, "though the conceptions originally denoted by 'evolution' and 'development' were

country with a special philosophical teaching, that of Mr Herbert Spencer, which, whilst in many points coinciding with scientific views of development, has some special and peculiar features which will occupy us further on in our survey of thought. Having sought therefore for a term which is to comprise all the contributions to scientific thought which deal with the change and development of natural objects and events, I propose to use the older word "genesis," and to call this view "the genetic view of nature": it is, in general, the view which seeks to give answer to the question,

3. "Genesis."

shown to be untenable, the words retained their application to the process by which the embryos of living beings gradually make their appearance; and the terms 'development,' 'Entwickelung,' and 'evolutio' are now indiscriminately used for the series of genetic changes exhibited by living beings, by writers who would emphatically deny that 'development' or 'Entwickelung' or 'evolutio,' in the sense in which these words were usually employed by Bonnet or by Haller, ever occurs." The word evolution has, however, acquired in the English language, mainly through the influence of Mr Spencer's writings, a much wider sense than evolution in biology implies: in fact, it takes the place of the German "Werden," a word much used in the philosophical writings influenced by the Hegelian doctrine, which indeed taught a logical or dialectical development of things, as Herbert Spencer and his school teach a mechanical development. There seem to be given to us by observation only two elementary processes of change, or of "Werden" (in Greek γίγνεσθαι, in French "devenir," in English "be-coming," in Latin "fieri," in German also the synonym "geschehen"). These are, on the on one hand, the process of mechanical motion, and on the other hand the process of logical thought : the one being the movement of external things, ultimately of atoms, the other the spontaneous movement of what Hume called ideas. When the thinking mind fixes its attention on the "fieri" rather than the "esse" of things there are accordingly two clues available, the mental or the physical, the logical or the mechanical. Many times taken up in earlier ages, both have been consistently applied only in the nineteenth century, the latter by Herbert Spencer, the former fifty years earlier by Hegel, whose philosophy is fundamentally as much a logical as the former is a mechanical system of evolution. The narrower meaning of evolution in biology is usually given in French by the word "transformisme," in German by "Entwickelungslehre" or "Darwinismus." See on the general subject Prof. James Sully's able article on "Evolution" in the 9th ed. of the 'Ency. Brit.'

How have things come to be what they are? What is their history[1] in time?

The first great philosopher of modern times who seems to have approached the question of the genesis of the objects of nature in the modern scientific spirit was Leibniz, who, in composing his local history of the origin of the Guelphs and the antiquities of Brunswick, pushed his researches into prehistoric times and made use of the geological and mineralogical data supplied in the Harz forest and mountains to arrive at conjectures as to the past history of the earth. His ideas, based upon local facts and observations on stratification and fossil remains, were collected in a famous tract entitled 'Protogæa,' which during his lifetime was only known in abstract,[2] and was published in 1749, many

4.
Leibniz's
'Protogæa.'

[1] Although the word "genesis," through its use in the Scriptures, has acquired the meaning of a narrative of the origin or beginning of things, this meaning is not necessarily implied in the word γίγνεσ-θαι, and the genetic view of nature, or things in general, may limit itself to the study of observable, actual change, renouncing altogether the question of origins. The German words, "werden" and "geschehen," are in this respect less ambiguous and less ambitious, and many philosophers may accordingly prefer "evolution" to "genesis."

[2] On the connection of Leibniz's genetic studies with his History of Brunswick, which expanded under his hands into the 'Annales imperii occidentis Brunsvicenses' (edited by Pertz in the first three volumes of 'Leibnizens Gesammelte Werke,' Hannover, 1843-47, 4 vols.), see the introduction by Scheidt to his complete edition of the 'Protogæa,' Göttingen, 1749

(reprinted in the second volume of Dutens' 'Leibnitii Opera Omnia,' 1768); the words of Leibniz himself in the 'Plan' of his History (quoted by Pertz, vol. i. p. xxiii): "Præmittetur his annalibus quædam dissertatio de antiquissimo harum regionum statu qui ante historicos ex naturæ vestigiis haberi potest"; the address of Ehrenberg, 'Ueber Leibnitzens Methode' (Berlin, 1845); the account in Guhrauer's 'Life of Leibniz' (1846, vol. i. p. 205, and an interesting note in the appendix). Fontenelle, who knew of the 'Protogæa' only by the abstract (ed. 1693) in the Leipsic 'Acta,' and from correspondence with Eckhardt, Leibniz's executor, says in his 'Eloge de Leibniz': "Il la [viz., the History] faisait précéder par une dissertation sur l'état de l'Allemagne, tel qu'il était avant toutes les histoires et qu'on pouvait le conjecturer par les monuments naturels qui en étaient restés; des coquillages pétrifiés dans les terres,

years after his death. He conceived that both fire and water[1] had been at work in forming the surface of the earth, and suggested that similar examinations of other localities[2] would be required in order to arrive at general conclusions. Such were subsequently supplied by Werner, de Saussure, Pallas, Hutton, Cuvier, and William Smith, before the systematic exploration of the whole globe became in the nineteenth century one of the tasks of geological science. A few years after the publication of Leibniz's speculations, which pointed to an accumulation of local observations as the means of arriving at a history

des pierres où se trouvent des empreintes de poissons ou de plantes qui ne sont point du pays, médailles incontestables du déluge," &c., &c. How very much Leibniz was—in this as in many other ideas—in advance of his age can be seen from his correspondence with the Swiss naturalist Scheuchzer of Zürich : " Merentur Alpes vestræ, si quis alius Europæ locus, hanc eruditi inquilini curam et cæteros montes utili exemplo præibunt, quem admodum magnitudine vincunt. . . . Germanorum nostrorum non ea est diligentia quam vellem : itaque Historias regionum naturales habemus nullas, cum Angli Scotique nobis egregiis exemplis præiverint" (quoted by Guhrauer in the note referred to). An interesting reference is made in § xvii. of the 'Protogæa' to the use of the microscope, then only recently invented, and largely used by Leuwenhoek in connection with the examination of the formation and crystals of the celebrated " Baumann cave" : " Et velim microscopia ad inquisitionem adhiberi, quibus tantum præstitit sagax Leuwenhoekii diligentia, ut sæpe indigner humanæ ignaviæ,

quæ aperire oculos, et in paratam scientia possessionem ingredi non dignatur." A very fair account of the contents of the ' Protogæa' is given in W. D. Conybeare's ' Report on the Progress . . . of Geological Science ' in the first volume of Brit. Assoc. Reports, p. 366, &c.

[1] 'Protogæa,' § iv. : " Donec quiescentibus causis atque æquilibratis consistentior emergeret status rerum. Unde jam duplex origo intelligitur firmorum corporum ; una, cum ab ignis fusione refrigescerent, altera cum reconcrescerent ex solutione aquarum. Neque igitur putandum est lapides ex sola esse fusione. Id enim potissimum de prima tantum massa ac terræ basi accipio."

[2] Ibid, § v. : " Hæc vero utcumque cum plausu forte dici possint de incunabilis nostri orbis, seminaque contineant scientiæ novæ, quam Geographiam naturalem appelles. . . . Et licet conspirent vestigia veteris mundi in præsenti facie rerum, tamen rectius omnia definiunt posteri, ubi curiositas mortalium eo processerit, ut per regiones procurrentia soli genera et strata describunt."

of the earth, another philosopher of the highest rank took an important step in the direction of the study of the genesis of things natural, on the largest scale. It was Immanuel Kant, the philosopher of Königsberg, who, stimulated by the perusal of the cosmical theories of Thomas Wright of Durham,[1] applied the principles of the Newtonian philosophy in a first attempt to trace out the great stages in the formation of a planetary system.

5.
Kant's
nebular
theory.

[1] The work of Wright is not so rare as it is represented to be by foreign writers, as I picked up two copies from a second-hand catalogue several years ago. It is chiefly interesting as having induced Kant to venture on his genetic speculations, which appeared anonymously at Königsberg in 1855, and for a long time remained unknown. About the same time as Kant, the celebrated mathematician J. H. Lambert published his ' Cosmological Letters on the Structure of the Universe ' (Augsburg, 1761), many ideas in which coincide with the later expositions of Herschel and Laplace, which were based on quite different considerations. The speculations of Wright, Lambert, and Herschel were what we may call morphological, whereas it is the merit of Kant and Laplace to have built upon the ideas as to the architecture of the universe a plausible theory of its genesis. A full account of Wright's suggestions, which were accompanied by very beautiful mezzotint engravings executed by himself, is given by Prof. R. A. Sampson of Durham in the ' Proceedings of the Society of Antiquaries' of Newcastle - upon - Tyne, vol. vii. p. 99.

Kant's theory has been dealt with by Helmholtz in his Königsberg address (1854), "Ueber die Wechsel-wirkung der Naturkräfte " (' Vor-träge und Reden,' vol. i.), by Faye ('Sur l'Origine du Monde,' Paris, 1885, 2nd ed.), by C. Wolf ('Les Hypothèses Cosmogoniques,' Paris, 1886, which contains a translation of Kant's work), and by G. F. Becker (Amer. Journal of Science, 1898). It is, however, to be noted that recent writers on Astronomy are inclined to speak of the genetic theories of the universe very much in the same way as Humboldt treated them in his 'Kosmos,' which professedly excluded the historical aspect in favour of a purely descriptive treatment, recognising the many difficulties which stand in the way of a consistent elaboration of the "nebular hypothesis." See A. Berry's 'History of Astronomy' (1898), p. 409 ; R. Wolf, 'Handbuch der Astronomie' (vol. i., 1890), p. 594 ; G. H. Darwin, 'The Tides' (1898), p. 302 ; also J. Scheiner, 'Der Bau des Weltalls' (Leipzig, 1901). On the additional great support which has been given to a genetic conception in general in the second half of the nineteenth century by Thermodynamics and Spectrum Analysis I shall speak later on. The writings of M. Faye in France, and of Sir Norman Lockyer in this country, utilise to the fullest extent the arguments derivable from these sources, and mark a great contrast to the manner in which cosmological questions were treated by A. von Humboldt.

The speculations of Wright had been purely geometrical. He had drawn attention to the apparent unity of organisation in the stellar system, as established by the accumulation of stars in a certain belt, popularly called "the milky way." He also suggested that the whole system was moving in a certain direction. Kant pointed out the analogy with the solar system, in which, viewed from the centre, the planetary masses would likewise appear situated in a narrow belt, moving all in the same direction. From these data he proceeds to show how, taking for granted an initial movement and the action of gravitation, the formation of rings, like those of Saturn, can be explained; further, how these might be broken up and concentrated in satellites. In fact, he recognised how, under the influence of gravitation, the solar system might have been gradually formed out of matter which was previously scattered through the whole of that space which the system still occupies. Kant also descended somewhat further into detail, and proceeded to discuss the possible retardation of the earth's rotation through tidal friction.[1]

[1] The tract in which Kant develops his views on this subject was occasioned by a prize offered by the Berlin Academy in 1754 for an answer to the question whether the time of revolution of the earth had suffered any retardation, and if so, through what causes ? Kant did not compete for the prize, deeming his reflections not capable of being sufficiently perfected to deserve to be submitted. So he simply published them in a local Königsberg paper, from which they were later reprinted in the collected works, forming one of the first of Kant's publications. At the end of this tract he announces his ' Cosmogonie' which appeared the following year with the title 'Natural History of the Heavens,' &c. Kant had the satisfaction of seeing many of his speculations verified by the subsequent discoveries of inductive research, notably through Sir William Herschel's observations of nebulæ ; and the German edition of Herschel's great memoir ' On the Construction of the Heavens' ('Phil. Trans.,' 1784), which appeared in Königsberg in 1791, by Sommer, contains an extract from Kant's

The two lines of speculation, originated by Leibniz and Kant as to the genesis of things on this earth and in the universe, mark two distinct ways of approaching the genetic problem. They were both isolated, and it was not till well on in the course of our century that they were again taken up and independently developed— the one by geologists, the other by physical astronomers. They remained for a long time without mutual influence ; till, within the last generation, they were brought together, their different results deduced, and a reconciliation attempted. To this I shall revert later on.

6. Laplace.

Forty years after Kant, Laplace put forward his so-called nebular hypothesis at the end of the popular exposition which he gave of his mechanical theory of the heavens. He apparently knew nothing of Kant's attempt, and his views differ materially from those of Kant, in so much as he assumes in the rotating nebular mass an attracting nucleus from which, in the course of condensation through attraction, the planetary rings and bodies were thrown off as the centrifugal velocity balanced the attracting forces. For a long time this sketch of a possible genesis of the planetary system was paraded in popular

work. The merits of Kant have only been tardily recognised ; they were unknown to Laplace, and only imperfectly known to more recent authorities, such as Helmholtz and Lord Kelvin, who were fully prepared to do him justice. Lord Kelvin, in his Rede Lecture of 1866, refers to Kant as the first to publish " any definite estimate of the possible amount of the diminution of rotatory velocity experienced by the earth through tidal friction " ('Pop. Lects. and Addr.,' vol. ii. p. 65), and in the controversy which took place between him and Huxley on "Geological time" the theories of Kant were frequently referred to. See his lecture on "Geological Time," 1868 (loc. cit., p. 10, &c.) ; Huxley on "Geological Reform," 1869 (reprinted in 'Lay Sermons,' No. XI.) The best account in the English language of Kant's contributions to cosmogony will be found in an article by G. F. Becker in the 5th vol., 4th series, of the 'American Journal of Science,' 1898.

works on astronomy as an established theory, whereas Laplace himself had put it forward with great reserve, and only as a likely suggestion.[1]   There is, however, no doubt that it powerfully influenced the minds of many students of nature in the direction of a genetic view of phenomena.

The attempts referred to so far can be described as belonging to the Romance of Science.   I now come to the more solid contributions—to a real genetic theory of the things of nature.   These are not much older than our century.   They belong to two entirely independent lines of research which were followed up in England and on the Continent respectively—the former in palæontology, the latter in embryology.   Although they were carried on quite independently of each other, they had this in common, that they both resorted to a study of life—as preserved in geological strata or as now existing around us—for a guide in comprehending the genesis of Things on a larger scale.

It may be well to remark here that the contemplation of the phenomena, the forms and the processes exhibited in the living portion of creation, has not always, and even not generally, in the course of history led to those theories which our age is elaborating, and which will in future times possibly be looked upon as one of its char-

[1] Laplace himself says: "Je présente cette origine du système planétaire avec la défiance que doit inspirer tout ce qui n'est point un résultat de l'observation et du calcul." The elaborate exposition of the architecture and system of the universe contained in A. von Humboldt's 'Kosmos,' which was professedly inspired by Laplace (see 'Kosmos,' vol. vi. p. 8), gives us little, if anything, about the history of the universe, professing to be only a "Weltgemälde" and not a "Welterklärung." The time for genetic theories had not yet come, and both Kant's and Laplace's cosmogonies are only casually referred to.

acteristic achievements — the genetic view. There is another view which a superficial glance at organic life, with its well known phases of birth, culmination, and decay, has frequently impressed upon the observer; there seemed another lesson to learn than that which our age is trying to master.

7.
"Cyclical"
view.

That other view can best be termed the "cyclical" view of things, the doctrine that every thing runs in a cycle [1] and repeats itself, that all change is periodic and recurrent, that there is nothing new under the sun. [2]

[1] Mr Thomas Whittaker has given me various references to the writings of ancient philosophers which bear on this subject. He finds the cyclical or recurrent aspect of the world-process prominently put forward by the Stoics. Zeller ('Philosophie der Griechen,' vol. iii. I. p. 136, &c., 2nd ed.) says in his account of the stoical philosophy: "Out of the original substance the separate things are developed according to an inner law. For inasmuch as the first principle, according to its definition, is the creative and formative power, the whole universe must grow out of it with the same necessity as the animal or the plant from the seed. The original fire—according to the Stoics and Heraclitus—first changes to 'air' or vapour, then to water; out of this a portion is precipitated as earth, another remains water, a third evaporates as atmospheric air, which again kindles the fire, and out of the changing mixture of these four elements there is formed —from the earth as centre—the world. . . . Through this separation of the elements there arises the contrast of the active and the passive principle: the soul of the world and its body. . . . But as this contrast came in time, so it is also destined to cease; the original substance gradually consumes the matter, which it segregated out of itself as its body, till at the end of this world-period a universal world-conflagration brings everything back again to the primæval condition. . . . But when everything has thus returned to the original unity, and the great world-year has run out, the formation of a new world begins again, which is so exactly like the former one that in it all single things, persons, and phenomena return exactly as before; and in this wise the history of the world and the deity . . . moves in an endless cycle through the same stages." Zeller, in a note to this passage, remarks that "the conception of changing world-periods is frequent in the oldest Greek philosophy; the Stoics found it first in Heraclitus. The further statement, however, that the succeeding worlds resemble one another down to the minutest detail, is to be found, to my knowledge, before Zeno only in the Pythagorean school . . . and is connected with the doctrine of metempsychosis and the world-year."

[2] Mr Whittaker quotes a passage from Aristotle's 'Metaphysics,' towards the end of the 12th book (Berlin ed., p. 1074, b. 10-12): "Κατὰ τὸ εἰκὸς πολλάκις εὑρημένης εἰ τὸ δυνατὸν ἑκάστης καὶ τέχνης καὶ φιλοσοφίας καὶ πάλιν φθειρομένων.

Poets and philosophers have repeated this theme in endless variations, probably without improving upon the
classical and perfect expression which it has found in
ancient [1] poetry and in the sacred writings. History has
been written with the professed object of gaining, by
analogy, an insight into the drift of modern or future
events, and economic and political theories have been
based upon the likelihood of a recurrence of what has
happened before. Especially has the teaching been
impressed upon us that the universal fate of all development is to lead to death and decay, and to make room
for the endless repetition of the same recurring phases

Every art and every kind of philosophy having probably been found
out many times up to the limits
of what is possible and again destroyed;" and remarks, "This
notion of cycles refers to human
civilisation, not to the universe,
which is one eternal system with
a fixed central mass, and with its
outer part in a moving equilibrium. Empedocles undoubtedly
had a theory of recurrent cycles
in the universe. The four elements,—which he first brought together as elements of the whole,
early thinkers having taken one or
other of them as a first principle
from which the rest are evolved,
—according to Empedocles, are
necessarily aggregated and segregated by the predominance of principles which he calls love (φιλία)
and hate (νεῖκος). The four periods
are : 1. Predominant love (the
σφαῖρος), a state of complete aggregation ; 2. decreasing love and increasing hate or strife ; 3. predominant strife (ἀκοσμία, complete
separation of the elements); 4. decreasing strife and increasing love.
These are cosmic periods. It has
been supposed—Zeller takes this
view—that we are living in the

fourth cosmic period, the period of
increasing love."
    [1] The best known passage is that
from the celebrated fourth eclogue
of Virgil, where, after describing the
return of the golden Saturnian age,
the poet continues (vv. 31-36) :—

"Pauca tamen suberunt priscæ vestigia
        fraudis,
Quæ tentare Thetim ratibus, quæ cingere
        muris
Oppida, quæ jubeant telluri infindere
        sulcos.
Alter erit tum Tiphys, et altera quæ
        vehat Argo
Delectos heroas : erunt etiam altera bella,
Atque iterum ad Trojam magnus mittetur
        Achilles."

Dugald Stewart (' Philos. Works,'
vol. iii. p. 167) refers to this
with the following quotation from
Clavius's ' Commentary on the
Treatise on the Sphere,' by Joannes
Sacro Bosco : " Hoc intervallo, qui-
dam volunt, omnia quæcumque in
mundo sunt, eodem ordine esse
reditura, quo nunc cernuntur," and
he also attributes this theory of recurrence to an extreme application
of the mathematical spirit (vol. iv.
p. 207). How this idea of recurrent cycles fascinated and haunted
Fr. Nietzsche see Seth's article,
' Contem. Rev.,' vol. 73, p. 734.

of existence.[1]   This view was considerably strengthened by the popular interpretation of the teaching of modern astronomy, which laid great stress on the periodicity of the planetary movements, and the stability and inherent readjustment of the solar system.   Also the insight gained by the first application of chemical knowledge to

[1] The idea of recurrent, periodic repetition seems opposed to the modern idea of progress and development as taught by Leibniz and Herder abroad, by Spencer in this country ; still it seems almost impossible in a purely mechanical system to avoid introducing the conception of an ultimate recurrence, so long as one deals with finite space, time, or number, however great they may be.   The only escape seems to be in assuming an infinite process or an immaterial principle which is not subject to mathematical treatment, the latter being inherently one of repetition.   It is interesting to note how Herbert Spencer at the end of 'First Principles' relapses into the cyclical conception : "Thus we are led to the conclusion that the entire process of things, as displayed in the aggregate of the visible universe, is analogous to the entire process of things as displayed in the smallest aggregates.   Motion as well as matter being fixed in quantity, it would seem that the change in the distribution of matter which motion effects, coming to a limit in whichever direction it is carried, the indestructible motion thereupon necessitates a reverse distribution.   Apparently, the universally coexistent forces of attraction and repulsion, which necessitate rhythm in all minor changes throughout the universe, also necessitate rhythm in the totality of changes—alternate eras of evolution and dissolution.   And

thus there is suggested the conception of a past during which there have been successive evolutions analogous to that which is now going on ; and a future during which successive other such evolutions may go on—ever the same in principle but never the same in concrete result " (' First Principles,' 1st ed., p. 536).   The other great system of modern philosophy which aims at a reconciliation of the mechanical and spiritual aspects —the philosophy of Lotze—though it dwells less than Spencer's system on the genetic problem, gives a different view of cosmic development.   "The series of cosmic periods cannot be a number of phases, in each of which the one purpose of the universe does in fact maintain itself : it must rather be a chain, each link of which is bound together with every other in the unity of one plan.   The One can manifest itself in various forms only when such variety of forms is necessary for the expression of its meaning—in a definite order of succession only when this order corresponds to a craving for development in its nature.   As we required that each section of the world's history should present a harmony of the elements firmly knit throughout, so we must now require that the successive order of these sections shall compose the unity of an onward advancing melody " (' Microcosmus,' Eng. transl. by Hamilton and Jones, Book IV. chap. 3).

physiology and agriculture in the school of Liebig, and the first chapters of meteorology, seemed to favour the idea that the elements and forces of nature were engaged in cyclic movements which return again and again in the same fashion. To the same cyclical view the doctrine of the fixity of species, as well as that of the repetition of various creations, lent further support; hence it continued up to the middle of our century [1] to be fre-

[1] In Germany Moleschott's 'Kreislauf des Lebens,' a popular exposition of the conceptions developed in the second quarter of the century through chemistry and embryology, represented adequately the cyclic conception of life and development in a catching phrase. Much later we find — *inter multa alia* — in Michael Foster's 'Text-book of Physiology' a concise description of the process in nature which has always served as a type for the cyclic conception : " When the animal kingdom is surveyed from a broad standpoint it becomes obvious that the ovum, or its correlative the spermatozoon, is the goal of an individual existence ; that life is a cycle beginning in an ovum and coming round to an ovum again. . . . The animal body is in reality a vehicle for ova ; and after the life of the parent has become potentially renewed in the offspring, the body remains as a cast-off envelope whose future is but to die." Another example may be found in Mohr's 'Geschichte der Erde,' where the circulation of different elements in nature is considered. The conception of periodic cycles has found poetical expression in Rückert's beautiful poem, "Chidher," which is evidently the poetical rendering of an Arabian legend quoted by Lyell (' Principles,' vol. i. p. 31) :—

"Chidher, the ever youthful, spake :
I passed a city on my way,
A man in a garden fruit did break,
I asked how long the town here lay ?
He spoke, and broke on as before,
'The town stands ever on this shore,
And will thus stand for evermore.'

And when five hundred years were gone
I came the same road as anon,
Then not a mark of the town I met.
A shepherd on the flute did play,
The cattle leaf and foliage ate.
I asked how long is the town away ?
He spake, and piped on as before,
'One plant is green when the other's o'er,
This is my pasture for evermore.'

And when five hundred years were gone
I came the same road as anon,
Then did I find with waves a lake,
A man the net cast in the bay,
And when he paused from his heavy take,
I asked since when the lake here lay ?
He spake, and laughed my question o'er,
'As long as the waves break as of yore
One fishes and fishes on this shore.'

And when five hundred years were gone
I came the same way as anon.
A wooded place I then did see,
And a hermit in a cell did stay ;
He felled with an axe a mighty tree.
I asked since when the wood here lay ?
He spake : 'The wood's a shelter for evermore,
I ever lived upon this floor,
And the trees will grow on as before.'

And when five hundred years were gone
I came the same way as anon,
But then I found a city filled
With markets' clamour shrill and gay.
I asked how long is the city built,
Where's wood and sea and shepherd's play ?
They pondered not my question o'er
But cried : 'So was it long before,
And will go on for evermore.'
And when five hundred years are gone
I'll go the same way as anon."

quently put forward and popularly accepted. It is useful then to note that in the course of the second half of the century we were more and more grow-ing out of the cyclical and realising the meaning of the genetic [1] view of things natural. We have been taught in astronomy to inquire into the origin of our solar or any similar system and the conditions of its duration, to ask concerning the central heat of the sun whence it came and how long it will last—a question unknown to Laplace,—to consider the effects of tidal friction, to learn that all the movements in nature are irreversible as distinguished from completely reversible ones, which only exist in abstraction; and, finally, we are met with the doctrine of the immortality of the germ-plasma, an idea, the meaning and significance of which I shall have to explain later on. All these novel theories and views combine to impress upon us the general significance of the terms "genesis, evolution, develop-ment," the fact that everything in and around us, in spite of the seeming recurrence of smaller movements and phenomena, and of the periodicity of the minuter and elementary changes, is slowly, continuously, and inevit-ably tending in a definite direction, which is certainly not that of a cyclical recurrence.

Leaving aside for a moment these more general views, which have been clarified in the course of our century, it is interesting to note how they gradually emerged in

8.
Supplanted
by genetic
view.

9.
Geology.

[1] Perhaps it would be more correct to say that we were learning to consider the changes within the larger cycles, confining ourselves to the study of one branch only of the periodic or cyclical movement of things around us, that branch which we are pleased to call the ascending or progressive branch.

the teachings of the several natural philosophers who initiated the genetic conception of natural phenomena. One of the earliest who broke with the older and introduced the modern methods was James Hutton, who towards the end of the preceding century led that school in geology which is called after him, and which violently opposed the ideas introduced from the Continent. The controversy culminated in the wrangle of the Neptunists and Vulcanists, those who looked to the agency of water and those who upheld that of fire as the principal cause of geological change. This difference, which at the time impressed the popular mind, is hardly that by which, in a history of scientific thought,[1] this controversy has become important. Hutton's position is marked rather by his opposition to catastrophism, and by his doctrine that geological changes, such as the decay and reproduction of rocks, were going on with the utmost uniformity, being always in progress. This he opposed to the Wernerian view, which believed in the existence of certain " fundamental rocks," which were "triumphantly

[1] The great merits of James Hutton, his extensive and original geological studies, his opposition to catastrophism, were overlooked through the theoretical discussions and the unfortunate title of his book. The world had grown tired of ' Theories of the Earth ' and the discussion of fundamental problems. A spirit of observation had set in ; the Geological Society was formed, and theories were for the time discountenanced. (See vol. i. p. 290, note 1, of this 'History.') The attacks also of Kirwan and De Luc, which turned upon the stale argument that Hutton's ideas were opposed to the scriptural records, had their effect in circles in which everything connected with the revolution against Church and State was distasteful. As Huxley has told us, Hutton came before his time. To him belongs the merit of having initiated the line of research and reasoning which, through the brilliant labours of Charles Lyell a generation later, swept away the older geology, and prepared the way for the genetic study of nature on a large scale. (See the " Historical Sketch " in the first volume of Lyell's ' Principles of Geology,' and Huxley's address on " Geological Reform," 1869.)

appealed to if anybody ventured to doubt the possibility of our being able to carry back our researches to the creation of the present order of things." [1]   Hutton destroyed these characters, which were considered by many as sacred, and declared that in the economy of the world he could find " no traces of a beginning nor signs of an end."   And yet, as Lyell has shown, his principles were only imperfectly carried through, for though he maintained that " the strata which now compose our continents have once been beneath the sea, and were formed out of the waste of pre-existing continents," [2] he imagined that when the decay of old continents had furnished the material for new ones these were upheaved by violent and paroxysmal convulsions.   He therefore required " alternate periods of general disturbance and repose, and such he believed had been and would for ever be the courses of nature." [3]   A strange mixture of the genetic and cyclical views of natural phenomena !

10.
Hutton.

Professor Huxley [4] has explained these seeming inconsistencies in the theory of Hutton, whom, together with Sir Charles Lyell, he has described as having founded the " uniformitarian " school of geology, by the influence which the discoveries of physical astronomy, brought out at that time by Laplace and his contemporaries, had upon Hutton.   Thus Hutton writes : " From seeing revolutions of the planets, it is concluded that there is a system by which they are intended to continue those revolutions.   But if the succession of worlds

[1] See Lyell, 'Principles,' 3rd ed vol. i. pp. 90, 91.

[2] Ibid., p. 89.   [3] Lyell, p. 92.

[4] Huxley, on " Geological Re- form," quotes largely from Hutton's ' Theory of the Earth ' (1758) and Playfair's ' Illustrations of the Hut- tonian Theory ' (1802).

is established in the system of nature, it is in vain
to look for anything higher in the origin of the earth.
The result, therefore, of this physical inquiry is, that
we find no vestige of a beginning, no prospect of an
end." The beginnings of the genetic view of geological phenomena, which in Hutton were still mingled with
catastrophism, were further developed by Sir Charles
Lyell in his celebrated 'Principles of Geology.' When
he entered upon his geological researches, which were
conducted during his very extensive travels all over
Europe, a new element had already been introduced
into science, of which neither Hutton nor Werner had
been able to avail themselves extensively. This was the
identification of geological strata according to the fossil
remains which were contained in them,—a realisation
of the plan of work already dimly foreshadowed in
Leibniz's 'Protogæa,' but nevertheless accepted even by
Humboldt as only a doubtful indication.[1] This valuable
branch of geological science had been started by William
Smith in his 'Tabular View of the British Strata' in
1790, and further elaborated in his geological map of
England (1815), which was the fruit of his own unaided labours, "for he had explored the whole country

[1] The Wernerian school are generally accused of having neglected
the historical record afforded by
fossil remains, and Humboldt, in
his 'Essay on the Superposition of
Rocks in both Hemispheres' (1823),
says (Eng. transl., p. 52): "In
the present age naturalists are no
longer satisfied with vague and
uncertain notions, and they have
sagaciously observed that the greatest number of those fossils, buried
in different formations, are not
specifically the same; that many
species which they have been enabled
to examine with precision vary with
the superposed rocks. . . . Ought
we to conclude from this assemblage of facts that all the formations are characterised by particular
species? that the fossil shells of the
chalk, of the muschelkalk, of the
Jura limestone, and of the Alpine
limestone, all differ from each other?
This would be, in my opinion, to
carry the induction much too far."

on foot without the guidance of previous observers or the aid of fellow-labourers,"[1] and "had thus singly effected for the whole of England what many celebrated mineralogists had only accomplished for a small part of Germany in the course of half a century."[2] Simultaneously with Smith in England, Cuvier and Brongniart were exploring the Paris basin. Thus the three different nations of Europe with whom I am mainly concerned in this work furthered independently the main divisions of geological inquiry. "The systematic study of what may be called mineralogical geology had its origin in Germany, where Werner first described with precision the mineral character of rocks; the classification of the secondary formations belongs to England, where the labours of Smith were steadily directed to these objects; the foundation of the third branch, that relating to the tertiary formation, was laid in France by the splendid work of Cuvier and Brongniart."[3] To these words of Lyell we can now add that the theoretical explanations were first suggested, and the correct line of reasoning on this accumulated evidence initiated, by Sir Charles Lyell himself.

The key to the doctrines of Lyell was the study of existing causes — the attempt to show how the slow agencies which we now see at work in nature around us are sufficient to explain the successive changes[4]

[1] Lyell, 'Principles,' vol. i. p. 101.

[2] An expression of d'Aubuisson, quoted by Dr Fitton, 'Phil. Mag.,' vols. i. and ii., also 'Edin. Rev.,' Feb. 1818.

[3] See Lyell, loc. cit., p. 103.

[4] Id. ibid., vol. iii. p. 273: "It is only by carefully considering the combined action of all the causes of change now in operation, whether in the animate or inanimate world, that we can hope to explain such complicated appearances as are exhibited in the general arrangement of mineral masses."

which the recognisable strata of the earth's crust with their fossil remains indicate as having occurred in former ages. It was an attempt to " reconcile the former and the present state of nature." [1] This was to break with the idea of great and general convulsions, to which the Continental school resorted in their explanations, and it also meant upsetting the vague notions which set a limit to the time [2] which should be allowed for the operations of natural causes. It is possible to admit that in both directions, in their uniformitarian explanation and in their geological time-reckoning, the new school frequently went too far, the indications of actual catastrophes and paroxysmal convulsions being to many observers quite unmistakable. On the other side, the arguments based upon physical astronomy, mechanics, and thermodynamics, which afford an independent basis for geological time-reckoning, were not yet elaborated,[3] or were deemed too crude [4] to be of value; and for a good while geologists were permitted

[1] Lyell, vol. i. p. 114.

[2] Id. ibid., p. 241 : "When difficulties arise in interpreting the monuments of the past, I deem it more consistent with philosophical caution to refer them to our present ignorance of all the existing agents, or all their possible effects in an indefinite lapse of time, than to causes formerly in operation but which have ceased to act."

[3] See Lyell, vol. i. p. 154, &c., also vol. ii. p. 274 : "It has long been a favourite conjecture that the whole of our planet was originally in a state of igneous fusion, and that the central parts still retain a great portion of their primitive heat. Some have imagined with the late Sir W. Herschel that the elementary matter of the earth may have been first in a gaseous state, resembling those nebulæ which we behold in the heavens, and which are of dimensions so vast that some of them would fill the orbits of the remotest planets of our system. . . . Without dwelling on such speculations which can never have any direct bearing on geology," &c.

[4] See Lyell, vol. i. p. 206, where he refers to "astronomical causes of fluctuations in climate," and to the calculations of Sir J. Herschel and the fact that "this matter is still under discussion," and that "MM. Fourier and Herschel have arrived at very different opinions."

to draw indefinitely on the great bank of time,[1] just as in
former ages they had been quickly brought to book by
existing prejudices.[2]

Whilst these contributions to the genetic view of
nature on the large scale were being independently
worked out, the sciences which deal with the minute
and hidden phenomena of organic growth had made great
progress in the same direction. Here a definite scheme
of development was quite evident to the most casual
observer. In these sciences indeed we have to do with
what is called in the German language " the history of
development " *par excellence*, a term which is inadequately
rendered by " Embryology " in French and English. For
it is an error which has frequently and for long periods
obscured the correcter view to assume that the changes
and processes which characterise the development of
embryonic or germ life are essentially different from
those which exist in the larger and more complex adult
organism. The abolition of the fundamental distinction
between the processes of embryonic and of adult or full-

12.
Embryol-
ogy.

[1] Lyell, vol. iii. p. 358 : " Confined notions in regard to the
quantity of past time have tended
more than any other prepossessions
to retard the progress of geology,
. . . and until we habituate ourselves to contemplate the possibility
of an indefinite lapse of ages having
been comprised within each of the
more modern periods of the earth's
history, we shall be in danger of
forming most erroneous views in
geology."
[2] One of the first to attack the
uniformitarian doctrine in geology
and to apply the principles of
modern physical science to geological and cosmical questions in this
country was Lord Kelvin. His
influence belongs, however, mainly
to the post-Darwinian period, and
begins with his celebrated memoir
' On the Secular Cooling of the
Earth ' (Edin. Trans., 1862, reprinted in the 3rd vol. of 'Math.
and Phys. Papers,' p. 295). See
also the 2nd vol. of his ' Popular
Lectures and Addresses.' According to the introductory statement
in the former paper his doubts
regarding the uniformitarian teaching began as early as 1844. I shall
refer to these speculations at the
end of this chapter.

grown life, the unification of thought on these matters, is quite as important in the history of science as the abolition of the supposed fundamental difference between animal and vegetable growth or between normal and abnormal (or pathological) development.   The reduction of all these seemingly so different changes to the one great problem of cellular structure, cellular growth, and cellular division marks one of the greatest achievements of our century. " Our position with regard to the cell is similar to that of investigators towards the whole animal or vegetable body a hundred years ago, before the discovery of the cell theory." [1]

Anticipations of this generalisation, of the condensation of the whole problem of animal and vegetable embryology, of generation, growth, and organic development in the formula, " omnis cellula ex cellula," have indeed existed since the time of Harvey, who, in addition to the great discovery of the circulation of the blood, laid down the thesis, " omne vivum ex ovo." [2]   The further correct

[1] See O. Hertwig, "The Cell," ' Outlines of General Anatomy and Physiology.'   Transl. by Campbell, 1895, p. 11.

[2] One of the best expositions of Harvey's ideas is to be found in Huxley's article on " Evolution in Biology " in the ninth edition of the ' Encyclopædia Britannica.'   He there also refers to Aristotle's opinions.   " One of Harvey's prime objects is to defend and establish, on the basis of direct observation, the opinion already held by Aristotle, that in the higher animals at any rate the formation of the new organism by the process of generation takes place, not suddenly by simultaneous accretion of rudiments of all, or of the most important of the organs of the adult, nor by sudden metamorphosis of a formative substance into a miniature of the whole, which subsequently grows, but by epigenesis, or successive differentiation of a relatively homogeneous rudiment into the parts and structures which are characteristic of the adult."   In the sequel of his exposition, after maintaining epigenesis or after-formation against evolution in the older sense or preformation, Huxley, however, makes a passing remark that " though the doctrine of epigenesis, as understood by Harvey, has definitely triumphed over the doctrine of evolution, . . . it is not impossible that, when the analysis of the process of develop-

generalisation which he ventured to put forward, that growth and development of the germ or embryo consisted in the addition or formation of new parts and structures through division or differentiation, was, however, obscured and cast into the shade by the opposite doctrine, termed evolution, according to which every form or particle of organisation was minutely pre-formed in an invisible germ, and growth consisted merely in a process of enlargement, as a particle of "dry gelatine may be swelled up by the intussusception of water." The supporters of this doctrine, to which the celebrated names of Leibniz, Boerhaave, Haller, and Bonnet belonged, seemed unable to conceive of any force in nature which was capable of producing organisation, and were thus compelled to accept in some form or other the doctrine of the pre-existence of germs, a theory which has in modern times been revived under an altered form.

13.
Epigenesis
and evolu-
tion.

The real foundation of scientific embryology, of the study of the genesis of vegetable and animal organisms, is now pretty unanimously [1] traced to Caspar Friedrich Wolff, whose 'Theoria generationis' appeared in 1759. His observations refer alike to plant and to animal life, and his distinct object was to refute the theory of evolu-

14.
C. F. Wolff.

ment is carried still further, and the origin of the molecular components of the physically gross, though sensibly minute, bodies which we term germs is traced, the theory of development will approach more nearly to metamorphosis than to epigenesis. . . . The process, which in its superficial aspect is epigenesis, appears in essence to be evolution in the modified sense adopted in Bonnet's later writings; and development is merely the expansion of a potential organism or original pre-formation according to fixed laws."

[1] See J. A. Thomson, *loc. cit.*, p. 121. Yves Delage, 'L'Hérédité,' p. 357, note; and especially O. Hertwig, 'The Biological Problem of To-day,' transl. by P. C. Mitchell (Heinemann's Scientific Handbooks, 1896), p. 4, &c.

tion and replace it by the correcter doctrine of epigenesis
—*i.e.*, of repeated or after-formation.   Haller [1] thought
very highly of this attack on his own view, but was
not convinced by it; and although in botany Wolff's
views on the cellular structure of plants were adopted
in France by Mirbel, and those on metamorphosis were
unknowingly reproduced by Goethe, his influence on embryology dates actually only from the year 1812, when
Meckel translated one of his treatises and thus drew
attention to his great merits.   Wolff tried to refute the
theory of evolution or pre-formation, supplanting it by
that of epigenesis or after-formation, through actual
observations of the development of germs in plants and
animals in definite instances.   In botany his views,
after lying dormant for a long period, led ultimately to
the famous cellular theory of Schleiden and Mohl.   In
zoology, shortly after Meckel's republication of his treatise
in 1812, there were published the researches of Pander,
who, in his treatise on the development of the chick,
"gave a fuller and more exact view of the phenomena
less clearly indicated by Wolff, and laid the foundation
of the views of all subsequent embryologists." [2]

Pander was a Russian by birth, and so was his greater
contemporary and friend, Karl Ernst von Baer,[3] a man

15.
Pander and
K. E. von
Baer.

[1] As Prof. J. Arthur Thomson
says ('Science of Life,' p. 120), "A
single sentence, 'Es gibt kein
Werden — there is no Becoming,'
sufficiently indicates Haller's position."

[2] J. A. Thomson in article "Embryology" ('Ency. Brit.,' 9th ed.,
p. 165).

[3] The work of von Baer (1792-
1876) remained for a long time unknown and unrecognised outside
of Germany.   Huxley made him
known in this country by translating extracts from his principal
writings for Taylor's 'Scientific
Memoirs' in 1853, nearly thirty
years after von Baer had begun the
brilliant series of his researches.   It
can be said of him that he, even
more than his forerunners, Pander
and Döllinger, withdrew natural

who occupies a unique position in the history of natural science. He introduced the principle and aspect of development into the midst of those studies which, under the important but one-sided influence of Cuvier and his school, were in danger of being confined within the limits of morphology and comparative anatomy. Through a long series of most important embryological investigations, conducted during the years 1819-1837, he demon-

science from the spell under which it was kept for a long time in the West of Europe by the great authority of Cuvier. Geographically also, von Baer's activity was centered in Königsberg (where he was one of a brilliant company who made the University celebrated) and St Petersburg. Though a great admirer of Cuvier, whose biography he wrote, and an adherent of the doctrine of animal types, which he independently arrived at, he introduced three distinct lines of research into his scientific labours, to all three of which Cuvier was either foreign or distinctly averse — viz., microscopic research, study of embryological development, and the philosophical spirit of the "Naturphilosophie." He was not dazzled by the latter ; but whilst avoiding its extravagances and premature generalisations which then flooded German science, he always appreciated the search for the connection and unity of all the things of nature which was characteristic of that school. Baer stood, historically and philosophically, in the middle between the extreme morphological and genetic views represented respectively by Cuvier before and by Darwin after him. Already in 1815, when studying under Döllinger at Würzburg, he was guided by the idea that "nature follows in her creations certain general themes (types), and that she varies these in the different species." Von Baer

also combined the geographical and anthropological interest, so largely represented by Humboldt and Ritter, with his morphological and genetic studies. In fact, it is doubtful whether in any naturalist of the very first order the different interests which the nineteenth century inherited and created were more equally and impartially balanced than in him. The embryological researches of von Baer stimulated many ardent students in Germany, such as Purkinje, Rathtke, Bischoff, and it is mainly through them that this branch of science was cultivated and made generally known. The name of the distant originator thus became somewhat forgotten, so that in French science we do not find von Baer as frequently and appreciatively mentioned as he deserves. Ample information on von Baer's scientific and personal character can be found in later publications : foremost in his 'Autobiography,' published in 1865 ; in his 'Life,' by Stieda (1877) ; and in an elaborate work by Professor R. Stölzle, entitled 'K. E. von Baer und seine Weltanschauung' (Regensburg, 1897). This work contains very ample and useful references and extracts from Baer's writings and correspondence. Very important are also von Baer's miscellaneous writings and essays, which were published by Vieweg in Brunswick, in three parts (2nd ed., 1886).

strated in the completest manner the truth of epigenesis. In fact, he had recognised development as the "sole basis of zoological classification; while in France Cuvier and Geoffroy St Hilaire were embittering each other's lives with endless merely anatomical discussions and replications, and while in Germany the cautious study of nature was given up for the spinning of Natur-philosophies and other hypothetical cobwebs." [1]

The position which Karl Ernst von Baer occupies in the history of science and thought is in many respects interesting and unique. He lived early enough in the century to experience the full influence of Cuvier's authority, and lived long enough to witness the great change which Darwin's writings brought on in all the natural sciences; whereas his great contemporary, Johannes Müller, passed away before the name of Darwin was known outside of his own country. In unison with Müller, and yet in an independent manner, he effectually liberated German science from the undue influence of the speculative school. And he has, probably more than any other great naturalist, recognised the importance of the three aspects which a contemplation of natural objects forces upon us: the apparent or real fixity of certain forms (the morphological view), the continued and orderly change [2] of these forms (the genetic view), and the apparent or real existence of a

[1] Huxley in Taylor's 'Scientific Memoirs,' New Series, p. 176.

[2] Very important in this respect is a lecture delivered by von Baer in 1834, with the title 'Das allgemeinste Gesetz der Natur in aller Entwickelung (reprinted in the Brunswick edition, vol. i. p. 39 *sqq.*) "We must conclude that, so far as observations now give materia for inferences, a transformation of certain original forms of animals in the succession of generations is very probable, but only to a limited extent (p. 60), a view which von Baer maintained to the end against extreme Darwinism (see p. 37).

design in this process of change (the teleological view).
Though his own researches did so much to give prominence to the genetic view, to the conception of development, he retained and elaborated the doctrine of types ;
and though he effectually handled the modern methods
of the mechanical or exact sciences, he realised the full
importance of studying the things and processes of
nature in their actual and living connection,[1] and not
merely in the artificial isolation of the laboratory or
the dissecting-room. And he never became an adherent
of the doctrine so prevalent with many of the followers
of Darwin, that the apparent purpose of forms and
processes in organic nature could be mechanically explained. During the period of his greatest scientific
activity he was little known outside of Russia and
Germany ; in England, Carpenter and Huxley alone
drew attention to his embryological and genetic studies ;
but since the tide of Darwinism has somewhat subsided,
or has ceased to be all-absorbing, it is to the writings
of Baer that many naturalists revert. In fact they
belong to the few books of this class written during
the pre-Darwinian age that bear to be read and re-read
with profit by those who take a philosophical and not
merely a historical interest in the development of

16.
Von Baer's
comprehen-
sive views.

natural science. Perhaps the fact that von Baer was
as great in relation to the morphological as he was
in relation to the genetic and the teleological conceptions of natural phenomena prevented him from
producing that revolutionary impression on the minds

[1] See the introduction to the second part of his ' Entwickelungs- geschichte der Thiere' (Königsberg, 1837).

of his contemporaries which Darwin did, and for which he indeed largely prepared the way. Instead of opposing the genetic change and development of the forms of natural objects to their apparent fixity, he rather reconciled both views with each other by maintaining [1] "that in order to obtain a just insight into the mutual affinities of animals it is before all things necessary to distinguish the different *types of organisation* from the different *grades of development.*" He considered that [2] "the idea of animal organisation does not vary at equal intervals, but is realised in certain principal forms which again break up into variations of a lower grade"; and he [3] "arrived at the four principal divisions of the animal kingdom established by Cuvier." In 1828, in his work on the 'Development of Animals,' he discusses [4] "the prevalent notion that the embryo of higher animals passes through the permanent forms of the lower animals"—*i.e.,* "the doctrine of the agreement of individual metamorphosis with the ideal metamorphosis of the whole animal kingdom." Von Baer had himself added greatly [5] to

[1] See Huxley's translation, *loc. cit.*, p. 178.

[2] Ibid., p. 182.

[3] Ibid., p. 183.

[4] See K. E. von Baer's 'Ueber Entwickelungsgeschichte der Thiere Beobachtung und Reflexion,' Königsberg, 1828. The above extracts are taken from the fifth scholion: "Ueber das Verhältniss der Formen, die das Individuum in den verschiedenen Stufen seiner Entwickelung annimmt." See also Huxley's Translation, *loc. cit.*, pp. 186, 189.

[5] Prof. J. A. Thomson summarises as follows von Baer's own results: "It was von Baer who first clearly discriminated the great events in a life-history; (*a*) the primary process of egg-cleavage, and the establishment of the germinal layers; (*b*) the gradual differentiation of the tissues (histogenesis); and (*c*) the blocking out of the organs (organogenesis), and the shape-taking of the entire organism (morphogenesis) ('Science of Life,' p. 123). The classical work of von Baer is dedicated to his friend Pander, from whom and Döllinger he acknowledges having received the first impulses towards

the existing knowledge of the early development of
the germs of animals by discovering the ovum in the
body of the mammalia before fructification, and by this
and other discoveries secured his claim to be considered
the greatest embryologist of his own age, and perhaps
of all time.   He goes on to examine to what extent the
morphological differences which the animal kingdom exhibits in its various members can be taken as a guide to
the genetic differences in the growth and development of
the higher organisms.   He, in fact, tried to ascertain
how far the facts of classification throw a light on the
facts of development, how far the changing embryo of
the higher animal gradually passes through the permanent
forms of the lower animals.   He combats the idea that
the classification or morphological arrangement can be
uni-serial—*i.e.*, brought into one continuous line or order.

his researches. He wishes to distinguish carefully between facts
and theory, and is very cautious
as to the latter, a trait which
runs through all his writings. It
is also very interesting to see how
in his biography of Cuvier (posthumously published by Stieda) he
considers it a merit of that great
naturalist not to have indulged
in genetic theories. " It is evident that Cuvier in his youth had
also a genetic system in view, such
as Oken afterwards followed up,
but that he must soon have found
out that this task was unattainable
for him. He abandoned it, and
sought rather to draw from the
manifoldness of the formed product inferences regarding the conditions of its genesis. Thus he
arrived at the teleological conceptions which he developed on various occasions. German naturalists

drew from all this, especially in
the age of Schelling's 'Natur-philosophie,' the conclusion that Cuvier
was not a philosophical mind. To
me it seems that we recognise in it
Cuvier's desire for clearness. He
dropped the higher task because
he found that it would not lead
him to clear views" ('Lebensge-
schichte Cuvier's von K. E. von Baer,'
ed. Stieda, 1897, p. 72). English
readers, to whom the genetic view
has only become familiar since
Darwin or perhaps Lyell, will find
with astonishment how in the
writings of Baer, before Lyell and
even before the appearance of
Cuvier's final system, genetic ideas
were thought to be prevalent, and
were criticised elaborately and received with the utmost caution
even by the great propounders of
the doctrine of development.

Animals differ according to the type of organisation to which they belong.   Thus the "embryo of the vertebrate animal is from the very first a vertebrate animal, and at no time agrees with an invertebrate animal."[1]   Having, however, once fixed the existence of special organic forms, he asks whether within the limits of such form no law can be discovered to formulate the development of the individual.   He believes there can,[2] and he proceeds to explain it in terms which for the most part might appear unaltered in the most modern work on evolution. He states that the more special type is developed from the more general, "and that the more different two animal forms are, so much the further back must their development be traced to find them similar."   Indeed he thinks it probable that "in the condition of the actual germ all embryos which are developed from true ova agree," and he anticipates the cellular theory of Schwann, established by observation ten years later, by suggesting that the simple vesicle is the common fundamental form "from which all animals are developed, not only ideally but actually and historically."[3]   In further examining the process of development, von Baer introduces the very suggestive term[4] *differentiation*.   "The higher and lower development of the animal coincides perfectly with that histological and morphological differentiation which gradually arises in the course of the development of the individual."[5]   Development, in fact, is the estab-

[1] *Loc. cit.*, p. 220 ; transl., p. 210.
[2] Ibid, p. 221.
[3] *Loc. cit.*, p. 224 ; transl., p. 213. On this anticipation see, however, von Baer's later explanation in 'Reden, &c.,' vol. ii. p. 250.

[4] The German term is "Sonderung," which Huxley renders by the English term "Differentiation."
[5] *Loc. cit.*, p. 229, 230 ; transl., p. 219.

lishing of differences, and in reality " the embryo never passes through the form of any other animal, but only through the condition of indifference between its own form and others." And he sums up his reflections by stating that the " development of an individual of a certain animal form is determined by two conditions : first, by a progressive development of the animal by increasing histological and morphological differentiation ; secondly, by the metamorphosis of a more general form into a more special one." [1]

17.
Von Baer's
views in
modern
terms.

In order better to understand the difference which separates these various reflections, though breathing so much the air of the more modern theory of evolution, from later views, and to prepare for a real comprehension of the great step taken by Darwin, it will be helpful to resort to modern nomenclature. None of the terms of that vocabulary which was invented by Darwin and his followers to bring home to the popular mind the main points of his revolutionary doctrine are to be found in the earlier writings of von Baer. Nevertheless they are useful in defining the views of the great naturalists who preceded Darwin. Since we have become familiar with the idea of the origin and the transmutation of the different animal and vegetable species, we are accustomed to apply the genetic view not only to the growth and development of individual living things in nature, but to everything else. When von Baer speaks of development, when he tells us that " the history of development is the true source of light for the investigation of organised bodies," he means development in the narrower sense,

[1] *Loc. cit.*, p. 231 ; transl., p. 220.

that which Haeckel has termed " Ontogenesis," the genesis of the individual being.   From this Haeckel distinguishes " Phylogenesis," the genesis of the phyla, the genera, and species.   Now, in discussing the relation of the order which prevails in the natural systems of animals to the stages of development of individual embryos, von Baer does not seem to have had before his mind the genesis of one species out of another, a view which he in fact ridicules [1] after a very modern fashion.   He looked

[1] *Loc. cit.*, p. 200 ; transl., p. 187 (1828) : " This idea—viz., that the higher forms of animals in the single stages of the development of the individual, from its first origin to its completed development, answer to the permanent forms of the animal series— . . . could not fail to be widely accepted, since it was supported by a multitude of special demonstrations.   Certain of its advocates were so zealous that they no longer spoke of similarity but of perfect identity, and assumed that the correspondence had been demonstrated in all cases and to the minutest details. . . . By degrees it became the custom to look upon the different forms of animals as developed out of one another, and then many appeared to forget that this metamorphosis was after all only a mode of conceiving the facts. . . . At length, in sober seriousness, and with all due particularity, we were informed exactly how they arose from one another.   Nothing could be easier.   A fish, swimming towards the shore, desires to take a walk, but finds his fins useless. They diminish in breadth for want of use, and at the same time elongate. This goes on with children and grandchildren for a few myriads of years, and at last, who can be astonished that the fins become feet ?   It is still more natural that the fish in the meadow, finding no water, should gape after air, thereby, in a like period of time, developing lungs ; the only difficulty being that in the meanwhile a few generations must manage to do without breathing at all.   The long neck of the heron arose from a habit its ancestors acquired of stretching out their necks for the purpose of catching fish. . . .   An immediate consequence of the assumption of this idea as a natural law was that a view which had once been very general, but had subsequently been pretty generally given up,—that of the universal progression of the different forms of animals,—gradually got footing again. . . .   It must be confessed that the natural law being assumed, logical consequence required the admission of the view in question.   There was then only one road of metamorphosis, that of further development, either attained in one individual (individual metamorphosis) or through the different animal forms (the metamorphosis of the animal kingdom) ; and disease was to be considered as a retrogressive metamorphosis, because universal metamorphosis, like a railroad, allows motion backwards or forwards, but not to one side."

upon this order as systematic only, and ideal;[1] he thinks
merely of arrangement or "taxonomy." We may say
that he deals with phylotaxy (called at that time taxonomy), not with phylogenesis. He conceives that ontogenesis, the historical development of the individual
thing, throws light on the "mutual relations of organised bodies";[2] he wishes to make ontogenesis helpful
in taxonomy or in phylotaxy. This term did not then
exist, but it is useful in order to enable us to understand the change which came over natural science when
the attempts at phylotaxy were succeeded by the schemes
of phylogenesis, when reasons were established for taking
in real earnest the idea then fancifully[3] put forward that
the natural order of living beings represented the order
in which they had developed out of each other in time.
These reasons did not at that time exist.

18.
Phylotaxy
and phylo-
genesis.

A suggestion in this direction had indeed been thrown
out, and an elaborate theory had been published about

[1] In his later writings von Baer
notes especially the difference between a purely ideal and a genetic
or genealogical relationship. See
'Reden, &c.,' vol. ii. p. 386 (2nd ed.)

[2] 'Entwickelungsgeschichte'
(1828), p. 231; transl., p. 221.

[3] In a later publication of von
Baer's (see 'Reden, &c.,' 2 Theil,
No. V., "Ueber Darwin's Lehre")
the aged author tries to define more
exactly the part which his early
writings played in the gradual
establishment of a genetic conception of nature. If Haller arrived
ultimately at the dictum "es gibt
kein Werden," we may say that von
Baer as emphatically asserted the
opposite, that "es gibt kein Sein."
In Baer we have progressed from the
study of the "esse" (fixed forms) to
that of the "fieri" (processes of
change and development). See the
expositions in the introduction to
the article on Darwin. He there
also mentions Meckel and Oken as
the two principal exponents of the
extreme view then put forward and
opposed by himself, that the human
being in its development passes
through the different higher forms
of the animal creation, and he
maintains that Johannes Müller,
who had in the first edition of his
'Physiology' accepted this view,
struck it out in the second. He
also refers to a passage in a Memoir
of 1859, published just before the
appearance of the 'Origin of
Species,' in which he maintains his
belief "that formerly organic forms
were less rigid."

ten years before von Baer [1] took up "the subject, which then presented itself as the richest which an anatomist could take up, the history of development," and twenty years before his first larger publication on this subject. Lamarck's [2] 'Philosophie Zoologique' appeared in 1809. Though known to von Baer, it does not seem to have ever been much appreciated by him, but it was the first serious attempt to deal with phylogenesis, as von Baer's researches were the first consistent studies in ontogenesis.

19.
Lamarck.

It is of interest to inquire into the reasons which induced Lamarck to form opinions so entirely different from those which, through the influence and the authority of Cuvier, were then prevalent among naturalists, and to oppose the idea of variability and of descent to that of

[1] Von Baer himself describes—using these words—how in the year 1819 the play of accident or good fortune "threw this subject into his hands." Stieda, p. 67.

[2] Since the interest in the speculations of J. Baptiste de Lamarck (1744 - 1829) has been revived through the writings of Charles Darwin, the historical antecedents of his ideas have also been studied, and his as well as Geoffroy's theories have been brought into connection with the views contained in Buffon's 'Epoques de la Nature.' See especially the interesting analysis in Edmond Perier's 'La Philosophie Zoologique avant Darwin,' 1884. "Ainsi surgissent, posés par Buffon, ce partisan d'abord si résolu de la fixité des espèces, tous les problèmes dont la solution aura été sans aucun doute la pensée dominante de la seconde moitié de ce siècle. . . . Et toutes ces grandes idées que Buffon devine en quelque sorte, vers lesquelles il est invinciblement entraîné par la puissante et rigoureuse logique de son génie, sont précisément celles qui commencent aujourd'hui, appuyées sur un ensemble imposant de recherches, à triompher de tous les scrupules" (p. 68). "Trois grands hommes y vont poursuivre, par des voies diverses, l'œuvre de Buffon : Lamarck, Geoffroy St Hilaire, et Cuvier" (p. 72). For the historical connections of Lamarck's ideas see also Huxley's article in the 9th ed. of the 'Ency. Brit.,' in which he points to a great change which took place in Lamarck's views between 1794 and 1809. In fact, the theories which have given to Lamarck so distinguished a position in the history of the genetic view of nature belong to the latter half of his long life. I know of no other recent example of so late a development of quite original ideas except perhaps the critical philosophy of Kant.

the fixity and independence of species. And it is equally interesting to mark the causes which militated against the more general acceptance of his views, and which cast the ' Philosophie Zoologique ' into oblivion. To the first question Lamarck has himself, in the introduction [1] to his great work, furnished us with the means of replying. He there tells us that when the real study of natural history began, and each of the different kingdoms of nature received the due attention of naturalists, animals with a backbone—viz., mammalia, birds, reptiles, and fishes—received the greater attention.[2] Being in general larger, with parts more developed and more easily determinable, they, as it were, obtruded themselves on the attention of man, for whom they are both more useful and more formidable. The other large group of animals, classed together first by Lamarck himself as " Invertebrates," are mostly very small, with organs and faculties less developed, and thus much further removed from man and his interests. Of this by far more numerous class of beings, those called insects had alone at the end of the former century received considerable attention, whereas all the others, classed together by Linnæus as " worms," formed a kind of chaos, an unknown land.

---

[1] Lamarck's later genetic views are contained in the ' Philosophie Zoologique,' which appeared in 1809, and was republished with a biographical notice by Charles Martin in 1873. I quote from this edition. His principal ideas are also summarised in the introduction to his great work, ' Histoire des Animaux sans Vertèbres' (1816), which in fact he represents as containing the "pièces justificatives de ce que j'ai publié dans ma Philosophie Zoologique." This great work was republished in 1837 by Deshayes and Milne - Edwards. I quote from this edition, which is in three volumes.

[2] See ' Philosophie Zoologique,' Discours préliminaire, vol. i. p. 29 ; also 'Animaux sans Vertèbres,' Introduction, vol. i. p. 11.

It was to some extent accidental [1] that Lamarck, after having devoted himself for many years to the exclusive study of plants, should on the occasion of the foundation of the different chairs for the natural sciences at the "Museum" suggested by Lakanal, have allotted to him the cultivation of this department, unknown to himself as it was to others, and where even the systematising genius of Linnæus had abstained from trying to make order. Thus it came about that Lamarck brought to the study of the animal world a mind trained in a very different region of science,[2] and that he approached this study

[1] See the "Introduction Biographique," by Martins, 'Philos. Zool.,' I. xiii. "La Convention gouvernait la France, Carnot organisait la victoire. Lakanal entreprit d'organiser les sciences naturelles : sur sa proposition, le Muséum d'histoire naturelle fut créé. On avait pu nommer des professeurs à toutes les chaires, sauf pour la zoologie ; mais dans ces temps d'enthousiasme le France trouvait des hommes de guerre et des hommes de science partout où elle en avait besoin. Étienne Geoffroy Saint-Hilaire était âgé de vingt-et-un ans, il s'occupait de minéralogie sous la direction d'Haüy. Daubenton lui dit : ' Je prends sur moi la responsabilité de votre inexpérience ; j'ai sur vous l'autorité d'un père ; osez entreprendre d'enseigner la zoologie, et un jour on puisse dire que vous en avez fait une science française.' Geoffroy accepte, et se charge des animaux supérieurs. Lakanal avait compris qu'un seul professeur ne pouvait suffire à la tâche de ranger dans les collections le règne animal tout entier. Geoffroy devant classer les vertébrés seulement, restaient les invertébrés, à savoir les insectes, les mollusques, les vers, les zoophytes, c'est-à-dire le chaos, l'inconnu. Lamarck, dit M. Michelet, accepta l'inconnu . . . il avait tout à apprendre, tout à créer dans ce monde inexploré, ou Linné avait pour ainsi dire renoncé à introduire l'ordre méthodique qu'il avait su si bien établir parmi les animaux supérieurs." Lamarck was accordingly about fifty when he undertook this novel study, which, as Huxley pointed out, was to work such a change in his views (loc. cit.)

[2] He had written in six months his 'Flore française,' which was prefaced by his 'Clé dichotomique.' This was in 1778. "Rousseau avait mis la botanique à la mode ; les gens du monde, les dames s'en occupaient. Buffon fit imprimer les trois volumes de la 'Flore française' à l'imprimerie royale" (loc. cit. p. 11). Lamarck had also qualified as a naturalist by extensive travels in many European countries as a companion to Buffon's son.

from that side which at the time was the least known,
and probably the least promising: he approached it,
as it were, from below. But this had the consequence
of giving to his original mind in two ways a special
direction. First of all, it enabled him to look at natural
objects from a more general point of view, not as a
zoologist or as a botanist, but as a naturalist and a
biologist—*i.e.*, from the more general view of the phenomena of Life.[1] Indeed he himself seems to have been

20.
The term
"Biology."

the first, if not to use, at least to introduce in his
published writings, the term "biology."[2]   And secondly,

[1] 'Philos. Zool.,' Discours pré-
lim., p. 31: "Le vrai moyen de
parvenir à bien connaître un objet,
même dans ses plus petits détails,
c'est de commencer par l'envisager
dans son entier ; par examiner
d'abord, soit sa masse, soit son
étendue, soit l'ensemble des parties
qui le composent ; par rechercher
quelle est sa nature et son origine,
quelles sont ses rapports avec les
autres objets connus ; en un mot,
par le considérer sous tous les
points de vue qui peuvent nous
éclairer sur toutes les généralités
qui le concernent." P. 32 : "La
nécessité reconnue de bien observer
les objets particuliers a fait naître
l'habitude de se borner à la con-
sidération de ces objets et de leurs
plus petits détails, de manière
qu'ils sont devenus, pour la plupart des naturalistes, le sujet principal de l'étude. Ce ne serait
cependant pas une cause réelle de
retard pour les sciences naturelles,
si l'on s'obstinait à ne voir dans les
objets observés que leur forme,
leur dimension, leurs parties ex-
ternes, mêmes les plus petites,
leur couleur, &c., et si ceux qui
se livrent à une pareille étude
dédaignaient de s'élever à des considérations supérieures, comme de

chercher quelle est la nature des
objets dont ils s'occupent quelles
sont les causes des modifications ou
des variations auxquelles ces objets
sont tous assujettis, quels sont les
rapports de ces mêmes objets entre
eux, et avec tous les autres que
l'on connait," &c.

[2] Lamarck in his 'Hydrogéologie,' in an appendix (p. 188)
which seems to be a rehearsal of
his opening lecture of 1801, announces a work, 'Biologie,' as a
sequel, being the third and last
part of the Terrestrial Physics.
This work was not published, but
was probably comprised in his
'Philosophie Zoologique.' See Prof.
A. S. Packard's excellent work on
Lamarck, 'The Founder of Evolution, his Life and Work,' London
and New York, 1901. As Lamarck's writings are very scarce
and his teaching only imperfectly
understood, frequently misrepre-
sented, even by competent authorities, and in popular opinion surrounded by mystery and sometimes
treated with ridicule, the work of
Prof. Packard is most welcome.
It contains copious extracts—unfortunately all translated — from
the earlier biological writings and
lectures, which are otherwise al-

it introduced him to the study of animal life from that side where organisation, the phenomena and the organs of life were the simplest, rudimentary as it were, and unformed.   Here the great differences of form, the morphological differences which the observation of the higher and more developed creatures force upon our attention, disappear; not the marked differences, but the numerous relations, the endless varieties and resemblances, seem to command our consideration.   These seem to be much more likely to " make us understand the beginnings of all organisation as well as the cause of its complexity and of its development." [1]   Now in descending in the scale of the living objects of nature, Lamarck was struck by the fact that many of the phenomena of life which in the higher animals seemed to originate within were in the lower creatures produced

most inaccessible.   According to Huxley (Lecture " On the Study of Biology," 1876, and " Evolution in Biology," 'Ency. Brit.,' 9th ed.), there were simultaneously three independent attempts to treat the phenomena of organic life as a whole and in connection, emanating from Bichat and Lamarck in France, and from G. R. Treviranus in Germany.   The great but unfinished work of the latter, with the title 'Biologie oder Philosophie der lebenden Natur,' was begun in 1796, when the author was only twenty, but the first volume was not published till 1802, one year after Lamarck's 'Hydrogéologie.'   Haeckel in his 'Natürliche Schöpfungs geschichte' gives some account of Treviranus' ideas (Band I. Vorlesung 4). . Although so much has been written about " Biology," the definition of the science is still uncertain.   Prof. Goebel says: " The word Biology is one of those conceptions of modern times which have not yet arrived at a generally accepted limitation.   Some understand by it the whole science of living things, others only the doctrine of the phenomena of life in contrast to the purely descriptive branches."   (' Pflanzenbiologische Schilderungen,' Marburg, 1889, vol. i. p. 1).   With Lamarck biology was only one division of a general science of nature, for he says (' Hydrogéologie,' p. 8): " Toutes ces considérations partagent naturellement la physique terrestre en trois parties essentielles, dont la première doit comprendre la théorie de l'atmosphère, la Météorologie, la seconde celle de la croûte externe du globe, l'Hydrogéologie ; la troisième enfin, celle des corps vivants, la Biologie."

[1] Philos. Zool., vol. i. p. 30.

or excited from outside, and he was thus led to the
conception that nature herself, through the environment,
did a great deal for the lower creatures which in the
gradual development of the higher ones she knew how
to make them do for themselves.[1] In fact, the idea is
worked out in the 'Philosophie Zoologique,' that if we
commence the study of living creatures from below, and
from the side of vegetable life, we are inevitably led
to the conviction that the surrounding conditions and
influences, the environment, are gradually and slowly
modifying the elementary organisms, and through habit
and inheritance[2] developing the higher ones, endowing
them with more specialised organs and more complex
powers and activities.

Lamarck is aware that these ideas sound strange and
novel, and he is quite prepared to admit in the reception
of them by his readers the same inevitable force of habit
which, as it only permits gradual modification of the forms

21.
" Environ-
ment."

---

[1] Philos. Zool., 'Avertissement,'
p. 13 : "Ayant remarqué que les
mouvements des animaux ne sont
jamais communiqués, mais qu'ils
sont toujours excités, je reconnus
que la nature, obligée d'abord d'emprunter des milieux environnants
la puissance excitatrice des mouvements vitaux et des actions des
animaux imparfaits, sut, en com-
posant de plus en plus l'organisation animale, transporter cette
puissance dans l'intérieur même de
ces êtres et qu'à la fin elle parvint
à mettre cette même puissance à la
disposition de l'individu." P. 12 :
"Ayant considéré que sans les
excitations de l'intérieur, la vie
n'existerait point et ne saurait se
maintenir en activité dans les
végétaux, je reconnus bientôt qu'

un grand nombre d'animaux devaient se trouver dans le même
cas ; et comme j'avais eu bien des
occasions de remarquer que, pour
arriver au même but, la nature
variait ses moyens, lorsque cela
était nécessaire, je n'eus plus de
doute à cet égard."

[2] Ibid., p. 13 : "Je pus saisir le
fil qui lie entre elles les causes
nombreuses des phénomènes que
nous offre l'organisation animale
dans ses développements et sa
diversité, et bientôt j'aperçus l'importance de ce moyen de la nature,
qui consiste à conserver dans les
nouveaux individus reproduits tout
ce que les suites de la vie et des
circonstances influentes avait fait
acquérir dans l'organisation de ceux
qui leur ont transmis l'existence."

of nature, so also opposes a great resistance to any sudden change of opinion. " But it is better," he says, " that a truth once perceived should struggle a long time to obtain merited attention than that everything that the ardent imagination of man produces should be easily accepted." [1] Whereby it may appear to us worthy of note that Lamarck did not stop to reflect on the existence of those sudden changes by which such powers as the " ardent imagination of man " are continually breaking through the slow action of habit. The doctrine of the mutability and variability of species, of the influence of the environ-ment on the habits, and through them and inheritance on the forms of living creatures, was thus opposed to the prevalent doctrine of the fixity of species and the permanence and recurrence of types. Through these generalisations, and through the larger view which Lamarck took of the phenomena of nature and of life, he stepped outside of that school of natural studies which was then dominant in his country, and approached the teachings of the German philosophers of nature, such as Schelling, Oken, and Steffens, with whom Goethe is frequently associated, who, rather than limit themselves to the patient study of detail, indulged in fanciful theories on the origin of life, the genesis and metamor-phosis of forms, and the ideal significance of natural phenomena and processes. A wide gap separated the speculations of the author of the ' Flore française,' the ' Histoire des Animaux sans Vertèbres,' and the ' Mémoires sur les Coquilles fossiles des environs de Paris ' from those of the German school, yet it cannot be denied that in

22.
The "Natur-philoso-phie."

---

[1] Philos. Zool., p. 15.

many passages of the 'Hydrogéologie,' where he speculated on matters of chemistry, geology, and meteorology without the necessary foundation of facts, such as he possessed in botany and zoology, he laid himself open to the criticism and ridicule [1] of his more cautious opponents. Thus it happened that the most original contributions to science were forgotten or disregarded for more than half a century, after which time Lamarckism became a familiar term in speculative science, denoting one of the great ideas with which the genetic view of nature operates — viz., the influence of environment, adaptation, acquired habits, in the development of living organisms.

23.
Lamarck
and von
Baer.

In the history of the genetic view of nature, the position of Lamarck may be regarded as, in a certain sense, complementary to that of von Baer. Both brought the study of living forms back to that of their origins —Lamarck to the study of the lowest forms of animal creation, the great variety and abundance of which he was the first to attempt to put into some order; von Baer to the study of the embryonic beginnings of the higher organisms, on which important subject he was one of the first to throw some light. Though widely

[1] See, *inter alia*, what Cuvier wrote in his 'Eloge de Lamarck,' which was read posthumously in the Academy by Silvestre, 26th November 1832 ('Mem. de l'Acad. des Sciences,' vol. xiii. p. xx), with omissions to tone down its severity : "Quelque intérêt que ces ouvrages excitassent par leurs parties positives, personne ne crut leur partie systématique assez dangereuse pour mériter d'être attaquée ; on la laissa dans la même paix que la théorie chimique"; and further on he touches on one of the weakest points of all genetic speculations (p. xxii) : "Le temps sans borne qui joue un si grand rôle dans la religion des mages, n'en joue pas un moins grand dans toute cette physique de M. de Lamarck, et c'était sur lui qu'il se reposait pour calmer ses propres doutes et pour répondre à toutes les objections de ses lecteurs."

different in their mental attitude, the two men agreed in looking for the advancement of natural science in an understanding of the simpler, unspecified, and undifferentiated forms or stages of existence out of which they conceived the more complex to have grown or developed by a process of specialisation or differentiation. Many other naturalists and philosophers contributed, partly independently, partly through the influence of Lamarck's systematic and von Baer's embryological labours, to elaborate the same view and strengthen the same tendency of thought and research. Nor were there wanting suggestions as to the ultimate philosophical drift of the line of reasoning. It is doubtful whether these speculations, like those of Oken in his ' Physio-philosophy,' did not retard rather than promote the acceptance of the genetic view by scientific thinkers: [1]

[1] On the position of Goethe and Oken in the history of the genetic view, see Carus, ' Geschichte der Zoologie,' p. 723 ; von Baer, ' Reden und wissenschaftliche Abhandlungen,' Bd. II. p. 258, &c. Both consider Lamarck as the real originator of a scientific theory of Descent. Von Baer gives an amusing account of the extent to which, as early as 1829, actual genealogical trees were given in Jacob Kaup's ' Skizzirte Entwickelungsgeschichte und natürliches System der Europaeischen Thierwelt.' Von Baer sums up his historical account in the following words (p. 264) : " In general I believe that at that time, when the succession of different animals and plants in the history of the earth—and generally from imperfect to more perfect organisms —occupied the thoughts of naturalists, and when, at the same time, the study of development of single organisms had taken a new start, the notion of their Transformation was pretty generally accepted." The view expressed here by von Baer would probably have to be limited to German naturalists at that date. It must, however, be admitted that the fairest exposition and criticism of the arguments of Lamarck at that early date is probably to be found in Lyell's ' Principles of Geology ' (vol. ii. Bk. III. chap. i. to iv.) He there also considers the arguments derived from embryology as contained in the researches of Thiedemann, confirmed by Serres (' Anatomie Comparée du Cerveau,' 1824), and comes finally to the result that—1. " There is a capacity in all species to accommodate themselves." 2. " That the mutations thus superinduced are governed by constant laws." 3. That "some acquired peculiarities of form, structure, and instinct are

they belong, therefore, more to the history of philosophical than to that of scientific thought.   There is,
however, one instance of which it is necessary to take
a passing notice.

In the year 1844 a book appeared which in nine
years, up to 1853, ran through nine large editions.   It
was anonymous,[1] and bore the title 'Vestiges of the

24.
The
'Vestiges.'

transmissible to the offspring."   4.
That "indefinite divergence" from
the original type is "prevented."
5. That "the intermixture of distinct species is guarded against by
the aversion of the individuals composing them to sexual union."   6.
That "it appears that species have
a real existence in nature, and that
each was endowed, at the time of
its creation, with the attributes
and organisation by which it is
now distinguished."   The reviewers
of Lyell's work—such as Whewell
('Quarterly,' vol. xlvii. p. 113)—
treat Lamarck with much less
gravity than Lyell himself, who
evidently had studied the 'Philosophie Zoologique' carefully and with
much interest ; which, I am afraid,
was not the case with many others
who then and long after only quoted
certain extreme passages and examples which had been spread in
general literature in a garbled
fashion.   Contrast in this respect
what Lyell wrote to G. Mantell in
1827 ('Life of Lyell,' vol. i. p. 168),
where he admits having "devoured
Lamarck with pleasure,"and though
disagreeing with him, admits that
it is impossible to say "what
changes species may really undergo," with the remarks of Charles
Darwin—otherwise so careful and
moderate—when he talks of "Lamarck nonsense" ('Darwin's Life
and Letters,' p. 23) and his "veritable rubbish" (p. 29), and attributes to him statements which such
a careful student of his writings as

Prof. Packard had been unable to
trace (see his work on 'Lamarck,'
1901, p. 74).   One would be inclined to agree with Darwin that
such absurdities have done the subject more harm than good, but to
attribute them rather to garbled
paraphrases and quotations by Lamarck's critics(see Darwin to Hooker,
1853, 'Life,' vol. ii. p. 39) than to
Lamarck himself.   More than thirty
years after the publication of the
'Principles,' when, in consequence
of the appearance of the 'Origin of
Species,' the subject of Transmutation was much discussed, Lyell
wrote to Darwin that he had re-
read Lamarck, and admitted that,
"remembering when his book was
written, he felt he had done him
[Lamarck] injustice" ('Life, &c.,
of Sir Charles Lyell,' 1881, vol. ii.
p. 365).   In the same letter Lyell
states that forty years ago (1823)
Prévost, a pupil of Cuvier's, told
him his conviction "that Cuvier
thought species not real, but that
science could not advance without
assuming that they were so."

[1] The anonymity of the work was
long maintained, and though, after
various guesses as to the authorship—attributing it, e.g., to Lyell or
Darwin—had been made, it was generally believed that Robert Chambers (1802-1871) was the author,
this was not publicly admitted till
Alex. Ireland—the last survivor of
the few friends to whom the secret
was committed — published (1884)
the twelfth edition of the book,

Natural History of Creation.' This book contained a very clear and popularly intelligible statement of the genetic or development hypothesis as applied to cosmic, geological, and organic phenomena. The importance of the book did not lie in its own original contributions, but in the great controversy which it occasioned. In this controversy most of the arguments for and against the

with an introduction, in which he "told for the first time" the "story of the authorship." It is of interest, after the lapse of half a century, to read the various—mostly hostile—criticisms of the book in the reviews and magazines of the day. The attacks came from two distinct sides : from scientific authorities, who — each in his own specific branch—challenged the correctness of single facts, mostly without inquiring whether, in spite of many misstatements, sufficient evidence was not after all adduced to prove the main thesis ; and, secondly, from both scientific and popular writers, who used the well-known arguments, that the teaching of the book was unorthodox, both in a religious and scientific sense. In fact, they displayed in a great degree scientific and religious dogmatism and intolerance, and in some cases considerable temper. To this larger section of the critical attacks belonged the reviews in all the leading periodicals of the day, headed by the 'Edinburgh Review' (Adam Sedgwick), the 'North British' (Sir David Brewster), the 'Eclectic,' the 'North American' (Bowen and Asa Gray), the 'British Quarterly.' Tolerance and appreciation were, however, shown by some of those more recent reviews which were professedly the organs of freedom, enlightenment, and progress, notably the 'Prospective' (F. W. Newman) and the 'Westminster' in two articles, in

the first of which the genetic view of the 'Vestiges' is suggestively contrasted with the purely descriptive of the 'Kosmos.' Looking at the whole controversy, the 'Westminster Review' (xliii. 130) seems, in the light of history, justified in maintaining that, after "having attentively considered the objections which have been urged in numerous able criticisms to the theory and the arguments of the author," after noting that "learned men have discovered that he is less familiar than they with the pedantry of science," that "they have triumphed in the detection of slips of the pen, mistakes in technicalities, and some inaccuracies of fact," the conclusion is nevertheless justified that "these detract but little from the merit of a work which may be fairly characterised as the most skilful generalisation that has yet (1848) appeared of the results of geological, astronomical, and physiological researches made to bear upon the history of the first and most momentous of all problems—the order and plan of creation." It is known that some scientific men of first rank, such as Baden Powell of Oxford, and the physiologist W. B. Carpenter (who, according to Huxley, was the only authority in this country acquainted with the 'Entwickelungsgeschichte' of von Baer), distinctly supported the doctrine of the 'Vestiges' ; and Darwin himself, who had studied the 'Vestiges' with evident care

genetic aspect, which have since become familiar, were very ably stated by scientific as well as by popular writers. Earlier anticipations of the genetic view were recalled, the historical sketch given in Lyell's 'Principles' was supplemented by reference to many great and many forgotten authorities, who in more or less distinct terms had given expression to their belief in a gradual development of the existing forms and phenomena of nature out of simpler beginnings, which they described with more or less precision. It cannot be denied that the enormous literature which accumulated during the ten years following the publication of this book unsettled

25.
Popular
influence.

the popular mind in this country, and prepared it for a really able, dispassionate, and exhaustive exposition of the whole subject, and especially of the crucial problem to which it was narrowed down, the question regarding the fixity or variability, the historical origin and development or the sudden creation and persistence, of animal and vegetable species. The genesis of the cosmos as suggested by Laplace, the geological history of our earth as worked out by Lyell, the fact of organic growth and development as given by embryology, seemed clear

(see 'Life of Darwin,' vol. i. p. 333), gave probably the fairest verdict on the book in the historical preface to the later editions of his own great work, where he says : "The work, from its powerful and brilliant style, though displaying in the earlier editions little accurate knowledge and a great want of scientific caution, immediately had a very wide circulation. In my opinion, it has done excellent service in this country in calling attention to the subject, in removing prejudice, and in thus preparing the ground for the reception of analogous views" ('Origin of Species,' 6th ed., 1872, p. xvii). In a history of European thought it is well to mention that the 'Vestiges' had no influence on the Continent, for reasons partially stated in the text. A little later, however, a similar "scandale" (as the 'Grande Encyclopédie' has it— art. "R. Chambers and L. Büchner") arose in Germany on the publication of 'Kraft und Stoff.'

and plausible enough, but there remained the last strong-hold of the older view, the existence of definite forms of animal and vegetable life. Were these to be merely classi-fied and reduced to separate types, as the morphological view was contented to reduce them, or was the growing evidence of variability to be interpreted in favour of a gradual development of the higher out of the lower and simpler forms of life? Above all, how was the highest type of all, man himself, to be regarded in such a com-prehensive scheme of development? In Germany many great naturalists[1] were quite prepared for a consistent genetic or developmental view of nature; in France at that time the question was not agitated at all, the sug-gestive writings of Lamarck and St Hilaire having been

26.
Genetic view in Germany and France.

[1] This does not refer to the earlier writings of Goethe, Oken, Treviranus, and others, whose merits, since the appearance of the 'Origin of Species,' have been variously estimated by Huxley in England and by Haeckel in Ger-many : their speculations had, with the generalisations of the 'Natur-philosophie,' been swept away by the inductive school represented in botany at that time by von Mohl, Nägeli, and Hofmeister ; in zoology by the embryological school with von Baer at its head. Of W. Hof-meister (1824-1877), whose labours begin about ten years before the appearance of Darwin's great work, Julius Sachs says : "The results of his 'Comparative Researches' (1849 and 1851) were magnificent beyond all that has been achieved before or since in the domain of descriptive botany, . . . the conception of what was meant by the development of a plant was completely changed, . . . the reader was presented with a picture of the genetic connection between cryptogams and phanero-gams which could not be reconciled with the then reigning belief in the constancy of species. . . . When, eight years after Hofmeister's 'Comparative Researches,' Dar-win's theory of descent appeared, the affinities of the large divisions of the plant-world lay so openly, so deeply founded, and so clearly be-fore the eyes of students of nature, that that theory had only to recog-nise what had been made evident in this line by genetic morph-ology" ('Gesch. d. Botanik,' p. 215, &c.) In another direction Nägeli, by his mechanical theory of "the growth and internal structure of organisms," which he reduces to "physical, chemical, and mechanical processes" (1860), fell in with Dar-win's attempt to "reduce the earlier purely formal consideration of or-ganic structures to a causal (genetic) view" (ibid., p. 373).

entirely overruled by the authority of Cuvier.[1] In England, where geology and natural history were always popular pursuits, the question was one of more than scientific interest: it was one which had been appropriated by general literature,[2] and the larger bearings of

[1] Huxley describes the position of France and Germany to the doctrine of descent as follows: "In France the influence of Elie de Beaumont and of Flourens, to say nothing of the ill-will of other powerful members of the Institute, produced for a long time the effect of a conspiracy of silence. . . . Germany took time to consider; Bronn produced a . . . translation of the 'Origin' . . .; but I do not call to mind that any scientific notability declared himself publicly in 1860. None of us dreamed that in the course of a few years the strength (and perhaps, I may add, the weakness) of 'Darwinismus' would have its most extensive and most brilliant illustrations in the land of learning. If a foreigner may presume to speculate on the cause of this curious interval of silence, I fancy it was that one moiety of the German biologists were orthodox at any price and the other moiety as distinctly heterodox. The latter were evolutionists à priori already," &c. ('Life of Darwin,' vol. ii. p. 186). The two men abroad to whose opinion English biologists of that day would probably attach the greatest value were Karl Ernst von Baer and Milne-Edwards. The former "wrote to Huxley in August 1860, expressing his general assent to evolutionist views" (loc. cit., p. 186, note). It was von Baer from whom Huxley admits to Leuckart that he learnt the "value of development as the criterion of morphological views" ('Life of Huxley,' vol. i. p. 163). Von Baer later on qualified his adher-

ence, admitting development only within the regions of the different types which he had established (see the second volume of his collected papers). The opinions of the great contemporary French zoologist, Henri Milne-Edwards (1800-1885), are fully given in the last chapter of his very interesting 'Rapport sur les progrès récents des Sciences zoologiques en France' (1867), where he also refers to the writings of Isidore Geoffroy Saint-Hilaire, who in France continued to some extent the line of research and reasoning which, through his father, Etienne Geoffroy, and Lamarck, dates back to Buffon, Bonnet, and other philosophical naturalists, of whom, under the name of "Transformistes," M. Edmond Périer has given a connected account in his very valuable historical work, 'La Philosophie zoologique avant Darwin' (1884). Milne-Edwards remained to the end unconvinced by the arguments of Darwin. He had already in 1853 set forth his ideas referring to the general problems of zoology, and he repeated them in 1867 (loc. cit., p. 432 sqq.) It is, however, well to note that ever since 1827 (loc. cit., p. 453, note) he had contributed largely to the furtherance of the genetic view by his principle that progress in nature depends on division of labour. In his subsequent writings he dwells with much success on this principle of the "division of physiological labour." (See Spencer, 'Biology,' vol. i. p. 160.)

[2] About ten years after the controversy about the 'Vestiges' had

which had been fully demonstrated to the educated and reading public. There has always existed in this country a class of literature which is almost entirely wanting, or has died out, on the Continent. The value of this class of literature has been differently gauged, but it never-

filled the columns of the foremost British periodicals, we find in Germany a similar agitation originating through the publication of several works which have since been generally considered as the purest expression of Materialism. The controversy begins in 1852 with the publication of Rudolf Wagner's 'Physiological Letters,' Moleschott's 'Kreislauf des Lebens,' and Carl Vogt's 'Bilder aus dem Thierleben'; it came to its height after the appearance (in 1855) of L. Büchner's 'Kraft und Stoff,' and occupied the meeting of scientific and medical men which was held in Göttingen in 1854. The subject belongs essentially to the history of philosophical thought, and can be studied in the very fair and exhaustive 'History of Materialism' written by F. A. Lange, with a distinctly idealistic tendency (English translation, three vols., by Thomas, 1880). I mention the subject in this connection, because in Germany and England attempts were made about the same time to found a general philosophy of life upon the teachings of science. This had been done about two generations earlier in France by the "Sensualistes" and the "Idéologues." For a French public neither the English nor the German controversy presented any essentially new feature, or disclosed any novel argument. The older orthodox conceptions had been abandoned very largely in France in the eighteenth century, and at once replaced by conceptions derived from science. In Germany a similar movement took place, likewise during the eighteenth century; but, instead of exact science, it was the prevailing idealistic philosophy which was appealed to for the purpose of gaining new foundations, and science only came in when the speculative restoration was generally considered to have failed. In England, which had really supplied the beginnings both for the French sensualistic philosophy through Locke, and for German criticism through Locke and Hume, the older orthodox foundations were not materially shaken before the middle of the nineteenth century. The author of the 'Vestiges' distinctly appeals to science, though in a religious spirit, desiring to make it helpful for a general philosophical, and not merely an industrial, purpose. Again, the English movement, which really culminated in Herbert Spencer, differs from the German, being more influenced by biological conceptions, whereas in Germany the extreme system of Büchner took purely mechanical, though ill-defined, ideas—force and matter —as the shibboleth. It is significant, as showing the great general importance of Darwinism, that through it both the controversy over the 'Vestiges' in England and that over 'Materialismus' in Germany were soon cast into oblivion, though they had both to some extent prepared the way (see Lange, 'Gesch. des Mat.,' p. 570, Ausg. 1867; and Haeckel, 'Schöpfungsgeschichte,' vol. i. p. 98, 9 Aufl.)

theless forms an important feature in the development of English thought, if not also of English science. It is the apologetic literature, those works which deal with what have been termed the "Evidences." In the absence of any scientific theology based upon accurate historical research and philosophical criticism, such as has existed with many good and some evil results since the end of the eighteenth century in Germany, the need was felt for defending or interpreting those answers to the great problems of Nature, Man, and Life, which seemed bound up with the Christian belief, or suggested by the sacred writings. The teaching of science had not become, as in France, a purely secular occupation; instruction was not separated from education; apologetics had not become doubtful through the bad faith and duplicities of cynics like Voltaire, nor ridiculous through the puerilities of shallow writers such as Campe in Germany. Many serious minds were occupied with the growing discrepancies between scientific and popular religious teaching, and believing they could discern the drift of the former, they made various more or less successful attempts to effect a reconciliation between the moving and developing conceptions of scientific thought and the fixed and unalterable ideals of religious belief. Such attempts must be doomed to failure, or at best they offer an individual solution, interesting only if it happens to be the inspiration of a poet or if it represents the creed of one of the few great and soaring intellects which appear once or twice in a century. The conviction is gradually gaining ground that scientific and religious thought emanate from two separate centres, that although they inevitably come into frequent contact, the study of their independent origin and history and their different psychological method is more valuable than a temporary and merely ephemeral compromise of their respective doctrines. Happily this country has produced many great and a few thinkers of the first order, in whom the greatest that scientific thought has achieved was in harmony with a truly religious spirit. In contemplating these illustrious examples, and bowing before their greatness, the popular mind will probably find its conviction of the possibility of an ultimate reconciliation of both aspects more strengthened than by leaning on the doubtful support of a voluminous apologetic literature, which proposes to give general proofs where only individual faith can decide.

I deemed it appropriate to offer these few remarks on the whole of the voluminous literature[1] from Butler

[1] The largest and best known type of publication in this class of literature, which is practically unknown on the Continent, but which belongs to our period, is found in the Bridgewater Treatises "On the Power, Wisdom, and Goodness of God, as manifested in the Creation." The circumstances under which this series was published are set forth in the preliminary notice to the first treatise. The Earl of Bridgewater, heir to the title and fortune of Francis Egerton, third Earl of Bridgewater, who constructed from the plans of James Brindley, and in accordance with the idea of his father, Lord Chancellor Egerton, the first of the large canals in England, from his coal mines at Worsley to Manchester and Liverpool, left in his will to the Royal Society the sum of £8000, which, with its accruing interest, was to be paid to the person or persons selected by the President and appointed to write and publish one thousand copies of a work with the above title, — "illustrating such work by all reasonable arguments, as, for instance, the variety and formation of God's creatures in the animal, vegetable, and mineral kingdoms; the effect of digestion, and thereby of conversion; the construction of the hand of man, and an infinite variety of other arguments; as also by discoveries, ancient and modern, in arts, sciences, and the whole extent of literature." The series contained works by such foremost men of science as Sir Charles Bell, William Whewell, William Prout, and William Buckland.

to Drummond whilst I was dealing with the 'Vestiges,' because the latter is probably the last example of that class of books in which purely scientific thinkers took any great interest. Similar publications which have since appeared have made no impression on the course of scientific thought, though they may have won a place in the popular literature of their day. To bring about that complete separation and independence of the scientific and the religious arguments in this country which has been recognised during the whole of the nineteenth century on the Continent, two books have probably contributed more than any others : Dean Mansel's Lectures,[1] 'On the Limits of Religious Thought,' through its unanswerable logic ; and Darwin's 'Origin of Species,' through treating fearlessly a scientific argument which was based upon observation and expanded by legitimate inference without any reference to the ulterior consequences which might be drawn from it. It required some courage to attack a problem beset with such difficulties and which had become hackneyed

28.
Mansel and
Darwin.

[1] It is a remarkable coincidence, showing the general tendencies of English thought about the middle of the century, that Dean Mansel's "Bampton Lectures" appeared just a year before the 'Origin of Species.' The argument of the Lectures "On the Limits of Religious Thought" was that which was elaborated by Sir William Hamilton on the lines of Kant's 'Critique of Pure Reason' in his celebrated article in the 'Edinburgh Review' on the "Philosophy of the Unconditioned." A further appreciation of this line of reasoning, which had its beginning in Hume's sceptical writings a hundred years previously, belong to a different section of this 'History.' We shall there see that in the negative portion of this analysis lie also the germs of the ideas put forward by Herbert Spencer and Huxley under the well-known terms of the "Unknowable" and "Agnosticism," and there is no doubt that both Hamilton and Mansel had a considerable influence in forming Huxley's attitude in this respect. He says, in 1863 ('Life,' vol. i. p. 242): "I believe in Hamilton, Mansel, and Herbert Spencer so long as they are destructive, and I laugh at their beards as soon as they try to spin their own cobwebs."

through periodical and popular literature. Others who, before Darwin, treated similar controversial subjects, such as Whewell, Babbage, Herschel, Lyell, Baden Powell, and the author of the 'Vestiges,' had always taken into account the possible inferences which might be drawn from their scientific statements, and had oftentimes toned them down so as not to offend existing opinions.[1] Darwin thought it more modest and more becoming for an independent scientific thinker to state his side of the question completely and simply, without presuming to attack or to support a view of things which lay outside of the dominion and the powers of science. And this is not the least of the many reasons why his work has created an era, especially in this

[1] The position adopted by several of the eminent forerunners of Darwin is interestingly analysed by Huxley in the chapter on the " Reception of the ' Origin of Species '" contributed to the second volume of the ' Life and Letters of Charles Darwin.' Of Lyell, who had come nearest to the doctrine of unbroken descent of species, Huxley says (vol. ii. p. 193) : " I see no reason to doubt that if Sir Charles Lyell could have avoided the inevitable corollary of the pithecoid origin of man—for which to the end of his life he entertained a profound antipathy — he would have advocated the efficiency of causes now in operation to bring about the condition of the organic world, as stoutly as he championed that doctrine in reference to inorganic nature." And Lyell himself wrote to Darwin in 1863 (' Life of Lyell,' vol. ii. p. 365) : " I remember that it was the conclusion he [Lamarck] came to about man that fortified me thirty years ago against the great impression which his argu- ments at first made on my mind." Treviranus, the author of the ' Biologie,' the contemporary of Lamarck, was quite consistent in his views of descent and mutability, for he declares against catastrophism, believes in the evolution of higher species from the zoophytes, and even in that of a higher species than man (see ' Biologie,' vol. ii. p. 225, &c.) Neither in Germany nor in France, at the beginning of the century, did those prejudices exist which in 1859 prevented even Darwin from developing to the full the consequences of his main thesis. This was done in his later works. See his letter to A. R. Wallace, 22nd Dec. 1857 (' Life,' vol. ii. p. 109) : " You ask whether I shall discuss ' man.' I think I shall avoid the whole subject, as so surrounded with prejudices ; though I fully admit that it is the highest and most interesting problem for the naturalist. My work, on which I have now been at work more or less for twenty years, will not fix or settle anything."

country, not only in the region of scientific, but quite as much in that of philosophical, thought.

29.
Triumph of
the genetic
view.
So far as the purely scientific aspect is concerned, the 'Origin of Species' firmly established the genetic or developmental in the place of the morphological view, or the earlier purely systematic and classificatory treatment of the objects and processes of nature ; and it is interesting to note how the period from the publication of the 'Vestiges' to that of the 'Origin of Species,' the fifteen years from 1844 to 1859, was also the period during which Humboldt published his '.Kosmos'—the *résumé* of the labours of a lifetime. This was the consummation of that aspect of nature which I have termed the purely morphological one, and which in his mind was expanded to the panoramic view : the attempt to unroll before his readers a picture or panorama of the whole world as the scientific mind was then able to see it. Nature appeared mapped out in bold and characteristic lines and colours, without allowing the questions of past history or future development,— the origin, life, and fate of the cosmos,—to present itself at all. The fact that this latter question was professedly excluded as foreign, or premature, is probably the reason why the book attracted so little attention in this country, where a new manner of treating all the problems of natural science was being inaugurated ; but it is interesting to learn from Darwin that his whole life was influenced[1]

[1] See 'Life and Letters of Charles Darwin,' vol. i. p. 25 : "During my last year at Cambridge I read with care and profound interest Humboldt's 'Personal Narrative.' This work, and Sir J. Herschel's 'Intro- duction to the Study of Natural Philosophy,' stirred up in me a burning zeal to add even the most humble contribution to the noble structure of natural science. No one or a dozen other books influ-

and his studies directed by reading and re-reading Humboldt's 'Personal Narrative.' The 'Kosmos' of Humboldt closed the older, the 'Origin of Species' of Darwin opened the new, epoch of natural science: the former was retrospective, the latter prospective. Both works owe their origin to a visit to the same portion of the globe, to a study of the subtropical scenery and life of South America — Humboldt having visited the inland, Darwin specially the maritime and island scenery.[1] It is further of interest to note how the

30.
Humboldt's
'Kosmos'
and the
'Origin of
Species.'

enced me nearly so much as these two. I copied out from Humboldt long passages about Teneriffe," &c. Also vol. i. p. 337 : "I never forget that my whole course of life is due to having read and re-read as a youth Humboldt's 'Personal Narrative.'"

[1] Besides Darwin and Lyell, to whom, of British naturalists as representing the genetic view in the middle of the century, I have so far confined my remarks, there were at that time two other eminent men working in the same direction. The views of these two were likewise much influenced by travel and by the study of plant and animal life in distant countries. I refer to Sir J. D. Hooker and Mr A. Russel Wallace. The important part which these men played in the gradual conception and birth of the ideas which were for the first time comprehensively set forth in the 'Origin of Species' is lucidly and impartially told by Huxley in the well-known chapter which he contributed to the second volume of the 'Life and Letters of Charles Darwin,' edited by his son, Professor Francis Darwin, in 1887. Few episodes in the history of thought have been treated with greater mastery. Few botanists have

possessed a greater personal knowledge of different and greatly varying floras than Sir J. D. Hooker, who succeeded to the position and labours of his father, Sir W. J. Hooker, at Kew. After having accompanied Captain Ross on his Antarctic expedition for the discovery of the South magnetic pole, he became best known by his 'Himalayan Journal' (1854). It was in constant correspondence and intercourse with Hooker that Darwin, from 1844 to 1859, wrote his first great work. The important original contributions of Mr Wallace are well known, and the story how his paper, "On the Tendency of Varieties to depart indefinitely from the Original Type," reached Darwin when he had got half through the larger work which he was then writing, how this coincidence hastened the publication of the two papers by Wallace and Darwin, which "contained exactly the same theory," in the 'Journal of the Linnæan Society' (Zoology, vol. iii. p. 45), has been told by Lyell and Hooker (ibid., letter to the secretary), and by Darwin himself (Autobiography, in 'Life,' &c., vol. i. p. 84). No mystery lies upon the history of the first enunciation of the doctrine of natural

same year which witnessed the appearance of the work
of Darwin was also that of the invention of Spectrum
Analysis, that great instrument by which astronomy,
doomed by the purely mathematical treatment to become simply " une question d'analyse," was once more
enrolled among the natural sciences; the means being
supplied for that natural history of the heavens which is
now one of the most progressive and fascinating branches
of science. The reader who has realised from the foregoing exposition how the genetic view of nature was
anticipated by earlier writers on cosmology, such as
Leibniz and Laplace, how it obtained in geology through
Hutton and Lyell, how it became dominant in embryology through von Baer, and how the morphological
treatment broke down through the recognition of the
variability of species and the impossibility of defining
clearly the landmarks of zoological and botanical classification, will readily understand the importance and
timeliness [1] of Darwin's work, which proposed to deal

selection, no national or personal
jealousies obscure the issues which
were then at stake ; neither of the
two great naturalists has ever put
forward any complaint that the
other has not fairly and generously
dealt with his own merit. Since
the death of Darwin Mr Wallace
has written the well-known book
which, under the title of ' Darwinism ' (London, 1889), gave to many
readers the first comprehensive
account of the celebrated theory
which is generously identified with
the sole name of only one of its
original propounders.

[1] Both propounders of the theory
of natural selection have in their
subsequent writings referred to
those who prepared the way be-

fore them, and Mr Wallace has
taken special pains to explain why
a doctrine which was so well prepared, and even anticipated, had
not been more distinctly accepted
before the appearance of the ' Origin
of Species' ("Darwinism," chap. i.) :
" Notwithstanding the vast knowledge and ingenious reasoning of
Lamarck, and the more general
exposition of the subject by the
author of the ' Vestiges of Creation,'
the first step had not been taken
towards a satisfactory explanation
of the derivation of any one species
from any other. Such eminent
naturalists as Geoffroy St Hilaire,
Dean Herbert, Professor Grant,
von Buch, and some others, had
expressed their belief that species

specially with the actual fact and the function of variation in the domain of living beings. He pushed the
problem of variation and variability into the foreground,
and discussed one of its main features—viz., its possible
effect and results. Since his time the eye of every
botanist, every zoologist, and every embryologist has
been directed towards the variability, transition, and
genesis of forms, to their history rather than to their
portraiture, whereas before him it was mostly attracted
by their seeming fixity and recurrence. Variations have
been studied on the large and on the minute scale in
geological strata at home and abroad, and the vexed
question has been raised as to their causes and laws,—
Darwin having been mainly occupied with their existence
and operation, the results which they brought about, the
gradual alterations of the forms of living things. On
this side he tells us that he found an important clue
through reading a book which had appeared at the very
end of the eighteenth century, Malthus's ' Essay on the
Principle of Population.'[1]

arose as simple varieties, and that
the species of each genus were all
descended from a common ancestor ;
but none of them gave a clue as to
the law or the method by which
the change had been effected. This
was still ' the great mystery ' " (p.
6). " Darwin, by his discovery of
the law of natural selection and his
demonstration of the great principle
of the preservation of useful variations in the struggle for life, has
not only thrown a flood of light on
the process of development of the
whole organic world, but also established a firm foundation for all
future study of nature " (p. 9).

[1] This essay appeared first in

1798, and in the enlarged and much
improved form in which it is now
known in 1803. Darwin seems to
have come upon it accidentally. In
his Autobiography (' Life,' vol. i.
p. 83) he writes : " In October 1838
—that is, fifteen months after I had
begun my systematic inquiry—I
happened to read for amusement
' Malthus on Population,' and being
well prepared to appreciate the
struggle for existence which everywhere goes on, from long-continued
observation of the habits of animals
and plants, it at once struck me
that under these circumstances
favourable variations would tend
to be preserved, and unfavourable

32.
Malthus.
The ideas and reflections contained in this celebrated
essay, which has played a prominent part in the philosophical literature of economics, could not have occurred
to any one who had studied human society or nature
merely in individual specimens or isolated cases; for
they referred not so much to the natural history of a
single being, as to the peculiar relations and complications which arise in a community or society of beings,
some of these being applicable quite as much to animal
and plant life as to the life of men. In fact, it was a
chapter in the science of bionomics. Malthus, Darwin,
and Wallace were not " laboratory naturalists, to whom
the peculiarities and distinction of species, as such, their
distribution and their affinities, have little interest as
compared with the problems of histology and embryology, of physiology and morphology." [1] The problem of
population, whether it refers to man or other living
creatures, is one that will force itself upon those who
study nature and mankind on the large, on the outdoor,
scale, not as does the collector or dissector of specimens.
How has the face of the earth been peopled by plants,
animals, and human beings ? What are the forces which

ones to be destroyed. The result
of this would be the formation of
new species. Here, then, I had
at last got a theory by which to
work," &c. Prof. Haeckel, in his
'History of Creation,' has dwelt
exhaustively on this connection of
Darwin with Malthus, quoting a
letter of Darwin's to him, dated 8th
October 1864, in which he says that
for years he could not comprehend
how any form should be so eminently adapted to its special conditions of life, but that when
through good fortune Malthus's
book on Population came into his
hands, the idea of natural selection
came into his mind ('Schöpfungs-
gesch.,' chap. vi.) In the first
paper which Darwin published in
the 'Journal of the Linnæan
Society' ("Letter to Asa Gray,"
vol. iii. p. 51), he uses the term
"Natural Selection," and refers in
the abstract which he there gives
to Malthus ; whereas Wallace (ibid.,
p. 56)introduces the term "Struggle
for Existence."

[1] Quoted from Wallace, 'Darwinism,' preface, p. vi.

ensure the multiplication, what are those which check
the increase, of population ?   As all living things are
dependent on each other, forming the great household or
economy of nature or the smaller one of human society,
a certain adjustment must exist by which a definite place
and part are allotted to every individual and to every
class of individuals.   Malthus had studied the problem
from a political point of view.   Here it was felt to be
of human and social importance, but his principle was
applicable to all living creatures.   For everywhere, even
in the remotest and only recently discovered countries,
we see at work the luxuriant and productive powers of
nature on the one side, on the other side the many
difficulties and obstacles by which they are forcibly and
automatically kept in check, resulting in the ever-recurring spectacle of a " struggle for existence."   The more
we penetrate into the hidden and remoter provinces of
nature, into the luxuriant " fauna and flora " of tropical
regions, or realise the enormous population among the
lower forms of life, the more the conviction forces itself
upon us that the apparent equilibrium is only maintained
by the phenomenon of " crowding out " on a scale compared with which the spectacle unfolded by Malthus in
his special application to human societies is quite a miniature display.   This process of " crowding out " must have
been at work during the untold ages which modern
geology has made known to us, and the effects of it
must indeed have been extraordinary, and well worthy
of study.   That living beings, if left to their natural
instincts, multiply at an enormous rate, and would,
except for certain automatic checks, in a very short time

33.
" Struggle
for exist-
ence."

people the whole habitable portion of the globe, is a
fact which has only been realised since Malthus, and,
on a much larger and more general scale, Darwin and
Wallace have drawn attention to it.[1] This being
generally admitted, the questions arise : What are these
automatic checks, and what results do they produce ?
It is evidently quite a new line of reasoning, unknown
to former naturalists, or only sporadically and fragmentarily pursued by them; but it introduces us at once
into nature itself, away from the class-room and the
museum, where we hear of the forces and laws of nature
in their abstract mathematical development, or where we
behold specimens arranged peacefully and lifelessly side by
side.   We are face to face with the fierce and continuous
conflict which is unceasingly going on around us, and
realise the endless changes which it must be producing.

34.
Outdoor
studies.

Among the many influences which the Darwinian
view has had in opposite directions on the thought of
our age, none is greater or more fundamental than
this, that whereas before Darwin naturalists stepped

---

[1] On the publication of the
'Origin of Species,' Darwin received many letters pointing out
earlier anticipations of his views.
The more important of these—bearing upon descent and change—have
been referred to in the present
chapter. The special principle of
natural selection seems to have
been already foreseen by Dr Wells
in 1813, and published in his
famous 'Two Essays upon Dew and
Single Vision' in 1818. "In this
paper he distinctly recognises the
principle of natural selection, and
this is the first recognition which
has been indicated" ('Origin of
Species,' historical sketch to later
editions). Another anticipation was
that of Patrick Matthew in 1831, in
his work on 'Naval Timber and
Arboriculture.'   "Unfortunately
the view was given very briefly in
scattered passages in an appendix
to a work on a different subject, so
that it remained unnoticed until
Mr Matthew himself drew attention to it in the 'Gardeners'
Chronicle' on April 7, 1860. . . .
He clearly saw the full force of the
principle of natural selection "
(loc. cit., p. xvi). Neither of
these writings was known to
Darwin in 1859.

out of doors only from curiosity, and in search of new
specimens, prompted by the love of travel and adven-
ture, or as companions to commercial and colonising expeditions, they are now forced to do so, because one of
the greatest agencies in nature—" the struggle for existence "—can only be studied in nature herself.   Before
Darwin the study of nature was artificial; through his
influence it has become natural.   From the point of
view of the history of thought, this is surely a much
greater result than any of the several theories or special
arguments which are connected with his name.   These
are indeed numerous, each making, as it were, a distinctly new departure in scientific reasoning, characterised by that unmistakable sign [1] of all that is really
novel in the realm of thought, the creation of a new
vocabulary of distinct terms and phrases.   Varieties
were known to botanists before Darwin, but who studied
" variation " and " variability "? or who spoke of the
" divergence of character "?   Breeders of stock and
pigeon-fanciers knew what " selection " meant, but the

[1] The late Hewett Cottrell
Watson, author of the 'Cybele
Britannica'—one of a most valuable
series of works on the topography
and geographical distribution of
the plants of the British Islands—
wrote to Darwin shortly after the
publication of the 'Origin of
Species,' 21st November 1859:
" I am tempted to write you the
first impressions, not doubting that
they will, in the main, be the
permanent impressions. Your leading idea will assuredly become
recognised as an established truth
in science—i.e., 'Natural Selection.'
It has the characteristics of all
great natural truths, clarifying
what was obscure, simplifying what
was intricate, adding greatly to
previous knowledge. You are the
greatest revolutionist in natural
history of this century, if not of
all centuries. . . . Now these
novel views are brought fairly before the scientific public, it seems
truly remarkable how so many of
them could have failed to see their
right road sooner. How could Sir
C. Lyell, for instance, for thirty
years read, write, and think on the
subject of species *and their succession*, and yet constantly look down
the wrong road?" ('Life of Darwin,' vol. i. p. 352, and vol. ii. p.
226.)

terms " natural selection " and " sexual selection " appeared for the first time in Darwin's writings. The
" struggle for existence," and the resulting " survival of
the fittest " individuals, represent definite processes always
going on consciously or unconsciously in nature and in
human society ; nor is it less significant that many other
phrases have been coined, by which the same idea has been
made useful in other domains of research.   " Hybrids,"
" mongrels," " rudimentary organs," and " monstrous "
developments, which in earlier times were subjects of
mere curiosity, have been raised to scientific importance
as indicative of the concealed and mysterious agencies
by which natural forms are altered or maintained, and
natural processes encouraged or checked.   " Environment " and " adaptation " open out great vistas of inquiry, whilst nearly all those different lines of search
and of reasoning have latterly become centred in the
great problem of " heredity "—the central question of
biological science.   In addition to these, the older
terms of the naturalists and anatomists have received
new interpretations.   It has been shown by Darwin
himself how the vague endeavours of system-makers,
since Linnæus, after a " natural " as distinguished from
a merely " artificial system of classification " of living
beings, implied " something more " than mere resemblance, and that this something more is " propinquity
of descent—the only known cause of the similarity
of organic beings—it being the bond, hidden by various
degrees of modification, which is partially revealed to
us by our classifications." [1]   In the light afforded by

[1] ' Origin of Species,' 1st ed., p. 413.

this idea, the whole work of classification has since Darwin's time been taken up anew; and though it is probably premature to fix upon any elaborate scheme as likely to afford a correct view of the main lines of descent in the two great realms of animal and plant life, single pedigrees, such as those of the rhinoceros and the horse, have, with the assistance of the geological record, been successfully worked out, the missing links having unexpectedly turned up.[1]

In addition to this great service of directing the glance of the naturalist outside, and of helping to overcome the bewildering effects which the aspect of nature must produce on every one who is not prepared for research by some definite aim and a distinct habit of reasoning, the Darwinian spirit has further proved its usefulness by the great increase of our knowledge of the things and phenomena of nature which has taken

[1] "It is certain that, before the theory of descent was accepted or even discussed, genealogical trees were used to represent possible relationships among human races, or possible affinities among animals. It was used as a 'graphic' way of expressing classification, and was true just in proportion as the classification was true. The naturalist traveller, Peter Pallas, was one of the first to use it to express affinities among animals, though it is possible he saw a deeper meaning in his symbol. But when the theory of descent took hold on men's minds, the genealogical tree became more than a graphic register of affinities,—it was used to express the supposed facts of descent. To Ernst Haeckel belongs the credit, or, as some critics would say, the responsibility, of introducing the use of genealogical trees into zoology and botany. In his 'Generelle Morphologie' (1866) and in his 'Schöpfungsgeschichte' (1868, 9th ed. 1897), he displayed numerous genealogical trees designed to show the descent of various stocks and types of animals and plants. There can be no doubt that in so doing he focussed the idea of descent into vividness, and, by the very definiteness of the notation, forced naturalists to a criticism of the reality of the supposed lines of descent. Prof. L. von Graff says of Haeckel's 'Stammbäume,' 'There is due to them the immortal credit of having given the first impetus to the grand revolution in the animal morphology of the last decades'" (J. A. Thomson, 'The Science of Life,' 1899, p. 15).

place since the publication of Darwin's works, by the industry of friend and foe, with the object of proving or of disproving and modifying Darwin's theories. Whole chapters, such as those referring to the fertilisation of plants through insects, to the part which colour plays in the world of flowers or in the plumage of birds and in the wings of butterflies and moths, have been added to our handbooks of natural history;[1]

37.
Fertilisation
of plants and
"Mimicry."

[1] Two remarkable instances may be mentioned. It was known to Christ. Conrad Sprengel that many flowers are "dichogamous"—*i.e.*, that though the organs for self-fertilisation exist in the same flower, nevertheless, because of a want of timekeeping or for other reasons, pollination is done by crossing, wherein the visits of insects are instrumental through elaborate existing arrangements. "Variously coloured spots serve as honey-guides and pathfinders to the exploring insects, hairs protect the nectar from rain and yet offer no obstacle to desirable visitors, other arrangements secure that the insects are dusted with pollen" (J. A. Thomson, 'The Science of Life,' p. 192). Sprengel published his observations in a remarkable book (1793) with the title 'The Secret of Nature discovered in the Structure and Fertilisation of Flowers.' Such was the enthusiasm of this true naturalist, that he, "after being ejected from the rectorate of Spandau for neglecting his flock in favour of flowers, settled down to a frugal life in Berlin, and gave lessons in languages and botany. The commonest plant became new by what he had to say about it; a hair, a spot, gave him opportunity for questions, ideas, investigations" (ibid., p. 191). Sachs ('Gesch.,' p. 449) considers Sprengel's little work to contain "the first attempt to explain the genesis of organic forms out of definite relations to their environment." For sixty years this bionomical classic was forgotten. Darwin in 1841 heard of it through Robert Brown, who, according to Dr Gray ('Nature,' 1874, p. 80), "in common with the rest of the world, looked on Sprengel's ideas as fantastic." The book impressed Darwin, who in 1837 had written in his notebook: "Do not plants which have male and female organs together, yet receive influence from other plants?" as being "full of truth." (See 'Life of Darwin,' vol. i. p. 90; vol. iii. p. 257.) The other important research which has been much stimulated by the two great propounders of Darwinism, is the study of the meaning of colours in plants and animals and the allied subject of "Mimicry." "It is the wonderful individuality of the colours of animals and plants that attracts our attention — the fact that the colours are localised in definite patterns, sometimes in accordance with structural characters, sometimes altogether independent of them, while often differing in the most striking and fantastic manner in allied species. We are thus compelled to look upon colour not merely as a physical but also as a biological characteristic, which has been differentiated and specialised by

the older division of zoology and botany having to a large extent been removed by a study of the interdependence of the many forms of living things and their connection with peculiarities of climate and soil. The Darwinian attitude to the study of natural objects has also introduced into the natural sciences the exact spirit of research,—accurate measurements, together with elaborate countings, being resorted to in order to decide the range of variability of species, the rate of increase in numbers, and the proportion of the surviving to the lost or wasted specimens. A large amount of statistical information [1] has thus been accumulated, and natural history is becoming to some extent an exact science. That it will ever be so to a very large extent is doubtful: it is one of the great merits of Darwin that he has introduced a special method into the sciences of nature— the method of a judicious balancing of evidence. He was fully "aware that scarcely a single point was discussed in his works on which facts cannot be adduced, often apparently leading to conclusions directly opposite to those at which he arrived, and that a fair result can be obtained only by fully stating and balancing the facts

38.
The judicial method.

natural selection, and must, therefore, find its explanation in the principle of adaptation or utility" (Wallace, 'Darwinism,' p. 189). The term "Mimicry" was first introduced by H. W. Bates in his paper on "Mimetic Butterflies," read before the Linnæan Soc., Nov. 1861, and hailed by Darwin ('Life,' vol. ii. p. 392) as "one of the most remarkable and admirable papers" he ever read. The subject had been passed over in the first editions of the 'Origin,' but was introduced in later editions, and has always served as one of the most valuable illustrations and proofs of the theory of natural selection. The whole matter is admirably expounded by Mr Wallace in his long article in the 'Westminster Review,' July 1867, reprinted in his 'Contributions to the Theory of Natural Selection' (1870, pp. 45-129), and again in 'Darwinism.'

[1] On the development of statistical methods in the service of the theory of evolution, see chap. xii. below.

and arguments on both sides of each question."[1] It is quite a different process of investigation and method of thought from that which the abstract sciences use, where every agency is first considered in its isolated action and mathematically calculated, and a complex effect is rightly looked upon as merely the resultant of specific, well-defined forces, compounded according to rigid dynamical formulæ. That the whole of nature, as well as all observable phenomena, are in reality only the result of such a composition of definite simple actions, and can be studied as such, may be quite correct; but that this method, however useful in isolated cases, and especially however fruitful in the application to artificial mechanisms, will never lead to a just comprehension of any large cluster of phenomena, or to an appreciation of the totality of things which surrounds us, must be evident to any one who at once appreciates the rigidity and universality of mathematical calculations, and sees how soon they fail to become of practical use when we attempt to attack any complex problem through them. Now, all processes in nature herself, as distinguished from the laboratory, are eminently complex, and far transcend the powers and grasp of the mathematical calculus, so far as the human mind is able to employ it. In fact, the outdoor naturalist must attack the problem of nature and life by quite a different method : he must, like a judge, confront and appreciate the evidence of many witnesses who are speaking on all sides to him, and he must, with an open and unbiassed mind, judiciously combine such evidence in the sentences which he passes or the

[1] 'Origin of Species,' 1st ed., p. 2.

generalisations which he attempts. Absolute mathematical certainty is almost unknown in such cases : they
can only be made out with more or less clearness and
probability.

It seems to me that the new phase into which scientific
thought has entered, mainly through the influence of
Darwin, has not been sufficiently appreciated by those of
his critics who have compared his methods with those of
earlier philosophers and naturalists. Darwin has been
called by some the Newton of the natural sciences,[1] and
again by others his method has been unfavourably contrasted with that of Newton and Cuvier.[2] Some of these

39.
Darwin and
Newton
compared.

[1] It is in many instances only
a *façon de parler*. Maxwell similarly called Ampère the Newton of
Electrodynamics ; and Young has
been called the Newton of Optics.
Mr Wallace says ('Darwinism,' p.
9) : " We claim for Darwin that he
is the Newton of natural history,
and that, just so surely as that the
discovery and demonstration by
Newton of the law of gravitation
established order in place of chaos,
and laid a sure foundation for all
future study of the starry heavens,
so surely has Darwin, by his discovery of the law of natural selection and his demonstration of the
great principle of the preservation
of useful variations in the struggle
for life, not only thrown a flood of
light on the process of development
of the whole organic world, but also
established a firm foundation for all
future study of nature."

[2] The most important publication of this kind is the late Professor Albert Wigand's work, in
three volumes, 'Der Darwinismus
und die Naturforschung Newton's
und Cuvier's' (Braunschweig, 1874-
1877). The author significantly
classes Humboldt also among those

who belong to that period and
school of research which has—unfortunately, in his opinion—been
superseded by the modern genetic
treatment (see vol. iii. p. 14). It is
not likely that a perusal of these
volumes will, in the mind of the
reader, change the current of
thought which is now, even more
than twenty-five years ago, running
in genetic lines, nor will it do anything towards diminishing the sense
of importance which attaches to
this modern movement. Nevertheless, the book is valuable as
giving a very complete *résumé* of
what was said " pro and con " Darwinism during the first fifteen years
of its existence. It is interesting
to see what a small part French
scientific opinion played during that
period as to the theories of descent
and mutability of species, which had
both their origin and their first great
exponents in France. The book
does not appear to have had much
influence in its time, but more
recently the criticisms of Wigand,
von Baer, and other writers seem
to receive greater attention since
the central biological problems have
been pushed into the foreground. Of

comparisons refer to the law of "natural selection," which is placed in parallel with Newton's law of "universal gravity." Now, although "natural selection," the automatic process which ensures the survival of the fittest and the extinction of the less adaptive members in a crowd of living beings, is a definite formula which allows us to understand and clearly define one of the many factors which are at work in the development, in the genesis and growth, of living beings, it is only one. It is not a prime mover or force, like the force of gravity; it is a check upon the over-luxuriance of other existing forces of production and development. These are only very imperfectly known; whereas Newton not only discovered the "law of gravitation," but also the correct expression for the general and all-pervading laws of motion which obtain, even where gravitation or any similar force ceases to be a valid conception. Again, Newton's greatness does not rest on the "law of gravitation" alone, but much more on the general foundations of dynamics and natural philosophy which he has laid. So also Darwin's greatness is not limited to the formula of "natural selection," but depends on the novel conception which he has introduced into the study of nature on the large scale and as a whole, viewing it as a scene of conflict and ceaseless development. From this time dates the study of nature as a whole [1] in contradistinction to that of natural

this I shall treat in the next chapter. See also the various writings of Hans Driesch, such as 'Analytische Theorie der organischen Entwicklung' (Leipzig, 1894); 'Die Biologie als selbständige Grund-wissenschaft (1893), especially p. 7 of the latter.

[1] Though this was prepared, as Darwin himself points out, by A. von Humboldt.

objects and processes. The general laws which obtain in this great field, and which would correspond to Newton's laws of motion—the laws of variation and of heredity—have not yet been discovered; but it is again Darwin more than any other naturalist who has called attention to these prime movers in the living universe. He has pushed into the foreground the two great problems of "variation" and "heredity." [1]

40.
Unsolved
problems.

[1] Darwin in his subsequent writings urged another important problem, to which he had already in his first and greatest work drawn passing attention. This is the agency of "sexual selection." It occupies by far the larger portion of his third great work, which appeared in 1871 with the title 'The Descent of Man and Selection in Relation to Sex.' In the introduction he says, "During many years it has seemed to me highly probable that sexual selection has played an important part in differentiating the races of man ; but in my 'Origin of Species' I contented myself by merely alluding to this belief. When I came to apply this view to man, I found it indispensable to treat the whole subject in full detail. Professor Haeckel is the sole author who, since the publication of the 'Origin,' has discussed in his various works, in a very able manner, the subject of sexual selection, and has seen its full importance." The problem of "sexual selection" is introduced in the 'Origin' (p. 87) in the following words : "Inasmuch as peculiarities often appear under domestication in one sex, and become hereditarily attached to that sex, the same fact probably occurs under nature ; and if so, natural selection will be able to modify one sex in its functional relations to the other sex, or in relation to wholly different habits of life in the two sexes, as is some-times the case with insects. And this leads me to say a few words on what I call Sexual Selection. This depends not on a struggle for existence, but on a struggle between the males for possession of the females : the result is not death to the unsuccessful competitor, but few or no offspring. Sexual selection is thus less rigorous than natural selection." A great deal has been written about sexual selection, and in general it may be said that the question belongs to quite a different category from that of natural selection. Some of the foremost champions of the latter doctrine, notably Mr Wallace, reject sexual selection as unnecessary in the whole scheme. The characteristic feature of natural selection is this, that it is a purely automatic process, dependent on overcrowding, whereas in sexual selection it becomes much more difficult to see how the process works automatically. Nowadays the question of natural selection is hardly any longer doubtful ; it is a fact. As to sexual selection, the statistical proofs that there is a superabundance from which to choose are still wanting. To understand sexual selection, or even to define it, we need to form some conception of the reason and origin of sexual differentiation, and this cannot be arrived at without a theory of life

And, besides this, it is well to remember that Newton was condemned by some of his contemporaries on the basis of the philosophy of Bacon; Fresnel and Young were condemned on the ground of Bacon and Newton combined. In like manner the novel line of reasoning adopted or largely cultivated by Darwin has been attacked as being opposed to Bacon, Newton, and other great thinkers before him. In all these cases it is the results, and not the theory, of the process of reasoning which have justified its continued employment. Without attempting to elaborate the parallel too minutely, we may say that as Newton created Natural Philosophy and took one brilliant step in fixing for all time one of the great laws of the material universe, so Darwin has founded the study of nature as distinguished from that of the objects and processes of nature, and has enunciated one of the great factors which obtain in the living portion of nature: through him a history of nature, the genetic view of nature on a large scale as distinguished from the older natural history, has for the first time became conceivable. The word history indeed suggests other analogies. Political history, what we ordinarily term history proper, has in the course of our century undergone changes and developments similar to those in the history of nature. Confined once to a casual, un-methodical, uncritical, and incomplete record of isolated

which rests on something more than the two purely statistical or numerical facts of overcrowding and of variation—*i.e.*, the fact that no two individuals are absolutely alike. The importance of the phenomenon of sex in the economy of living nature has been studied, and given rise to many theories. A very good account of these will be found in P. Geddes and J. A. Thomson, 'The Evolution of Sex,' 1889. In the following chapter, where I deal with the various attempts to define "Life," I shall revert to this subject.

events or biographies, it has been gradually united and organised as a whole, largely through the same judicial sifting of manifold evidence and elaboration of critical methods of research. Of this I hope to treat in a different portion of this work: here I only wish to draw attention to the enlarged aspect, which in both instances has, through the same process of development, come over our studies. When once we rise from the contemplation and examination of details and single facts, and grasp the connection and economy of the whole as a subject worthy of special attention, we involuntarily introduce two new elements into our research—the element of conjecture and the element of speculation. The former is needed to fill up the many gaps which we find in the actual records when we wish to string them together into a united and intelligible whole; the latter is the inquiry into the general principles which underlie any and every development of the kind we have in view. The creation by Darwin of the science and history of nature, as distinguished from the science and history of natural objects and single processes, has been accompanied and strengthened by the appearance of conjectural and speculative attempts; just as the cultivation of the science of general history has gone hand in hand with, and has been supported by, the brilliant results of philological conjecture and the philosophy of history.[1] Of

41.
Genetic view on a large scale.

---

[1] In an eloquent passage Professor Parker compares the work of the naturalist of to-day with that of the philologist. This passage occurs in his Memoir on the Fowl (1868), and is quoted in his book 'On the Morphology of the Skull' (by Parker and Bettany, London, 1877, p. 362):

"Whilst at work I seemed to myself to have been endeavouring to decipher a palimpsest, and one not erased and written upon again just once but five or six times over. Having erased, as it were, the characters of the culminating type —those of the gaudy Indian bird

these I shall treat elsewhere. It may be a question capable of very opposite answers whether the philosophy of history, such as it has been offered in the brilliant generalisations of Kant, Herder, Hegel, and Buckle, has really aided the science of history proper; whereas no question can arise as to the indispensable service that has been rendered to historians by the criticism and conjectural emendation of texts and other monuments of antiquity. With Darwinism the matter stands differently: no person who peruses the great and increasing literature of the subject can deny the enormous assistance which the philosophical ideas of evolution have rendered to the cause of Darwinism—how the latter, when it appeared, found ready made, though then only slightly appreciated, the philosophical canons and terms which were so well fitted to its systematic enunciation and literary *mise en scène*. This was the independent work of Mr Herbert Spencer.[1] The other well-known

42.
Philosophi-
cal theories.

43.
Herbert
Spencer.

—I seemed to be among the sombre grouse ; and then, towards incubation, the characters of the sand-grouse and hemipod stood out before me. Rubbing these away in my downward work, the form of the tinamou looked me in the face ; then the aberrant ostrich seemed to be described in large archaic characters ; a little while and these faded into what could just be read off as pertaining to the sea-turtle ; whilst underlying the whole the fish in its simplest myxinoid form could be traced in morphological hieroglyphics."

[1] The part and position which belongs to Mr Herbert Spencer in the history of evolution as a scientific doctrine has not yet received due attention or adequate recognition. There is, however, no doubt that the principal features of the genetic view of natural phenomena were clearly before his mind as early as 1852, when he wrote his short essay on " The Development Hypothesis " in 'The Leader,' republished in the first volume of his 'Collected Essays.' It has been pointed out by Romanes (' Darwin and After Darwin,' vol. i. p. 257) that though the attempts towards a genetic conception of organic nature were numerous, if not abundant, before Darwin, yet this view only broke through and became dominant on the appearance of the theory of natural selection. He says : " If we may estimate the importance of an idea by the change of thought which it effects, this

name which is so frequently associated with Darwin, especially in Germany, is that of Professor Haeckel, whose ' Generelle Morphologie' and ' History of Creation' have done much to introduce the spirit of Darwinism into German literature.   These works also represent the

44.
Haeckel.

idea of natural selection is unquestionably the most important idea that has ever been conceived by the mind of man.   Yet the wonder is that it should not have been hit upon long before ;" and after referring to the forgotten anticipations of Wells and Matthew, Romanes proceeds : "Still more remarkable is the fact that Mr Herbert Spencer — notwithstanding his great powers of abstract thought and his great devotion of those powers to the theory of evolution, when as yet this theory was scorned by science—should have missed what now appears so obvious an idea."   In this connection it is interesting to note how those general canons of evolutionary thought which were established by Spencer before the publication of the ' Origin' were brought into general recognition by scientific men only when the definite mathematical or statistical formula of natural selection was announced, and that, after the lapse of a whole generation, it is not this precise formula but the general conception of evolution which, according to many of the foremost naturalists, will obtain ; the part which natural selection plays being uncertain and variously estimated by the many adherents of the theory of evolution.   See, *inter alia*, the article on " Evolution in Biology " by Huxley in the ' Ency. Brit.,' 9th ed., vol. viii. p. 751 : "How far natural selection suffices for the production of species remains to be seen.   Few can doubt that, if not the whole

cause, it is a very important factor in that operation. . . . The importance of natural selection will not be impaired even if further inquiries should prove that variability is definite and is determined in certain directions rather than in others by conditions inherent in that which varies."   See also the Address of Lord Salisbury at the meeting of the Brit. Assoc. at Oxford in 1894, and the subsequent remarks of Huxley in seconding the vote of thanks (' Life of Huxley,' vol. ii. p. 378) : "The essence of this great work (the ' Origin of Species ') may be stated summarily thus : it affirms the mutability of species and the descent of living forms, separated by differences of more than varietal value, from one stock. . . . And yet it is also true that if all the conceptions promulgated in the ' Origin of Species' which are peculiarly Darwinian were swept away, the theory of the evolution of animals and plants would not be in the slightest degree shaken."   In fact, the general principles of mechanical evolution, as first systematised by Mr Spencer, received recognition only through a definite formula, but may, after all, survive that special doctrine.   It is further very evident how the parallel with Newton's formula of gravitation entirely breaks down if we look at matters in this light ; every subsequent discovery having only tended to confirm that special mathematical relation, and proved the all-important part it plays in nature.

first brilliant attempt to fill up conjecturally the broken
lines of development and descent as the Darwinian conception of living nature postulates them.[1] As a first
and daring approximation, they deserve to have assigned
to them a prominent place in the history of the scientific thought of our age. In elaborating his pedigrees, Professor Haeckel has taken up and more clearly
defined the analogy between the development of the
embryo in the higher organisms and the supposed transition from lower to higher forms which is found in the
classification of the genera or species of animals and
plants. He has termed this analogy the great law of
biogenesis, of the development of life in the individual
(τὸ ὄν), and the species or tribe (τὸ φῦλον), expressed
also as the parallelism of ontogenesis and phylogenesis.
Long before Darwin and the appearance of the theory of
descent this analogy[2] was pointed out in a restricted

[1] The later editions of the 'Origin
of Species' contain the following
reference to Haeckel (6th ed., p.
381): "Prof. Haeckel, in his 'Generelle Morphologie,' and in other
works, has brought his great knowledge and abilities to bear on what
he calls phylogeny, or the lines of
descent of all organic beings. In
drawing up the several series he
trusts chiefly to embryological characters, but receives aid from homologous and rudimentary organs, as
well as from the successive periods
at which the various forms of life
are believed to have first appeared
in our geological formations. He
has thus boldly made a great beginning, and shows us how classification will in the future be
treated." And Huxley (art. "Evolution," p. 752) says: "Whatever
hesitation may not unfrequently

be felt by less daring minds in
following Haeckel in many of his
speculations, his attempt to sys-
tematise the doctrine of evolution,
and to exhibit its influence as the
central thought of modern biology,
cannot fail to have a far-reaching
influence on the progress of
science."

[2] As to the early anticipations of
this so-called "law of biogenesis,"
they are given with more or less
completeness by many modern
writers, such as Huxley in his
article on Evolution (1878, 'Ency.
Brit.'), P. Geddes (ibid., art. "Reproduction"), Yves Delage ('L'Hérédité,' &c., p. 159), J. A. Thomson
('The Science of Life,' p. 133, &c.)
The most important earlier statement is that quoted by Huxley
from Meckel's 'Entwurf einer Dar-
stellung der zwischen dem Embryo-

sense by Meckel, von Baer, and Serres. It has sometimes been termed von Baer's law, though von Baer
very carefully guarded himself against many popular
versions of the analogy, applying it only within the
limits of the four great groups or plans of organisation
into which he divided the animal kingdom.[1] In his

zustande der höheren Thiere und dem permanenten der niederen stattfindenden Parallele' (1811): "There is no good physiologist who has not been struck by the observation that the original form of all organisms is one and the same, and that out of this one form all, the lowest as well as the highest, are developed in such a manner that the latter pass through the permanent forms of the former as transitory stages. Aristotle, Haller, Harvey, Kielmeyer, Autenrieth, and many others, have either made this observation incidentally, or, especially the latter, have drawn particular attention to it, and drawn therefrom results of permanent importance for physiology." Louis Agassiz, in his celebrated "Essay on Classification" (1859), though rejecting the doctrine of descent, "insisted, nevertheless, on the correspondence between stages in embryonic development and the grades of differentiation expressed in the classification of living and extinct animals" (Thomson, 'The Science of Life,' p. 134).

[1] "A careful examination of von Baer's 'laws' shows that he did not accept the recapitulation without many saving clauses. He believed in it much less than many a modern embryologist, such as F. M. Balfour or A. Milnes Marshall" (Thomson, p. 133). Before the publication of Haeckel's 'Generelle Morphologie' the naturalist who seems to have most clearly expressed the recapitulation theory

was Fritz Müller, who in 1864 published his famous tract 'Für Darwin,' which appeared in 1868 in an English translation by Dallas, with the title 'Facts and Arguments for Darwin.' The work of Fritz Müller, who for many years lived in the Brazils, isolated and secluded, and devoted to scientific observation, was welcomed by Darwin as one of the first and greatest supports to his doctrine: the author was singled out by him as the "prince of observers," and frequently referred to in the later editions of the 'Origin of Species.' Delage considers him to have first expressed the fundamental biogenetic law ('L'Hérédité,' pp. 159, 469), and this is in agreement with Haeckel's own declaration in the 13th chapter of the 'History of Creation.' It is, however, well to mention that the recapitulation theory has found little favour with botanists ; that Haeckel himself admits that the parallelism between ontogenesis and phylogenesis is general and not exact ; that there is a tendency to abbreviation ; that recent adaptations (called by him "kainogenetic") may mask more ancient ("palingenetic") features, &c. See J. A. Thomson, 'The Science of Life,' p. 135. Ziegler, in his recent excellent review of the 'Present Position of the Doctrine of Descent' (Jena, 1902, p. 12), admits that the theory of parallelism has "perhaps not realised all the expectations" which were cherished thirty years ago.

time also no attempt was made to bring phytogenesis
—the genesis of plant-life—into line and order with
zoogenesis, the genetic arrangement of animals.   It is
Haeckel's undoubted merit to have attempted for the
first time to carry out this general scheme on a large
scale, and by means of detailed pedigrees, beginning
with the undefined organisms in which as yet the
peculiar characters of animal- and plant-life do not
appear to be differentiated, and ascending in two great
trunks into the vegetable and animal kingdom, and
thence through many ramifications into the several
classes, families, genera, species, and varieties of living
things, to construct the supposed real natural system
for which systematists had been unconsciously searching
since the age of Ray and Linnæus.   For the purpose of
elaborating this great scheme he employs not only the
great law of heredity, according to which ancestral
characters are reproduced in development, but also the
older law of adaptation to the existing environment, as
pointed out by Lamarck.   Haeckel, in fact, combines the
views of Darwin and Lamarck, which other naturalists
are more or less inclined to keep apart, whence has
arisen the well-known division into the two great schools
of the neo-Darwinians and neo-Lamarckians.[1]   Though

45.
Combines
Darwin and
Lamarck.

[1] Natural selection being an admitted fact among living things,
like gravitation in the physical
universe, three distinct problems
arise : First, how far does it reach ?
the scope of the principle.   The
subsequent writings of Darwin were
mainly occupied with this question,
though—as we shall see later—he
also ventured upon an important
suggestion as to the underlying
problem of inheritance.   Secondly,
the fact or principle itself requires
to be traced to deeper-lying causes.
We may say natural selection is a
vera causa, but not a *prima causa* :
it is a true but not a prime cause.
The investigations regarding "variation" and "heredity" work along
this line of research, and form the

Haeckel's work is, as he himself admits, highly conjectural,[1] it has done much to extend and popularise the

whole domain of modern post-Darwinian biology. The problem is far from being solved, though it is perhaps nearer a solution than the question as to the cause of gravitation. Thirdly, there is the ambitious attempt to construct a general philosophy of life by means of the new principle, or some modification or amplification of it. After Newton had discovered universal gravitation, the attempt was made by Boscovich and the French school of mathematical physics to use the idea of attraction at a distance as a general physical theory. Of those who, before or after Darwin, attempted the more ambitious task, we may take Herbert Spencer, Ernst Haeckel, and Nägeli as three distinct representatives. They, however, agree in one point—viz., in considering natural selection to be insufficient, and in admitting other agencies, which are largely drawn from the suggestive writings of Lamarck. The section of these philosophical writers who consider Lamarck's principles to be more fundamental than Darwin's, and who are largely represented by American naturalists (notably E. D. Cope and A. Hyatt), are called neo-Lamarckians. The best account of their views will be found in the last chapter of Professor Packard's book, 'Lamarck, the Founder of Evolution' (1901). The following passage quoted there (p. 391) from a much earlier memoir (1877) gives a very clear account of the reasoning of this school: "Darwin's phrase, 'natural selection,' or Herbert Spencer's term, 'survival of the fittest,' expresses simply the final result, while the process of the origination of the new forms

which have survived, or been selected by nature, is to be explained by the action of the physical environments of the animals, coupled with inheritance - force. The phrases quoted have been misused to state the cause, when they simply express the result of the action of a chain of causes which we may, with Herbert Spencer, call the 'environment' of the organism undergoing modification; and therefore a form of Lamarckianism, greatly modified by recent scientific discoveries, seems to meet most of the difficulties which arise in accounting for the origination of species and higher groups of organisms." It is also well to note that Mr Wallace, though not a Lamarckian, considers the principle of natural selection insufficient especially to explain the higher developments of mental life. (See 'Darwinism,' p. 463, &c.)

[1] "It is evident that our 'phylogeny' is and remains an edifice of hypotheses in the same way as her sister, historical geology. For she tries to gain a connected view of the course and causes of events long past, the direct investigation of which is impossible. Neither observation nor experiment can give us direct information regarding the endless processes of change through which the existing animal- and plant-forms have emerged out of lengthy ancestral stages. . . . The empirical documents of our history of descent will always remain largely incomplete, however much through continued discoveries our region of knowledge of individual things may increase." (Haeckel, 'Systematische Phylogenie,' 1894, vol. i. preface, p. vi.)

genetic view of nature, drawing likewise into this circle
of ideas the great departments of anthropology and
geography; in fact, it amounts to rewriting the 'Kosmos'
of Humboldt on genetic instead of on purely descriptive
lines. But in perusing these and similar writings of
modern times, we feel on the one side that we are
gradually getting out of the depths of science, not only
into the domain of conjecture, without which a knowledge of the past cannot be gained, but also into the
regions of philosophical thought, which proceeds on
other lines than those prescribed to science, and which
will claim our attention in a special portion of this
work. On the other side, in using so confidently the
ideas of descent and adaptation, we feel that we are
appealing to two great empirical facts, the facts of
heredity and of variation of living things, on which the
genetic view of nature, when applied to the living
portion of creation, rests, but which are scarcely even
defined in clear terms, much less explained. In fact,
we are face to face with the problem and definition of
life itself. Neither the morphological nor the genetic
view of nature is limited to the living world, although
both views originated there, and were from thence extended to the larger domain of inorganic and cosmical
phenomena. Into these larger views which try to
grasp the forms of nature in their apparent rest or in
their endless change and history, the phenomena of
life have been fitted by the help of three definite conceptions — the conception of the cell as the morphological basis or unit of all life, and the two conceptions of inheritance and variation, by which living

46.
**Philosoph-
ical prob-
lems.**

47.
**Problem of
life.**

forms are partially maintained and continuously altered.[1] These three conceptions deserve and have received special attention by a class of students who, since the beginning of the nineteenth century, have termed themselves biologists. On what lines of reasoning their studies have been conducted, and to what general results they have led, I propose to discuss in the following chapter, which might be appropriately entitled the "Biological view of Nature" in the narrower sense of the term. In order to distinguish the studies which I shall have to deal with in that chapter from those which have occupied us in this and the last chapter, which deal largely but not exclusively with living things, I have preferred to give to it the title, "On the Vitalistic[2]

[1] To these — according to some naturalists — might be added the factor of adaptation, so prominently put forward by Lamarck and his followers. But adaptation is one of the causes of variation, as natural selection is a consequence. The latter is a physical necessity wherever overcrowding exists; whereas the scope of adaptation, which is an undeniable fact so far as individuals are concerned, is, so far as it regards inheritance — i.e., the development of the race — a much controverted question. It comes under the larger problem of the influence of environment, and will occupy us again in later chapters. Among the most valuable contributions to this subject are Mr Herbert Spencer's articles on the "Factors of Organic Evolution," published in the 'Nineteenth Century' in 1886, and separately, with additions, in 1887. In these essays he also shows how Darwin himself in his later writings includes the influence of environment as an important factor in development. (See p. 29 sqq. of the reprint.)

[2] As the two terms "biological" and "vitalistic" might, according to their etymology, mean the same thing, it may be appropriate to offer some explanation of the reasons which have induced me to adopt the latter term for the purpose indicated in the text. Biology means the science of life. This can only be studied in living things. Living things, however, are formed entirely of the same elementary substances as we find in inorganic or not living things, and are very largely formed through the same chemical and physical processes as we find among the latter. And as our scientific — i.e., exact, accurate, and useful — knowledge has all begun with the study of inorganic phenomena, it is natural that biologists should have attacked the problems of living nature from the side of the similarity or sameness which they presented when compared with lifeless nature. The main progress in physiology

view of Nature." Clearly both the morphological and
the genetic views of nature remain incomplete unless
they embrace the forms and the processes of life. It
is the problem from which both started and to which
both lead. They, as it were, presuppose its possible
solution. Let us see what has been done in the course
of our century to effect it.

Before we do this it is well to draw attention to
the great strengthening which the genetic or developmental view of nature has received, since the time of
Darwin, from other quarters — notably from that of
general physics and chemistry in their application to
geology and astrophysics.[1]

and medicine during the last hundred years has come from that
quarter. This large class of studies
can be carried on without facing
the problem of life at all ; and thus
it happens that we may have a very
large biological literature in which
the word life hardly occurs, and
in which we seek in vain for a
definition of life. We must, therefore, have a term which singles out
from the enormous mass of biological literature that smaller portion which professedly deals with
those properties and phenomena
which are peculiar to the living as
distinguished from the lifeless creation. I have chosen for this purpose
the term vitalistic ; but I may
note that in using it I do not limit
myself to that class of thinkers
who are usually termed "Vitalists,"
because they are led to, or start
with the assumption of, a special
vital principle. Even those who,
in studying the phenomena of life,
arrive at or start from the denial of
such a principle are included under
the vitalistic view, just as Kant is
rightly termed a metaphysician

although the outcome of his philosophy may be considered to be
the destruction of metaphysics in
the sense which was current in
his age.

[1] A general scheme of evolution,
or of development as it was more
frequently termed, which would
embrace equally cosmical and terrestrial processes, the lifeless and
living world, was clearly before the
mind of Schelling and his followers,
notably Oken and Steffens. The
vagueness and extravagancies of
this school brought the idea into
discredit, and the remedy applied
by Hegel, to put a logical process in
the place of fantastic suggestions,
ruined it utterly in the eyes of the
cultivators of exact research. Only
very few of the great students of
organic development, but among
them the greatest, von Baer, retained a just appreciation of the
great aims of Schelling. The study
of development abroad was almost
entirely limited to embryology. In
other sciences the "statical" aspect
ruled supreme. In the face of this
somewhat retrograde movement

In the second chapter of this volume, which treated of the physical view of nature, and developed the various ideas which cluster around the term "energy," I showed how, in the middle of the century, through the introduction of these ideas, a new clue was gained wherewith to penetrate the connection of natural phenomena in time and space. Before that time the conservation of matter, the rule that matter can neither be lost nor created, guided research by trying to account for the apparent loss or gain of matter whenever and wherever changes take place in the material world. The science of chemistry with its instrument the balance was built on the foundation of this axiom. When, through the labours of Mayer, Helmholtz, and Joule, the further axiom became established that, besides matter, there exists in the material universe a second quantity (or substance) termed "energy," which, like matter, can be changed, but which, like matter, can neither be created nor annihilated, the questions began to be asked, "If we

48.
Genetic view strength-ened by physics and chemistry.

abroad, the merit of Mr Spencer in urging the "dynamical" aspect long before the 'Origin of Species' put forward a definite mechanical agency is so much greater, and he himself says ('Factors of Organic Evolution,' p. 5): "Of the few . . . who, espousing the belief in a continuous evolution, had to account for this evolution, it must be said that though the cause assigned (viz., the modification of structures resulting from modification of functions) was a true cause, . . . it left unexplained the greater part of the facts. Having been myself one of these few, I look back with surprise at the way in which the facts which were congruous with the espoused view monopolised con-sciousness and kept out the facts which were incongruous with it—conspicuous though many of them were." Mr Spencer was also probably the first who defined in mechanical terms, applicable to cosmical, lifeless, and living pheno-mena alike, the process of develop-ment, adopting the term evolution. This fitting of the process of or-ganic development into the general formula of evolution, and the sub-sequent announcement by Darwin of the mechanical agency of over-crowding and selection, has had the effect of strengthening im-mensely the genetic view of nature, but also of obscuring and pushing into the background the special problem of life.

receive energy, where does it come from ? if we lose energy, where does it go to ? " It was recognised that the great store of energy on which we at present depend is the heat of the sun, which is partly used or wasted by daily radiation, partly stored in the separated energies of chemical substances, such as were produced by the agency of solar heat in bygone ages; the deposits of coal in the bowels of the earth being a prominent and important example. Where does the heat of the sun come from, and how is it maintained ? These were some of the questions which began to be asked. The genesis of the cosmos, as suggested by Laplace and fancifully elaborated by popular writers, had taken note only of the matter in the sun and in the planetary system, and had disregarded the heat [1] or energy which the sun supplied, and on which the historical changes on the surface of our globe have almost entirely depended. "But physical laws are for our mental vision," as Helmholtz says, "like telescopes which penetrate into the farthest night of the past and the future." [2] Shortly before the pioneers of the mechanical theory of heat published their

[1] "When Playfair (in his 'Illustrations of the Huttonian Theory') spoke of the planetary bodies as being perpetual in their motion, did it not occur to him to ask, What about the sun's heat? Is the sun a miraculous body ordered to give out heat and to shine for ever ?" (Lord Kelvin in 1868, "On Geological Time," 'Popular Lectures and Addresses,' vol. ii. p. 45.) "The old nebular hypothesis supposes the solar system and other similar systems through the universe which we see at a distance as stars to have originated in the condensation of fiery nebulous matter. This hypothesis was invented before the discovery of thermodynamics, or the nebulæ would not have been supposed to be fiery ; and the idea seems never to have occurred to any of its inventors or early supporters that the matter, the condensation of which they supposed to constitute the sun and stars, could have been other than fiery in the beginning " (id., 1871, ibid., vol. i. p. 184).

[2] See 'Vorträge und Reden,' 3 Aufl., vol. i. p. 57.

first theoretical and experimental essays, experiments had already been made by Sir John Herschel at the Cape, and independently by Pouillet in France, with the object of measuring the annual expenditure of heat by the sun. They had found it to be an enormous quantity.[1] They represented it popularly by the thickness of a crust of ice on the surface of the earth, which the heat radiated annually by the sun would be able to melt, and they found this to be about 30 metres or 100 feet. Mayer was the first who seems to have put the question definitely : How is this enormous expenditure of heat defrayed, which would, if not in some way compensated, have resulted, even in historical times, in a great lowering of the temperature of the sun, and hence also of that on the surface of our globe, such as is contradicted by all historical evidence ?   The answer which Mayer gave to this question was based upon an application of his conception of the equivalence of heat and the energy of mechanical motion.   As the sun, according to the cosmogonic hypothesis [2] of Laplace, was originally formed by

49.
The heat of the sun.

[1] These measurements were made in 1837, and very nearly agreed. The resulting figures can, of course, only be considered as rough approximations : they have been considerably increased by more recent observations.   See A. Berry, 'A Short History of Astronomy,' p. 397.

[2] It does not appear that Mayer brought his "meteoric" hypothesis of the generation and maintenance of the heat of the sun into connection with the nebular hypothesis of Kant and Laplace.   In fact, in his first mention of it in his communication to the Paris Academy in 1846 he says simply : "En con-sidérant le grand nombre que nous voyons, comme bolides ou étoiles tombantes, nous ne pouvons pas doubter qu'à tout moment des myriades d'astéroides semblables à une grêle épaisse se jettent dans tous les sens sur le soleil où ils perdent la force vive de leur mouvement" (Mayer's 'Schriften und Briefe,' p. 264) ; and M. Faye remarks that the fact that Mayer's ideas are opposed to Laplace's theory of the origin of the solar system explains how it came about that his theories were never reported on or explicitly mentioned.   Leverrier also seems to have ridiculed the meteoric hypothesis, according to

the gathering up of cosmical matter which, under the force of gravitation, was in rapid motion—so the heat of the sun originated through the conversion of the energy of this arrested motion into heat. This process of gathering up of cosmical or meteoric matter is still going on, and it makes up for the loss or expenditure of solar heat through radiation. Helmholtz, in the sequel of his investigation into the conservation of energy, likewise takes up this problem, and while admitting to some extent Mayer's theory,[1] shows that even without the accession of cosmical matter, the mere contraction through gravitation of the gaseous substances of the sun would result in a continual production of heat. His calculations show that the amount of this contraction, resulting in a diminution of the sun's apparent diameter, would not be great enough to be perceptible during historic ages. The theory of Helmholtz has in general been accepted as

which the sun's heat was kept up by breakfasting and dining on meteorites. (See Wolf, 'Handbuch der Astronomie,' vol. ii. p. 433.) It is on the other side equally interesting to see how Herbert Spencer, for whom the nebular hypothesis was a principal example of cosmic evolution, failed to avail himself of the strengthening support it received through thermodynamics (see 'Essays,' vol. i., "On the Nebular Hypothesis," 1858). Had Mayer brought his ideas into connection with Laplace's cosmogony, he probably would have hit upon the correcter version, the contraction theory, which it was reserved for Helmholtz to propound in 1854.

[1] The subject was about the same time taken up by William Thomson (Lord Kelvin), first in a paper "On the Mechanical Energies of the Solar System" (Trans. Edin. Roy. Soc., 1854), and continued in a series of papers and addresses, reprinted in his mathematical, &c., papers (vol. ii.) in the 1st volume of his 'Popular Addresses,' and in an appendix to Thomson and Tait's 'Natural Philosophy.' He shows that the form of the meteoric theory propounded by Mayer, and independently by Waterston (Brit. Assoc., 1853), is as little able to explain the maintenance of the sun's heat through known historic ages as the chemical theory of combustion, which was already abandoned by Mayer in 1846, and finally adopts Helmholtz's form of the meteoric theory as the most likely. ('Pop. Lect.,' vol. i. p. 365, &c.; p. 373, &c.)

a valid explanation of the maintenance of solar heat.   In fact, " as to the sun, we can now go both backwards and forwards in his history upon the principles of Newton and Joule." [1]

But further means for testing the correctness of these theories were afforded by the invention, in 1859, of Spectrum Analysis.   It was found that the composition of the light of luminous bodies, as revealed by prismatic scattering in the spectrum, enabled us to tell a good deal about the nature of the body itself from which the light emanated.   We can tell whether the body is shining with its own or with reflected light, what are the constituents of the incandescent body, whether it is an incandescent solid or an incandescent gas; also whether the body is in motion or not.   The nebular hypothesis supposed that the planetary system owed its origin to incandescent, perhaps gaseous, matter, which, through the force of attraction, was collected in different centres: the discoveries of thermodynamics and of spectroscopy have enabled us to expand and correct some of the assumptions of this theory, and to add new features to its minuter elaboration.   It is not necessary that the matter which was originally scattered through space and was gathered into attracting centres should be itself incandescent or gaseous; it may have been cold and solid like dust; rising in temperature and becoming incandescent only through the conversion of arrested motion into heat, which again was maintained for some time through accession of new matter or progressive shrinkage, but which must in a calculable time be radiated away, leaving a

50.
Spectrum
Analysis.

[1] Lord Kelvin, *loc. cit.*, vol. ii. p. 131.

cold, heavy, lifeless, and lightless body behind.[1] The action of attractive power would sometimes reveal the existence of cold bodies, with specific gravity much in excess of our earth, as in the case of the satellite of Sirius, and the spectroscope would reveal clusters of stars or nebulæ in the various stages of development, such as the nebular hypothesis suggested as making up the genetic process of our planetary system. Much uncertainty and much conjecture must of course exist in these chapters of science, which those who are in full possession of the accumulated and yet very imperfect facts may venture to elaborate in a more or less plausible or fanciful manner. Such attempts to write the history of the universe have been made in an original fashion by M. Faye in France[2] and Sir Norman Lockyer[3] in this country. They have tried

51.
Genesis of
the cosmos
—Faye and
Lockyer.

[1] See Helmholtz, 'Vortrage und Reden,' vol. ii., 3rd ed., p. 88, &c.

[2] 'Sur l'Origine du Monde,' 2nd ed., Paris, 1885. The author, finding the celebrated cosmogonic hypothesis of Laplace in "full contradiction" with the actual state of science, takes up an original theory of Descartes, that of vortices, in order to characterise not the actual, but the initial, stage of the solar system (see Preface): "Autrefois, je veux dire il y a une vingtaine d'années, on avait les coudées franches pour imaginer un système cosmogonique : il suffisait de l'accommoder aux notions contemporaines d'Astronomie solaire et de mécanique céleste. Il n'en est plus de même aujourd'hui, car la thermodynamique assigne à notre Soleil une provision limitée de chaleur, l'Analyse spectrale nous révéle la constitution intime des astres les plus éloignés, et la palé-

ontologie nous fait remonter à des époques où il n'y avait, sur notre globe, ni saisons, ni climats."

[3] Whereas M. Faye has ingeniously modified the original and older nebular hypothesis so as to account for the anomalies in the movement of some of the members of our planetary system, which were unknown or unexplained in Laplace's time, and has tried to account for the phenomena of loss and supply of heat which thermodynamical theory and palæontological records reveal, Sir Norman Lockyer has during more than thirty years been occupied with the elaboration of a special theory which tries to harmonise the revelations of the spectroscope as to the chemical constitution of the sun and other stars with the more recent developments of the atomic theory as suggested by chemical and electrical phenomena observed in our labora-

to do what Professor Haeckel has done in the more restricted field of the history of the living creation. Whilst these attempts are by many scientific authorities con-

tories. His speculations, based upon his own observations as well as those of many other European and American authorities, such as Secchi, Dumas, Kayser and Runge, Rutherford, Rowland, Young, and, above all, of Sir W. Crookes and the late Professor Preston,—all of which, as well as many others, he generously quotes,—were given in three works 'The Chemistry of the Sun' (1887), 'The Meteoritic Hypothesis' (1890), and 'The Sun's Place in Nature' (1897). He has latterly collected the whole evidence in a brilliant and fascinating volume entitled 'Inorganic Evolution as studied by Spectrum Analysis' (1900). The central idea contained in these books, and elaborated with increasing detail and clearness, was suggested as early as 1873, when Sir N. Lockyer pointed out "that many of the difficulties would vanish if it were conceded that the 'atoms' of the chemist were broken up or dissociated into finer forms by the high temperatures employed in the new method of investigation" ('Inorg. Evol.,' p. 73). This "dissociation" hypothesis has been much criticised, and can only be firmly established by patient and prolonged research in that borderland which unites chemistry and astronomy. As the author says : "The chemist has little interest in an appeal to celestial phenomena, and astronomers do not generally concern themselves with chemistry. The region investigated by the chemist is a low temperature region, dominated by monatomic and polyatomic molecules. The region I have chiefly investigated is a high temperature region, in which mer-

cury gives us the same phenomena as manganese. In short, the changes with which spectrum analysis has to do take place at a far higher temperature level than that employed in ordinary chemical work." It is well to note that during and since the time when the dissociation hypothesis was first prominently put forward researches conducted on entirely different lines have led to similar views— i.e., to a further elaboration of the atomic hypothesis. M. Berthelot wrote in 1880 : " L'étude approfondie des propriétés physiques et chimiques des masses élémentaires, qui constituent nos corps simples actuels, tend chaque jour d'avantage à les assimiler, non à des atomes indivisibles, homogènes et susceptibles d'éprouver seulement des mouvements d'ensemble . . . il est difficile d'imaginer un mot et une notion plus contraires à l'observation ; mais à des édifices fort complexes, doués d'une architecture spécifique et animés de mouvements intestins très variés " (quoted in 'Inorg. Evol.,' p. 28). The first chemical confirmation of the dissociation hypothesis came in 1883 through the " beautiful researches on the rare earth Yttria," contained in Sir Wm. Crookes's Bakerian Lecture to the Royal Society. "In the lectures he gave a sketch of the train of reasoning by which he had been led to the opinion that . . . this stable molecular group had been (by a process termed 'fractionation') split up into its constituents " (ibid., p. 116) ; and already, in 1879, Sir Wm. Crookes had provisionally accepted the "dissociation" hypothesis (p. 74). Anomalies also in the periodic

sidered to be premature,[1] they have contributed much to impress on the thought of our age the genetic or developmental view on a large as well as on a minute scale.

law of Mendeléef were explained by utilising this hypothesis (p. 165), and in the sequel other authorities, such as Brodie and Rydberg, expressed themselves in the same sense (p. 164). These, and quite recently the electrical researches of Prof. J. J. Thomson (referred to *supra*, p. 192), support the view, originally suggested in a cruder form by Prout, that what we call elements are really compounds or aggregations or complexes, built up "from similar particles associated with the presence of electricity" ('Inorg. Evol.,' pp. 167, 190 ; also J. J. Thomson, 'Discharge of Electricity through Gases,' p. 198 *sqq*.)

[1] It would be unfair not to state that many works on astronomy are still written in which all genetic hypotheses are left out, the "statical" view being still the predominant one. Especially in Germany, it seems as if "inorganic evolution" is not very popular ; though a large amount of the best work in spectrum analysis of the stars has been done there by H. C. Vogel, Kayser and Runge, Scheiner, and many others. Dr Scheiner, in his valuable work (translated with the title 'A Treatise on Astronomical Spectroscopy,' by Prof. Frost of Dartmouth College, U.S.A., 1894), has some important criticisms on hypotheses and solar theories (see Preface, and the discussion of the Meteoritic Hypothesis in the German edition, Part II. chap. i.) In his 'Bau des Weltalls' (Leipzig, 1901) genetic views are not discussed. The older very valuable works of R. Wolf ('Gesch. d. Astronomie,' 1877, 'Handbuch der Astronomie,' 2 vols., 1890-92)

give only slight attention to "genetics," and consider even the "statics" of the universe though a possible yet a difficult problem (see the last-named work, §§ 298, 299). The latest and excellent 'History of Astronomy,' by Mr A. Berry (1898), is likewise reticent about the evolution of the universe, admitting only a general, fairly well-founded presumption in favour of a modified nebular hypothesis (p. 409). It would, therefore, be doubtful whether a history of science should, at the end of the nineteenth century, give much room to these modern genetic theories in astronomy. It is different with a history of scientific thought. However premature and venturesome it may appear to purists in science to elaborate such hypotheses, there is no doubt that the genetic arguments and lines of reasoning have got a firm hold of many great thinkers in the physics of the universe as well as in biology, and that the genetic view of nature in general has received very strong support from the several trains of reasoning and the rapidly increasing revelations of spectrum analysis of cosmical and terrestrial objects, as set forth in Sir N. Lockyer's interesting volumes. Already thirty years ago Lord Kelvin said of the spectroscope : "It is not merely the chemistry of sun and stars, as first suggested, that is subjected to analysis by the spectroscope. Their whole laws of being are now subjects of direct investigation ; and already we have glimpses of their evolutionary history through the stupendous power of this most subtle and delicate test.

It is intelligible that these different lines in the genetic view of nature—the different trains of reasoning which, in the course of our century, have started independently in astronomy, in geology, and in natural history—should, as they develop and expand, come into contact, and in the event either support or invalidate each other.   The former was the case when the geological record, the discoveries of palæontology, were brought in to throw light on the history and development of species ; the stories of nature, as written from the point of view of the embryologist, the systematic zoologist and botanist, and the palæontologist, seemed more and more to confirm and support each other.   The same cannot be said if we write the history of our earth from the point of view of the geological record on the one side and from that of the purely physical data afforded by thermodynamics on the other.   Lord Kelvin has shown [1] that the untold

52.
Palæonto-
logy and
geophysics.

We had only solar and stellar chemistry ; we now have solar and stellar physiology" (Presid. Address, Brit. Assoc., 1871.   See 'Popular Lectures and Addresses,' vol. ii. p. 180).

[1] The literature of the subject begins with Lord Kelvin's Address to the Geological Society of Glasgow, February 27, 1868, which had been preceded by a paper read before the Royal Society of Edinburgh in 1865, briefly refuting the "Doctrine of Uniformity in Geology." The address began with the words : "A great reform in geological speculation seems now to have become necessary," and in the sequel stated : "It is quite certain that a great mistake has been made—that British popular geology at the present time is in direct opposition to the principles of natural philo-

sophy." These papers are reprinted in the 2nd vol. of 'Popular Lectures and Addresses' (see pp. 10 and 44).   The attack was taken up by Huxley in his Address to the Geological Society for 1869, reprinted in 'Lay Sermons,' &c., 1891, p. 198.   In a rejoinder to this, delivered in the same year at Glasgow (loc. cit., p. 73), Lord Kelvin shows how the current geology was in the habit of looking upon geological time as "an element to which we can set no bounds in the past any more than we know of its limits in the future" (quoted from Page's 'Text-book '), that Darwin's arguments themselves involve an almost unlimited duration of the conditions admitting the operation of natural selection, since, in his view, "in all probability a far longer period than 300 million

ages with which geologists, since the time of Lyell, have been accustomed to reckon, are not supported by our present knowledge of the periods during which the so-called secular cooling of the earth has been going forward—the period which has elapsed since the "consistentior status" of Leibniz set in. He has thus put before natural philosophers a problem—the reconciliation of the geological and the thermophysical record—in which the genetic view of nature must be greatly interested. But even more important than all this is the doctrine of the dissipation of energy, referred to in the second chapter of this volume—a doctrine of which

53.
Dissipation
of energy.

years has elapsed since the latter part of the secondary period" ('Origin of Species,' 1st ed., p. 287). He shows that Hutton and the uniformitarians were misled by a belief in the so-called stability of the solar system, which took no notice of the effect of tidal friction, nor of the phenomena of radiation and cooling in the past, still less of the law of dissipation of energy, and maintains that the modern ideas of evolution are in a sense a return to the older conceptions of Leibniz, Newton, and other more recent geologists (*loc. cit.*, p. 111). Since the subject was thus brought prominently forward, astronomers, physicists, and geologists have not only—as Huxley expected them to do (see 'American Addresses,' 1886, p. 93)—adduced arguments in order to arrive at an approximate idea how long the earth may have been able to maintain organic life, but biologists have been induced to revise the postulates of the extreme —almost infinite—slowness, and of the uniform continuity of organic changes, originally contained in the Darwinian theory. The influence of these researches upon biological

and genetic reasoning has been to emphasise the sudden changes, the ruptures in the continuity of development. In England the great work of Mr William Bateson ('Materials for the Study of Variations,' 1894) has familiarised us with the idea of "Discontinuity" in the origin of species. On the Continent the rapid or even sudden appearance of variations is not a new idea, though the original suggestion of Maupertuis (1748), which was taken up and elaborated by Geoffroy St Hilaire (see Yves Delage, 'L'Hérédité,' p. 291), was forgotten. In quite recent years the reconciliation of the "persistence of species" with their "variability," and of the "geological" with the "biological" records, has been much furthered by the theory of "Mutation" of the celebrated Dutch botanist de Vries. His view is that "every species has its beginning and its end ; it behaves in this way like an individual." He refers to the experiments on heredity and crossing of butterflies of Standfuss, who has been led to maintain the existence of sudden or "explosive" transformations ; and he

the mechanical and cosmical importance was clearly foreseen by Lord Kelvin in 1852, but which is hardly
assimilated yet by scientific, much less by popular,
thought.

The two doctrines of the conservation of matter and
of energy would lead to the idea that nature is a kind
of *perpetuum mobile,* nothing in the way of matter or
energy being lost; and that such a reversal of her processes is possible as we are accustomed to deal with in
purely mechanical contrivances.   But a closer examination of the processes of nature, as distinguished from
those of artificial machines, revealed the fact that,

speaks of "periods of mutation"—
i.e., of rapid change of species, of
which he gives various instances.
He concludes that "as many steps
as the organisation has taken since
the beginning, so many periods of
'mutation' must have existed."
He considers the vital processes to
be built up out of "units."   "Of
such units there are probably in
the higher plants several thousands,
and their ancestors must have run
through as many periods of mutation."   He concludes with the
following words : "Although such
calculations are naturally exposed
to much criticism, they nevertheless lead on very different roads to
identical results.   Lord Kelvin,
who a few years ago collected and
examined critically the various data
referring to this subject, arrives at
the conclusion that provisionally,
and with all reservations, the duration of life on the earth can be
placed at 24 millions of years.   We
accordingly take this figure for our
biochronic equation.   And as we
can with great probability estimate
the number of elementary properties in one of the higher plants
at some thousands, it follows that
the interval of time between two
periods of mutation must have
lasted several thousands of years."
(See de Vries's Address to the German Assoc. of Science at Hamburg
in 1891, 'Verhandelungen,' &c., p.
202, &c. ; also Lord Kelvin (Phil.
Mag. (5.) 47, p. 66).   Mr Wallace
has, from an entirely different point
of view, been led to the conclusion
that "certain definite portions of
man's intellectual and moral nature
could not have been developed by
variation and natural selection alone,
and that, therefore, some other influence, law, or agency is required
to account for them."   This would
account for an apparent, though
perhaps not an actual, break in the
continuity of all natural processes,
which, in the dictum *natura non
facit saltum,* has received a very
general expression and acceptance.
This dictum—supported by the
authority of Leibniz—is, however,
by some modern thinkers de-
nounced as a scholastic and antiquated aphorism.   (See Yves
Delage, 'L'Hérédité,' &c., p. 266.)

though matter and energy be indestructible, the succession of phenomena, the changes and processes which we call the genesis or history of things, are dependent on the condition in which energy exists; it being a general tendency for energy not to be lost, but to become unavailable; change and action, the life of things everywhere, depending on an equalisation of existing differences, say of level or temperature, or quicker and slower motions. This great property of natural, as distinguished from purely mechanical, processes, explains the fact that the processes of nature are irreversible, that the clock cannot be turned back, that everything moves in a certain direction. Various attempts have been made to explain mechanically this remarkable property of all natural processes, which seems to lead us to the conception of a definite beginning and to shadow forth a possible end—the interval, which contains the life or history of nature, being occupied with the slow but inevitable running down or degradation of the great store of energy from an active to an inactive or unavailable condition.

54.
Mystery of
the actual
processes of
nature.

This doctrine of the degradation or dissipation of energy leads us one step farther towards an understanding, or at least a description, of the processes of nature, but also of their mystery. It has been urged that, as we always only deal with a small portion of existing things, we have no right to apply conceptions which are based upon a restricted observation to the totality of things in the universe. For instance, we know nothing of what becomes of the energy radiated away into empty space. This is a reflection we should always bear in mind. We have also been reminded that the theories of the so-called stability of the planetary system which were propounded in the earlier years of our century, and which have found their way into popular treatises on astronomy, are only approximations. On the other side, we have daily before our eyes the ever-recurring instances of the building up and running down of natural forces in smaller systems. These we term organisms, the living things of nature. It is from and through them that we first learnt to look upon the whole of nature as having a history and a life. Imperceptibly we have been led to study life, the genesis of things, on the large scale and in the abstract, and in doing so have lost sight of the life which goes on around and near us. Both the morphological and genetic views of nature started with a biological interest, but have gradually lost sight of it. It is time to come back to it and to see what real progress has been made during our century in the study of life itself—the truly biological view of nature. This will be the object of the next chapter.

CHAPTER X.

ON THE VITALISTIC VIEW OF NATURE.

In the foregoing chapters, where I have treated of the several distinct aspects of nature which have become helpful in science, I have always used the word nature in its widest sense as comprising everything which is revealed to us by our external senses, directly or indirectly.

The title of the present chapter may suggest to some of my readers that I am now narrowing down the meaning of the word,—the vitalistic view of nature being possible only where life is present. The astronomer might say, Life is only known to exist in an infinitesimally small portion of the universe, on the surface of our planet. This infinitesimal area has nevertheless for us the greatest importance, inasmuch as all that we know of the larger outlying world is only won by inference from observations made in this restricted portion. Independently of this, the conception of life itself has always fluctuated between the two extremes of considering it as a universal property of all matter, or on the other hand as quite a casual and accidental occurrence attached to conditions which, from a wider point of view, are extremely rare and exceptional.   Between these two views, the cosmical and the terrestrial, the wider [1] and the narrower views of life, biological theories have fluctuated even in our century, and are still fluctuating.

1.
The cosmi-
cal and the
terrestrial
views.

[1] One of the foremost upholders of the wider conception of animation as a universal property of all matter is the celebrated German naturalist, Prof. Ernst Haeckel of Jena. See, *inter alia*, his Address "Ueber die heutige Entwickelungslehre im Verhältnisse zur Gesammtwissenschaft," 1876, reprinted in 'Gesammelte populäre Vorträge,' &c., part ii., Bonn, 1879, p. 119: "The recent controversies regarding the properties of the Atoms, which we must accept in some form or other as the ultimate elementary factors of all physical and chemical processes, seem to be most easily settled by the assumption that these smallest particles of mass, as centres of force, possess a permanent soul, that every atom is endowed with sensation and motion," &c., p. 109: "Arriving at this extreme psychological consequence of our monistic doctrine of development, we attach ourselves to those ancient conceptions as to the animation of all matter which, in the philosophy of Democritus, Spinoza, Bruno, Leibniz, Schopenhauer, have already found varied expression." The cosmical origin of life has also been put forward by such authorities as Helmholtz and Lord Kelvin, as long ago as 1871. (See Helmholtz's lecture "On the Origin of the Planetary System," 'Popul. Vorträge,' &c., vol. ii. p. 91, and Lord Kelvin's celebrated address to the Brit. Assoc. at Edinburgh in 1871, reprinted in 'Pop. Lects.,' &c., vol. ii. p. 199, &c.) This theory of "Panspermia," of the cosmical or ubiquitous nature of the germs of life, has also been proposed by biologists such as H. E. Richter (1865), and has been more fully elaborated by Prof. W. Preyer since the year 1880 : it has received further support in the genetic theories of the chemical elements and compounds put forward by him in 1891 ('Die organischen Elemente und ihre Stellung im System,' Wiesbaden), and in 1893 ('Das genetische System der chemischen Elemente,' Berlin). Of the fourteen elements which are common to organic substances, he says (p. 49) "that they belong to the oldest elements"; that "they admit of more varied relations," and "agree with the assumption that, before being condensed as at present on the surface of the earth, they formed at higher temperatures more stable protoplasms which might be in other places the carriers of life"; and he has no doubt "that there existed before the present terrestrial phytoplasma and zooplasma another plasma, which ultimately came from the sun" (p. 50). In fact, Prof. Preyer asks whether, instead of living being evolved from dead matter, the latter is not rather a product of the former. See also the reference to organic evolution as a cosmical process in Sir N. Lockyer's 'Inorganic Evolution' (1900, p. 168). In many of the writings of the celebrated German physicist and philosopher, Gustav Theod. Fechner, the fact is emphasised that we never see the organic developed out of the inorganic, but that everywhere the living generates not only the living but more frequently the inanimate. See Lasswitz, 'G. T. Fechner,' Stuttgart, 1896, p. 130, &c.

No theory of the nature and origin of life has gained
universal acceptance: the very alphabet of biology, or
the science of life, has still to be written. We fancy
we possess some knowledge of certain forms or processes
which are common to all living matter, but the description of these has to be kept in the most general, not to
say the vaguest, terms: quite unlike the rudiments of
other scientific theories which deal with mathematically
defined conceptions expressed in distinct language and
formulæ.

2.
Vagueness
of biological
theories.

For instance, if we take one of the best founded of
modern biological theories — the cellular theory [1] of
living matter — we notice that the pretty definite
description which the early supporters of this theory—
Schleiden and Schwann—gave of this morphological
unit of vegetable and animal structure has been dis-
placed by much vaguer descriptions. Schleiden and

[1] The history of the cellular
theory has been written from various points of view in all the three
languages. I give the titles of a
few out of the great abundance
of excellent treatises. Foremost
stands the work of Prof. Oscar
Hertwig of Berlin, 'The Cell:
Outlines of General Anatomy and
Physiology.' English transl. by
Campbell (1895). Then there is
the more recent book by Prof.
Valentin Häcker of Freiburg,
'Praxis und Theorie der Zel-
len- und Befruchtungslehre' (Jena,
1899). In the French language
we have the great compendium of
biological theories by M. Yves
Delage, 'La Structure du Protoplasma et les Théories sur l'Hérédité,'&c. (Paris, 1895). In English
we have the valuable treatise of
Prof. E. B. Wilson, 'The Cell
in Development and Inheritance'
(1896), and the excellent little work
of Prof. James Arthur Thomson,
'The Science of Life' (1899). Of
high importance are also the older
works of the great master and
brilliant expositor in biological
science, Claude Bernard, notably
his celebrated lectures entitled
"Leçons sur les Phénomènes de la
vie communs aux animaux et aux
végétaux" (1878 and 1879), which
every philosophical student of
biology should read, as well as his
excellent posthumously published
little work, 'La science experi-
mentale,' 1890. Of him M. Dumas
says that he has "épuisé ses forces à
l'étude du grand mystère de la vie,
sans prétendre à pénétrer toutefois
son origine et son essence" ('Sci.
Exper.,' p. 6).

Schwann defined the cell as "a small vesicle with a firm membrane enclosing fluid content."[1] But the cellular theory was gradually replaced by the protoplasmic theory of Max Schultze, the distinct membrane was found to be frequently absent, and there only remained "a small mass of protoplasm endowed with the attributes of life." The cell, which had once been compared to a crystal, became a very complicated and indefinite thing: it became, in the conception of biologists, an "organism."[2] Further, the nucleus or kernel to which Schleiden attached great importance in his cellular theory was, for a while, quite lost sight of—it being for a long time held that there exist nonnucleated cells. Elaborate theories, such as that of Haeckel,[3] were founded upon this view, till in more

---

[1] O. Hertwig, 'The Cell,' p. 5 n.

[2] Treatises on the subject now usually begin with an apology, the word cell being considered misleading. Thus Hertwig says (loc. cit., p. 8), "It is evident that the term 'cell' is incorrect. That it has, nevertheless, been retained may be partly ascribed to a kind of loyalty to the vigorous combatants who conquered the whole field of histology under the banner of the cell-theory, and partly to the circumstance that the discoveries which brought about the new reform were only made by degrees, and were not generally accepted at a time when, in consequence of its having been used for several decades, the word cell had taken firm root in the literature of the subject."

[3] "Since, in consequence of the inadequacy of former methods, no nuclei had been discovered in many of the lower organisms, the existence of two kinds of elementary cells was assumed — more simple ones, consisting only of a mass of protoplasm, and more complex ones, which had developed in their interior a special organ, the nucleus. The former were called cytodes by Haeckel (1866), to the simplest solitary forms of which he gave the name of Monera; the latter he called cellulæ, or cytes. But since then the aspect of the question has been considerably changed. Thanks to the improvements in optical instruments and in staining methods, the existence of organisms without nuclei is now much questioned." (Hertwig, 'The Cell,' p. 54. See also Häcker, p. 239.) On the other side M. Delage says ('L'Hérédité,' p. 37), 'Après avoir découvert un noyau chez la plupart des monères et des cytodes et même chez les Bactéries, on a, par une induction à mon sens un peu hâtive, nié l'existence d'organismes sans noyau."

recent times, owing to improvements in the microscope, the existence of organisms without nuclei has become doubtful. To complicate matters still more, to the nucleus have been added the nucleolus, the vacuoles, the central or pole corpuscles of the cell, &c. It is quite evident from this short reference to the changes which the definition of the morphological unit of living matter has undergone, that no complete and accurate description lending itself to measurement and calculation could be based upon it. The conception, useful as it may be, has therefore not permitted of predictions, such as mechanical, physical, and even chemical science, abound in. " Has one ever," says Delage, " in a single instance divined in advance the least of those structures which the microscope has unveiled ? Has one divined the transverse striation of muscles, the cilia of vibratile epithelia, the prolongations of nerve-cells, the action of the retina or the arcades of Corti, the chromosomes of the nucleus, the centrosome of the cytoplasma ? "[1] Or, to take an example not from the morphology but from the physiology of organic cellular bodies. It is a very general and a very useful property of cells that they readily absorb substances ; in fact, this property is one of the most valuable aids in microscopic exam-

3. Impossibility of prediction.

[1] ' L'Hérédité,' &c., p. 746. Prof. Weismann, in his celebrated ' Essays upon Heredity ' (Engl. transl. by Poulton, &c., p. 255), claims for the theory of descent that " it has rendered possible the prediction of facts, not indeed with the absolute certainty of calculation, but still with a high degree of probability. It has been predicted that man, who, in the adult state, only possesses twelve pairs of ribs, would be found to have thirteen or fourteen in the embryonic state ; it has been predicted that, at this early period of his existence, he would possess the insignificant remnant of a very small bone in the wrist, the so-called *os centrale*, which must have existed in the adult condition of his extremely remote ancestors."

ination, insomuch as the different behaviour of different parts of the cellular body towards organic staining solutions reveals to the observer differences of structure otherwise indistinguishable. Yet Professor Pfeffer,[1] who has studied the absorbing powers of cellular substances with much care, states that these cannot in the least be foretold, but can only be determined empirically; nor is the fact that cells require some substances for their life, while others are harmful, sufficient to enable us to predict that either will be absorbed or rejected. Again, hybridisation has been much studied by gardeners and breeders, and also, since the time of Darwin, by naturalists; nevertheless, the result of cross-fertilisation of individuals belonging " to different families or species, or even only to different varieties," cannot be theoretically foretold, but " can only be discovered by means of experiment." [2]

This ignorance in which we are still placed as to the forms as well as functions of living matter, has been a subject of much comment by biologists all through the

[1] See W. Pfeffer, ' Ueber Aufnahme von Anilinfarben in lebende Zellen.' Untersuchungen aus dem botanischen Institut zu Tübingen. Quoted by Hertwig, ' The Cell,' p. 136.

[2] Hertwig, ' The Cell,' p. 310. Another point, strongly urged by Claude Bernard, is, that a knowledge of structure in living beings—*i.e.,* anatomical knowledge—in no wise suffices to explain the functions, does not lead to physiological knowledge. See ' La Science Expérimentale, p. 105, " L'impuissance de l'anatomie à nous apprendre les fonctions organiques devient surtout évidente dans les cas particuliers où elle est réduite à elle-même. Pour les organes sur les usages desquels la physiologie expérimentale n'a encore rien dit, l'anatomie reste absolument muette. C'est ce qui a lieu par exemple pour la rate, les capsules surrénales, le corps thyroïde, &c., tous organes dont nous connaissons parfaitement la texture anatomique, mais dont nous ignorons complètement les fonctions. De même, quand sur un animal on découvre un tissu nouveau et sans analogue dans d'autres organismes, l'anatomie est incapable d'en dévoiler les propriétés vitales."

century, nor can it be stated that uniformity of opinion exists even yet as to the cause of this ignorance. The enormous progress which has been made in our knowledge of the different properties of living things has had an effect on the minds of those searchers to whom we are mostly indebted for it, similar to that produced on a wanderer who ascends an unexplored and distant peak. Ever and anon, after scaling the eminence just before him, he beholds a new and greater one rising into view, which he contemplates with mixed feelings of discouragement and of eager desire for advance. But whereas our wanderer must know that the very greatest height or distance is none the less a measurable and attainable quantity, what hope has the biologist to encourage him on his way ? No other—as it appears to some—than the assurance that he is all the time exploring an unknown country, whereas the final achievement is impossible to him through the inaccessibility of the position or the limitation of his own powers. Others, indeed, from time to time have not taken this despondent view, but, elated by the triumphs which every new step has afforded them, have persistently maintained that some day the last step will be taken and the central peak really gained.

4.
Oscillation
of biological
thought.
The history of biological thought, as distinguished from biological knowledge, presents us with the spectacle of a repeated oscillation between these two extreme views : on the one side the continually recurring conviction that the problem of life is insoluble, and, on the other, the assertion that it is soluble, though

it is admittedly as yet unsolved. Biological knowledge itself has progressed on the same lines as chemical, physical, and mechanical knowledge; it registers the progressive conquest of new regions of phenomena exhibited by living matter through the methods which have been discovered in the abstract sciences: but it has generally been felt that this knowledge does not exhaust the subject; that there is some principle involved which we know not; and that we cannot think about the living portion of creation without consciously or unconsciously admitting the existence of this principle. The unknown—nay, possibly, the unknowable—element or factor must be admitted to exist, and it involuntarily governs our reflections on that which we know. To show the difference between reflections on biological and on other phenomena, which, though equally unknown, yet do not contain an admittedly unknown factor, it may be useful to refer to the scientific way of dealing with meteorological phenomena. The science of meteorology is probably as young as that of biology, if not younger. Prediction of the weather is probably even more uncertain than the prognosis of a physician at the bedside of a patient suffering from a malignant disease. Yet no one would suggest that there is a special meteorological principle involved, as in the case of the phenomena of life and death there is a special biological principle. We are quite satisfied that purely mechanical and physical and possibly chemical processes make up the whole of the weather problem, and that the difficulty of the latter is simply one of

5.
The unknown factor.

complexity and intricacy. A similar [1] attitude has in the course of our century frequently been taken up with regard to the problem of life, but it has always been abandoned again.[2] We are still told that "in

[1] See, for instance, what Huxley, who, in his earlier writings, might be termed a vitalist (cf. his address "On the Educational Value of the Natural History Sciences," 1854, and his own criticism thereof in the preface, dd. 1870, in 'Lay Sermons and Addresses'), says in his article "Biology," 1875, in the 'Ency. Brit.,' vol. iii. p. 681 : "A mass of living protoplasm is simply a molecular machine of great complexity, the total results of the working of which, or its vital phenomena, depend—on the one hand, upon its construction, and on the other, upon the energy supplied to it ; and to speak of 'vitality' as anything but the name of a series of operations, is as if one should talk of the 'horology' of a clock." Similarly Claude Bernard, in his 'Leçons sur les phénomènes de la vie,' &c., vol. i. p. 379, says : "En un mot, le phénomène vital est pré-établi dans sa forme, non dans son apparition. . . . La nature est intentionelle dans son but, mais aveugle dans l'éxecution." Both Huxley's comparison of an organism with a clock and the quotation from Claude Bernard suggest a parallel between the dictum of Archimedes : "δός μοι ποῦ στῶ καὶ τὸν κόσμον κινήσω," and a possible one of a biologist : "Give me an organism, and I will explain its action mechanically." In another place Claude Bernard says (loc. cit., ii. p. 524) : "L'élément ultime du phénomène est physique ; l'arrangement est vital."

[2] Examples of this could be multiplied indefinitely. I take one from an entirely different field. Prof. Kerner von Marilaun, the celebrated botanist, says ('The Natural History of Plants,' transl. by Dr Oliver, 1894, vol. i. p. 52) : "In former times a special force was assumed—the force of life. More recently, when many phenomena of plant life had been successfully reduced to simple chemical and mechanical processes, this vital force was derided and effaced from the list of natural agencies. But by what name shall we now designate that force in nature which is liable to perish whilst the protoplasm suffers no physical alteration, and in the absence of any extrinsic cause ; and which yet, so long as it is not extinct, causes the protoplasm to move, to inclose itself, to assimilate certain kinds of fresh matter coming within the sphere of its activity and to reject others, and which, when in full action, makes the protoplasm adapt its movements under external stimulation to existing conditions in the manner which is most expedient ? This force in nature is not electricity nor magnetism ; it is not identical with any other natural force, for it manifests a series of characteristic effects which differ from those of all other forms of energy. Therefore I do not hesitate again to designate as vital force this natural agency, not to be identified with any other, whose immediate instrument is the protoplasm, and whose peculiar effect we call life." Another example is that of Prof. Virchow, to whom we are indebted for the great revolution which the application of the novel conceptions of the cellular theory has worked in the

accepting a mechanical conception," we must not " fall into the very common mistake of trying to explain vital processes as being due directly to mechanical causes." It has been quite as impossible to banish the word life from the biological vocabulary as it has been to banish the word " ought " from the ethical. Biological knowledge has become purely chemical, physical, and mechanical, but not so biological thought. The question " What is life ? " still haunts us. Let us see what position the foremost representatives of modern biological research have taken up to this question. We find that they can be divided into two classes.

First, there are those who have studied the pheno- mena of living matter solely by the means which the advancing sciences of dynamics, physics, and chemistry have placed at their command. To them biology is an applied science. The question " What is life ? " is, ac- cording to their view of method, only to be solved by degrees, by bringing the forms and processes manifested in the living world more and more under the sway of observation, measurement, and possibly calculation. The central problem as to the essence of life and the

6.
The purely scientific aspect.

field of pathology. After having assisted in banishing the older vitalism, he, to the dismay of many of his own school, reintro- duced the conception of a vital principle in a well-known review entitled " Old and New Vital- ism," in his own journal (vol. ix. p. 20). " Indeed, the living body consists, so far as we know, of substances of the same kind as we find in 'lifeless nature,' and these substances have not only no other properties and powers in the living body, but they do not even lose any of them. . . . Never- theless, we cannot see how the phenomena of life can be under- stood simply as an assemblage of the natural forces inherent in those substances : rather do I consider it necessary to distinguish as an es- sential factor of life an impressed derived force in addition to the molecular forces. I see no ob- jection to designating this force by the old name of vital force."

consensus of many mechanical, physical, and chemical processes in the living organism does exist, but it can only be answered by attacking it from all sides and reducing it to ever narrower issues. The stronghold in which life is intrenched is to be conquered by surrounding it on all sides by the attacking forces of dynamics, physics, and chemistry. It will have to yield some day, though that day may be far off. The number of those who treat biology in this way has increased very much ever since Descartes,[1] and still more Lavoisier, applied

---

[1] The claims of Descartes to be considered as one of the founders of modern physiology are put forward by Huxley in several of his addresses, notably in that of 'On Descartes' Discours,' &c., 1870 ('Lay Sermons,' &c., p. 279); and in that on 'The Connection of the Biological Sciences with Medicine,' 1881 ('Science and Culture,' p. 325). In the latter address he says: "Now the essence of modern, as contrasted with ancient, physiological science, appears to me to lie in its antagonism to animistic hypotheses and animistic phraseology. It offers physical explanations of vital phenomena, or frankly confesses that it has none to offer. And, so far as I know, the first person who gave expression to this modern view of physiology, who was bold enough to enunciate the proposition that vital phenomena, like all the other phenomena of the physical world, are, in ultimate analysis, resolvable into matter and motion, was René Descartes. . . . And as the course of his speculations led him to establish an absolute distinction of nature between the material and the mental worlds, he was logically compelled to seek for the explanation of the phenomena of the material world within itself" (p. 335). It is interesting to contrast with this announcement of the banishment of the animistic aspect from modern physiology what Prof. Bunge says in the introductory chapter to his well-known 'Text-book on Physiological and Pathological Chemistry' (Engl. transl. by Woolridge, 1890): "The mystery of life lies hidden in activity. But the idea of action has come to us, not as the result of sensory perception, but from self-observation, from the observation of the will as it occurs in our consciousness, and as it manifests itself to our internal sense" (p. 7). "Physiological inquiry must commence with the study of the most complicated organism, that of man. Apart from the requirements of practical medicine, this is justified by the following reason, which leads us back to the starting-point of our remarks: that in researches upon the human organism we are not limited to our physical senses, but also possess the advantage afforded by the 'internal sense' or self-observation" (p. 11). "The essence of vitalism does not lie in being content with a term and abandoning reflection, but in adopting the only right path of obtaining knowledge, which is possible, in starting

the purely scientific or exact method to the study of the organism.

But biology is not only a subject of purely scientific interest.   There is a second and larger class of students —those who study biology as the basis of the art of healing, the medical profession.   To them the question of life and death, of the normal or abnormal co-operation of many processes in the preservation of health or the phenomena of disease, is of prime interest : the knowledge of the mechanical, physical, and chemical properties and reactions of living matter, of the construction of the organs and their functions, is only the means to an end.   Before the time of Lavoisier, with the solitary exception of Descartes, biology was studied only by medical men ; indeed to them both the existence and the progress of the science were entirely due.   For them the paramount questions must always be, " What is life ? What is its origin ?   What is death ?   What are its causes ?   What is disease ? "   To this class of students we are indebted for again and again bringing forward and trying to answer these fundamental, these central questions.[1]

By the other, the smaller yet increasing class of purely scientific biologists, we are being continually told that these questions are premature or metaphysical,[2] and

*7.
Influence of medicine.*

from what we know, the internal world, to explain what we do not know, the external world " (p. 12).

[1] See, for example, the two very interesting and suggestive addresses by Prof. Ed. von Rindfleisch of Würzburg, 'Ärztlich Philosophie' (Würzburg, 1888), and ' Neo-Vitalismus' (Verhandl. d. Ges. deutscher Naturforscher und Ärzte zu Lübeck, 1895, vol. i. p. 111).

[2] See Claude Bernard, 'La Science Expérimentale,' 3me ed., p. 211 : " La vie est l'idée directrice ou la force évolutive de l'être ; . . . mais l'erreur serait de croire que cette force métaphysique est active à la façon d'une force physique. . . . La force métaphysique évolutive par laquelle nous pouvons caracteriser la vie est inutile à la science, parce qu'étant en dehors des forces

that the answer which we may give to them is of no scientific importance and of no scientific value. The question, "What is electricity? What is the ether?" cannot yet be answered; nevertheless the sciences which deal with the properties of the ether or of electrical bodies are advancing daily. So also—we are told—does the science of biology progress, even though we leave the question "What is life?" unanswered. This would be a tenable position if the living organism were like an electrical or an optical apparatus, constructed by man himself with the modicum of knowledge which he possesses. But the living organism, the eye that can see or the nervous system that is in action, or even the smallest "autonomous" cell, visible only with the microscope, are each an apparatus constructed by nature with the employment of all the intricate agencies which are at her command. In dealing with such an apparatus, we are again and again tempted to ask, "What is life? On what does the normal and healthy co-operation of all parts in the living organism depend? In what does it consist?" Fragmentary knowledge may be well enough so far as it goes, but every medical practitioner must painfully feel it to be altogether insufficient. Where practical interests are involved we cannot indefinitely postpone our answers. Science can wait and

physiques elle ne peut exercer aucune influence sur elles. Il faut donc ici séparer le monde métaphysique du monde physique phénoménal qui lui sert de base, mais qui n'a rien à lui emprunter. . . . En résumé, si nous pouvons définir la vie à l'aide d'une conception métaphysique spéciale, il n'en reste pas moins vrai que les forces mécaniques, physiques, et chimiques, sont seules les agents effectifs de l'organisme vivant, et que la physiologiste ne peut avoir à tenir compte que de leur action. Nous dirons avec Descartes: on pense métaphysiquement, mais on vit et on agit physiquement."

content itself with the known and the knowable.   Practice is placed face to face with the unknown and the
unknowable.[1]   Thus the question will again and again
be asked, "What is life?"   And for the benefit or
injury of mankind theories will exist which profess to
handle this delicate problem successfully, even as
weather-prophets will always exist though the necessary
knowledge for accurate prediction is still wanting.

One of the first in time and eminence in the course of
the nineteenth century to whom we are indebted, not

8.
Practice
urges the
question :
What is
Life?

9.
Bichat.

[1] See what Theod. Bischoff, one
of the first and foremost German
anatomists of the new school, says
in his Éloge of Liebig (München,
1874), p. 60.   "Inorganic science is
not any way induced and is much
less obliged to forsake the road
from the known to the unknown.
But what would have been the
result, what would still be the
result, if, in all our researches into
organised nature, and yet more in
all our actions which have reference to our state of health or ill-
health, we had proceeded, or were
now to proceed, only from data
firmly established as to cause and
connection ?   Could we then so much
as take a morsel into our mouths
or treat a cold otherwise than with
fear and trembling ?   Physiologists
and doctors have surely always been
ready to proceed according to the
methods of exact science so far as
this was developed.   But so long as
this gave but a stone instead of
bread, acceptance could not be
thought of ;   necessity compelled
us to make some attempt towards
the solution of questions, to invent
some language in order to gain an
understanding ;   and through this
frequently an erroneous procedure
has arisen which outlives the means
for its correction."   "Physiology,"
says Du Bois-Reymond (Éloge of
Joh. Müller, 'Reden,' vol. ii. p.
199), "is the only science in which
one is obliged to speak about things
which one does not know.   Chemistry need not treat of unknown
compounds, nor physics of undiscovered forces ;   botany and zoology
do not mind what kind of animals
may still move about unknown
among unknown vegetation in unexplored regions.   But in physiology, even if we confine ourselves
to man, a definite number of things
is given which must be dealt with.
The spleen, the thyroid gland, the
thymus, the suprarenal capsules ;
many parts of the brain, ganglia,
nerves, the labyrinth of the ear—all
these are there, and must, according
to the customary view, be there for
something.   Manifold suppositions
as to the functions of these parts,
seemingly supported or invalidated
by pathological experience, have
put in the place of absolute darkness a twilight which is richer in
delusions though not in certainty.
The expounder of our science is
obliged to lead his pupils through
this twilight on an anxious path,
and then meet in return with that
discouragement which really is
owing to the subject itself."

indeed for the name, but for the modern science and direction of biology, was Xavier Bichat, who during the short period of his remarkable career (1771 to 1802) remodelled biological studies. He approached the sub-ject from the side of medicine and in a philosophical spirit. In 1800 there appeared two treatises, one on the membranes and tissues, and another entitled " Recherches physiologiques sur la vie et la mort." These by their titles already reveal the twofold aspect of biological science which drew the attention of Bichat and his school. First, the attempt to reform biological and medical knowledge by a close anatomical examination of organic tissues in their normal and diseased states, for the purpose of which he, within a very short time, ex-amined six hundred corpses. The fuller account of his researches is given in the four volumes of the 'Anatomie Générale' (1801) and in the posthumous five volumes of the 'Anatomie Descriptive,' completed by some of his numerous pupils and followers after his death. In these works Bichat created the science of histology without resorting to the microscope, which was to do such good service in the hands of those who came after him, and without that application of physical and chemical principles which during his time (notably by Lavoisier and his school) had been applied with much success in the theory of animal combustion and in the foundation of another new science—that of organic chemistry. The reasons which inclined Bichat to distrust the microscope were the delusive nature of the revelations of the imperfect instruments then in use. They disappeared when, in the course of the next thirty years, the instrument was gradually improved. The reasons which prevented Bichat from treating biology as an application of physics and chemistry lay deeper, and were rooted in the second great idea which governed him and his school—his "Vitalism." As stated above, those who have studied the phenomena of life can be divided into two classes. There are those who have been struck by the resemblance of the processes and phenomena in living matter with those in dead or unorganised matter: their attention has been directed more and more to establishing a parallelism between organic and inorganic nature, and they have frequently ended in the conviction that their parallelism warrants us in asserting their ultimate identity. There have been others who have been impressed with the essential and fundamental difference between organic and inorganic processes and phenomena. To them, all attempts to reduce the living process to a mechanism seem to have failed, and however much they have appreciated the insight gained by the other class of students, they have deemed it equally important to emphasise the essential difference—the independence, originality, and incommensurability of the phenomena of life. The latter can be called Vitalists in the broadest sense of the term. Bichat belonged to them. As the former class of students have frequently arrived at the thesis that organic and inorganic processes are ultimately identical, so the latter have frequently arrived at the thesis that they are fundamentally opposed and antagonistic. Bichat gives expression to this view in his celebrated definition of life, as the totality of those

10.
His vitalism.

11.
His definition of life.

functions which resist death. He adopts, on the one
side, the method of looking for the explanation of the
phenomena of matter in the properties of matter. In
the introduction to the 'Anatomie Générale,' he says: [1]
"The connection of the properties as causes with the
phenomena as effects is an axiom which has become
almost tiresome to repeat nowadays in physics and
chemistry: if my book establishes an analogous axiom
in the physiological sciences, it will have fulfilled its
purpose." But being convinced of the essential difference
of the object with which the physiologist is concerned,

[1] Claude Bernard (1813-78), from whose various writings the passages of Bichat are mostly taken, has very fully analysed the theoretical views of his eminent predecessor. The following books belong to the best, in substance and notably in style, that have been written on the subject: 'La Science Expérimentale,' 3me ed., 1890; especially: 'Definition de la vie,' p. 149, &c.: 'Leçons sur les Phénomènes de la vie communs aux animaux et aux végétaux,' 1878, especially vol. i. p. 57, &c.; 'Rapport sur les progrès et la marche de la Physiologie générale en France,' 1867. Introduction. Although Bichat was a vitalist, he took a first and important step in the direction of getting out of the vitalistic conceptions which he inherited from Haller, and which had assumed a special form in the Montpellier school. Through his foundation of physiological research upon an anatomical study of tissues, he localised the problem of physiology. Had he proceeded further on the lines he himself started, he would have thrown off, like his successors, notably Magendie, the hypothetical distinction between physical, chemical, and vital properties, and become a pure ex-

perimentalist. The founder of this purely experimental school in France was Magendie (1783-1855). It is interesting to note that prior to Magendie in France, Charles Bell in London had led up to experimental physiology in England by his famous distinction between sensory and motor nerves (1811). But, according to Claude Bernard, this anatomical distinction required experimental verification in a living animal. Magendie furnished this in 1822, and, together with this corner-stone of modern physiology, laid the foundations of the art of vivisection, with all its wonderful discoveries and its disfavour in certain quarters. There is no doubt that for many years Paris became, through this innovation, the centre of medical teaching on the Continent. As to the distinctive merits of Bell and Magendie, see Claude Bernard's exhaustive examination ('Physiol. gén.,' p. 11, &c.), but also Du Bois-Reymond's Eloge of Johannes Müller ('Reden,' vol. ii. p. 176, &c.) According to him the "Thesis" of Bell was not generally considered to be proved till after Müller's experiments in 1831.

he does not advance to the position that the same method will lead to parallel results. "There are," he says, "in nature two classes of things, two classes of properties, two classes of sciences. Beings (things) are organic or inorganic, their properties are vital or non-vital, the sciences are physical or physiological." He did not anticipate that a faithful examination of the properties of organised matter, of membranes and tissues —which should not be limited to lifeless corpses—would more and more reveal that their properties, the forces acting on and in them, could be analysed into the same forces as those we find in the inorganic world.[1]

[1] According to Claude Bernard ('Physiol. gén.,' p. 5, &c.), three things were wanting at the beginning of the nineteenth century to place physiology on a satisfactory basis. The first—anatomical knowledge of the structure of living matter—was brilliantly established by Bichat. But Bichat was not a physiologist : he neglected the second requisite, the study of the continual conflict between the living organism and the mechanical influences of the "milieux," the environment. "Il faudra"—says Bernard—"tenir compte de deux ordres de conditions : 1°, des conditions anatomiques de la matière organisée qui donnent la nature ou la forme des phénomènes physiologiques ; 2°, des conditions physico - chimiques ambiantes qui déterminent et reglent les manifestations vitales." A third impulse was wanted in physiology : "il fallait la ramener définitivement à la méthode des sciences expérimentales ; il fallait la pousser avec vigueur dans la direction des expériences sur les organismes vivants, afin de la détourner de la voie des hypothèses et des explications prématurées dans laquelle elle s'était si souvent égarée. Un grand physiologiste français, Magendie, mon maître, est venu, au commencement de ce siècle, exercer cette action générale sur la science physiologique, en même temps qu'il l'enrichissait par ses propres découvertes. Magendie fut élevé dans l'école anatomique de Paris, mais il n'était point disposé à suivre les successeurs de Bichat dans leurs explications hypothétiques. Doué d'un esprit précis et pénétrant, sceptique et indépendant, il fut lié de bonne heure avec Laplace, qui le patronna. Par cette influence il se trouva encore fortifié dans son antipathie innée pour les explications physiologiques dans lesquelles on ne se payait que de mots. Puis, par une tendance spontanée de réaction qui, à cette époque, fut très utile à la physiologie, il s'arrêta à l'expérimentation empirique, c'est-à-dire au résultat brut de l'expérience considérée en dehors de toute interprétation et de tout raisonnement."

Bichat, as Claude Bernard has told us,[1] thus clearly and eloquently found the expression or "formula for the fleeting ideas of his age. All the ideas of his contemporaries regarding life, all their attempts to define it, are, in a way, only the echo and paraphrase of his doctrine." We find it repeated by surgeons like Pelletan, who practised in the Hôtel Dieu, and by great naturalists like Cuvier, who founded comparative anatomy. To both of these life was a contest, a struggle, as it is at the end of the century to the Darwinians; but it was a struggle of the living forces against the dead, whereas nowadays it is the struggle of the living for supremacy amongst each other or a process of adaptation to external conditions. Whilst there is this great difference between these two views characterising respectively the beginning and the end of our century, they have one point in common——they both emphasise the unrest, the continued change, the extreme mobility which distinguishes living matter. But even this distinction has ceased during the course of the century to impress us so much as it did Bichat; since the stability of the solar system proclaimed by Laplace has ceased to charm astronomers, and the dictum of ancient science has been refuted: "materiam cœli esse inalterabilem." [2]

12.
Vitalism and
Darwinism.

[1] 'La Science Expérimentale,' p. 164.

[2] Claude Bernard (*loc. cit.*, p. 172, &c.) dwells on this point with great eloquence. "Aujourd'hui l'esprit des astronomes est familiarisé avec l'idée d'une mobilité et d'une évolution continuelle du monde sidéral. Les astres n'ont pas toujours existé, dit M. Faye; ils ont eu une période de formation; ils auront pareillement une période de déclin, suivie d'une extinction finale. . . . Les astronomes, avant de connaître les lois des mouvements des corps célestes, avaient imaginé de puissances, des forces sidérales, comme les physiologistes reconnaissaient des forces et des puissances vitales. Kepler lui-même admettait un esprit recteur sidéral par l'influence

After the age of Bichat, and largely through his influence,—*i.e.*, through the cultivation of anatomical researches,—the pendulum swung in the direction of proving more and more the parallelism of organic and inorganic processes. It reached its maximum swing in that direction about the second third of the century. Since then it appears to have again returned in the opposite direction. Let us follow this movement somewhat more closely, and see how the stronghold in which the innermost secret of life is intrenched has been attacked from all sides by all the processes and methods of the mechanical, physical, and chemical sciences, and how it has persistently refused to surrender.[1] There was a time when the leading repre-

duquel les planètes suivent dans l'espace des courbes savantes sans heurter les astres qui fournissent d'autres carrières, sans troubler l'harmonie réglée par le divin géomètre." Another property which was once thought peculiar to and characteristic of living organisms, that of regeneration after mutilation, of "redintegration," is now known to exist also in lifeless structures: "M. Pasteur a signalé des faits de cicatrisation, de rédintégration cristalline, qui méritent toute notre attention. . . . Ces faits . . . se rapprochent complètement de ceux que présentent les êtres vivants lorsqu'on leur fait une plaie plus ou moins profonde " (ibid., p. 173).

[1] Bischoff, in his Éloge of Liebig, who remained all his life a vitalist, says (p. 57): " We must, indeed, as in the exact sciences, guard against letting a mere word step in as an explanation, wherever our insight into the conditioning causes has been insufficient, as was indeed repeatedly done formerly, when a word was considered to be a suffi-

cient reason. We must consider it to be the continual duty of organic science to wage, as it were, a constant war against this organic force, and to dispute its territory wheresoever possible. If, for example, a talent like his succeeds in deducing many morphological traits of the higher animal organisms from the mechanical conditions of growth in the embryo, &c., we shall gratefully accept the proof ; but we must all the while not forget to ask the further question, by whom these mechanical conditions have been brought together. If it be further true that the cells of the embryo perform the most extraordinary wanderings, in order to arrange themselves into the various tissues and organs of the animal body, we shall welcome this as a very interesting and remarkable phenomenon in the obscure region of development ; but we have received no light on the question who acts as guide to the wandering cells. Similarly, if chemistry should some day succeed in forming albumen ar-

sentatives of the medical profession considered it
unworthy and degrading to treat the human frame
as a mechanism, and to approach it by the methods
used in other sciences. "For the vitalist physician,"
says Helmholtz,[1] "the essential part of the vital processes did not depend on natural forces which act
according to fixed laws. What these could do appeared of secondary importance, and a study of them
hardly worth the trouble. He thought to be face to
face with something soul-like,"—the anima of Stahl,
the vital force of the vitalists,—" which had to be met
by a thinker, a philosopher, a man of spirit. •. . . Aus-
cultation and percussion were practised in the hos-
pitals,[2] but I have heard it said that these were crude

tificially, we shall probably be able
to date from that day an entirely
new period in natural science, but
this artificial production of albumen
will never be feasible through the
simple affinities of the elements,
but only by producing a new
arrangement in organic substances
already formed by the plant. We
shall gratefully receive all such
increase of our knowledge : we do
not require wonders and belief in
miracles for the vital force, but
only a name for the effects of
which we do not know the
causes. . . . Neither the ancient
primæval ooze nor the modern
Bathybius, neither the remote
monads nor the recent monera,
neither protoplasm, nor nucleus
and cell and their development,
confessedly so simple and easily
understood up to self - conscious
man, give us the smallest clue
to the forces at work and their
origin. This induces us to ascribe
them to a force, regarding the
essence of which we indeed know

no more than we know of any
cause that cannot be further analysed. But we admit in doing
so the imperfection of our knowledge, and do not deceive others
by suggesting that mechanical
science could solve the secret of
organised nature."
[1] ' Vorträge und Reden,' vol. ii.
p. 179.
[2] Chr. Fried. Nasse (1778-1851),
since 1822 professor at Bonn,
where, together with Walther,
Joh. Müller, and others, he cultivated the physiological method
in medicine, "was, as it seems,
the first German doctor in whose
clinical institute physical diagnosis
was introduced. From 1820 onward percussion was practised ;
since 1821 the stethoscope was
regarded as an indispensable instrument" (Haeser, ' Geschichte
der Medizin,' 3rd ed., Jena, 1881,
p. 912). "The thermometer was
first used extensively at the bedside by James Currie (1756-1805).
His ' Medical Reports on the effect

mechanical devices which a physician with a clear mental vision did not require: moreover, the patient would thereby be degraded and treated as a machine. Feeling of the pulse was the most direct method of ascertaining the reactive power of the vital forces, and was delicately practised as the most important process. Elderly practitioners considered counting with a second-watch as hardly good taste: taking the temperature was not thought of.   As to the eye-mirror, a highly celebrated surgical colleague told me he would never use the instrument, it being dangerous to throw brilliant light into suffering eyes: another declared the mirror might do well for oculists with poor sight; he himself possessed very good eyes and did not need it. . . . A celebrated professor of physiology had an argument with his colleague in physics regarding the images in the eye.   The professor of physics invited him of physiology to come and see the experiment.   This was indignantly refused: a physiologist should have nothing to do with experiments, which might do well enough for a physicist."

The first great attack upon the organic system of forces, upon the citadel of life, was made by chemistry, and was led by Lavoisier and the great school of chemists which continued his work.   In consisted in the application of the theory of combustion, in which oxygen played such an important part, to the processes of respiration,

14.
Attack from
the side of
chemistry.

of water, cold and warm, as a remedy in fever and other diseases,' London, 1797, "contains observations on the variations of the body-temperature. . . . But these attempts had little success. Not till the middle of the nineteenth century was the importance of medical thermometry recognised, first through the classical work of von Bärensprung (1851), then through that of Traube, but mainly through Wunderlich " (ibid., p. 930).

nutrition, and the generation of animal heat.[1] Already in
1783 Lavoisier and Laplace had presented a memoir to
the Paris Academy of Sciences, in which they attributed
the generation of animal heat mainly to a process of
combustion which took place by the conversion of oxygen into fixed air during the process of respiration.
Lavoisier continued his researches on these and other
similar physiological processes, such as perspiration,
along with Séguin. They presented a joint memoir
on the subject in 1790. It is also known, through
the posthumous publication of Lavoisier's scientific
papers in 1862, long after Liebig had brought out his
series of researches on this matter, that the former had
entertained very correct views on the economy of organic
life as it exists in the balance of the animal and vegetable creations. After Lavoisier, the application of the
new science of chemistry to questions of the individual
and collective life of organisms was extended in a series

[1] The two great discoveries of oxygen and of the electric current at the close of the eighteenth century were not long in being applied to the reform of medical doctrine. In both instances exaggerated theories were not wanting. Fourcroy, himself a medical student by profession and one of the most ardent followers and promoters of the new chemistry, who, moreover, edited a journal with the title 'La médecine éclairée par les sciences physiques' (1790-92), found it nevertheless necessary to give warning against the premature introduction into medical teaching of the new ideas of chemistry. Of this many instances existed, both in France and Germany, such as the 'Essai d'un système chimique de la science de l'homme' (1798), by J. P. T. Baumes of Montpellier, against which Fourcroy aimed his criticisms in a letter to Humboldt. On these extravagances see Haeser, 'Geschichte der Medicin,' vol. ii. p. 737, &c. ; also Dr A. Hirsch, 'Gesch. d. medicin. Wissenschaften in Deutschland' (München, 1893, p. 567). There is no doubt that opposition to this one-sided application of some chemical or physical theory, or of some special therapeutic method, which might be valuable to a limited and restricted degree, partly accounted for the fact that the more thinking members of the profession clung to the notion of a vital force or principle, as yet undefined but nevertheless existent.

of very valuable but unconnected researches in all the different countries where chemistry was cultivated. Priestley, in England, had noticed the purifying effect of plants on air; De Saussure, in a series of remarkable experiments, carried on in the last years of the eighteenth century at Geneva, established the fact that in sunlight plants increase the quantity of carbon and other constituents in their tissues. Ingenhousz in Holland and Senebier in France had shown that in the presence of sunlight bubbles of oxygen gas are given off by plants when plunged under water, and had traced this oxygen to its source, the carbonic acid in the atmosphere. Sir Humphry Davy had applied chemistry to agriculture; and, much later, German physiologists like Tiedemann and Johannes Müller had recognised the necessity of explaining the processes in the living body chemically. All these labours, however, were detached, and their value was little known. It was therefore a very timely proposal which issued from the British Association in 1839, that a report on the present state of organic chemistry should be drawn up. For this task no less a person than Justus Liebig was selected.[1] The event

[1] The sources of information on Liebig's great work in revolutionising the science of life through his application of organic chemistry to agriculture and physiology are numerous. In particular there are two addresses by Vogel and von Bischoff, delivered in the Munich Academy in 1874, Hofmann's "Faraday" lecture, delivered in the Royal Institution in 1875, and a very able summary, drawn mainly from these sources by Mr W. A. Shenstone, in Cassell's 'Century Science' Series (1895), entitled "Justus von Liebig, his Life and Work." Bischoff's address contains a very full discussion of Liebig's vitalistic sympathies. His great influence was established as much by his special scientific discoveries as by his method of teaching,—by his early attempts to popularise science and make it an educational power through his well-known 'Familiar Letters.' He was in this respect a pioneer, as after him Helmholtz and Du Bois-Reymond were pioneers in spreading scientific ideas by means of popular lectures and addresses.

marks an epoch equally in the science of organic chemistry proper and in the life-work of Liebig. The necessity of collecting and systematising the scattered labours of chemists and physiologists in this department was simultaneously felt in France, where Liebig's friend and rival, Dumas, published his 'Essai de Statique chimique des Êtres organisés' as a conclusion to his course of

Liebig broke through the barriers which in his age separated science in Germany from general culture, and the university professor from the man of the world. From France he learnt the merit of a clear style, and from England the higher art of popularisation. His fame did not grow slowly and surely like that of Helmholtz, spreading almost imperceptibly from narrower into ever wider circles : he took the world by surprise, and stirred up everywhere inquiry, opposition, and controversy. He ventured on great and sweeping generalisations and on daring experiments and prophecies, with the result that in the final establishment of truth his opponents had frequently as great a share as himself. Notable instances are his so-called "mineral theory" of manuring and his theory of fermentation. Through the former the great division which separated the processes in the living from those which obtained in the inanimate (mineral) world was broken down ; and through the latter the modern notions of the ubiquity and continuity of life were to a large extent established, as will be seen in the sequel of this chapter. The correct notions which he entertained as to the necessity of the mineral ingredients (phosphoric acid, lime, potash, &c.) in plant-manures, which he started in opposition to the older "humus" or "vegetable mould" theory, was on the point of being refuted by his

insistence on making his chemical fertilisers insoluble, ignorant as he then was of the absorbing and retaining function of mould ; but, a generation after, the prevailing predilection for soluble manures was again much modified by the introduction of the "Thomas slag," and the enormous improvements in the process of extreme pulverisation. Prof. Vogel in his above-mentioned address gives many extracts from Liebig's writings, referring to the final and corrected expression of the chemical theory of fertilisation. These are so characteristic of Liebig's habit of thought and his whole mental attitude, that I transcribe them : "When I knew the reason why my fertilisers would not act, I felt like a man who had received a new life, for through this all processes of agriculture were explained, and now that the law is known and lies clearly before our eyes, there remains only the wonder that we did not see it long ago : but the human mind is a queer thing,—what does not fit into the circle of ideas once given, does not exist for it. . . . I had sinned against the wisdom of the Creator, and for this had received merited punishment. I wanted to improve His work, and in my blindness I thought that in the wonderful chain of laws which bind life to the surface of the earth, one link was missing which I, a helpless worm, could supply " (loc. cit., p. 34).

chemistry at the Medical School of Paris in 1841. With him was associated Boussingault, the man who, next to Liebig, did most for the elaboration of the true principles of agricultural chemistry.

To Liebig, organic chemistry did not mean the chemistry of the carbon compounds as it is defined nowadays, and has largely become since Dumas himself introduced into science the fruitful method and idea of substitution. This idea extended the facilities of the laboratory chemist enormously,[1] but also marks the altered view which has since taken hold of organic chemistry, the alliance with arts and industries rather than with an understanding of the economy and the phenomena of living organisms. From the moment of that alliance dates the division of organic chemistry into the two great branches of the chemistry of carbon compounds and the chemistry

15.
Change in
organic
chemistry.

---

[1] It is well known that organic chemistry during Liebig's lifetime outgrew the canons and the circle of ideas in which he moved, and that he complained of not being able to understand the papers in his own periodical, the 'Annalen,' &c. Liebig originally opposed Dumas' ideas on substitution, but in the end admitted himself defeated, when, through Hofmann, he became convinced "that the character of a chemical substance does not depend so much as he had supposed on the nature of its constituent atoms, and depends very largely also on the manner in which these atoms are arranged. Some years afterwards, at a dinner given by the French chemists to chemical visitors to the Exhibition of 1867, Liebig made his defeat on this occasion the source of a happy retort to Dumas, who had asked him why of late years he had devoted himself exclusively to agri-cultural chemistry. "I have withdrawn from organic chemistry," said Liebig, "for with the theory of substitution as a foundation, the edifice of chemical science may be built up by workmen: masters are no longer needed" (Shenstone, 'J. von Liebig,' 1895, p. 61). Already, in 1838, Liebig and Wöhler, in their investigation on uric acid and its derivatives, prophetically suggested the twofold development which organic chemistry was destined to take: "From these researches the philosophy of chemistry must draw the conclusion that the synthesis of all *organic* compounds which are not *organised* must be looked upon not merely as probable, but as certain of ultimate achievement" ('Annalen,' &c., vol. xxvi. p. 242). In fact, we have now a chemistry of organic and one of organised substances.

of organised nature. From this organic chemistry of the modern school Liebig turned away—continuing to lead research in the older and less fashionable direction. This choice is explained by the peculiarity of his great mind, which, while investigating details, never lost sight of the organic whole of natural processes, and which allowed itself many a flight of imagination into unexplored regions. In fact, if we review the work of Liebig from the side of the history of thought rather than from that of science, we must assign to it a very great and lasting influence. He was probably the first man of science who conceived the twofold meaning which belongs to the words, life and organism, a meaning which was known and appreciated by practical men, but which had, at that time, hardly received scientific recognition.[1] Life is not only defined, as Bichat put it, by the contrast with death; it is just as much defined by the idea of co-operation or solidarity: life is not only the property of individual beings, but also of the collection or society of several individuals in a larger organism. As such, political economy had conceived it long before Liebig's time, but Liebig was probably the first scientific thinker who studied the economy of nature, who fully realised the interdependence of animal and plant life, and tried to reduce this larger life of living things to scientific data and laws. Through him and his school two terms have become current in scientific and popular literature which, especially in the

16.
Influence of
Liebig.

[1] The idea of the dependence of living things on the environment, on the "milieu," was indeed fully recognised and emphasised by Lamarck (see p. 314 *supra*); but the philosophical ideas of that great thinker were then unknown and disregarded.

German tongue, have characterised the new ideas then introduced into science, and have brought them home to the intelligence of the educated classes. These two terms have only been inadequately rendered[1] in any other modern language: they are the words "Stoff-wechsel" and "Kreislauf des Lebens." The former de-notes the continual change of matter connected with maintenance of form in all living things; the latter denotes the continual interchange which exists between the separate members and the different provinces of the living creation, the circulation of living matter and living processes. Liebig looked upon nature on the large and on the small scale as an economy, as a household, and he applied himself to study the conditions of its exist-ence, of its normal and abnormal states. Through Liebig chemistry entered into close alliance with political economy, or, as it is termed abroad, national economics.

17.
"Stoff-wechsel" and "Kreis-lauf des Lebens."

We shall see immediately how the progress of science has, in the further course of the century, tended to emphasise this twofold aspect and define it more clearly; how the individual organism, the bearer of life, has been traced to smaller and smaller dimensions and units, and how, correspondingly, life as we see it on the larger scale has more and more revealed itself as consisting in co-operation, in the collective action of societies made up of individuals. We have on the one side the doctrine of the "Autonomy of the Cell," so eloquently proclaimed by Professor Virchow; on the other side the doctrine of

18.
"Autonomy of the Cell."

---

[1] We shall see farther on how the word "Metabolism," with its two subordinate terms "Anabol-ism" and "Catabolism," is even more expressive than the German term "Stoffwechsel."

"Division of Physiological Labour." the "Physiological Division of Labour," the happy expression invented by the great French zoologist, Henri Milne-Edwards.

Whilst Liebig was working at the great problems of the economy of life, and making chemistry subservient to the interests of agriculture, physiology, and pathology, another influence was exerted—mainly in Germany—on the study of the processes which take place in the living organism. This influence had its source in an application of the principles of dynamics and the more modern teachings of physics.[1] It emanated from two distinct centres— from Leipzig, where the brothers Weber[2] taught how to

[1] In many passages of his interesting and brilliant "Addresses" Du Bois-Reymond has dwelt on the great revolution which came over physiological studies about the middle of the century, characterising it as a special German achievement. Claude Bernard has given us an interesting account of a corresponding, but not identical, change of ideas in the great medical schools of Paris. Quite recently Sir Michael Foster has created in this country an interest in the history of medicine, notably of physiology, and has on various occasions given us masterly summaries of the results of his historical research. I may refer specially to his very lucid and fascinating monograph on Claude Bernard (London, 1899, in Fisher Unwin's 'Masters of Medicine' Series). Another authority in modern physiology, Prof. M'Kendrick of Glasgow, has treated in a companion volume of Helmholtz, dwelling mainly on his physiological labours, based upon his brilliant application of physics and mathematics. The two monographs exhibit very clearly two distinct influences which have been at work in remodelling the science of physiology and the conceptions of the phenomena of life.

[2] Regarding the position and influence of the three brothers Weber, I may refer to former passages of this history (vol. i. p. 196 ; vol. ii. chap. vi. *passim*). The greatest of the three —Ernst Heinrich Weber (1795-1878) —occupies a unique position in the development of the "science of life" in Germany. He seems never to have come under the influence of the then prevalent "philosophy of nature," and he had accordingly, unlike Liebig and Johannes Müller, nothing to unlearn. See on this point Du Bois-Reymond's Éloge of Müller in 'Reden' (vol. ii. p. 216), also Ludwig's Éloge of Weber (Leipzig, 1878, p. 10). Weber represents in the purest form the influence which physics, based upon experiment and measurement, had upon the development of the study of organic form and function, as Liebig represents in the purest form the influence of chemical research and reasoning. In this respect Liebig was more nearly related to the Paris school, Weber to the Berlin school, which he greatly influenced.

apply strict experimental research, combined with actual measurements, to physical, organic, and psychical phenomena, which had so far escaped all exact treatment; and from Berlin, where in the person, and still more in the school, of Johannes Müller, the great and complex phenomenon of life in the higher organisms was analysed into various mechanical and physical processes, each connected with some well-defined organ which was more and more recognised as possessing the properties of a physical apparatus. A great deal of the work of the numerous members of this school consisted in unravelling with the microscope the structure of such organic apparatus, and studying its action by physical measurements and experiments. As examples and models of this kind of work we have Du Bois-Reymond's 'Researches in Animal Electricity' (1848), and Helmholtz's 'Physiological Optics' (1867, second edition, much enlarged, 1896), and 'Physiological Acoustics' (1862). In the course of these labours it was found that the older ideas of "Stoffwechsel," and the conception of the circulation of matter as it was taught in the school of Liebig, required to be corrected and extended. I have referred in an earlier chapter [1] to the interesting circumstances under which our modern notions of the conservation of energy first dawned independently upon Mayer and Helmholtz whilst studying the phenomena of heat in the animal organism. In the school of Liebig we meet with an occasional attempt to extend the idea of "Stoffwechsel," the exchange of material or of elementary matter in the living body of animals and

19.
Johannes
Müller.

[1] See *supra*, chap vii.

plants, so as to embrace likewise the imponderables—
heat, light, electricity, &c. We find Mohr treating of
heat and animal energy as substances which must be
counted among the elements or prime materials known
to chemists—just as the French chemists of Lavoisier's school enumerated the imponderable along with
the ponderable elements of nature: even Liebig's first
edition of the 'Chemical Letters' is not quite averse
to such an interpretation. The ideas on this matter
were, however, vague, and needed defining. When
Mayer attempted a first step in this direction, Liebig did
not see the value of it. The subject was only cleared up
when Helmholtz, in 1847, showed that all so-called
living forces were the different manifestations of a
certain quantity of power to do work — later termed
energy — and that this power could show itself in
actual change and motion, or be stored up in tensions
in the system, later called "potential energy." After
this, "Stoffwechsel" appeared not only as an exchange
of material, but also as a change in the form of energy,
whereby potential or latent energy could be accumulated
in the organism and let loose, as the latent power of
an explosive substance is let loose by the pulling of
a trigger.

One of the immediate consequences of these varied
researches—all tending to show how the conception
formerly established in chemistry, physics, and dynamics
could be utilised in the description of the phenomena of
living matter, how the complex phenomenon of life
could be split up into a number of separate chemical
and physical processes, which could be imitated in

the laboratory, and how the living organism could be analysed into a complex of separate apparatus or machines, acting on intelligible mechanical and physical principles—was a radical change of the conception of vital force and the vital principle. It ceased in the opinion of many to be opposed to other non-living forces, as it was with Bichat; according to others it was non-existent, or at all events useless; others again reduced it to a purely regulative function, or even a mere idea. A popular philosophy founded upon the unknown principle of matter, and the equally unknown and even less clear principle of force, promulgated the notion that science had succeeded in banishing all spiritual entities, and was able to explain everything on purely mechanical principles. Vitalism and animism were at an end; there only remained mechanism and materialism. It is well to note that none of the great men to whom we are indebted for the real extension of our knowledge of biological phenomena favoured or embraced this view. The reasons which kept them from drawing what seemed to some the inevitable consequences of their discoveries were manifold.

*20.
Influence of doctrine of energy.*

*21.
Mechanism.*

As I stated before, there are two ways of approaching the problems of nature, and two interests by which our researches can be guided. The one is the abstract mathematical method, which begins with the simplest definable and measurable elementary processes, and tries to imitate the complicated phenomena of nature by more and more intricate combinations of these elementary processes. The other is the more concrete method inspired by practical interests. The mechanical, physical, and chemical methods of analysis and synthesis follow the former way, and they generally arrive at satisfactory explanations of isolated parts of the actually existing phenomena, or of special and simple cases. Notably, they create the artificial world of manufactured things, such as instruments, machines, chemical and mechanical compounds. They may at times make it appear as if this process of putting together, continued indefinitely, would ultimately reach the real things which we behold in inorganic, organised, and even in animated nature. At all events no other way, it might seem, is open to science, and the only thing that delays our progress is the bewildering intricacy and complexity of things natural. At the beginning of our century, when, through Laplace and his school, many seemingly complicated phenomena of nature, notably those of physical astronomy, yielded to the processes of analysis just described, there seemed for the moment a possibility of building up a complete philosophy of nature on such a groundwork. Laplace himself indulged in a frequently quoted prophetic vision of this kind. When, in the middle of the century, some molecular phenomena, notably those of light, had likewise yielded to the calculus, and when correcter views as to the nature of forces had further brought another and different world of phenomena into a calculable form, it seemed likely that even the mysterious processes of living organisms might be subjected to similar reasoning. It seemed time to abandon the familiar conception of a special vital force, and to hand over physiological problems likewise to the physicist, the chemist, and the microscopist. A regular crusade was accordingly started in Germany by philosophers, as well as by naturalists and biologists, against the vitalists—those who believed in a special principle of life; and an impression was created in the minds of thinking outsiders that a purely mechanical explanation of life and mind was finally decided on, and within possible reach. Among those who assisted in bringing about this impression, I need only single out two names—those of Hermann Lotze,[1] the philosopher of Göttingen, and of

22.
Lotze and
Du Bois-
Reymond.

[1] The position which Lotze occupies in the history of the conceptions of life or of vitalism is peculiar. If we read works dealing specially with the history of medicine, such as those of Haeser or Hirsch, we do not come across the name of Lotze at all, and it is only in quite recent times, fifty years after the appearance of Lotze's writings dealing with vitalism, that experts in physiology have reverted to his discussion of the subject. See notably the following: 1. Rauber, "Formbildung und Formstörung in der Entwickelung von Wirbelthieren" ('Morphol. Jahrbuch,' Band vi.), 1880. 2. Wilhelm Roux, "Einleitung zu den Beiträgen zur Entwickelungsmechanik des Embryo," 1885 (reprinted in 'Gesammelte Abhandlungen,' vol. ii. p. 11, Leipzig, 1895). 3. O. Hertwig, 'Zeit und Streitfragen zur Biologie' (Heft 2, Jena, 1897), pp. 23-29. 4. Carl Hauptmann, 'Die Metaphysik in der modernen Physiologie' (Jena, 1894), p. 3. These and many other recent references go back to Lotze's article, "Leben und Lebenskraft," in Rud. Wagner's 'Handwörterbuch der Physiologie,' 1842; and to his larger publications, 'Allgemeine Pathologie und Therapie als mechanische Naturwissenschaften' (Leipzig, 1842), and 'Allgemeine Physi-

ologie des Körperlichen Lebens' (Leipzig, 1867). The reasons why Lotze's expositions were so little regarded at the time were probably twofold. He taught that the phenomena of life constituted a mechanical problem. This was enough to dismiss in the eyes of many empirical naturalists the further, but not easily comprehended, statement of Lotze that life was not merely a mechanical problem. The definition and solution of the second part of the problem was much more difficult, aud Lotze delayed his expositions on this side of the question for ten years, when he published his 'Medicinische Psychologie oder Physiologie der Seele' (1852), which contained a metaphysical introduction apparently little in harmony with the supposed purely mechanical or even materialistic standpoint of his earlier writings. In the meantime several important works had appeared which carried out in wider or narrower regions the purely mechanical or inductive and experimental treatment, and quite revolutionised physiological and medical studies. I need only mention such works as Jacob Henle's 'Allgemeine Anatomie' (1840), and his 'Handbuch der rationellen Pathologie' (1846-53). Henle, as von Kölliker

Du Bois-Reymond, the eminent physiologist of Berlin. The former owed much of his scientific training to the school of Ernst Heinrich Weber in Leipzig, the latter to that of Johannes Müller in Berlin. Both agreed in denouncing the conception of a vital force—as it was then called—as illogical, and moreover as scientifically useless. But whilst Lotze distinctly stated that his criticisms on this subject were only addresssd to scientific thinkers, and promised a further philosophical

says, "correctly saw that the work of Bichat had to be remodelled on the foundations laid by Schleiden and Schwann," an undertaking in which von Kölliker himself laboured with the greatest success. But above all must be mentioned the appearance of Rud. Virchow's 'Cellular Pathology' (1858, Engl. transl. by Chance, 1860), "in which he himself explains that he does not give a system but a general biological principle," and in so doing lays the foundation for the entire exact treatment of pathological cases. It is, however, well to note that Virchow does not regard life as a purely mechanical problem. The works of such authorities as Henle and Virchow give as much or as little philosophy and discussion of general principles as physiologists of the exact school required for about thirty years. Those masters, indeed, had themselves grappled with the philosophical problem, and had arrived at a formulation which sufficed to lead research into fruitful paths for a new generation of experts who themselves were not philosophically educated. The term vital force disappeared, and in the specialist medical literature of a lengthy period even life itself was hardly any longer discussed. Thus a firm basis was laid on which

mechanics, physics, and chemistry could be usefully applied. A similar silence as to general problems reigns in the great school which for two centuries built on the principles laid down by Newton in natural philosophy. Similarly in chemistry, the foundations laid by the atomic theory sufficed for the greater portion of the century following its enunciation. We have seen in earlier chapters of this work how, even in these much more firmly established mechanical sciences, our century has witnessed before its end discussions again arising as to fundamental questions and leading principles. A similar fate has come over biological science, and with it a renewed interest in the writings which stand at the entrance of that epoch which was so rich in the unravelling of definite and special problems. Authorities like Prof. O. Hertwig warn us now of that "other extreme which sees in vital processes nothing but chemico-physical and mechanical problems, and thinks it finds the true science of nature only in so far as it is possible to reduce phenomena to the motions of attracting and repelling atoms, and to submit them to calculation" ('Die Lehre vom Organismus,' an Address, Jena, 1899, p. 8).

investigation of the question, Du Bois-Reymond [1] gave
the impression, in his earliest deliverance, that the

[1] Du Bois-Reymond's position in
the vitalistic controversy is interesting and instructive, inasmuch
as he considerably modified his
opinions in course of time. His
first deliverance on the subject is
to be found in the preface to his
celebrated ' Untersuchungen über
Thierische Elektricität' (March
1848). This discussion of the
subject followed soon after the
deliverances of men like Berzelius
(1839), Schwann (1839), Schleiden
(1842), Lotze (1842), on the same
subject, which are stated to have
been "ineffectual." After the
lapse of twenty-four years Du
Bois-Reymond approached the
subject again in his celebrated
address at the German Association
of Sciences at Leipzig, 1872, entitled "Ueber die Grenzen des
Naturerkennens." This deliverance
created a great sensation : the
pamphlet appeared in many
editions and translations, and
only in this country failed to
get adequately noticed. A further
explanation of the views expounded in it was given by the
author (1880) in an oration at
the meeting held annually in
honour of Leibniz in the Berlin
Academy on the 8th of July. It
bears the characteristic title "Die
sieben Welträthsel." These documents together contain the author's
"philosophical creed," which ends
in "Pyrrhonism," out of which
there seems no escape except
through "Supernaturalism," which,
however, begins where science
ends. (See note 1 to the last-
mentioned address.) All three
documents are reprinted in the
two volumes of 'Reden' (Leipsic,
1886-87), from which I quote. In
the interval of a quarter of a century which lay between the first and
second deliverance great changes
had come over scientific thought.
The mechanical view, which had
been put forward in an extreme
form in 1848, when it was prophe-
sied that "physiology, giving up its
particularistic interest, would disappear in the great united estate
of natural philosophy, would be
entirely dissolved in organic
physics and chemistry" (vol. ii. p.
23), had had time and opportunity
to show its power and its limits.
It had gained through greater
facility of application (such as
Ludwig's automatic curve - plot-
ting), through the larger conception of "Stoffwechsel" as
denoting "metabolism" of matter
and energy. The author himself
had introduced a new definition
of life as a "dynamical equilibrium " in the place of older
descriptions (vol. ii. p. 25) ; and,
above all, Darwin had shown the
possibility of a mechanical explanation of so-called "final causes"
in nature. The author himself
was one of that great school,
emanating from Johannes Müller,
but now represented by the still
greater Helmholtz, which had
pushed the mechanical or exact
treatment to its furthest limits,
to the analysis of the phenomena
of the nervous system in its highest activity, those of sensation
and perception. It is therefore
highly significant that, instead of
confirming the earlier dictum, that
the exact treatment would halt
only at the most advanced point—
viz., the manifestation of "free
will,"—the author is now forced to
admit that not only is the "origin"
of all motion quite obscure, but
likewise the lowest forms of
animation or consciousness are
not to be explained mechanically,

question was definitely settled and the road quite clear for research. To those—and they comprised the second class of thinkers referred to above—who were unwilling or unable to follow Lotze and Du Bois-Reymond into the details of their criticism of the illogical conception of force as employed in the term "vital force," but who looked at the great facts of economy, design, and recurrent order which are exhibited in the living creation, these criticisms had little that was convincing. If the term "vital force" was illogical, some other term such as "vital principle" might be substituted. The enormous difference between the phenomena of living and of dead matter remained and impressed itself on them. Liebig, and many naturalists in France and Germany, had approached the study of nature from the practical side. Their methods were not mathematical but rather experimental, and very frequently not limited to the laboratory and dissecting-room, but carried out in the workshop of nature itself. In spite of his successful attempts to establish clearer views regarding the economic processes of living nature and the application of chemical analysis, Liebig[1] to the end

the mystery which attaches to all beginnings as well as to the great transitions in the ascending scale of natural phenomena being further emphasised and forcibly driven home in the last-named address, which, as has been said, bears the title "The Seven Enigmas." The three deliverances of Du Bois-Reymond, together with the copious notes and references which he gives in the latest reprint, serve as a very good and lucid exposition of the inherent difficulties of the problem, and should be studied by every one who desires to be at home in the ancient and modern literature of the subject. The position of the author has been many times criticised. See, *inter alia*, Kaufmann, 'Die Metaphysik in der modernen Biologie' (Jena 1894), *passim*.

[1] Lord Kelvin in his essay "On the Dissipation of Energy" (reprinted in 'Popular Lectures,' &c., vol. iii. p. 464) has the following interesting note: "The influence of animal or vegetable life on matter is infinitely beyond the range of any scientific

of his life never satisfied himself that the phenomena of life can be mechanically explained: he remained, in the face of much criticism, a Vitalist.   So did Wöhler in Germany—so did most of the eminent physiologists in France and in England.   The crusade against Vitalism, which was started in Germany, seems to have had little influence on them.   In 1854, six years after Du Bois-Reymond's essay on Vital Force, and twelve years after that of Lotze, Huxley [1] could still, in the first of his 'Lay Sermons' "On the educational value of the natural history sciences," express opinions on the difference between living and not-living bodies which were distinctly vitalistic, maintaining, much in the same way as Liebig did in the later editions of his chemical letters, that "the phenomena of life are dependent neither on physical nor on chemical, but on vital forces"; and if, in 1870, he could himself state that he had long since grown out of this view, it is interesting to discover what were the arguments which brought about this remarkable change.   I will at once state what seems to me to be the great influence which combated Vitalism in this country, which greatly strengthened the anti-vitalistic or mechanical views in Germany, but which, as little as the methematical and philosophical criticism of Lotze and Du Bois-Reymond, ever took real hold of biological thought

23.
Liebig's
vitalism.

inquiry hitherto entered on. About twenty - five years ago I asked Liebig if he believed that a leaf or a flower could be formed or could grow by chemical forces.   He answered, I would more readily believe that a book on chemistry or on botany could grow out of dead matter by chemical processes."

[1] The address referred to was re-printed in 1870 in the well-known volume, entitled 'Lay Sermons, Addresses, and Reviews,' with a "prefatory letter" to Tyndall, in which the following passage occurs: "The oldest essay of the whole contains a view of the nature of the differences between living and not-living bodies, out of which I have long since grown."

in France, where a modified kind of vitalism still prevails.[1] It is the far-reaching influence of the reasoning which sprang out of Darwin's theory of descent.

[1] The older ideas of vital forces have in all the three countries been combated by authorities of the very first order, but, characteristically, in a very different manner — the phenomena of living bodies having been attacked from different sides. In Germany the mechanico-physical school was for a time the dominant one. In France the dominant school was the so-called experimental, also termed the vivisectional, school, founded by Magendie. Between these two extreme positions, both equally opposed to the older vitalism, there stood in the middle, with a less strongly pronounced antagonism to earlier conceptions, those who, like Liebig in Germany, Dumas and Boussingault in France, approached the phenomena of life mainly by the methods and reasoning of the new science of chemistry. This school had a profoundly modifying influence on the extreme views of the experimental school in France. It made itself felt mainly through Claude Bernard. In Germany this influence was felt later, after that of Darwinism had somewhat subsided. In England it was the doctrine of descent pure and simple which combated the older vitalism : the question became one of origins, and vitalism, as such, could be temporarily ignored. The facts of variation, overcrowding, natural selection, and inheritance, presented such a mass of material, waiting to be sifted and arranged by exact methods, that the problem of the essence of life and its beginnings was set aside. Accordingly, the attempts both of Darwin and Huxley to grapple with the central and final problem of vitalism are very few ; the latter only repeating what had been said long before him by thinkers of a very different school. The question was not answered, because, for the progress of the sciences and for their successful application in medicine, it did not require to be answered. It became a purely philosophical question, and the only English writer of authority who seriously grappled with it was Mr Herbert Spencer in his 'Principles of Biology.' Darwin in 1863 wrote to Hooker ('Life,' vol. iii. p. 18) : "It is mere rubbish thinking at present of the origin of life ; one might as well think of the origin of matter." Huxley, in a letter from the year 1884 ('Life,' vol. ii. p. 67), compares life with a whirlpool, a favourite simile of Cuvier's (see *supra*, vol. i. p. 129), but is doubtful as to comparing it with a machine. M. Delage names Chevreul ('Considérations générales sur l'analyse organique et ses applications,' 1824) : "Il a eu le mérite d'écrire que la Force vitale n'explique rien, qu'elle aurait besoin elle-même d'être expliquée avant de prétendre expliquer autre chose, et que les phénomènes de la vie ont leur cause directe dans les principes immédiats constitutifs de la matière organisée. Il n'établit cependant sur cette donnée une théorie de la vie, car il conclut, au contraire, que, eût-on ramené les phénomènes vitaux à leurs causes prochaines et aux forces qui régissent la matière inorganique, on ne serait pas encore en état de comprendre comment l'être organisé en se reproduisant répète avec une constance si remarquable les caractères de son espèce." Even François Magendie, the great founder of the purely experimental school of physiology, says of Bichat's celebrated 'Recher-

In order to enable my readers to comprehend clearly the great change which has come over biological thought through Darwin's writings and reasonings, I must now introduce an idea which I have so far intentionally avoided in discussing the various scientific views of nature. This is the idea of final causes, the apparent existence of a purpose (in German *Zweck*), or an end (in German *Ziel*) in all processes of nature, but preeminently in those of the living portion of creation. In all writings prior to Darwin a great deal is made of final causes in nature, of the teleology of living processes. The phenomena of life seemed safely intrenched in the citadel of final causes : no mechanism could explain them away. The very fact that organisms were compared with machines, admitted the existence of a definite end and purpose; for it is the peculiarity of every humanly constructed machine or instrument that it serves a definite purpose which, in the mind of the inventor or maker, suggested the peculiar arrangement or organisation which we behold. The criticisms of Lotze [1]

ches,' &c. : " Les esprits sévères et amis des progrès des sciences . . . ont regretté que l'auteur opposât sans cesse la vie aux lois physiques, comme si les êtres vivans n'étaient pas de corps, avant d'être des végétaux ou des animaux " ("avertissement " to the 4th ed. of Bichat's 'Recherches,' &c., 1822).

[1] The lengthy discussions of Lotze contained in the writings quoted above are not easy to understand, and it is not surprising that, beyond the elimination of the conception of vital force as useless to the purely scientific student, his real meaning was at the time not grasped at all. In fact, we may say that Lotze, though ceasing to be a vitalist, remained an animist. Discarding vital force, he retained the conception of a soul in a manner which drew upon him the ridicule of those whom, like Carl Vogt, he had converted to pure materialism. This has had the consequence, that in more recent times his whole philosophy has been stigmatised as dualistic, and that he has been accused of having halted half-way. His real meaning can be gathered more easily from his later and more mature writings : for his contemporaries it must have remained to a great extent enigmatical. See C. Haupt-

and Du Bois-Reymond [1] did not do away with this very
evident property of living things, but only maintained

mann ('Die Metaphysik in der
Physiologie,' 1894, p. 7): "However convincingly Lotze destroyed
the conception of a vital force, he
had no desire to criticise in a similarly destructive manner the principle of a soul, though both have
grown up in the same climate, in
the fertile country where substances blossom, &c. . . . And
although he emphatically, and in
many ways, urged that all organism
is a definite form and arrangement
of mechanism, he nevertheless
accorded to the principle of inherent disturbances (soul, will) a
partial control over the functions
of the animal body," &c. Accordingly this view set only the physiology of plant-life quite free for a
purely mechanical treatment, which
it received — after the suggestive
beginnings made by Schleiden—
mainly at the hands of Julius
Sachs, from whose 'Lectures on
Plant Physiology' (1887) Kaufmann gives the following very characteristic extract : "The organism
is only a machine put together
out of different parts ; . . . in a
machine, even if only made by
human hands, there lies the result
of deepest and most careful thought,
and of high intelligence, so far as
its structure is concerned," &c. (p.
623).

[1] The two great facts which stare
every unbiassed student of nature
in the widest sense in the face,
and which always upset a purely
mechanical view, are Purpose and
Will. Lotze recognises both, and
in all his writings never forgets or
ignores them. Naturalists, who
for the nonce are deeply interested
and fully absorbed in the analysis
of some definite organ, or some
special chemical power in the
organism, may usefully ignore

these two facts, of which the first
only intrudes itself if we rise to a
general, a comprehensive aspect;
the second is a result of individual
experience.   Nor did Du Bois-
Reymond ignore these facts.   It
is interesting to see how he deals
with them in his earlier and later
writings.   In the earlier period
he eliminates the problem of free
will as not a scientific problem
at all, and gets over the question
of purpose by a reference to the
evident existence of purpose in inanimate nature also,—an idea which
really comes ultimately back to an
assumption of a general animation
of the whole of nature, such as
has been maintained by many philosophers and naturalists in very
various forms.   See, for instance,
the further remarks of Julius Sachs
in the passage quoted above.   But
there is no doubt that this method
of viewing the teleology of nature did
not really satisfy Du Bois-Reymond,
for in the reprint of his paper on vital
force he refers to it as superficial
('Reden,' vol. ii. p. 26), having in
the meantime adopted the explanation of Darwin, whose "highest
title to glory" will, "so long as
philosophy of nature exists," be
this, that he to "some extent
allayed the agony of the intellect
that ponders over the problems of
existence " ('Reden,' vol. i. p. 216).
In 1887 he holds that what he
wrote as late as 1859, before the
appearance of the 'Origin of
Species'.—for instance his celebrated Éloge of Johannes Müller—
is antiquated, though it still gives a
valuable picture of the "tormenting
confusion of those who could not
free themselves from the embarrass-
ing fetters of the fixity of species,
the incompleteness of the palæontological records, and, more than all,

that this end or purpose was attained by purely mechanical processes, that no new force, called vital force, need be assumed to exist, that it was the adequate and sole object of science to disclose the mechanism by which the various ends of life were attained. The very idea of life, the vitalistic element or factor, was chased away beyond the region of the knowable, and remained merely an idea in the realm of thought, as it was for Descartes and Leibniz, and as it has remained, up to recent times, for von Baer and for Claude Bernard, and for all those who do not accept the Darwinian explanation. For Lotze, Du Bois-Reymond, and Claude Bernard [1]

25.
Lotze and Claude Bernard.

of final causes ; in one word, of all pre-Darwinian Darwinians" (vol. ii. p. 299).

[1] Du Bois-Reymond ('Reden,' vol. ii. p. 557) claims that the greater part of the progress in modern physiology belongs to Germany, in spite of the great talent and originality of Claude Bernard. He thus describes the different position of the three countries : "One branch of physiology especially emanated from Germany — general physics of muscle and nerves. Whereas in England experimental physiology lay fallow, while it moved in France in vivisection and zoochemistry, being held down in both countries by vitalism, German science was the first to advance to the investigation of the surviving organs, especially of the frog, looking upon them as apparatus built up by nature, extremely complicated, yet conceivably only machines." This was spoken in 1880. Since that time a certain change has come over physiological reasoning, notably even in the very centre of the physico - chemical school at Berlin. In 1899 Prof. O. Hertwig warns us of the other extreme, opposed to the older vitalism, "which would lead us to a one-sided and equally inadequate conception of the vital process . . . which would see in it merely a chemico - physical and mechanical problem, and would recognise the genuine science of nature only so far as it is possible to reduce phenomena to motions, . . . and to subject them to mathematical calculation" ('Die Lehre vom Organismus,' an Address, Jena, p. 8). How far Du Bois-Reymond in later years modified his earlier notions, we can to some extent see from his published addresses. We know that the French school, with Claude Bernard as its most illustrious representative, never fell into the mistake of looking at the living organism as a physico-chemical machine, and we may be inclined to attribute this to a large extent to those experiments on the living organism which were first instituted by Magendie, which, under the hands of Claude Bernard, led to the discovery of the action of the pancreatic juice, of the glycogenic function of the liver, of vaso-motor nerves, and of the effects of poisons:

purpose exists in nature, notably in living nature; it is its very characteristic, its definition—the very " quid proprium " of life,[1] but it is useless as a scientific conception. It remains a problem for the philosopher, but the

all of them epoch - making discoveries which revolutionised physiological science, and which it is difficult to conceive of as having been made without vivisectional methods. We have also a remark from the pen of the late Prof. Georg Wiedemann, that Helmholtz himself, that greatest master in the line of mechanico-physical reasoning on the processes and organs of the higher senses and the nervous system, foresaw the necessity of resorting for further progress to vivisectional research, to which he had a personal dislike. (See Wiedemann's Introduction to the third volume of Helmholtz's 'Wissenschaftliche Abhandlungen,' p. xxiv.)

[1] In many passages of his later writings Claude Bernard has dealt with the definition of life : most fully in the posthumously published volume entitled ' La Science Expérimentale' (3rd ed., 1890). He there arrives at the final statements (p. 207) : "Je pense, quant à moi . . . que les phénomènes chimiques dans l'organisme sont exécutés par des agents ou des procédés spéciaux ; mais cela ne change rien à la nature purement chimique des phénomènes, &c. . . . Les agents des phénomènes chimiques dans les corps vivants ne se bornent pas à produire des synthèses chimiques, . . . mais ils les organisent. . . . Parmi ces agents . . . le plus puissant et le plus merveilleux est sans contredit l'œuf, la cellule primordiale qui contient le germe, principe organisateur de tout le corps. Nous n'assistons pas à la création de l'œuf ex nihilo, il vient des parents, et l'origine de sa virtualité évolutive nous est cachée. . . . Il y a comme un dessin vital qui trace le plan de chaque être et de chaque organe ; . . . ils semblent dirigés par quelque condition invisible dans la route qu'ils suivent, dans l'ordre qui les enchaîne. . . . C'est cette puissance ou propriété évolutive que nous nous bornons à énoncer ici qui seule constituerait le quid proprium de la vie, car il est clair que cette propriété évolutive de l'œuf, qui produira un mammifère, un oiseau ou un poisson, n'est ni de la physique, ni de la chimie. . . . En disant que la vie est l'idée directrice ou la force évolutive de l'être, nous exprimons simplement l'idée d'une unité dans la succession de tous les changements morphologiques et chimiques accomplis par le germe depuis l'origine jusqu'à la fin de la vie. . . . La forcela métaphysique évolutive par laquelle nous pouvons caractériser la vie est inutile à la science, parce qu'étant en dehors des forces physiques elle ne peut exercer aucune influence sur elles. Il faut donc ici séparer le monde métaphysique du monde physique phénoménal qui lui sert de base mais qui n'a rien à lui emprunter. Leibniz a exprimé cette délimitation dans les paroles : ' Le corps se développe mécaniquement, et les lois mécaniques ne sont jamais violées dans les mouvements naturels ; tout se fait dans les âmes comme s'il n'y avait pas de corps, et tout se fait dans le corps, comme s'il n'y avait pas d'âmes.' . . . Nous dirons avec Descartes : on pense métaphysiquement mais on vit et on agit physiquement."

naturalist may neglect it, or at best can only use it as an "heuristic" help, as an indication where to look for the special mechanical contrivances which he is trying to unravel. It seems to me that the position which such thinkers take up towards the objects or individuals of living nature is similar to that of a mathematical student who clearly comprehends the solution of an algebraical problem, but who himself would be unable to find it. He may all his life remain in this attitude without being able to find any solution himself: he has got complete hold of the mechanism, but not of the idea, of mathematical reasoning. The student of nature could thus hope eventually to understand the mechanism of life, but the idea is beyond his comprehension. This can be expressed by saying: the mechanism of life is ultimately comprehensible, though highly intricate; the idea of life is transcendental, incomprehensible. Let us not trouble ourselves about the manner in which life first originated, but let us study the mechanical processes by which it is maintained, by which its various ends are accomplished. Let us study the mechanism of the clock, though this may not tell us the story of its maker nor the process of its manufacture. Those who cling to the conception of a vital force or principle would probably not even admit as much as this. It is doubtful whether Liebig to the end, whether Huxley in his earlier period, and Du Bois-Reymond in his later writings, would have admitted even this position.

We are now prepared to understand the novel position which the Darwinian conception of natural processes introduced so far as the teleology of nature is concerned,

26.
Darwinism and final causes.

—how it dealt with final causes, with the apparent existence of a purpose, an end in the processes of nature,
notably of the living organism.

It must here be remembered that the question how
living things come to exhibit traces of design and purpose has really nothing to do with the nature and processes of life : it is not necessarily a biological question.
Every machine shows the same marks of design, but is
not therefore alive. The influence of Darwin's principle
of natural selection, of overcrowding and consequent
struggle for existence and survival of the fittest specimens, has therefore not been in the direction of explaining any of the vital processes which are at work in the
individual organism. It is at best merely a statistical
relation, a peculiar phenomenon occurring only in a large
or congested group of living and self-multiplying beings :
it presupposes the facts of reproduction, heredity, and
variation ; it does not explain them. Hence I dealt
with Darwin's ideas in the last chapter, and did not
introduce them under the present heading of Biological
Thought. As we shall see later on, Darwin did recognise the necessity of attempting also a biological
explanation.

The possibility of explaining the marks of design as
merely apparent depends on the conception of the genetic
process acting on a large, a gigantic scale : individual
things put forth ever new developments by which they
eventually overtop their neighbours, ultimately advancing to such a degree of excellence and individual perfection that to an outside beholder the few surviving
specimens give the impression of having been origin-

ally designed. In fact, they only exist because those numberless individuals which could not grow in a sufficient degree perished in the struggle. Only those individual specimens survived in whom, in one or a few directions, something specially excellent was produced at the expense of development in other directions. In the mass, the crowd are sacrificed—*i.e.*, automatically crushed, in favour of the few: in the individual, one special growth is automatically pursued at the expense of a general but less enduring—*i.e.*, self-assertive—development. The end—the seeming purpose—is produced in the process of production, it being merely something more enduring—*i.e.*, something better. It conveys the impression to an outside beholder of having been consciously set at the term of the process of development; in reality it was produced simultaneously. The mountain peak which towers above its neighbours, and gives a distinctive rounding off and finish to a landscape, may be conceived as having been built up by the selective action of the natural artist who brought together the best materials and placed them in their most enduring positions: in reality it owes its existence only to one out of the numberless throes of nature which happened to take place with stronger materials and in more stable forms of arrangement and grouping, or it is due to the denudation of the strata surrounding it. The end and purpose of any natural development is that which it can itself automatically produce and endow with most distinctive and enduring characters, for this only survives at the expense of weaker productions: there is a natural result in development, but there need not be a purpose. The

27.
"Natural result" against "purpose."

contemplation of the result may permit us to trace backward the process by which it was brought about; but we are not warranted in assuming that it existed independently, like the plan of a building or the purpose of an instrument. In the place of a growth according to a prearranged plan, Darwin put the conception of an automatic adjustment called "natural selection"; in the place of a conscious end or purpose he put the conception of a mere result, a product, the "surviving fittest."[1]

The development and proof of Darwin's ideas gave a new impetus to biological research, as it did also to the science of the history and economy of nature. The fact that the phenomenon of selection, or rather of automatic crowding out, presupposes intimate relations and contact of every living thing with numberless other similar and dissimilar beings, led naturalists into the open air, to

[1] A very full appreciation of the great change that has come over the sciences of nature through the influence of Darwin will be found in the various writings and addresses of Prof. Haeckel, notably in his address to the German Association in 1877 at Munich, "Ueber Entwickelungslehre" (reprinted in 'Gesammelte populäre Vorträge,' vol. ii. p. 97). A more critical examination, referring specially to the central biological problems, is the address by Du Bois-Reymond, delivered in 1876 in the Berlin Academy, and reprinted in 'Reden,' vol. i. p. 211, with valuable literary notes. He there discusses how far the principle of natural selection, in addition to the general doctrine of descent, has been adopted or opposed, and refers to the outstanding difficulties. "One of the greatest difficulties," he says (p. 226), "presents itself in physiology in the so-called regenerative power, and — what is allied to it — the natural power of healing : this may now be seen in the healing of wounds, in the delimitation and compensation of morbid processes, or, at the farthest end of the series, in the re-formation of an entire freshwater polyp out of one of the two halves into which it had been divided. This artifice could surely not have been learnt by natural selection, and here it appears impossible to avoid the assumption of formative laws acting for a purpose. They do not become more intelligible by the fact that the regeneration of mutilated crystals, observed by Pasteur and others, points to similar processes in inanimate nature. Also the ability of organisms to perfect themselves by exercise has not found sufficient appreciation with regard to natural selection."

outdoor research, into the arena of real life.   On this
I dwelt in the last chapter.   Ideas of a cognate kind
had already emanated from other schools, such as that
of Liebig,—the circulation of life in the different provinces of nature, the interdependence of different species
of living things.   Isolated investigations, like those of
Gärtner and Sprengel, of Huber and Lubbock, on insect
life, or of bacteriologists like Pasteur and Boussingault
on fermentation and fertilisation, received a fitting place
as important chapters in the economics of nature.   The
problem of life became twofold—the life of the community and the life of the individual : organisation and
individuation.   Two great questions presented themselves : What is an individual ? what is a society of
individuals ?   Physiologists were from of old accustomed
to ask the former ; economists like Rousseau and Adam
Smith had asked the latter question.   Both now became
questions for the biologist.   Physiology and economics
joined hands.   In isolated instances, as in those of Liebig
and von Baer, these two interests had already been united.
The real meaning and reason of this union now became
clear to every one : it revealed itself as founded on the
two characteristic features of life—individuality and co-
operation.   With the exception of the strong emphasis
put by Liebig on the latter side of natural, notably
organic processes, biologists before Darwin had mainly
studied the phenomena of individual life.   In two special
directions—in embryology and in the cellular theory—
they had made great progress.   I have already treated
of these advances in their bearing upon morphology, the
study of forms, and upon genesis, the study of change

28.
Organisation
and individ-
uation.

29.
Biology and
economics.

and development.   Let us see how they affected biology proper—the study of life.

The early propounders of the cellular theory were evidently much influenced by the then existing theories which explained the constitution of inorganic chemical substances by atoms and by the processes of crystallisation.   The progress of science, however, was in the direction of showing more and more that these borrowed conceptions are quite inadequate.   Reasoning or thinking on organised matter is quite different from that which refers to unorganised substance.   Chemists and physicists deal with atoms as imaginary units, which form the ideal groundwork for constant arithmetical proportions or for the action of calculable mechanical forces measured by observable movements.   Biologists, whether dealing with plants or animals, approach the cells which they regard as the units of living matter with the microscope—an instrument which, till quite recently, has only been sparingly used in chemical research.   The units of the chemist far transcend our powers of vision; the units of the biologist are to some extent accessible to our senses.   All organisms have been found to be analysable by the aid of the microscope into similar morphological constituents called cells, which present very similar forms and functions.   This has had the advantage of permitting the phenomena of life to be analysed into a few fundamental processes common to all living things; the great diversity of the larger organisms, and the more conspicuous phenomena of life, being conceived as put together in various ways out of these elementary units, which exhibit in varying degrees of intensity the living processes common to all. Just so a state or human society is made up of a large number of individuals, all having the same human nature, who carry on the different functions peculiar to each with varying degrees of efficiency. The conception of the cell as the unit or type of all living matter, and the further discovery that there exist unicellular beings which are not essentially different from the constituent living elements of the most complicated organisms, has brought physiological research to a focus. The difficulties in the study of biological phenomena have vanished as those of the organic chemist did on the introduction of the conception of valency, of the saturating powers of chemical substances. Accordingly, if we compare a text-book of these subjects written in the middle of the century with one belonging to the latter part of it, we find an enormous difference of treatment. It is instructive to contrast the introduction given in Johannes Müller's 'Elements of Physiology' and that of Professor Michael Foster's 'Text-book.' The former represents the most advanced knowledge obtainable at the end of the thirties—the latter that of a generation later. The former contains a lengthy introduction on general physiology—the latter a short one on the physiological properties of a living amœba,[1] a

30.
The cellular
theory.

[1] Already, in 1835, K. E. von Baer pointed out how the study of one small animal can revolutionise our entire reasoning. "Ninety years ago a naturalist discovers the hydropolyp, an insignificant slimy animal, not larger than a peppercorn, and how, without head, sense-organs, muscles, nerves, blood, and sexual organs it nevertheless is nourished, grows, feels, moves, and multiplies,—how it can even be divided, each part forming a whole : he observes it with much wonder for nine years with untiring perseverance. At that time many would, no doubt, consider such an occupation childish and unworthy, yet these diligent observations have slowly but ma-

unicellular organism which is taken as a type, a model
of all the phenomena of life. The former consists of
philosophical and abstract generalisations, gathered from
many sources; it treats of life in general, of the vital
force, of the difference between animal and plant life,
&c.: the latter sums up the whole matter of the treatise
under a few heads, taken from the life of the simplest
living thing. The generalisation has become an actual
observable example. This transition from the abstract
to the concrete, from the idea to the thing itself, is owing
mainly to those definite conceptions which in Müller's
time were being slowly elaborated: these were the cellular
theory, the larger conception of "Stoffwechsel" as contained in the term "metabolism," and the conception
of "differentiation of tissue" connected with division
of labour. The two former are already very clearly
foreshadowed in Theodor Schwann's microscopical researches; the latter takes us back to K. E. von Baer's
embryological researches, to which the Darwinian idea
of a struggle for existence, and the consequent tendency
to one-sided development of form and function, have
given an additional importance. Of the first and third
of these definite modern conceptions I have treated
above. The cell is the morphological unit of living
matter. The process of differentiation was recognised

terially influenced physiology, the
basis of medicine, and hence also
the latter; and it is incalculable
what many of those here present
have gained through such influence
in days of sickness or may still gain.
Whoever carefully studies the development of physiology, will be
convinced that it is mainly Trem-
bly's observations of the hydropolyp that have changed the former
aspect of things, and that the transformation of the general views of
life has altered the theory of sensation, circulation, &c., very materially, and is still active" ("Blicke
auf die Entwickelung der Wissenschaft," an address, reprinted in
'Reden,' vol. i. p. 109).

in the examination of dead embryos in various stages of development, and the idea of the division of labour is one flowing from the premises of the Darwinian theory—the facts of variability and overcrowding. The second conception, that of "metabolism," touches immediately upon the processes of life, and demands special treatment in the present chapter which deals with biological Thought.

The conception of a continuous exchange or circulation of matter and of energy in every living organism, and the study of this elementary typical form of the living process in the morphological unit of all living organisms, in the cell, seems to have originated with Theodor Schwann,[1] and is laid down in his 'Microscopical Researches,' published in 1839. On it is based the whole simplification and unification of biological thought which distinguishes the second from the first half of our century.   The study of the cell — its

31.
Schwann.

[1] On the change which came over general physiology about 1840, and the part he himself played, Theodor Schwann has expressed himself in a letter addressed to Du Bois-Reymond, which is given in the notes to the latter's Éloge of Müller, reprinted in the second volume of his 'Reden,' pp. 143-334. It forms one of the most important historical documents. The Éloge itself should be read together with Claude Bernard's 'Rapport,' &c., mentioned above (p. 384 n.), which gives the history of the great change from a more exclusively French point of view. In the letter mentioned above, from which also the quotations given in the text are taken, Schwann claims that the first instance in which an "evidently vital phenomenon was submitted to mathematical, numerical" rule, was his measurement of the carrying power of a muscle in relation to its contraction in 1836. The purely physical view of vital phenomena exhibited in this example was not adopted by Müller, nor yet the quickly following general principle of the cellular theory. Schwann refers to the third section of his 'Microscopical Researches,' in which he discards "vitalism," but admits in man ("on account of his freedom") an immaterial principle, and claims that this assumption divides him distinctly from the materialists.

formation, growth, division, and maintenance of form amidst change of matter and alternation of function—constitutes the "prolegomena" of physiology, and a comparison of Prof. O. Hertwig's recent publication on the "cell" with the introduction to Johannes Müller's 'Physiology' marks well the change of ideas which half a century has produced. And we must so much the more admire the clear anticipation of Schwann, as he was not in possession of the full conception of energy in its two interchangeable forms of kinetic and potential energy, which was developed in the course of the two decades following his publication. Schwann not only conceived the cell to be the morphological unit of all living matter, but he also saw that "cell formation must be the general principle of organic development, and that there can be only one such principle." In the third section of his 'Microscopical Researches' he founds on this "his theory of organisms, and rejects distinctly therein all teleological explanations based upon a vital force acting according to final purposes." He thus showed "that the only essential property of all living matter—viz., growth—is not inaccessible to a physical explanation," and he did this at a time "when Liebig had not yet taught physiologists the chemical changes which take place in living tissues." These ideas were only partially adopted by Johannes Müller and other leading physiologists of the day. Schwann's view could only be consistently elaborated in proportion as

32.
Circulation
of matter
and energy.
to the older conception of a "Stoffwechsel" (a chemical process) there was added that of a "Kraft"- or

" Energie-wechsel " [1] (a physical process). Bio-chemistry had to be supplemented by bio-physics. With a clear anticipation of the correcter and fuller view, Schwann introduced the Greek term " metabolê." It is the merit of Prof. Michael Foster to have domiciled this useful and all-comprising technical term in English physiological

[1] Du Bois-Reymond ('Reden,' vol. ii. p. 220) mentions this as the third important gain which physiological science had to register since the appearance of Müller's book; the first and second being the cellular theory and the mechanico-physical method, both largely owing to Schwann. This was written just before the great influence of Darwin began to be felt. In the ideas introduced by Helmholtz, which clarified the conception of force, he sees the " key which opens a comprehension of the 'Stoffwechsel' in plants and animals." The term " Stoffwechsel," also " Stoffumsatz," or simply " Umsatz," has been quite familiar in German physiological literature during the whole of the century. I cannot find any generally accepted term in English literature before the introduction of Schwann's term " metabolic phenomena," which, I believe, was first adopted by Sir M. Foster, and is now quite domiciled in English text-books and translations. The passage in Schwann's ' Microscopical Researches ' is as follows ('Sydenham Society's Translation,' p. 193) : "The phenomena attending the formation of cells may be arranged in two natural groups : first, those which relate to the combination of the molecules to form a cell, and which may be denominated the *plastic* phenomena of the cell ; secondly, those

which result from chemical changes, either in the component particles of the cell itself or in the surrounding cytoblastema, and which may be called *metabolic* phenomena ($\tau\grave{o}$ $\mu\epsilon\tau\alpha\beta o\lambda\iota\kappa\acute{o}\nu$, implying that which is liable to occasion or to suffer change)." It will be seen later on that the term metabolism is a peculiarly happy one, as it lends itself by a slight change in the prefix to denote the twofold process of building up and of running or falling down, which constitutes the changes peculiar to protoplasm as the constituent element of all organised substance. It is, accordingly, somewhat surprising that the term has found so little favour abroad. In France, where this twofold movement has long ago been recognised as one of the characters of the living process, the terms " composition et décomposition " (de Blainville), " organisation et désorganisation " (Claude Bernard), " assimilation et désassimilation,"have been variously adopted (see Claude Bernard,'Phénomènes de le vie,' vol. i. p. 36, &c.) M. Yves Delage (' L'Hérédité,' p. 53) says : " Les Anglais ont substitué à ces expressions si significatives : *nutrition, assimilation, désassimilation,* une terminologie qui a dû leur paraître bien belle, car ils l'ont tous adoptée avec un empressement remarquable ; c'est celle de métabolisme," &c.

literature, to have placed it at the entrance of his text-book of physiology, and thus to have given the student a somewhat more detailed description of the elementary functions of living matter than was afforded by the older term " vortex," employed by Cuvier.

33.
" Metabol-
ism."

These merits of Schwann, which attach more to the conception of " metabolism " than to that of the cell, are not reduced by our having to state that the latter conception has been entirely changed since his time. The cell of to-day is not the cell as Schwann conceived it. Of the pretty clearly defined structure or organ-isation of that biologist, with its wall (membrane), its kernel (nucleus), and its fluid contents (cell sap), nothing has remained but the cell contents, termed protoplasm by von Mohl; and the living process can no longer be considered as the function of a well-defined organ or machine. It is rather the fundamental property of an almost homogeneous substance, the mass of proto-plasm, in which the kernel is the only recognisable differentiated portion. The immediate effect of this de-structive analysis of the early conception of the cell was to destroy the idea that the living processes carried on in any special cell or organ are a result of its organisation, as the function of an apparatus is dependent upon the arrangement and combination of its parts. It has pro-moted the view that—for our understanding at least—the first thing to learn is the nature of the processes themselves. We have to look upon the visible structure of special cells and organs merely as " mechanical con-trivances, serving only to modify in special ways the results of the exercise of these fundamental activities, and in no sense determining their initial development." [1]

It seems, then, that we can date back to Schwann's ' Researches ' the origin of two distinct courses of Thought which in the second half of our century obtain in biological science. The first we may call the morphological or structural school of biology. It is based on the theory of the cell or some modified conception, and attempts to explain the fundamental processes which go on in living organisms from the structure of the elementary parts. As the most minute particles of

34.
Structural analysis of morphological elements.

[1] See Sir Michael Foster's excellent article on "General Physiology" in the 19th vol. of the ' Ency. Brit.,' 9th ed., p. 12. In this connection a passage from an early review of Huxley's, " On the Cell Theory," has been frequently quoted, according to which cells may be " no more the producers of the vital phenomena than the shells scattered in orderly lines along the sea beach are the instruments by which the gravitative force of the moon acts upon the ocean. Like these the cells mark only where the vital tides have been and how they have acted " (1853, in the ' Brit. and For. Med. Chirurg. Review,' reprinted in the first volume of ' Scientific Memoirs,' p. 277). According to this view, which has been further developed in more recent times, the cells would be "indications," not instruments, of the vital phenomena, which "are not necessarily preceded by organisation, nor are in any way the result or effect of formed parts, the faculty of manifesting them residing in the matter of which living bodies are composed, as such—or, to use the language of the day, the ' vital forces ' are molecular forces." It is interesting to quote together with this passage from Huxley, what was said forty years later by an eminent living physiologist, Prof. Max Verworn of Jena : " The fact has been established that a fundamental contrast between living organisms and inorganic bodies does not exist. In contradistinction to all inorganic nature, however, organisms are characterised solely by the possession of certain highly complex chemical compounds, especially proteids " (' General Physiology,' transl. by F. S. Lee, 1899, p. 126). " We can summarise our considerations and give simple expression to the problem of all physiology. *The life-process consists in the metabolism of proteids.* If this be true, all physiological research is an experiment in this field : it consists in following the metabolism of proteids into its details, and recognising the various vital phenomena as an expression of this metabolism which must result from it with the same inevitable necessity as the phenomena of inorganic nature result from the chemical and physical changes of inorganic bodies " (ibid., p. 136).

living matter, revealed by the most powerful microscope
aided by all the elaborate processes of staining, still
appear to be endowed with the fundamental properties
of life, such as irritability, contractility, and metabolism,
i.e., change in form and chemical constitution, the
object of this line of research, viz., the investigation
of the initial structure of the elements of living matter,
can only be reached by indirect means or by conjecture.
Structural chemistry and stereo-chemistry proceed by
similar methods of investigation, and have succeeded
by means of the atomic, molecular, and kinetic theories
of matter in bringing order and unity into a very large
portion of our knowledge of chemical combinations. The
morphological or structural biologist pictures to himself
very much more complicated arrangements of molecules
than the carbon tetrahedron of van 't Hoff or the benzine
ring of Kekulé, yet formed on similar principles; and
by continuing in his mind these combinations which,
as they become more complex, also become more unstable, he arrives ultimately at a very complex and
continually changing chemical structure, which he imag-
ines might be the beginning of the living process, the
element of organisation. This conception, so far as I
can find, was first introduced into biological literature
by Herbert Spencer. He has termed this element
of living matter " the physiological unit." The conception has been varied in endless ways by many subsequent biologists, all of whom have invented special
names for these elementary units of life out of which
they hope to put together the many observable protoplasmic and cellular tissues of the plant and animal

organism as Haüy attempted to build up crystals out of his "molécules intégrantes."   The most elaborate analysis of this conception is put forward in the ' Micellar Theory ' of the celebrated botanist Nägeli, which in Germany has found favour with many eminent biologists as a provisional programme of the various problems involved.   It is clear that the conception of the physiological unit opens out two distinct lines of research.   We can approach it on the one side by artificially producing in the chemical laboratory more and more of those chemically stable compounds which we find in the living organism.   After Wöhler had produced urea artificially in 1828, the number of these artificial syntheses greatly increased, and we are specially indebted to M. Berthelot for having shown how all the simpler chemical compounds contained in the organism can be put together by inorganic processes. Some of the more complex substances have likewise subsequently yielded to this synthetic method.   " It is possible," we are told, " that after a time our knowledge of chemistry may have advanced sufficiently to enable us to produce albuminous bodies artificially by synthesis." [1]   " We are already able artificially to build up, atom for atom, out of their elements a series of organic compounds, some of a very complicated character.   We no longer doubt that all the rest, even the most complex, will be thus produced; it is only a question of time." [2]   But the ways in which the

35.
Synthesis of organic substances.

---

[1] See O. Hertwig, ' The Cell,' p. 16.
[2] See G. Bunge, ' Physiological

Chemistry,' transl. by Wooldridge, p. 313.

chemist puts together these substances in the laboratory are rarely the methods adopted by nature in the living organism, and in many cases the product itself, though apparently the same, is yet essentially different.[1]

[1] This touches on a very important point, which is much emphasised in all the best modern treatises on the subject. Claude Bernard in all his writings insisted on the fundamental difference between the processes going on in the organism and those that go on in the laboratory of the organic chemist, though the two produce frequently the same apparent result. "Si les forces que l'être vivant met en jeu dans ses manifestations vitales ne lui appartiennent pas et rentrent toutes dans les lois de la physico-chimie générale, les instruments et les procédés à l'aide desquels il les fait apparaître lui sont certainement spéciaux. En effet, l'organisme manifeste ses phénomènes physico-chimiques ou mécaniques à l'aide des éléments histologiques cellulaires, épithéliaux, musculaires, nerveux, &c. Il emploie donc de procédés, c'est-à-dire des outils organiques qui n'appartiennent qu'à lui. C'est pourquoi le chimiste, qui peut refaire, dans son laboratoire, les produits de la matière vivante, ne saurait jamais imiter ses procédés, parce qui il ne peut pas créer les instruments organiques élémentaires qui les exécutent. Cela revient à dire que tous les appareils des êtres organisés ont une morphologie qui leur est propre" ('Rapport,' &c., 1867, p. 135). Quite recently Bunge (loc. cit., p. 313) has said, "All our artificial syntheses can only be achieved by the application of forces and agents which can never play a part in vital processes, such as extreme pressure, high temperature, concentrated mineral acids, free chlorine—factors which are immediately fatal to the living cell. . . . It follows that the animal body has command of ways and means of a totally different character, by which the same object is gained." A very interesting speculation, referring specially to this point, was put forward by the eminent physiologist, Prof. E. Pflüger of Bonn, in the year 1875. It is fully discussed in Verworn's frequently quoted work on General Physiology (pp. 304, 311, 482). The theory is based upon the remarkable part which the compound radicle cyanogen seems to play in the organism. Pflüger starts from the fundamental characteristics of the substance called proteid, with which life is inseparably connected. Proteid is known to exist in a stable form in food-stuffs, for instance in egg albumen. But this is not the same as the proteid contained in living matter. In the latter it is not stable, but is being continually decomposed. The decomposition was found to be due to the oxygen that occurs in the living proteid molecule. This oxygen, which is intramolecular, being continually received from outside by respiration, transforms the more stable molecule into an unstable labile molecule. In further following the clue afforded by this property, and comparing the decomposition products of living proteid with those obtained by artificial oxidation of dead proteid, Pflüger is led to the conclusion that the presence of the radicle cyanogen in the living proteid will explain the difference. "In the formation of cell-substance—i.e., of living proteid—out of food proteid, a change of the latter takes place, the atoms of

Another way of inquiry is to analyse the existing organic tissues still further by microscopic and chemical methods, in order to find out how they are built up. As the result of such inquiries we have a framework theory of protoplasm, a foam theory, a filament theory, a granular theory; and the attempt has been made to define living protoplasm as a colony of still smaller structural units termed " bioblasts." By this twofold method—by synthesis and by analysis—the biologist may attempt to approach the physiological unit, the seat and stronghold of the vital process.[1]

nitrogen entering into a cyanogen-like relation with the atoms of carbon, probably with the absorption of considerable heat." Cyanogen being a radicle possessing a great quantity of internal energy, the addition of it to the living molecule "introduces into the living matter energetic internal motion." The interest which attaches to the theory lies in this, that it allows us to form some conception how living matter originated. This problem is indentified with the problem, How does cyanogen arise? This we know is formed at an incandescent heat. " Accordingly, nothing is clearer than the possibility of the formation of cyanogen compounds when the earth was wholly or partially in a fiery or heated state. . . . If, now, we consider the immeasurably long time during which the cooling of the earth's surface dragged slowly along, cyanogen, and the compounds that contain cyanogen and hydrocarbon substances, had time and opportunity to indulge extensively their great tendency towards transformation, . . . and to pass over, with the aid of oxygen, and later of water and salts, into that self-destructive proteid, living matter.

. . . The first proteid to arise was living matter, endowed in all its radicles with the property of vigorously attracting similar constituents, adding them chemically to its molecule, and thus growing *ad infinitum*." This theory is interesting, as it is, so far as I know, the only attempt to reconcile the existence of living matter with the fact of the high temperature which once existed on the earth.

[1] A description of these several theories on the structure of protoplasm, among which the micellar theory of Nägeli, the foam theory of Bütschli, and the "bioblasts" of Altmann, have been elaborately developed, will be found in Prof. O. Hertwig's work on 'The Cell' (Engl. transl., p. 19, &c.), as also in M. Yves Delage's great work, 'L'Hérédité' (pp. 299-310). Verworn (*loc. cit.*, p. 87) draws special attention to the "alveolar" or "foam" theory, which, built upon investigations of Prof. Quincke, has "completely clarified our ideas upon the real nature of the protoplasmic structures so much observed. . . . As a result of these recent investigations the following picture can be formed of the finer morphological structure of proto-

There is, however, a second way open to the student of the phenomena of life, and this may be termed the "physical method," as opposed to the "structural." Thus chemists and physicists first establish the general laws of motion and change in dynamics and energetics, and subsequently apply them to special problems, such as those of physical astronomy or the chemistry of electrolysis and solution. Similarly the physiologist may study the processes common to all living matter, and look upon the action of a definite cell, tissue, or organ merely as an application of these general processes. From this point of view structural biology, like structural chemistry, only furnishes illustrations, not an explanation, of the vital processes : the special structure or organ is a result of the process or function— not its cause. As Prof. Michael Foster says, "We may throw overboard altogether all conceptions of life as the outcome of organisation, as the mechanical result of structural conditions, and attempt to put physiology on the same footing as physics and chemistry, and regard all vital phenomena as the complex products of certain fundamental properties exhibited by matter, which, either from its intrinsic nature or from

The 36. "physical" method.

plasm. Protoplasm consists of a ground mass in many cases completely homogeneous, in most cases very finely foam-like or honeycomb-like, in which lies embedded a greater or less quantity of very various solid elements or granules. In the foam-like protoplasm the granules always lie at the corners and angles where the foam-vacuoles come together, never in the liquid of the bubbles themselves." Some physiologists think that none of the descriptions of protoplasmic architecture help us much, and "hold to the fundamental principle that living matter acts by virtue of its structure, *provided* the term structure be used in a sense which carries it beyond the limits of anatomical investigation—*i.e.*, beyond the knowledge which can be attained either by the scalpel or the microscope" (Burdon Sanderson, 'Address,' Brit. Assoc., 1889, p. 607).

its existing in peculiar conditions, is known as living matter."[1]

Thus, instead of trying to penetrate to the physiological units and construct them through a process of imagination, this latter class of biological thinkers confine themselves to the task of describing in the simplest manner and as completely as possible the various properties of the living substance—*i.e.*, its functions.[2] And

37.
Properties
of the living
substance.

---

[1] 'Ency. Brit.,' article "Physiology," vol. xix. p. 12. See also an address delivered by Prof. Burdon Sanderson at the meeting of the Brit. Assoc. at Newcastle in 1889 ('Report,' p. 604) : " During the last ten or fifteen years histology has carried her methods of research to such a degree of perfection that further improvement scarcely seems possible. As compared with these subtle refinements, the 'minute anatomy' of thirty years ago seems coarse—the skill for which we once took credit seems but clumsiness. Notwithstanding, the problems of the future from their very nature lie as completely out of reach of the one as the other. It is by different methods of investigation that our better - equipped successors must gain insight of those vital processes of which even the ultimate results of microscopical analysis will ever be as they are now, only the outward and visible signs " (p. 608).

[2] As. Prof. Burdon Sanderson puts it in his ' Address,' it is a reversion to a position which is not new in the history of physiology. "The departure from the traditions of our science which this change of direction seems to imply is indeed more apparent than real. In tracing the history of some of the greatest advances, we find that the recognition of function has preceded the knowledge of structure. Haller's discovery of irritability was known

and bore fruit long before anything was known of the structure of muscle " (p. 607). " . . . In much more recent times the investigation of the function of gland-cells, which has been carried on with such remarkable results by Prof. Heidenhain in Germany, and with equal success by Mr Langley in this country, has led to the discovery of the structural changes which they undergo in passing from the state of repose to that of activity ; nor could I mention a better example than that afforded by Dr Gaskell's recent and very important discovery of the anatomical difference between cerebro-spinal nerves of different functions " (ibid.) What has to a great extent worked this important change in the methods and reasoning in physiology is the recognition of "plurality of function with unity of structure," a principle urged strongly by the experimental school of medicine, with Claude Bernard as its greatest representative. Notably this was the effect of his " demonstration that the liver had other things to do in the animal economy besides secreting bile. This, at one blow, destroyed the then dominant conception that the animal body was to be regarded as a bundle of organs, each with its appropriate function—a conception which did much to narrow inquiry, since when a suitable function had once been assigned to an organ

here we meet first of all with the great fact that a living thing cannot be conceived to exist alone; it is dependent upon its environment, and upon other living things of similar, never quite identical, and mostly very different nature. As a consequence of the conception which guided Lamarck in contemplating the living world— especially the crowd of living things which before him had remained unobserved — the influence of environment plays a greater and greater part in the study of every form of life. The further fundamental property of all living matter—that it absorbs through intussusception other matter which surrounds it, that it grows and multiplies by division, casting off some portions of its own substance as useful secretions or cumbrous and useless excretions—has the twofold result that every living thing modifies its own surroundings and that it creates a society of its like which, through an automatic process of crowding-out, exercises a kind of selection among its members, they being forced to accommodate themselves to circumstances and to each other.[1] The process suggested by Darwin as the rationale

---

there seemed no need for further investigation. Physiology, expounded as it often was at that time in the light of such a conception, was apt to leave in the mind of the hearer the view that what remained to be done consisted chiefly in determining the use of organs such as the spleen, to which as yet no definite function had been allotted. The discovery of the glycogenic function of the liver struck a heavy blow at the whole theory of functions." (Sir M. Foster in ' Claude Bernard,' p. 90.) On the necessary condition

of the experimental as distinguished from the anatomical method, namely, that it deals with the organism whilst it is alive, see the concluding remarks in Sir M. Foster's article on " General Physiology " in the ' Ency. Brit.,' vol. xix.

[1] The relations of living things to each other and to their environment admit of being contemplated in two ways, which may be best distinguished by a reference to human society, exhibiting as it does the two phenomena of co-operation and of competition. The former

of variation and development is more and more coming
to be recognised as an inevitable property of all growing
and multiplying living things. So far as the influence
on the environment, the medium in which it lives, is
concerned, we owe to the great French biologist, Claude
Bernard, the helpful conception of the inner medium,[1] as

is based upon harmony, the latter
upon conflict. The former aspect
is more particularly emphasised by
the French school of Lamarck, de
Blainville, and Claude Bernard ;
the latter more by the English
school of Malthus and Darwin ;
each starting apparently without
any reference to the other. Claude
Bernard in particular says ('Phénomènes de la vie,' vol. i. p. 67): "Pour
nous la vie résulte d'une conflit,
d'une relation étroite et harmon-
ique entre les conditions extérieures
et la constitution pré-établie de
l'organisme. Ce n'est point par
une lutte contre les conditions
cosmiques que l'organisme se développe et se maintient; c'est,
tout au contraire, par une adaptation, un accord avec celles-ci. . . .
L'être vivant ne constitue pas une
exception à la grande harmonie
naturelle qui fait que les choses
s'adaptent les unes aux autres ; il
ne rompt aucun accord ; il n'est en
contradiction ni en lutte avec les
forces cosmiques générales ; bien
loin de là, il fait partie du concert
universel des choses, et la vie de
l'animal, par exemple, n'est qu'un
fragment de la vie totale de l'uni-
vers."

[1] Although the biology of Claude
Bernard does not contain the
principle of descent and evolution
which so powerfully influenced the
contemporary writings of English
and German naturalists, one is
nevertheless reminded of the ideas
of Lamarck in reading the second

of his lectures on the ' Phenomena
of Life' (vol. i. pp. 65 - 124).
Lamarck had expressed the idea
that in the graduated scale of
living things we recognise an increasing independence with regard
to the external environment. (See
supra, chap. vii. p. 315.) Claude
Bernard says (p. 67): "Le mode
des relations entre l'être vivant et
les conditions cosmiques ambiantes
nous permet de considérer trois
formes de la vie, suivant qu'elle est
dans une dépendance tout à fait
étroite des conditions extérieures,
dans ude dépendance moindre, ou
dans une indépendance relative. Ces
trois formes de la vie sont : 1°, La
vie latente ; vie non manifestée.
2°, La *vie oscillante ;* vie à manifestations variables et dépendantes du
milieu extérieur. 3°, La *vie constante ;* vie à manifestations libres
et indépendantes du milieu extérieur." Examples of the "vie
latente" are to be found in the
vegetable and animal creation alike.
Grains of seed, desiccated animals,
germs, eggs, ferments, yeast, &c.,
are examples. All vegetables belong
to the class of the *vie oscillante*, also
among animals all invertebrates,
and among the vertebrates those
with cold blood. These depend on
cosmic conditions, the cold of
winter, and the reviving heat of
summer, &c. The higher animals
with warm blood whose temperature is constant are not in the
same way subject to the influence
of the external medium. They

it were the inner atmosphere which any large assembly of living units must necessarily create for itself. All larger organisms are complex societies of living units which depend not only on the external but also on the internal medium which bathes them. It was one of Claude Bernard's happiest generalisations to look upon the blood, not as a living tissue but as a means of communication of the living tissues of the organism, as an internal medium which bears the same relation to the constituent tissues that the external medium, the atmosphere, does to the whole body.

39.
The "internal medium."

One of the principal functions of this artificial medium or atmosphere which the larger organisms possess, create and maintain for themselves during their life, is to enable a particular elementary substance to get access to every living cell or tissue of the organism. This substance is oxygen, without which the continuance of life in the higher organisms seems impossible. That life is a process of combustion is accordingly a

possess "un *milieu intérieur* perfectionné" (p. 104). But they begin their existence as beings with an oscillating life when they are in the form of eggs. Of the *vie constante ou libre* Claude Bernard says : "Je crois avoir le premier insisté sur cette idée qu'il y a pour l'animal réellement deux milieux ; un *milieu extérieur* dans lequel est placé l'organisme, et un *milieu intérieur* dans lequel vivent les éléments des tissus. L'existence de l'être se passe, non pas dans le milieu extérieur, air atmosphérique pour l'être aérien, eau douce ou salée pour les animaux aquatiques, mais dans le *milieu liquide intérieur* formé par le liquide organique circulant qui entoure et baigne tous les éléments anatomiques des tissus ; c'est la lymphe ou le plasma, la partie liquide du sang qui chez les animaux supérieurs, pénètre les tissus et constitue l'ensemble de tous les liquides interstitiels, expression de toutes les nutritions locales, source et confluent de tous les échanges élémentaires. Un organisme complexe doit être considéré comme une réunion *d'êtres simples* qui sont les éléments anatomiques et qui vivent dans le milieu liquide intérieur. *La fixité du milieu intérieur est la condition de la vie libre indépendante*" (p. 113).

definition which has been put forth in various ways
ever since Lavoisier's time, when he and Laplace tried
to explain the existence of animal heat in this manner.
The progress of science in the course of the century
which followed Lavoisier has more and more confirmed
the importance of the *rôle* which oxygen plays, but has
also shown how very complex are the products of
oxygenation in the living organism,—how the living
processes are indeed chemical processes, but are quite
different from those of the chemical laboratory.   As
Claude Bernard says, "The chemistry of the laboratory
is carried on by means of reagents and apparatus
which the chemist has prepared, and the chemistry
of the living being is carried on by means of reagents
and apparatus which the organism has prepared." [1]
One of the great performances of living matter is
the production, another is the storing up and distribution, of oxygen.   But though we know that the
chlorophyll - containing cells of green plants, under
the influence of sunlight, are able to decompose that
very inert body, carbonic acid, breathed out by both
animals and plants, into free oxygen and carbon, allowing the carbon to be retained or utilised in the form
of more or less complex carbohydrates, and though

---

[1] See especially the extensive explanations in the ' Rapport sur les
progrès de la Physiol. gén.' (1867,
p. 133 *sqq.*): "Les phénomènes
physico-chimiques qui se passent
dans les corps vivants sont exacte-
ment les mêmes, quant à leur nature,
quant aux lois qui les régissent et
quant à leurs produits, que ceux
qui se passent dans les corps bruts;
ce qui diffère, ce sont seulement les
procédés et les appareils à l'aide desquels ils sont manifestés. . . . Il
est déjà prouvé qu'un grand nombre
de phénomènes qui s'accomplissent
dans les corps vivants peuvent être
reproduits artificiellement, en dehors de l'organisme, dans le monde
minéral.   Mais ce que l'on ne peut
pas reproduire, ce sont les procédés
et les outils spéciaux de l'organisme
vivant" (p. 222).

we also know that the red blood corpuscles in verte-brate animals convey oxygen in a concentrated form [1] through all the organs, giving it up wherever it may be wanted, the real chemical process concerned in the action of chlorophyll is not cleared up; [2] and " no one has been able hitherto to explain, by a reference to physical laws, the active functions of the heart and muscular wall," by which the circulation of the blood is effected. [3]

In the explanation of many physiological phenomena no idea has proved more fruitful than the con-ception of natural selection, introduced by Darwin to explain the growing diversity and the purposeful-ness of organisms. Coupled with the cellular theory, which looks upon every living organism as a society of self-accommodating individual units or cells, forced by circumstances into differentiation of form and into divided labour or function, it relieved biologists of that spectre of vitalism which still survived after Lotze and Du Bois-Reymond had placed the creative and formative influence outside of the mechanism—as the watchmaker lives outside of the watch, which exhibits only mechanical contrivances. That which puzzles the spectator of the watch, as it does the spectator of every

[1] See Bunge, ' Physiological Chemistry,' p. 275.

[2] "Iron plays an important part in vegetable life : we know that chlo-rophyll granules cannot be formed without it. If plants are allowed to grow in nutritive solutions free from iron, the leaves are colourless, but become green as soon as an iron salt is added to the fluid in which the roots are immersed. It is even sufficient merely to brush the surface of the colourless leaf with a solution of an iron salt to cause the appearance of the green colour in the part thus painted. Chlorophyll itself contains no iron, and we do not know in what way the iron is concerned in its produc-tion" (Bunge, loc. cit., p. 25). See also Hertwig, 'The Cell,' p. 153.

[3] Bunge, p. 7 ; cf. also p. 275.

organism, is the apparent design and purpose, without which neither could be conceived to have been formed.[1] Here, then, the idea that it was a process of natural choice, of automatic adjustment, which produced the apparent end and purpose at the moment when the structure itself was produced, came as a great relief.[2] It explained how it comes about that nature, even with unloaded dice, so often—yet not always—throws doublets. It permitted naturalists and physiologists to use purpose and final cause, not as an explanation, but as an indication where to look for causal—that is, for mechanical—connections. Accordingly the first systematic attempt to use natural selection in the explanation of the adjustment of the internal parts of an organism, which is due to Prof. Wilhelm

40. Natural selection within the organism.

[1] "The main problem which the organic world offers for our solution is the purposefulness seen in organisms. That species are from time to time transformed into new ones might perhaps be understood by means of an internal transforming force, but that they are so changed as to become better adapted to the new conditions under which they have to live is left entirely unintelligible" (Weismann on Nägeli's " Mechanisch-Physiologische Theorie der Abstammungslehre " in ' Essays upon Heredity,' Engl. transl., p. 257).

[2] See Du Bois-Reymond's Address, "Darwin versus Galiani" ('Reden,' vol. i. p. 211, &c.): " Here is the knot, here the great difficulty that tortures the intellect which would understand the world. Whoever does not place all activity wholesale under the sway of Epicurean chance, whoever gives only his little finger to teleology, will inevitably arrive at Paley's dis-

carded ' Natural Theology,' and so much the more necessarily, the more clearly he thinks and the more independent his judgment. . . . The physiologist may define his science as the doctrine of the changes which take place in organisms from internal causes. . . . No sooner has he, so to speak, turned his back on himself than he discovers himself talking again of functions, performances, actions, and purposes of the organs. The possibility, ever so distant, of banishing from nature its seeming purpose, and putting a blind necessity everywhere in the place of final causes, appears therefore as one of the greatest advances in the world of thought, from which a new era will be dated in the treatment of these problems. To have somewhat eased the torture of the intellect which ponders over the world-problem will, as long as philosophical naturalists exist, be Charles Darwin's greatest title to glory " (p. 216).

Roux in his work on the 'Struggle of the Parts in the Organism,' was hailed by Darwin as "the most important book on development that has appeared for some time." [1]   In modern books on physiology the process of selection is a familiar conception; but if in natural history, in the life of plants and insects, there still remain many extraordinary instances of selection

[1] The work appeared in 1880, and is referred to by Darwin in a letter to Romanes ('Life and Letters,' vol. iii. p. 244 ; 16th April 1881), where he suggests also a similar consideration of plant life and structure. It has been republished in Roux's 'Gesammelte Abhandlungen zur Entwickelungsmechanik der Organismen' (Leipzig, 1895, 2 vols.), with an interesting preface (vol. i. p. 139, &c.), and many historical and critical digressions.   It originally emanated from the earliest school of Darwinism in Germany, represented by Haeckel, Gegenbaur, and Preyer, at Jena. It has been found very suggestive, and has been the beginning of a very large controversial literature in Germany, in which the fundamental problems of biology have been discussed, and have received new formulations.   The idea of the struggle of individuals for survival, suggested by Darwin, is applied by Roux to the different parts and organs within the developing organism. Du Bois-Reymond almost contemporaneously published his brilliant and celebrated address on   " Exercise "   (" Ueber   die Uebung," 'Reden,' vol. ii. p. 404). In England Roux's suggestive treatise does not seem to have been much noticed, and Prof. Roux himself attributes this to the inadequate notice of the book by Romanes in 'Nature' (vol. xxiv. p. 505), in which his doctrine was erroneously compared with Spencer's ideas of "direct equilibration." Prof. J. A. Thomson, in 'The Science of Life,' refers to the importance of Roux's work (pp. 138, 229), and of his 'Archiv für Entwickelungsmechanik.' Roux has been classed by some of his critics among the "organicists," a school represented in France chiefly by Claude Bernard. The main thesis of this view seems to be that the phenomena of life consist in the play of two factors—the organisation and the environment of the living thing. Roux applies the process of natural selection and consequent adaptation, which Darwin sees at work in a crowd of living things, to the organisation of the individuals themselves, each of which is a microcosm, a society of autonomous units, say of cells. He has   accordingly   gone   a step farther   back   than   the   older " organicists," studying the development, the genesis of the organism on Darwinian lines.   M. Delage accordingly dates from him a   new   school   of   "organicism." " L'organicisme commence, à mon sens, avec Descartes (1642), se continue avec Bichat, Claude Bernard,   et   arrive   avec   Roux (1881) à une théorie si profondément modifiée, bien qu'elle dérive du même principe, qu'elle peut être   considérée   comme   toute moderne" ('L'Hérédité,' p. 408).

for which no teleological mechanism has been invented, still more are we baffled by the apparent "autonomy of the living cell," in consequence of which it is, *e.g.*, "able to select its food, retaining what is useful and rejecting what is harmful."[1] And what shall we say of the so-called "wandering cells, which are actually sent out by the organism in order to absorb in the alimentary canal food-stuffs, notably fat, returning with it into the blood, or to receive into themselves malignant bacteria, making them innocuous by a process of digestion?"[2] No mechanical physico-chemical explanation of this process is imaginable, and the word "selection," with which Darwin charmed away so many mysteries, has revealed new ones in their place.[3]

[1] See the very interesting and frequently quoted address by Prof. G. E. Rindfleisch (Würzburg, 1888), entitled 'Ärztliche Philosophie,' p. 13.

[2] Rindfleisch, *loc. cit.*, p. 15.

[3] In this connection it is interesting to refer to a discussion which was raised by the suggestive address of Prof. F. R. Japp, entitled, "Stereochemistry and Vitalism" ('Brit. Assoc. Report,' 1898, p. 813). It refers to the discovery by Pasteur of "chirality" in solutions of certain crystallised organic salts, on which I reported in vol. i. p. 450. "Pasteur regarded the formation of asymmetric organic compounds as the special prerogative of the living organism. Most of the substances of which the animal and vegetable tissues are built up—the proteids, cellulose—are asymmetric organic compounds." Now, in his experiments on fermentation Pasteur found that "the asymmetric living organism selected for its nutriment that particular asymmetric form" out of a mixture of two enantiomorphous compounds held in solution—"which suited its needs—and left the opposite form either wholly or, for the most part, untouched" (p. 817). Prof. Japp proceeds to consider the opinion then formed by Pasteur, "that compounds exhibiting optical activity have never been obtained without the intervention of life" (p. 818). This view, to which Pasteur adhered, and which he defended against eminent opponents, has been frequently challenged, and seemed definitely set aside by the explanation of Prof. Emil Fischer of Berlin, and by Jungfleisch's synthesis of racemic acid and its resolution into dextro- and lævo-tartaric acids. . . . "Consequently, the overwhelming marjority of chemists hold that the foregoing synthesis and separation of optically active compounds have been effected without the intervention of life, either directly

Another property of all living matter which has been seized upon to furnish a definition of life is its extreme mobility. It has been stated that the great difference between living and non-living matter is this—that the former is in a state of movable or dynamical equilibrium, whereas the latter tends always to a condition of rest or of statical equilibrium. This was especially urged by the late celebrated Du Bois-Reymond of Berlin, to whom we owe the greater part of our knowledge of the physical and chemical changes exhibited in the active nervous system. In comparison with this property of a dynamical equilibrium, explained by the analogy of a fountain of water or a vortex which change their substance whilst maintaining their form, other older distinctions which had been drawn between organised and unorganised bodies sank into insignificance.[1]

---

or indirectly" (p. 824). Prof. Japp and Prof. Crum Brown of Edinburgh are of the opposite opinion, inasmuch as in the view of the former "the action of life, which has been excluded during the previous stages of the process, is introduced the moment the operator begins to pick out the two enantiomorphs," as was done by Jungfleisch.

[1] Among the older discussions of the best way of defining life which belong to the second third of the century, we have in Germany the various writings of Du Bois-Reymond ('Reden,' notably vol. ii. p. 25) ; in France those of Claude Bernard ('Phéno-mènes de la vie,' notably vol. i. p. 21, &c.) ; in England the 'Biology' of Mr Herbert Spencer. The two last-named authors examine with some care the definitions of earlier writers. All three should be read

and re-read by any one who desires to arrive at a clear understanding of the subject. Du Bois-Reymond's definition shows the preponderating influence of the ideas which governed the Berlin school of physiology, and which centred in Helmholtz's tract on the Conservation of Energy. Claude Bernard defines life by the words "La vie, c'est la création." Organisation and disorganisation are the two sides of this process, organisation, and environment the two factors. The doctrine of evolution goes a step farther back, and attempts to analyse "organisation." The process of creation is to Mr Herbert Spencer a process of development. The word creation in the older sense ceases to have a meaning. Of more recent date are the discussions of the subject in the very interesting work of Carl Hauptmann, 'Die Metaphysik in der modernen Physio-

It is true that not all parts of a higher organism are subject to this continued change, but those that are not —such as the skeleton of an animal or the trunk of a tree—are automatically deposited by the living organism for the purpose of external or internal support, protection, or communication. They are the permanent mechanism by which the economy and administration of the society of living units or cells are kept up. These it has been possible, in many instances, to analyse into stable chemical compounds, which have been reproduced in

logie' (Jena, 1894, neue Aufl.), especially the last chapter. Still more recent is the very careful analysis contained in the new edition of Mr Spencer's 'Biology,' notably vol. i. p. 111 *sqq.* The final conclusion arrived at by these two latest philosophers has much in common. Both strive after a dynamic conception of life; both confess that such is at present unattainable—a desideratum, not an achievement. Hauptmann says (p. 386): "The most primitive life, from which alone the living world on this earth can have sprung, can only be assumed to be a species the members of which varied in manifold ways and propagated themselves. Here we have to do already with an eminently complex interaction of elementary processes. . . . We still absolutely lack every conception of such a dynamical system. . . . Likewise the origin of the simplest living substance is mechanically quite unknown and uncomprehended. . . . The individual forms of life stand in the midst of a yet unintelligible higher order of the material world." Similarly Mr Spencer (*loc. cit.*, p. 120): "We are obliged to confess that life in its essence cannot be conceived in physico-chemical terms. The required principle of activity, which we found cannot be represented as an independent vital principle, we now find cannot be represented as a principle inherent in living matter. If, by assuming its inherence, we think the facts are accounted for, we do but cheat ourselves with pseudo-ideas. . . . It needs but to observe how even simple forms of existence are in their ultimate nature incomprehensible, to see that this most complex form of existence is in a sense doubly incomprehensible. . . . While the phenomena (of life) are accessible to thought, the implied noumenon is inaccessible, ... only the manifestations come within the range of our intelligence, while that which is manifested lies beyond it" (p. 122). There seems ample evidence that under different forms of words Claude Bernard and Du Bois-Reymond, in his later writings, arrived at similar conclusions. See 'La Science Expérimentale,' p. 210, and "Die sieben Welträthsel" ('Reden,' vol. i. p. 381). "The mystery is the more profound the more it is brought into contrast with the exact knowledge we possess of surrounding conditions" (Prof. Burdon Sanderson, 'Brit. Assoc. Report,' 1889, p. 614).

the chemical laboratory by processes which were like
or unlike those going on in the organism itself. But
such stable compounds are not the bearers, they are
merely the collateral products, the accompaniments, of
the living process. The artificial production of organic
compounds, beginning with Wöhler's production of urea,
and ending with the production of albumen, do not
approach the problem of the production of living matter.
Could the chemist produce protoplasm, it would not be
living; or were he fortunate enough to hit upon one of
its many metamorphoses, it would die the next moment,
not having the inner structure or the external and
internal environment necessary for its self-conservation
and activity. Nor do we seem to get any nearer the
real secret by analysing more closely the chemical and
physical changes, the metabolism, the rhythmical processes
which constitute this activity. We call it nutrition or
respiration, assimilation and disassimilation, oxidation and
reduction—storing up and letting loose of energy. We
picture to ourselves the building up of more and more
complicated chemical molecules, containing thousands of
atoms, in a temporary and easily disturbed equilibrium,
and the subsequent breaking down again of these complex
structures by gradual decomposition or by sudden explo-
sions due to external stimuli, or by the still more mysterious directive action of conscious will: we liken them to
the pulling of a trigger, or the gathering up and letting
loose of a destructive avalanche by the motion of a flake of
snow on the top of a peak. We see how this metabolism,
this "Stoff- und Kraft-wechsel," goes on in the smallest
amœba in rhythmical movements, and how, in higher

organisms, it is divided into many stages, allocated to special cells or to quite distinct classes of beings, some of which, like plants, take upon themselves the first important steps of the anabolism, so that others—the animals—may carry it a stage higher, preparing a discharge, or catabolism, which becomes more and more effective, till it reaches the unique nervous function which accompanies the highest phenomenon of animal activity—the mental process. Claude Bernard[1] has put into classical words the rationale of this process. " If, in the language of a mechanic, the vital phenomena —namely, the construction and destruction of organic substance—may be compared to the rise and fall of a weight, then we may say that the rise and fall are accomplished in all cells, both plant and animal, but with this difference, that the animal element finds its weight[2] already raised up to a certain level, and that hence it has to be raised less than it subsequently falls.

[1] 'Phénomènes de la vie,' &c., vol. ii. p. 513. It is one of Claude Bernard's greatest merits to have corrected the earlier formula in which the circulation of matter had been expressed. Dumas and Boussingault had said : " L'oxygène enlevé par les animaux est restitué par les végétaux. Les premiers consomment de l'oxygène ; les seconds produisent de l'oxygène. Les premiers brûlent du carbone ; les seconds produisent du carbone. Les premiers exhalent de l'acide carbonique ; les seconds fixent de l'acide carbonique." On this passage Claude Bernard has the following comment : " Cette loi qui sous la forme précédente exprime avec vérité le mécanisme d'une des plus grandes harmonies de la nature est une loi cosmique et non une loi physiologique. Appliquée en physiologie, elle n'explique pas les phénomènes individuels : elle exprime comment l'ensemble des animaux et l'ensemble des plantes se comportent en définitive par rapport au milieu ambiant. La loi établit la balance entre la somme de tous les phénomènes de la vie animale et de la vie végétale : elle n'est point l'expression de ce qui se passe en particulier dans un animal ou une plante donnés " (p. 512). This false direction, which had been introduced into physiology a generation earlier, Claude Bernard corrected by the view that the circulation of matter takes place not only between the two kingdoms of nature but in every elementary organism.

[2] Or its potential.

The reverse occurs in the green plant cells. In a word, of the two movements, that of descent is preponderant in the animal, that of ascent in the vegetable." No one has done greater service to the fixing of our ideas on this subject than Dr Gaskell when he analysed the whole process, called "Metabolism" by Professor Michael Foster after Schwann, into the two complementary processes of Anabolism the upward, and Catabolism the downward, movement — the winding up and running down of the clock, the preparation and loading of the explosive and the discharge of the gun.[1]

42. Anabolism and Catabolism.

[1] The introduction of these terms is, however, connected with a special view — differing somewhat from that suggested by the formula of Claude Bernard—which is now very generally adopted in textbooks of physiology. Prof. Burdon Sanderson has given a lucid statement of this difference in his Address, entitled "Elementary Problems of Physiology," before the Brit. Assoc. in 1889 ('Report,' p. 613). He there says : "A characteristic of living process . . . is that it is a constantly recurring alternation of opposite and complementary states, that of activity or discharge, that of rest or restitution. Is it so or is it not? In the minds of most physiologists the distinction between the phenomena of discharge and the phenomena of restitution (Erholung) is fundamental, but beyond this unanimity ceases. Two distinguished men— Prof. Hering and Dr Gaskell— have taken, upon independent grounds, a different view to the one above suggested, according to which life consists not of alternations between rest and activity, charge and discharge, loading and exploding, but between two kinds of activity, two kinds of explosion, which differ only in the direction in which they act, in the circumstance that they are antagonistic to each other. Now, when we compare the two processes of rest . . . and discharge . . . with each other, they may further be distinguished in this respect, that whereas restitution is automatic, the other is occasional—i.e., takes place only at the suggestion of external influences. . . . It is in accordance with the analogy between the alternation of waking and sleeping of the whole organism, and the corresponding alternation of restitution and discharge, of every kind of living substance, that physiologists by common consent use the word stimulus (Reiz), meaning thereby nothing more than that it is by external disturbing or interfering influence of some kind that energies stored in living material are discharged. Now, if I were to maintain that restitution is not autonomic, but determined, as waking is, by an external stimulus, that it differed from waking only in the direction in which the stimulus acts—i.e., in the tendency towards construction on the one hand, towards destruction on the other— I should fairly and as clearly as

The modern theories of the cell, of metabolism, and selection, have also greatly influenced and modified our conceptions concerning the last and most important property of all living matter—viz., that it is self-reproductive. Older text-books on physiology treated of the great problem of generation—*i.e.*, the origin of a new individual —as a phenomenon of organised life which stood quite isolated ; and although the sexual difference in plants and animals had early led to certain analogies, to similar terminology, and to vague inferences, the mysterious phenomena of generation, and especially of sexual generation, were not brought into line with the general properties of all living matter till about fifty years ago. Even Johannes Müller in his great text-book on Physiology, which takes a much wider view of the subject than any work before it, treats of the reproduction of tissues and of generation in quite separate, seemingly disconnected, parts of his work. Into this uncertainty only little light was thrown by the original propounders of the Cellular theory, who, misled by the supposed analogy of cells and crystals, imagined that cells originated out of the surrounding cell sap, as crystals solidify out of the solution or mother liquor. Correcter views were gradually elaborated by botanists. Mohl emphasised the important part which protoplasm plays in the formation of cells. Nägeli established the process of intussusception as against external accretion ; anatomists like Max Schulze and Brücke joined hands,

43.
Reproduction.

possible express the doctrine which Dr Gaskell and Prof. Hering have embodied in words which have now become familiar to every student. The words in question—'anabolism,' which, being interpreted, means winding-up, and 'catabolism,' running down—are the creation of Dr Gaskell."

and the year 1863 is usually given as that in which
the protoplasmic theory was established. According to
this view protoplasm is the element or unit of all living
substance : it grows through assimilation (intussusception
and excretion), and multiplies (*i.e.*, gives rise to other
living units) by subsequent division. This process was
found to be fundamental : it describes the growth of
the simplest and the most complicated organisms as
beginning alike with a unit cell, which may or may
not grow by division; it is the formula of growth,
restitution, and generation (whether sexual orasexual);
and, what is equally important, it prevails also in pathological cases—*i.e.*, in the formation of diseased tissues.
In fact, the great generalisation which followed Harvey's
celebrated dictum, " omne vivum ex ovo," was put forth
by the late Professor Rudolf Virchow, the eminent
founder of cellular pathology, in his formula, " omnis
cellula e cellula." The formula has in more recent
times been further elaborated on the same lines of
thought in proportion as the importance of the nucleus
or cell kernel has been recognised, or as the granular
structure of protoplasm has been maintained ; leading
to analogous formulæ, such as " omnis nucleus e nucleo,"
" omne granulum e granulo." These formulæ [1] are the

---

[1] See Roux ('Gesammelte Abhandlungen,' vol. i. p. 393): "Uninterrupted durability is the indispensable condition of all that is
organic, although this does not
involve a distinction from inorganic
processes. This fact is expressed
by the fundamental theses : Omne
vivum ex ovo (Harvey), Omnis
cellula e cellula (Virchow), Omnis
nucleus e nucleo (Flemming)."

Hauptmann ('Die Metaphysik,'
&c., p. 334) says : " Altmann for-
mulates for himself in analogy
with these biological principles the
further principle, ' Omne granulum
e granulo.'" On Altmann's theory
of the " bioblasts " as elementary
organisms, see Yves Delage,
'L'Hérédité,' p. 498, &c., Hertwig,
'The Cell,' p. 24.

expression of anatomical observations and theories representing an enormous amount of research, labour, and ingenuity, but they involve no new line of reasoning, and they belong, accordingly, more to the history of Science than to that of Thought.

The first to attempt a mechanical explanation of the process of cellular division was Mr Herbert Spencer,[1] who, in his 'Principles of Biology' (1863), pointed out that there exists a limit of growth through assimilation or intussusception, inasmuch as volume and mass increase at a greater rate than the surrounding surface through which communication with the environment is afforded. A resultant tension brings about an increase of surface through rupture, and restores the balance between the contained mass and the surface. In his analysis of this process of readjustment, Spencer has given mechanical

45.
Spencer's
law of limit
of growth.

[1] The principle here referred to sometimes goes under the name of the Leuckart-Spencer principle, it having been suggested independently by Rudolf Leuckart, Herbert Spencer, and Alexander James. It requires, of course, a great many qualifications. See the 'Principles of Biology,' vol. i. part 2, chap. i. But "it follows from these considerations that the cell can never surpass a certain size; for if the disturbance of metabolism that arises because of the increasing disproportion between the more superficial and the deeper layers has reached a certain extent, the cell can no longer continue living in its existing form. Thus the remarkable fact is explained very simply, that no cells of constant form are known that are larger than a few millimetres in diameter, and thus we are made to understand why the development of large organisms is only possible by the arrangement of the living substance into an aggregate of small cells instead of into a single cell, for example, of the size of a man. . . . If, therefore, the living substance of such a cell is not to perish by growth, at some period in its growth a correction of this disproportion between mass and surface and of the disturbance of metabolism conditioned by it must come in: such a correction is realised in the reproduction of the cell by division. The reproduction of the cell by division is accordingly to be considered merely as a result of growth, and the morphologists for a long time have rightly termed reproduction a continuation of growth, 'a growth beyond the measure of the individual'" (Verworn, 'General Physiology,' Engl. transl., p. 530, &c.)

biologists a formula which, like his physiological units, has helped to give precision and direction to reasoning on these subjects. But as growth has a natural limit and leads to division, so reproduction through division appears to have a limit also. "Only the very lowest organisms, such as fission fungi, appear to be able to multiply indefinitely by repeated divisions: for the greater part of the animal and vegetable kingdoms the general law may be laid down that, after a period of increase of mass through cell division, a time arrives

46. Fusion of two elements.

when two cells of different origin must fuse together, producing by their coalescence an elementary organism which affords the starting-point for a new series of multiplications by division."[1]   Fertilisation is now known to be a cellular problem. As such it has been studied in favourable cases which permitted of direct observation, and what has been ascertained in those cases —exhibiting in general the same common features and phases of development—has by inference under the great generalisations of the cellular theory been extended to all living things in which sexual differentiation exists, be they animals or plants.[2]   The male and the female

[1] Hertwig, 'The Cell,' p. 252. The process may be looked at as an instance of the cyclical order of change. "The multiplication of the elementary organism, and with it life itself, resolves itself into a cyclic process. . . . Such cycles are termed generation cycles. They occur in the whole organic kingdom in the most various forms." Similarly Sir M. Foster ('Text-book of Physiology,' 5th ed., p. 1555), as quoted, *supra*, p. 289. We may add that from a still broader standpoint, which we may call that of

bionomics — in distinction from biology — the cycle never repeats itself, but, owing to overcrowding and selection, something different, more complex—*i.e.*, externally or internally better endowed—is produced. Philosophically we call this progress.

[2] There exists no more remarkable instance of the extension of natural knowledge by a process of very incomplete induction than the gradual firm establishment of the now universally adopted doctrine of fertilisation, no more brilliant refu-

elements concerned have both been recognised to be cells, both have been found to undergo, before what is termed the stage of maturity, similar preparatory changes. The changes represent, as it were, the last stages of their independent existence as living cells. After these changes have taken place they can only enter into a new cycle of existence, exhibiting new powers of growth and division by a process of fusion where each supplies what in the other is wanting to start on a new cycle of life—*i.e.*, of differentiation and development.

Thus the vague theories of former times, which reach far into the nineteenth century, the speculations of the Spermatists and the Ovists, have during the last thirty years, beginning with Pringsheim's observation in 1869 of the pairing of the swarm-spores of certain algæ,

---

tation of the purely enumerative, or all-case method. The number of instances in which the process of fertilisation, with its various preparatory stages and its consequences, can be actually observed is infinitesimally small compared to the number of different species and varieties in which it is endlessly repeated on lines which no biologist doubts to be essentially the same. M. Yves Delage says : " C'est une chose remarquable combien certains êtres, par des particularités en apparence sans intérêt ont facilité la solution de certains problèmes presque insolubles en dehors d'eux. *L'Ascaris megalocephala* [the round-worm of the horse, first observed by van Beneden in 1883], par le petit nombre de ses chromosomes, les Echinodermes [sea urchins, &c.] par la facilité avec laquelle ils acceptent la fécondation artificielle, ont fait faire, en dix ans, plus de progrès aux questions relatives à la fécondation que n'ont fait avant ou depuis tous les autres animaux réunis. Dans l'Ascaride, le testicule forme un long tube et les diverses phases de la spermatogénèse s'accomplissent dans les régions différentes de l'organe : il y a une zone à spermatogonies, une zone à spermatocytes en voie d'accroissement, une zone où se font les divisions réductrices et une enfin où les spermatides se transforment en spermatozoïdes " (L'Hérédité,' p. 133). See on the variety of objects which have lent themselves to the gradual unravelling of the processes of cell division, nuclear division, fusion of nuclei, cleavage and embryonic development, notably the volume of Prof. Val. Haecker, ' Praxis und Theorie der Zellen- und Befruchtungslehre' (Jena, 1899). A very lucid summary is contained in J. A. Thomson's 'The Science of Life' (1899).

and centring in van Beneden's discovery,[1] been replaced by definite conceptions capable of typical description. This typical process consists in the fusion of certain parts of the male and female cells, — the nuclei or kernels playing an important if not the essential part. Many biologists of the foremost rank, notably in Germany and France, have contributed to make clearer the various lines in this typical picture of the most mysterious process in the physical organism, whilst every new discovery has brought with it new and unanswered questions or given a novel aspect to older problems.

47.
New
problems.

Of these problems, those of heredity and variation are at present by far the most important. Both the cellular theory of living matter and the theory of natural selection, including the principles of differentiation and of the division of physiological labour, converge upon these two great facts of modern biology. The theory of natural selection pre-

[1] See last note. "Since the researches of O. Hertwig and others in 1875, it had been clear that each parent contributes a single germ-cell to the formation of the offspring; but the masterly researches of E. van Beneden (1883) showed that every nucleus of the offspring may contain nuclear substance derived from each of the parents, a conclusion which is visibly demonstrable for a few of the first steps in cleavage. In fact, van Beneden to some extent *proved* what Huxley had foreseen when he said, in 1878, 'It is conceivable, and indeed probable, that every part of the adult contains molecules, derived both from the male and from the female parent; and that, regarded as a mass of molecules, the entire organism may be compared to a web, of which the warp is derived from the female, and the woof from the male'" (J. Arth. Thomson, 'The Science of Life,' p. 129). Another theoretical anticipation is, according to Haecker (*loc. cit.*, p. 133), the "Idioplasma" of Nägeli: "The heritable substance, organised, possessing a complex structure, transmitted from one generation to another," which was "about the same time identified by Strassburger, O. Hertwig, von Kölliker, and Weismann, with the chromatin substance of the nucleus."

supposes the fact of heredity—that is, the transmission of characters peculiar to the parents (be they acquired by them or not), and the fact of variation, but it does not explain them. It does not give any intelligible description of the means which nature uses to secure that continuity of change which is marked on the one side by a faithfulness to certain typical forms, and on the other by a gradual development. The cellular theory permits us to comprise, under the general categories of cell-growth, cell-division, and cell-fusion, the great facts of the history of all living matter, but it does not explain how that apparent sameness of structure which the ultimate morphological unit, the cell, presents to our view, develops into that variety of recurrent forms which make up the wealth and the order in the world of natural objects. The older naturalists were divided into two distinct schools: one believed in pre-formation with development—the older meaning of " evolution "; the other in after-formation, or " epigenesis." The former foundered on the difficulty of explaining or making plausible how all the germs of hundreds of succeeding generations could be contained in the first ancestor; the latter failed to explain how nature was able to build up by mechanical forces out of unorganised matter a structure resembling the parent structures. The suggestion of a " nisus formativus," which we owe to the celebrated Blumenbach, is only a definition of the difficulty, not an explanation.

The three distinct ideas represented by these historic terms occur again in modern biology, though altered to suit the vast extension of actual knowledge of facts, and the three great generalisations mentioned above. Out of the three ideas of pre-formation, after-formation, and the directive principle, the three generalisations, namely, the cellular theory, natural selection, and metabolism, and the enormous number of facts collected by microscopists and naturalists of all kinds, many more or less ingenious theories of life have been put together. None of them has obtained, though some have had a very marked influence on biological science, and even on popular thought. Of these Prof. Weismann's theories of heredity are probably the best known. Without entering upon the enormous array of biological facts which have been marshalled by supporters and opponents alike, it will be of interest to point out the novel aspects and lines of reasoning which have come into prominence through the voluminous discussion belonging to this subject. They were prepared before the appearance of Weismann's writings by the changed and enlarged conceptions which the discoveries of the middle of the century introduced concerning the general phenomena of Life, Death, and Disease. Three distinct convictions regarding these three main aspects of the living portion of creation have been forced upon the scientific and popular mind. First, we have the modern doctrine of the ubiquity of organisms and germs, at least so far as our planet is concerned: beyond this sphere we can say that we know no more of the existence of living matter than past generations. Secondly, we have the generally recognised doctrine that spontaneous generation of living out of not-living matter is unknown and inconceivable under such conditions as

48.
Weismann
on heredity.

we can realise or imagine. And thirdly, hand in hand with the conviction of this unique but ubiquitous character of life, the impression of the mutual interdependence of living creatures has gained ground, and has especially influenced our ideas of the cause and treatment of disease.

In one of those luminous addresses in which he has rivalled the combination of literary with scientific clearness characteristic of the French genius, the late Prof. Huxley has written the history of Biogenesis [1] —*i.e.*, of the theories of the origin of life from the time of the Italian Redi down to Pasteur, showing how experiment and theory alternately supported and contradicted the doctrine that living matter could be formed out of not - living matter, till the great French biologist, by his refined experiments, entirely banished from the provinces of science and practice the once admitted fact that, after exclusion or destruction of all living germs, phenomena peculiar to life, such as fermentation and putrefaction, could be generated. Those great departments of medical practice, the antiseptic and aseptic treatment, with their enormous development of prophylactic and antitoxic methods, form the daily and ever-growing argument against abiogenesis

49.
Biogenesis.

---

[1] In his presidential address to the British Association in 1870, reprinted in 'Critiques and Addresses,' p. 218 *sqq.* A very readable and much earlier deliverance on "The Diffusion of Life" is that by K. E. von Baer, before the Academy of St Petersburg in 1838, reprinted in the first volume of his 'Reden,' &c., p. 161 *sqq.* In the preface of 1864 to this reprint, the illustrious author tells us that between 1810 and 1830 there were probably few naturalists who "did not consider the generation without parents of inferior organisms as proved, or at least as highly probable," and he himself would not at that time (1838) "declare it to be non-existent" (p. 173). In 1864 he describes the theory as having almost vanished, leaving the problem of the first beginnings of life in the numberless varieties, even after Darwin's hypothesis, unsolved (p. 177).

—*i.e.*, the generation of living out of dead or not-living matter.

But in proportion as abiogenesis or spontaneous generation has disappeared from our scientific text-books, life being recognised as a phenomenon between which and dead matter there exists no intelligible and no practical transition except that of destruction, the ubiquity of life has forced itself more and more on our attention. Not long ago, as Huxley [1] tells us, the adherents of spontaneous generation urged as an argument on their side that if biogenesis be true, innumerable facts and experiments prove " that the air must be thick with germs ; and they regarded this as the height of absurdity. But nature," as Huxley continues, " occasionally is exceedingly unreasonable, and Professor Tyndall has proved that ordinary air is no better than a sort of stirabout of excessively minute solid particles." It is now, after a generation has passed, hardly necessary to refer to any special experiments of Tyndall or of others, when the daily press brings us records of the number of billions of germs contained in a cubic inch of the atmosphere of large cities, precisely as it does of the mortality of their population. The cellular theory of disease has been succeeded and amplified by the bacillar theory, and no modern scientific fact has fastened on the popular mind with a stronger hold than the ubiquity of the micro-organisms, which, with beneficent or fatal results, assist everywhere—chiefly in the larger organisms—in the struggle for existence.

It is, moreover, only a logical inference that if living

[1] 'Critiques and Addresses,' p. 233.

matter is not being continually formed out of not-living matter, while it is an undeniable fact that living matter is continually and everywhere passing out of existence, the preservation of life is dependent upon an enormous self-overproduction which, combined with the process of natural selection, secures its permanence and the development of the highest forms of which it is capable. The continuity—*i.e.*, the interdependence—of all living forms in time and space guarantees the non-extinction of this phenomenon, which, for all that we know, is of a unique character. The modern scientific and popular view of life is that it is a unique phenomenon, that it is a ubiquitous phenomenon, at least within the area of what we call " our " world, and that it is a continuous phenomenon. The unique character or singularity of life has been directly demonstrated by the sameness of the ultimate units of all living matter, the cells, indirectly by the refutation of the older theory of spontaneous generation ; and has been enormously strengthened by the doctrine of descent, the phenomena of overcrowding, and the possibility of natural selection. The ubiquity of life— within certain limits—has been revealed directly by the microscope, and indirectly by the modern theories of disease, and of many forms of growth.[1] The continuity of

51.
The continuity of living forms.

[1] There is a striking passage in Nansen's ' Farthest North,' vol. i. p. 445, showing the ubiquity of organic germs : " When the sun's rays had gained power on the surface of the ice, and melted the snow, so that pools were formed, there were soon to be seen at the bottom of these pools small yellowish brown spots, so small that at first one hardly noticed them. Day by day they increased in size, and absorbing, like all dark substances, the heat of the sun's rays, they gradually melted the underlying ice and formed round cavities often several inches deep. These brown spots were . . . algæ and diatoms. . . . I actually found bacteria,— even these regions are not free from them."

life has—as an inevitable corollary—come more and more into prominence. It has been the subject of much discussion, as a phenomenon which is felt to require a mechanical explanation.

The problem of the continuity in time of the forms and properties of living matter forced itself on the great propounder of the modern theory of Descent, on Darwin. He looked upon the principle of " Reversion [1]—this power of calling back to life long-lost characters—as the most wonderful of all the attributes of inheritance."

52.
"Pan-
genesis."
At the end of his second great work, ten years after the appearance of the ' Origin of Species,' he ventured on a hypothetical explanation, his theory of " Pangenesis," " which implies that the whole organisation, in the sense of every atom or unit, reproduces itself; hence ovules and pollen-grains, the fertilised seed or egg, as well as birds, include and consist of a multitude of germs thrown off from each separate atom of the organism." [2] This idea, as the author himself admitted, and as has since frequently been pointed out, was not fundamentally new: it had been anticipated by Buffon in his celebrated " organic molecules," and since Darwin it has been restated and adapted in various modified forms. It is hardly an explanation, but it is a statement which emphasises the great fact of modern biology,—the fact brought out by the cellular theory, that the units of life are not the large visible organisms which were formerly studied by prefer-ence, but the innumerable, infinitesimal living beings

---

[1] 'Animals and Plants under Domestication,' vol. ii. p. 372.
[2] 'Animals and Plants under Domestication,' chap. 27, vol. ii. p. 358.

called cells which, through growth and reproduction by division and fusión, maintain life as a continuous unique phenomenon.

Into this view, which under the special form of pangenesis has not found much favour, but which, nevertheless, in some form or other, forces itself more and more on our attention, Professor Weismann has imported a further distinctive feature, not prominently brought out by Darwin, though it also dates farther back [1] than the present generation.

[1] The history of the knowledge and theory of sex and heredity has been written in English by Profs. Patrick Geddes and J. Arthur Thomson, in a book entitled ' The Evolution of Sex' (1st ed. 1889); in French by M. Yves Delage, in his much-quoted work, ' La Structure du Protoplasma et les Théories sur l'Hérédité et les grands problèmes de la Biologie' (1895). The latter work contains elaborate criticisms, and finally inclines towards a theory of life termed in France " Organicisme," the main idea of which is the assumption of two distinctive factors in all the phenomena of living matter—viz., " Organisation and Environment." This view, according to the author, has not yet gained sufficient strength to form a definite current of thought like the three earlier views defined by the terms " Animisme," " Evolutionisme," " Micromérisme." The first of these centres in the idea of vital force, the second in the older school of evolution ; the last begins with Buffon, and comprises the modern theory of Evolution with Spencer, Darwin, Haeckel, Weismann. Of the last M. Delage says : " Ce dernier est, pour le moment, l'ouvrage le plus parfait créé pour expliquer l'Hérédité et

l'Évolution. Nous croyons avoir montré qu'il est bâti d'hypothèses fragiles, invraisemblables, et, tout en rendant justice au talent de son architecte, nous conseillons de l'admirer de loin et de construire ailleurs " (p. 837). " Organicisme " is represented by W. Roux, Driesch, and O. Hertwig, and is historically traced back to Descartes (p. 838), and to von Baer and Claude Bernard (p. 720). To the theories of the others, " les Organicistes opposent le concours d'une détermination modérée et des forces ambiantes toujours agissantes, toujours nécessaires, non comme simple condition d'activité, mais comme élément essentiel de la détermination finale " (p. 720). As in this account the names of Roux, Driesch, and O. Hertwig are placed together, it is well to remark that since that time the two last-named authorities have in various polemical publications signified the divergence of their fundamental conclusions from the later attitude which Prof. Roux has assumed. For those of my readers who desire to get some insight into the drift of this most recent and advanced controversy, in which questions of principle, of scientific and philosophical method, alternate with discussions of minute

Growth by intussusception and assimilation has long been recognised as the characteristic property of all living matter, of every living cell. Mechanical causes suffice to explain the further process of division as a necessary consequence of continued growth, the formation of new cells out of existing ones, the process of reproduction. Only in the lower organisms, however, does reproduction exist simply as multiplication by division. In all higher organisms at least, reproduction by division seems connected with the phenomenon of death of a portion of the dividing organisms: a differentiation seems to set in between the new cells, some gradually losing their power of self-multiplication by division, and thus being doomed sooner or later to arrive at the end of their organic existence; while others retain this power or regain it by uniting with others—the process of fusion of male and female elements —and seem thus to be specially endowed with the work of reproduction—*i.e.*, the preservation of the continuity of life. The great morphologist Richard Owen, about the middle of the century, in a tract on Parthenogenesis, remarked that " not all the progeny of the primary impregnated germ-cell are required for the formation of the body in all animals: certain of the derivative germ-cells may remain unchanged and become included in

embryological development, assisted or disturbed by experiments carried on in microscopic dimensions, I recommend, besides the larger works of Hertwig and Roux, already referred to, the highly suggestive writings of Hans Driesch, notably his ' Analytische Theorie der organischen Entwickelung ' (1894), and ' Die Biologie als selbständige Grundwissenschaft ' (1893). As a very helpful introduction to the original views of this writer, English readers will welcome the concluding chapter of Prof. E. B. Wilson's book, 'The Cell in Development and Inheritance ' (1896).

that body, . . . so included, any derivative germ-cell or
the nucleus of such may commence and repeat the same
processes of growth by imbibition, and of propagation by
spontaneous fission as those to which itself owed its
origin." [1] We have here the first enunciation of that
idea of a differentiation between the germ-substance and
the body - substance, between that portion of living
matter which is destined to preserve the continuity of
life, and that other portion which, destined to differen-
tiate more and more into the aggregate of living cells,
each bearing a special form and carrying out a special
function in the economy of the higher organisms, is at
the same time doomed to death, gradually losing, as it
does, its power of assimilation, growth, and division—*i.e.*,
of self-preservation. Prof. Haeckel in 1866, and Dr
Jäger in 1877, elaborated the idea further, pointing out
that the "germinal" element or substance was that
portion which in the process of division is reserved
for the preservation of the species (the $\phi\bar{v}\lambda o\nu$, hence
termed the phylogenetic portion), whereas the "personal"
element or substance goes to form the body or individual
(the $\ddot{o}\nu$, hence termed the ontogenetic portion).[2]

*53.
Germ-sub-
stance and
body-sub-
stance.*

[1] Darwin quotes this passage in
a historical note to his theory of
"Pangenesis" in the concluding
chapter of his 'Animals and Plants
under Domestication' (vol. ii. p.
375). He adds further, "By the
agency of these germ-cells Prof.
Owen accounts for parthenogenesis,
for propagation by self - division
during successive generations, and
for the repairs of injuries. His
view agrees with mine in the
assumed transmission and multiplication of his germ - cells, but
differs fundamentally from mine in
the belief that the primary germ-
cell was formed within the ovarium
of the female, and was fertilised by
the male. My gemmules are supposed to be formed, quite independently of sexual concourse, by each
separate cell or unit throughout the
body, and to be merely aggregated
within the reproductive organs."

[2] Complete references to the
earlier statements of this theory,
which, through the various writings
of Prof. Weismann (since 1881,
when he read a paper, "On the
Duration of Life," before the

This provisional statement, which emphasises the now generally recognised difference between the germ-substance and the body-substance, requires, however, two further qualifications in order to embrace the great characteristic facts of life and death as modern embryology and the phenomenon of descent have unfolded them.

Only in rare instances can we observe the continuity of cells—*i.e.*, of those organisms which, so far as our knowledge goes, form the ultimate units of living matter. Weismann recognised, as did the great botanist Nägeli, and long before both of these the philosopher Herbert Spencer, that though in the cell, with its nucleus and protoplasm, we may have arrived at the last microscopically visible independent units of life, we must—with the atomic theory in chemistry—assume the existence of much smaller units in all living matter, compared with which even the nucleus of the cell is a very complex aggregate. If the continuity of life is dependent upon that of an underlying living substance, this substance must be only an infinitesimal portion of any visible cell or nucleus. The conception of a continuous germinal substance has thus taken refuge in the more refined conception of a germ-plasma, as distinguished from the body or somatic plasma: the former is immortal within the limits of the conditions of organic life, the latter is

54.
Germ-plasma and body plasma.

Naturforscher - versammlung at Salzburg, reprinted in 'Essays upon Heredity,' transl. by Poulton and others, Oxford 1889 ; see also the 'Studies in the Theory of Descent,' transl. by Meldola, 2 vols., 1882, and the earlier essays of Weismann mentioned in the preface, p. viii.),
has become both scientifically and popularly recognised and debated, are given in Geddes and Thomson, 'The Evolution of Sex,' p. 93 ; also in M. Delage's great work, p. 349, &c., and in Wilson, 'The Cell,' p. 295, &c.

perishable, mortal, doomed, after temporarily serving the purposes of individual development, to disappear from the category of living matter.

And secondly, it appears that the germinal substance or germ - plasma, when once differentiated from the personal substance or body-plasma, cannot, as a rule, perform unaided the function of continuous preservation of the species or phylum. In all the higher animals the germ-substance appears in two distinct seemingly complementary forms, and only by the fusion of these does the development of the germ-substance become possible.

*55.
Differentia-
tion of germ
plasma.*

The great difficulties which stand in the way of applying these conceptions (which have found an exhaustive exposition in Prof. Weismann's 'Essays on Descent and Heredity') to the vegetable kingdom have been pointed out, and have prevented their general adoption by biologists;[1] nor have the elaborate modifications introduced in Prof. Weismann's later writings tended to make them more acceptable; the idea, nevertheless, of a fundamental differentiation of the elements of living matter into germinal and personal has got hold of the scientific mind at the present day, and cannot be

[1] On the objections of Prof. Strasburger, who points to the fact that in the case of begonias the fragment of a leaf planted in moist sand can reproduce the whole plant ; of Prof. Vines, who shows that whole groups of champignons, which propagate annually, are nevertheless rich in genera and species, which have evidently descended from one another, see Yves Delage, 'L'Hérédité,' p. 526, &c. ; 'Nature,' vol. x. p. 621 ; also O. Hertwig, 'The Biological Problem of To-day,' transl. by P. C. Mitchell (1896), p. 40, &c. On the discovery of Weismann "that in parthenogenetic ova only one polar globule is formed, while there are always two in ova which are impregnated," and the "momentary" presumption in favour of his theory which it afforded, see 'Essays on Heredity,' p. 333, &c. ; Geddes and Thomson, 'Evolution of Sex,' p. 180, &c. ; and Delage, 'L'Hérédité,' p. 151.

passed over in a history of Thought. Moreover, it has
made itself felt by giving rise to two separate views of
the cause of variation—*i.e.*, of that phenomenon in the
living creation on which the entire modern theory of
descent is founded.

If it be true that the preservation of the species, the
continuity of living forms, is dependent on the germ-
plasma, whereas the somatic plasma, from this point of
view, only serves individual ends and is a receptacle or
temporary dwelling-place for the germs which it trans-
mits but does not create, the experiences of the body, its
changes and development, can have little or no influence
on the hidden germs and their further history.   Thus
Weismann is led to a denial of the influence of environment, of habit and acquired characters, except in
those cases where, as in the lower organisms, no differentiation has set in between the germinal and the
personal substance.   This amounts to a negation of those
modifying influences which Lamarck emphasised, and
which play such a great part in the theories elaborated
by Darwin, Haeckel, and especially by Herbert Spencer.
On the other side, it has led Weismann to lay a much
greater weight upon sexual selection and the effects
of crossing in the process of descent and the phenomena of heredity.   But for sexual selection, and the
endless combinations of different germ - plasmas, there
would, according to Weismann, be no variation, and
hence no development of the higher forms of life.   The
controversy turns mainly upon the inheritance of acquired
characters, of which indeed no genuine and authenti-

56.
Weismann *v.*
Lamarck.

cated case seems to have been established.[1]   On the other side the influence of crossing, of the repeated division and fusion of different germ-plasmas, to which Darwin in his later writings attached more and more importance, and on which Weismann relies exclusively for an explanation of variation and natural selection, is denied by some biologists to tend in the direction of the gradual growth of definite characters : they point rather to the obliterating and diluting influence of such promiscuous fusion, and they maintain that the presence of an environment which always acts in a constant manner [2] is indispensable.

If we now look back for a moment on the fundamental change of ideas which the century has brought about in the biological aspect of nature, we are bound truly to halt in astonishment.   In no department of thought have comparatively small beginnings and detailed discoveries, referring to infinitesimally small phenomena, led to such revolutionary ideas concerning those phenomena which most intimately affect our personal interests—the problems of life and death, of conduct and of health.   The whole of this change has been brought about by introducing and extending those

---

[1] It is needless to give special references, as all the recent works on the subject, which have been largely quoted in this chapter, deal with this point.   See, however, Yves Delage, 'L'Hérédité,' p. 196, for a very complete bibliography. He concludes as follows : "Il n'est pas démontré que les modifications acquises sous l'influence des conditions de vie soient généralement héréditaires, mais il paraît bien certain qu'elles le sont quelquefois. Cela dépend sans doute de leur nature.   D'ailleurs on ne sait pas quelle est dans ce résultat la part de la transmission des modifications somatiques aux cellules germinales et celle de l'action directe des conditions ambiantes sur celles-ci " (p. 221).

[2] Hertwig, 'The Cell,' p. 319.

methods of investigation and reasoning which have been learnt in the mechanical, physical, and chemical sciences: the processes of observation, measurement, and calculation. And yet it may be asked, have we come nearer an answer to the question, What is Life? At one time, for a generation which is passing away, we apparently had. But a closer scrutiny has convinced most of us that we have not. The study of life has indeed been transferred from the higher and more complex forms to the lower, the minuter, and the simpler; and now lingers by preference among cells, germs, and primitive organisms, out of which we have learnt to consider the higher ones as put together on the principles of co-operation, division of labour, and mutual accommodation. The problem "What is Life?" has in all this gained a twofold aspect. Wherein consists the peculiarity of the smallest unit of living as compared with not-living matter? In organisation we are told, in growth through intussusception, in metabolism; but we are far from being able mechanically to describe these phenomena or processes. The spectre of a vital principle still lurks behind all our terms.[1] On the other

57.
Two aspects of the problem of life.

[1] If we broadly summarise the properties peculiar to living things which the nineteenth century has dwelt on in an original manner under the three conceptions of adaptation (fitness), selection (natural or sexual), and organisation (order or harmony), the question presents itself, Is any of these much-used terms intelligible or definable without reference to something which is extraneous to the object we treat of, this reference existing in our own thinking or contemplating mind, and, if actually present in natural objects themselves, then also indicative of the existence of some immaterial principle? Though this is manifested in mechanical contrivances which it has left behind with its signature upon them, it is nevertheless vaguely analogous to the selective, purposeful, or orderly performances of a human intellect. The exclusive study of detail on the one side, the aspect of the whole on the other, will always induce opposite answers to this question. In addition to the literature given in the notes to this chapter, I may refer

side, the union or co-operation of many essentially similar units in a complicated organism brings out more and more, as we ascend in the scale of living things, a new phenomenon, a new kind of unity, that which we term "individuality," the wealth of an inner self-conscious life, to which the older school of biologists attached primary importance.   Life accordingly has now for us two sides —first, the life of the smallest, the most primitive unit of living matter, say the cell, the amœba, or, if you will, the idioblast, the gemmule, the germ-plasma, the physiological unit.   Secondly, the life of the complex society of cells, the higher organism in which the inner world with all its mental phenomena has become manifest.   How is the unity of this higher complex possible ?   In what does it consist ?   What can we know of it ?   Neither the physiological nor the psychological unity is intelligible to us.   An eminent biologist, to whom we owe the creation of an entire new science, the late Professor Virchow, the founder of Cellular Pathology, has told us recently [1] that only since biologists have ceased to try to understand the unity of life in the higher organisms, the psychological unity, and have realised the fact that the unity of life is in the autonomous cell, has biology in theory and practice made much progress.   Be it so.   It seems likely that the progress of biology depends entirely on the cultivation of the mechanical view ; but from another and

to the following tracts which deal specially with the problems of mechanism and vitalism.   Hans Driesch, ' Die mathematisch - mechanische Betrachtung morphologischer Probleme der Biologie' (Jena, 1891) ; O. Bütschli, ' Mechanismus und Vitalismus' (Leipzig, 1901) ; Eugen Albrecht, ' Vorfragen der Biologie' (Wiesbaden, 1899).

[1] In the Huxley Lecture of 1898.

equally legitimate aspect, the unity of the complex as the bearer of all the phenomena of higher or inner life is equally important. In many ways it is a counterpart of the other, showing a peculiar continuity of its own, that continuity which I have made the special subject of this work. In proportion as the biological view of nature has become the science of the cell, another science has grown up which sets itself to study this higher phenomenon of living matter, the phenomenon of mind, directly by the methods of the exact sciences. This is the modern Science of Psycho-physics. Even the microscopist and biologist of the most modern type are occasionally startled by phenomena akin to those which commonly are only visible in the highest organisms. Psychical existence, an inner side to the external phenomena of motion, has accordingly been attributed by eminent representatives of the mechanical view of biological phenomena to the lowest, the most primitive, unit of living matter. Another school of science has set itself to study this inner side of living organisms in its more perfect, as it were fullgrown, manifestations, and by appealing in addition to the facts only known by introspection or self-consciousness. With the history of this movement, so far as it belongs to exact science, I propose to deal in the next chapter under the general title of the Psycho-physical View of Nature.

58.
Transition
to psycho-
physics.

CHAPTER XI.

ON THE PSYCHO-PHYSICAL VIEW OF NATURE.

IN the three foregoing chapters I have attempted to trace
the development of the different aspects under which our
knowledge of the real things which surround us, and of
nature as a whole, has been extended in recent times. I
have brought these different aspects which respectively
consider things natural according to their forms, their
genesis, or their life and purpose, under the general name
of the biological as distinguished from the abstract view,
with which I dealt in the four previous chapters. The
abstract view tries to arrive at the general properties of
all things, which it has succeeded in our times in summing up under the great generalisations of Attraction,
Atomism, Kinetics, and the doctrine of Energy. The
biological view is interested not so much in general
properties as in real specimens—the things, beings, and
phenomena in which we see the general properties exemplified and become real and in their actual union or
totality which we call nature. The abstract sciences
started on their modern career with mathematics, and
progressed through the development and application of

1.
Abstract
and concrete
sciences.

the mathematical methods to the data furnished by observation and experiment; the biological or concrete sciences began with a study of living things, and have progressed immensely in our times by viewing these not in isolation, but in their relations to each other and to the surrounding lifeless world—the so-called environment. An exact treatment, that to which the term "scientific" has been pre-eminently applied, seems here also to depend largely, if not exclusively, on the degree to which the mathematical processes of numbering and measuring can be applied, and on the utilisation of the general results arrived at in the abstract sciences.

2.
Their
different
methods.

The method of the abstract sciences is that of building up from small beginnings, by the process of summation or integration, intricate complexes which not infrequently are found to correspond to phenomena of actual experience. It has at its command the unlimited resolving powers of the calculus, and the well-established assumption that things natural are made up of numberless particles entering into innumerable combinations. The whole is thus for the mathematical view the sum of its parts. The concrete or natural sciences, on the other hand, start with the ready-made things or creatures of nature, or on a larger scale with the great order and economy of our world or the universe, and only descend into the minutiæ of the observatory, the dissecting-room, or the laboratory, with the hope of better understanding the great and complicated objects of their study. The greatest progress in the abstract sciences has been made by those minds that could concentrate their attention on special points, not infrequently expressed in mathematical formulæ, and expand their view through applications: the greatest progress in the natural sciences has been made by those who started with a large and comprehensive view of things natural, and gradually descended into detail.   Newton, Lagrange, Fresnel, and Helmholtz are good examples of the former; Humboldt, von Baer, Claude Bernard, and Darwin of the latter.

Now, it is a frequent experience that in the study of things natural, through the unavoidable process of dissection and analysis, the subsequent synthesis or summing up has not carried the student back to the real thing from which he started, but to some artificial product differing essentially from the natural object.   The real essence of the thing seemed lost when its parts were examined by themselves or in their apparent aggregation.   A prominent example of this kind is to be found in the living organism.   Theories have accordingly been formulated which looked upon life as a special principle to be superadded to any conceivable aggregation of mechanical processes, in order to raise them from the lifeless into the living order of things.   The last chapter dealt with the various biological hypotheses, of which three are conspicuous: the purely mechanical, according to which the living organism is merely a very complicated chemical molecule; the vitalistic, which establishes an essential difference between the action and constitution of a living and a lifeless unit of matter; and an intermediate view, which looks upon organisms as manufactured machines built up according to some plan, design, or idea, the nature of which can be further inquired into, but which does not try to throw any additional light on the mechanism itself, the working of which, like that of a clock, can be described on purely mechanical lines and without reference to the idea which preceded its construction.

According to many prominent naturalists, the evident design and purpose which characterise so many phenomena of living matter are explained on purely mechanical lines by the inherent or forced teleology of living things, which through over-production have to submit to an automatic process of selection or survival. To others this automatic process does not seem to suffice, and they assume a principle of progress which acts in a regulative manner. This vitalistic view is further supported by taking into account an extensive class of phenomena which I have, so far, hardly noticed— the marvellous properties of the higher creations of the animal world which exhibit the phenomena of consciousness or of an inner experience. That these phenomena belong to the realm of natural science as much as any other properties of living things cannot nowadays be doubted. The division into natural and mental science can no longer be upheld, or only with a very different meaning from that which it had for a bygone age.

3.
Inner
experience.

It will be my object in this chapter to give an account of the various and changing aspects which this great phenomenon of an inner or conscious life has presented to naturalists—*i.e.*, to those who have approached the phenomena of Mind from the side of nature, and of the different lines of research and reasoning along which they have dealt with it. I shall comprise the whole of this section of scientific thought under the general term of Psycho-physics.[1]   It refers to the borderland or common ground where physical and mental or psychical phenomena meet or interact.

Although the term psycho-physics is quite modern, the idea of a special science dealing with the relations of mind and body, or of the physical and mental life of the human organism, has been prominently before the scientific world ever since Cabanis published his celebrated 'Rapports du Physique et du Moral de l'Homme,' in which the well-known passage occurs which has been frequently repeated, modified, and quoted with varying approval or reproach : [2] " In order to arrive at a correct

---

[1] The term was first used by G. T. Fechner in the well-known work bearing this title, of which I shall have more to say in the course of the chapter. This work, dealing mainly with a certain numerical relation, narrowed the term down to a special investigation, whereas the larger problem, the study of the interaction of mind and body by the methods of the exact sciences, was variously designated as physiological psychology, mental physiology, psycho-physiology or physiology of the soul. As there is a tendency to regard physiology more and more as the physics of the living organism, it is evident that physics is the larger term ; and in dealing with the relations of the physical and the psychical in the widest sense, the term psycho-physics seems the more appropriate.

[2] 'Œuvres complètes' de Cabanis (1834), vol. iii. p. 159. The simile has attained a sort of historical celebrity through the drastic version which was given to it by Karl Vogt in his 'Physiologische Briefe' (1847), p. 206, where, with a

distinct intention of rousing an æsthetic disapproval, he compares the function of the brain with the secretion of bile by the liver and of urine by the kidneys. This dictum, which he repeated in his controversy with Rudolph Wagner, led in the middle of the century, as Du Bois-Reymond tells us, to a kind of systematic championship of the soul, the comparison with the kidneys being looked on as a degrading offence. " Physiology, however, has no knowledge of such grades of dignity. As a scientific problem the secretion of the kidneys is to her of the same dignity as the investigation of the eye or the heart or any other so-called noble organ." Vogt used the simile as an illustration of his purely materialistic view. Lange ('Hist. of Materialism,' vol. ii. p. 242) shows that with Cabanis the dictum is by no means bound up with such a view, as he really was a pantheist. The mistake, says Du Bois-Reymond, does not lie in the comparison, but in the implied suggestion, that psychical

idea of those operations from which thought arises, we
must consider the brain as a particular organ, destined
specially to produce it in the same way as the stomach
and the intestines are there to perform digestion, the
liver to filter the bile, the parotid, maxillary, and sub-
lingual glands to prepare the salivary juice."

The argument which led Cabanis to draw this parallel
between the functions of the brain and those of other
organs of the human body was based upon the philosophy of Locke, which had been domiciled in France by
Condillac and Helvetius. This philosophy, in its popular
version, taught that all our thoughts and ideas were
ultimately made up of sensations.[1] On the other side,

activity could be "explained
through the structure of the brain,
as secretion can be explained from
the structure of a gland" ('Reden,'
vol. i. p. 129).

[1] Cabanis (1757-1808), in the preface to the 'Rapports,' &c., p. 11,
gives a list of contemporary French
writers who, following in the line
of Locke, to whom "philosophy is
indebted for the greatest and the
most useful impulse," have taken
up different sides of the doctrine.
Of their writings a very clear and
exhaustive analysis will be found
in M. Picavet's 'Les Idéologues,
Essai sur l'histoire des idées et
des théories scientifiques, philosophiques, religieuses, &c., en France
depuis 1789' (Paris, 1891). Cabanis's own position is very clearly
defined (p. 16) when he says that
"Les opérations de l'intelligence et
de la volonté se trouveraient confondues à leur origine avec les
autres mouvements vitaux : le principe des sciences morales, et par
conséquence ces sciences elles-
mêmes rentreraient dans le domaine
de la physique ; elles ne seraient

plus qu'une branche de l'histoire
naturelle de l'homme : l'art d'y
vérifier les observations, d'y tenter
les expériences, et d'en tirer tous les
résultats certains qu'elles peuvent
fournir, ne différeraient en rien
des moyens qui sont journelle-
ment employés avec la plus entière
et la plus juste confiance dans les
sciences pratiques dont la certitude
est le moins contestée." This was
written in 1802. M. Picavet says
of Cabanis with much truth :
"Le continuateur d'Hippocrate, de
Descartes et des philosophes du
XVIIIᵐᵉ siècle, a été un précurseur
de Lewes et de Preyer, de Schopenhauer et de Hartmann, comme de
Lamarck, de Darwin et de bien
d'autres penseurs qui appartiennent aux écoles les plus différentes,
et ne soupçonnent quelquefois
même pas que les idées dont ils
sont partis leurs sont venues in-
directement, mais par des inter-
médiaires authentiques, de l'auteur
des 'Rapports du physique et du
moral'" ('Les Idéologues,' p. 264).
M. Picavet also gives valuable explanations how it came about that

the physiologists of the eighteenth century, notably
Haller, had demonstrated that the properties of the
physical organism culminated in those of the nervous
system—irritability and sensibility. The phenomenon
of sensibility, of producing and combining—as it were
digesting—sensations, was thus the function of the brain,
or the central organ of the nervous system, as other processes were the functions of other organs or physiological
apparatus. Cabanis was led on from medical[1] studies,
as Locke had been before him, to the study of mental
and moral subjects, and he formed the conception of a
science of Man, or Anthropology,[2] divided into Physiology, the Analysis of Ideas, and Morals, which would
ultimately be of as much use for the practical purposes
of education and government as the exact study of other
natural phenomena then cultivated in France for the
purposes of medicine, industry, and material civilisation.

Although it may be admitted that Cabanis created[3]
physiological psychology, and that he cast far-reaching
glances into the neighbouring departments of animal,

the line of philosophical thought
so clearly indicated by Cabanis
was not more systematically developed in France at the time,
and, like many other lines of research which originated in that
country, had to be re-discovered
fifty years later in other countries.
The question is important, and
may occupy us later on. See,
however, regarding the disfavour
into which the "moral" sciences
fell owing to political reasons, vol.
i. p. 149 of this work.

[1] Cabanis blames in Condillac and
Helvetius that they knew nothing of physiology. "S'ils eussent
mieux connu l'économie animale,
le premier aurait-il pu soutenir le
système de l'égalité des esprits ? le
second n'aurait-il pas senti que
l'âme, telle qu'il l'envisage, est une
faculté, mais non pas un être ; et
que, si c'est un être, à ce titre elle
ne saurait avoir plusieurs des
qualités qu'il lui attribue" (ibid.,
p. 66).

[2] "C'est ce que les Allemands
appellent l'anthropologie ; et sous
ce titre ils comprennent en effet
les trois objets principaux dont
nous parlons" (Cabanis, 'Œuvres,'
vol. iii. p. 40).

[3] Picavet, loc. cit., p. 292.

embryological, and morbid psychology, from which he
expected much assistance, his ideas remained vague, as
did those of the contemporary school of the "Idéologues,"
among whom Destutt de Tracy [1] deserves honourable
mention as having conceived the plan of a psychological
treatment of grammar. Their merit lay more in drawing
the plans of the new science of psychology as a natural
science in its largest sense, and of urging its scientific
and exact treatment, than in making a real and fruitful
beginning on special lines.

It is a remarkable fact that the first attempt to
analyse in detail one of the special instances of psycho-
physical interaction came about a hundred years earlier
from that successor of Locke who has always been
counted as the extreme idealistic development of English
speculation. Bishop Berkeley's 'Essay towards a New
Theory of Vision' (1709) has been called "the veritable historical starting-point of psycho-physical investigation." [2] Although averse to any exact theory of the
universe, deeming it "beneath the dignity of the mind
to affect exactness," [3] and at war with the mathema-

7.
Berkeley's
'Theory of
Vision.'

[1] Picavet (p. 398) says of Destutt
de Tracy (1754-1836): "Venu par
les sciences à la philosophie, D.
de Tracy a donné à l'idéologie un
nom et un caractère positif. S'il
a cru, à tort, qu'il pouvait la
constituer de toutes pièces, il a
fort bien vu que, pour devenir
une science indépendante et com-
plète, elle devait s'appuyer sur la
physiologie et la pathologie, sur
l'étude des enfants, sur celle des
fous et sur celle des animaux. Il
l'a unie intimement à la grammaire
et à la logique, à la morale et à
l'économie politique, à la législation
et à la politique."

[2] Dr Edmund Montgomery, in
his very interesting and valuable
critical analysis of 'Space and
Touch,' three memoirs contained
in the tenth volume of the first
series of 'Mind' (1885), p. 385.
[3] See 'A Treatise concerning the
Principles of Human Knowledge,'
§ 109: "As in reading other
books, a wise man will choose to
fix his thoughts on the sense and
apply it to use, rather than lay
them out in grammatical remarks
on the language; so in perusing
the volume of nature it seems
beneath the dignity of the mind
to effect an exactness in reduc-

ticians,[1] as Hobbes had been before him, Berkeley had a clear conception of the following definite problem : By what succession of physical and mental experiences, by what "organic and vital data," do we become aware of space and of body or matter ?   His answer, which makes tactile sensations the base, has been advocated and quoted by English psychologists of the Association school up to the present day, and forms the text for their various explanations.

The genesis of space perception was much discussed in the circle of Locke's friends, Molyneux proposing the celebrated query [2] named after him, and Cheselden describing at length, in the Philosophical Transactions, the experiences of an adult blind patient who had received his sight by couching.   The eighteenth century brought other isolated researches of an experimental or mathematical nature, which may be regarded as the beginnings of an exact treatment of the relation of psy-

ing each particular phenomenon to general rules, or showing how it follows from them.   We should propose to ourselves nobler views, such as to recreate and exalt the mind," &c.   In the following paragraph Berkeley refers to the 'Principia' as "the best grammar of the kind " he was speaking of.

[1] A very full account of this controversy will be found in a paper by Prof. Geo. A. Gibson in the 'Proceedings of the Edin. Math. Soc.,' vol. xvii.

[2] The query is given in Locke's 'Essay,' Book II. ch. ix. § 8, as follows : " Suppose a man born blind, and now adult, and taught by his touch to distinguish between a cube and a sphere of the same metal and nighly of the same bigness, so as to tell when he felt one and the other, which is the cube and which the sphere.   Suppose, then, the cube and sphere placed on a table, and the blind man made to see : Query, whether by his sight, before he touched them, he could now distinguish, and tell, which is the globe, which is the cube ? To which the acute and judicious proposer answers, No."   For a full analysis of actual cases, such as that of Cheselden, and more recent ones, see Wundt, 'Physiologische Psychologie,' vol. ii. p. 233.   That Berkeley was, however, neither a psycho-physicist nor a physiological psychologist in the modern sense, is well remarked by Campbell Fraser in his essay on Berkeley (Blackwood's " Philos. Classics," 'Berkeley,' p. 45, &c.)

chical with physical phenomena. Fechner, the founder
of psycho-physics as an independent doctrine, refers
notably to two [1] such instances. They were contributed
by two great mathematicians, Daniel Bernoulli and
Leonhard Euler. The former pointed out that the value
which we attach morally to the addition to any material
possession is not measured by the actual magnitude of
such addition, but by the relation it bears to that which
we already possess. The first sovereign earned by a
poor and starving labourer has an almost infinite value
compared with what it has for a person already possessed
of a million. Laplace and Poisson referred to this statement of Bernoulli, and introduced the terms " fortune
physique," " fortune morale," showing that they stand
in a simple mathematical relation. The same relation
was shown by Euler to exist between our estimate
of musical intervals in the harmonic scale and the
difference of the number of vibrations of the strings
which produce the two notes. It was above a century before Fechner correlated these isolated remarks
with observations of modern psycho-physics in his
celebrated law, of which more anon.

8.
Bernoulli
and Euler.

On the whole, little progress was made during the
eighteenth century in the department of research I am
now dealing with; but the end of the eighteenth and
the beginning of the following century brought several
important discoveries, some of which were at the time
much over-estimated, whilst others were for a long time
forgotten or overlooked.

The first is the accidental discovery by Galvani in

[1] 'Psychophysik,' 1860, vol. ii. p. 548, &c.

1786, followed, fifteen years after, by Volta's greater invention. The late eminent Prof. Du Bois-Reymond, in various passages [1] of his scientific and literary writings, has told us of the recurrent fascination which the *fata morgana* of Electricity has exercised over those interested in the explanation of the phenomena of innervation; how this seductive clue has been, in the

9.
Animal
electricity.

[1] See vol. ii. pp. 212, 386, 528 of Du Bois-Reymond's 'Reden,' also his 'Untersuchungen über thierische Electricität' (1848), vol. i. pp. 30-128. One of the first to take up in the interests of nervous physiology the clue which Galvani's discovery afforded was A. von Humboldt, who published in 1797, three years before Volta's discovery, his valuable "Versuche über die gereizte Muskel- und Nervenfaser, nebst Vermuthungen über den chemischen Process des Lebens in der Thier- und Pflanzenwelt." A lucid account of Humboldt's work is given by Prof. Wundt in the third volume of the German edition of Bruhns' 'Life of Humboldt,' p. 301 *sqq.* "It is difficult," he says, "to picture to oneself nowadays the excitement which the observations of Galvani produced in the scientific world. . . . Such experiments had almost become a general subject of entertainment in cultured circles. . . . It almost appeared as if what at that time was looked upon as the most general property of living matter, irritability, were by the experiment of Galvani to be for the first time unveiled in its real essence. . . . At the time when Humboldt made his experiments the contest was still going on between the followers of Galvani and Volta." This referred to a physiological or purely physical explanation of the phenomenon.

"Barely three years after the publication of Humboldt's work the discovery of Volta's pile put an abrupt end to all theories which were based upon the physiological origin of galvanic phenomena. The brilliant development of physical galvanism from that moment pushed the physiological aspect of electricity for a long time into the background. . . . Humboldt's work was forgotten" (p. 310). In the meantime Humboldt had travelled in South America, where he had — *inter alia* — observed the "natural electromotors which stand in such extraordinary connection with the nervous system" of the electrical eel (*Gymnotus electricus*), giving a thrilling description of a battle between the horses and the eels which he witnessed in the waters of Calabozo. (See Humboldt's 'Personal Narrative,' vol. iv. p. 345 *sqq.*; also 'Ansichten der Natur,' vol. i. p. 33.) Interest in the subject of animal electricity was again revived by Italian physiologists about the year 1835. Nobili, Marianini, Santi-Linari, Matteucci repeated and enlarged the experiments of Galvani, and through the influence of Humboldt and Johannes Müller, the study of the whole subject was comprehensively taken up at Berlin by Du Bois-Reymond about 1840, and exhaustively treated in his great work on the subject (vol. i. 1848, vol. ii. 1860).

course of more than a century, alternately taken up with enthusiasm, and abandoned as misleading. At the turn of the centuries the mania for animal electricity was at its height. Men like A. von Humboldt took up the study with eagerness, and sovereigns like Napoleon offered special prizes, in the hope that here at last the secret of life and consciousness would be revealed. The school of the "Naturphilosophie" in Germany seized upon the suggestion of polarity and polar forces contained in the phenomena of galvanic action, and, supported by the still more mystical processes of the so-called animal magnetism which had been exhibited by Mesmer twenty years earlier, worked up these vague indications into fanciful theories of vitalism and animism. This brought the whole line of thought into discredit, drove away the soberer, more scientific students of nature, and retarded real progress in the knowledge of the electric phenomena of the muscular and nervous system for fully a generation. At length in the school of Johannes Müller the subject was again approached and was put on a firm scientific basis by Helmholtz, and notably by Du Bois-Reymond. It is now known that, as in inorganic, so also in organic systems, the energy proper to them can appear under the different forms of mechanical, thermal, electric or chemical energy, but also that in none of these can be found pre-eminently the principle of life, still less that of consciousness.

10.
Phrenology.

Another important line of research which has had an equally fluctuating development, being sometimes enormously exaggerated, to the damage of sound pro-

gress, sometimes repudiated and treated with wholesale contempt, was that started by Gall, who from the
year 1805 onward, and latterly in conjunction with
Spurzheim,[1] started on an anatomical description of the
brain as the centre of nervous and conscious mental

[1] The two most prominent teachers of phrenology were Franz Joseph Gall (1758-1828) of Pforzheim, and Joh. Christ. Spurzheim (1776-1834) of Trier, the former an excellent doctor, the latter a skilled anatomist. Their influence was centred in Vienna and Paris. In England and America phrenology dates its popularity from George Combe (1788-1858). The term phrenology was suggested by George Forster about 1815, ten years after Gall had started his 'Schädellehre' or 'Craniology.' Of eminent medical authorities, the great Broussais in France (1772-1838) and C. G. Carus (1789-1869) in Germany were both phrenologists, the latter attempting to give the doctrine a more scientific foundation. Though phrenology was never popular in France, where the Academy of Sciences from the beginning assumed a very sceptical attitude (see above, vol. i. p. 136 note), the opponents of Gall have always given him full credit for his ability, and for the great impulse he gave to anatomical science of the brain. Flourens, one of the most formidable critics of the doctrine of the special faculties, and consequently of the separate phrenological organs and their location, nevertheless says: "Gall fut un observateur profond, qui nous a ouvert, avec génie, l'étude de l'anatomie et de la physiologie du cerveau. . . . Je n'oublierai jamais l'impression que j'éprouvai la première fois que je vis Gall disséquer un cerveau ; il me semblait que je n'avais pas encore vu cet organe" (quot. by Langlois, ' Grande Encyclop.,' vol. xxvi. p. 801). Somewhat earlier than phrenology the science or art of physiognomics, which was known already and practised by the ancients, had a representative in Caspar Lavater of Zürich, who, from 1772 onward, published his 'Physiognomische Fragmente,' a work which, accompanied by engravings by Chodowiecki, created a great sensation in philosophical, literary, and artistic circles, the whole of Europe being divided into followers and critics of Lavater. Among the latter was the celebrated Lichtenberg of Göttingen. Among scientific men were Camper in Holland, and later Charles Bell in England ; the former putting forward the well-known theory of the "facial angle" as an external measure of intelligence, the latter publishing his 'Essay on the Anatomy of Expression' (1806). In more recent times no less an authority than Charles Darwin took up the subject in his work on the 'Expression of Emotions' (1872). Shortly before Ph. Piderit published his 'Wissenschaftliches System der Mimik und Physiognomik' (1867) ; Duchesne (1862) his 'Mécanisme de la physionomie humaine' ; and more recently the Italian Mantegazza his 'Physionomie et l'expression des sentiments' (French transl., 1885). A very readable essay on the subject will be found among Prof. Wundt's 'Essays' (1885). See also his 'Physiologische Psychologie' (vol. ii. p. 598, &c., 4th ed.)

action. The scholastic notion of the older psychologists which divided the mental life into different powers or faculties as the body was dissected into parts and organs, lent itself to the idea of a localisation of these faculties or powers in different spheres of the brain, which Gall by a hasty generalisation maintained to be distinguishable on the external surface of the skull. Though these popular and practical applications, which form the basis of phrenology, were speedily and easily refuted, having always been regarded with suspicion by the medical profession, the anatomical labours of Gall were taken up and continued by others. Opinions fluctuated between the different views of Flourens, who insisted upon the unity of the central organ, as did Herbart in psychology on the unity of the mind; of G. H. Lewes, who assigns to the spinal cord together with the brain an important and initiatory *rôle* in conscious life; and of Hermann Munk and Friedrich Goltz, who by carefully devised experiments on living animals, by electrical irritation, and by systematic removal of parts of the brain, have to some extent succeeded in delimiting the special " spheres in which the various sensory nerves deliver their messages, and where the latter are transformed into conceptions and mentally stored." [1] Paul Broca had already, about forty years ago, succeeded in localising the powers of speech.

[1] Du Bois-Reymond, 'Reden,' vol. ii. p. 558 : "Though there is, in principle, no hope that the causal connection between material processes in the brain and consciousness will ever become clear to us, this does not hinder our penetrating deeply into a knowledge of those processes, or prevent such knowledge being of the greatest importance and of fascinating interest. As a first step in this direction there presents itself naturally to our understanding the localisation of the different faculties into which we naturally and systematically

Whilst animal electricity and the examination of the brain were taken up with ardour, over-valued by popularisers, and developed into fanciful theories which postponed for a long time the sober inquiries of science, another very fruitful vein of reasoning and research was struck early in the century, but left unexplored for fifty years. Since then it has been followed with success and profit.

divide mental activity. Out of the desire for such localisation there sprang up the fundamental idea of the phrenological follies; but, as so often, here also scientific superstition contained a kernel of truth. In the same cortex of the brain in which Gall and Spurzheim located their badly-chosen thirty-five mental faculties, Munk now describes the spheres in which the various sensory nerves deliver their messages, and where the latter are transformed into conceptions and stored. Thus, for the first time in the domain of sensation and intellection, a local basis of mental activity has been demonstrated, as had been done before by Paul Broca in the domain of volition, in the localisation of the faculty of speech." Most modern psycho-physicists would probably accept this statement with slight modifications; it is therefore well to note that one of the foremost and most original workers in this field of research, Prof. Fr. Goltz, takes a different view of the result of the experiments of himself and others. He does not consider Munk's teachings as the foundation of a physiology of the brain, but looks upon them as a system of error, and "hopes to see the day when all the beautifully elaborated modern hypotheses of circumscribed centres of the cortex will be laid in the same grave in which Gall's phrenology rests" (quoted from Goltz's memoirs, 'Über die Verrichtungen des Grosshirns,' in Pflüger's Archiv, by Carl Hauptmann, 'Die Metaphysik in der modernen Biologie' (1804), p. 240). Prof. Ferrier, whose 'Functions of the Brain' (2nd ed.) is a standard work in the English language, takes up a less negative position; yet he says (p. 23): "We are still on the threshold of the inquiry, and it may be questioned whether the time has even yet arrived for an attempt to explain the mechanism of the brain and its functions. To thoughtful minds the time may seem as far off as ever." Prof. William James of Harvard, in his excellent 'Principles of Psychology' (2 vols., 1891), gives, in his first chapter, a succinct account of the "localisation-question," which, he thinks, "stands firm in its main outline" (vol. i. p. 162). The standard work in the German language is Prof. Wundt's 'Physiologische Psychologie' (2 vols., 4th ed., 1893), which gives in the first division (chaps. 4, 5) a very exhaustive account of the experimental and theoretical work on localisation. Prof. Wundt himself takes up a position lying between the doctrine of sharp delimitation and that of a denial of local distinctions (vol. i. p. 159), but admits that the whole question is still highly controversial, though latterly the apparent differences of opinion have been much toned down (vol. i. p. 240).

11.
Dr Young's
colour
theory.

The beginnings of this line of reasoning are to be found in the writings of Thomas Young, who here, as in several other directions, "marched far in advance of his age." [1] During the last decade of the eighteenth century Young had been occupied with the study of the phenomena of Light and Colours; and, being a student of medicine, he had given equal attention to the physical phenomena and the physiological sensations of Light, going back to the beginnings laid in Newton's writings on these two important branches of Optics.[2] I have treated of his epoch - making discoveries in physical optics in an earlier chapter. As to the physiological problem of colour sensations, he likewise reviewed Newton's work, and especially took up the remarkable fact noted by Newton, that it appears possible to refer the great variety of colour sensations to three primary elements, out of which the whole wealth of the colour scale—varying in intensity, tint, and saturation—can be made up. In two distinct points he made a definite

[1] Note, in many passages of Helmholtz's 'Physiologische Optik' (2nd ed., Braunschweig, 1896), and his often - quoted 'Vorträge und Reden,' the high esteem in which he held the work of Young.

[2] A very succinct and exhaustive account of how Young arrived at his colour theory is given in a paper by A. M. Mayer, of New Jersey, in the 'Phil. Magazine' for 1876 (5th series, vol. i. p. 111). Young first selected red, yellow, and blue as the three simple colour-sensations, but later modified his view in consequence of the experiments of Wollaston between the years 1802 and 1807. How little Young's theory was thought of may be seen from the words of Helm-

holtz, quoted by Mayer (p. 114): "The theory of colour, with all these marvellous and complicated relations, was a riddle which Goethe in vain attempted to solve; nor were we physicists and physiologists more successful. I include myself in the number; for I long toiled at the task without getting any nearer my object, until at last I found that a wonderfully simple solution had been discovered at the beginning of this century, and had been in print ever since for any one to read who chose. This solution was found out and published by the same Thomas Young who first showed the right method of arriving at the interpretation of Egyptian hieroglyphics."

advance upon Newton.   For the three primary colours
of the older opticians he substituted red, green, and
violet ; and for the remarkable fact that the simple
colours of the rainbow can be compounded out of these
three, he suggested a physiological reason—viz., that the
eye possesses three distinct colour-sensations or three
distinct senses in relation to light, dependent upon some
peculiarity of nervous structure or function.   Young
did not elaborate his ideas, but it is clear that in the
short passages in his ' Lectures on Natural Philosophy '
and earlier papers, there were contained a variety of
definite problems and hints which were destined to
lead research for a long time after.

The next great step in advance, which has revolutionised and permanently fixed our ideas on the action
of the nervous system, was taken about the year 1810
by Charles Bell, who discovered the anatomical difference
between the anterior and posterior roots of the nerves
of the spine, and also went a long way towards showing their different functions.   The point as regards
functions was established by means of experiments on
living animals by Magendie, and independently by
Johannes Müller.[1]   Upon the combined labours of these
three masters of anatomy and experimental physiology
is based the distinction between sensory and motor
nerves—namely, that the anterior nerves of the spine
are employed to carry the nervous stimulus outward
to the different organs (efferent or motor nerves), the
posterior and better protected nerves serving to carry

[1] On the respective merits of
Charles Bell, Magendie, and Johannes Müller, see the writings of
Claude Bernard and Du Bois-Reymond, referred to *supra*, p. 384 of
this volume.

the peripheral stimuli of the senses inward to the nervous centres (sensory or afferent nerves).

About the same time Johannes Müller, under the influence of Goethe's observations on the subjective colour-sensations and of Kant's doctrine of the innate forms of perception,[1] introduced another important distinction into the theory of the action of the sensory nervous apparatus. This doctrine is known by the name of the "specific energies." It has for a long time governed all physiological reasoning on the subject of our sense perceptions. In the words of Helmholtz, who more than any other has lent the great weight of his authority to an elucidation of this theory, "physiological experience has found that by the stimulus of any single sensible nerve-fibre, only such sensations can be pro-

---

[1] The doctrine of the "specific energies" of the sensory nerves, one of Joh. Müller's earliest speculations, which has governed a large section of psycho-physical research, at least in Germany, has grown out of the philosophical discussions in the 'Kritik der reinen Vernunft,' and the æsthetic treatment in Goethe's 'Farbenlehre,' both of which deal with the subjective element in our sense-perceptions. In this regard the reform of physiology in Germany contrasts with the contemporaneous reform by Magendie in France, whose extreme experimentalism Müller even ridiculed. See on the historical origin of Müller's psychophysics, Du Bois-Reymond's excellent "Eloge de Müller" ('Reden,' vol. ii. p. 159), also Helmholtz's lecture on "Goethe's Naturwissenschaftliche Arbeiten" ('Vorträge und Reden,' vol. i. No. 1, 1853), and his address before the Goethe Society in 1892. Helmholtz finds the cause which

misled Goethe in his optical experiments to be the same which misled Brewster—viz., the difficulty of obtaining really pure homogeneous light of any special tint. He worked with impure light and dull media. Helmholtz experienced great difficulties in obtaining the necessary purity in his own labours. Goethe, however, was not alone in studying with predilection the subjective colour-sensations. Du Bois-Reymond mentions Erasmus and Robert W. Darwin in England, and Purkinje in Germany, as working in the same field (loc. cit., p. 160). Müller's work is contained principally in the treatise, 'Zur vergleichenden Physiologie des Gesichtsinnes des Menschen und der Thiere nebst einem Versuche über die Bewegungen der Augen und über den menschlichen Blick' (1826), and in his larger work on Physiology. See also on Goethe's merits Helmholtz, 'Physiologische Optik,' p. 249.

duced as belong to the qualitative—or order—region of
one definite sense, and that every stimulus which can at
all affect this nerve fibre produces only sensations belonging to this definite order."[1] This means that, for
instance, any effective stimulus of the optic nerve
apparatus produces only and always the sensation of
light, whereas the same stimulus would in the auditory
nerve apparatus, if effective, produce the sensation of
sound. "The same vibrations of the ether which the
eye perceives as light, the nerves of the skin perceive as
heat. The same vibrations of air which the latter perceive as a tremor, the ear perceives as a musical sound."[2]
The quality of our sensations does not depend on the
stimulus but on the nervous apparatus.

Helmholtz has said[3] that the law of the specific
energies forms the most important advance which the
physiology of the senses has made in recent times, and
has even compared it with the discovery of the law of
gravitation.[4] As we shall see immediately, he has him-

[1] See Helmholtz, 'Handbuch der
Physiologischen Optik,' 2te Aufl.,
1896, p. 233.

[2] Helmholtz, 'Vorträge und Reden,' vol. ii. p. 224 ; also 'Physiologische Optik,' p. 249 : "Müller's law
of the specific energies marks an
advance of the greatest importance,
for the entire doctrine of the sense-
perceptions has since become the
scientific foundation of this doctrine,
and is, in a certain sense, the empirical exposition of the theoretical
discussion of Kant on the nature
of the intellectual process of the
human mind." Cf. also p. 584.

[3] 'Vorträge und Reden,' vol. i. p.
378 ; vol. ii. p. 181.

[4] This excessive appreciation of
Müller's theory is, however, very
much limited to Germany, and there
also almost entirely to what may
be called Müller's school, in which
Helmholtz is the central figure. In
England the doctrine was subjected
to a full criticism by George Henry
Lewes, an important thinker, whose
writings contain many original views,
which have in some instances since
been independently put forward by
other authorities. See his ' Physiology of Common Life' (1860, chap.
8) ; 'Problems of Life and Mind'
(vol. i. p. 135, 1874) ; 'Revue Philosophique' (Paris, 1876, No. 2) ;
'The Physical Basis of Mind' (1877,
p. 184). Without knowing of Lewes's
criticisms, Prof. Wundt was led to
a criticism of the doctrine from
the physiological side in the first

self made a very important application of it, by bringing it into connection with Young's colour theory. But before I refer to this, it will be well to note the different lines of research which were opened out by Müller's formula, and how they have led in many ways to very fruitful expansion of natural knowledge. In this respect it is indeed permissible to compare Müller's formula with that of gravitation, which, as we saw above, through the different ideas which it introduced, helped to guide research for fully a century. Müller in the original statement of his views had made use of the term " specific energy," and had applied this term to the process or sense of sight : he spoke of the seeing substance or apparatus of sight. Now this apparatus is a complicated one, consisting mainly of three parts—the external or

edition of his great work on Physiological Psychology in 1872. See the note on p. 332, vol. i., of the 4th German edition (1893). Wundt says (p. 331) : "Historically, the doctrine . . . is to be traced to the fact that the philosophical foundation of modern science, and especially of the science of sensation, rests on Kant. In fact, that doctrine is nothing else than a physiological reflexion of Kant's attempt to find the conditions of knowledge which are given *a priori*, or, what was mostly considered to be the same, subjectively. This is very evident in the case of a foremost representative of that doctrine — viz., Johannes Müller." In opposition to Müller and his school, Lewes and Wundt put forward a view which has been termed the doctrine of indifference of the function of the nervous elements. The difference between the two views is very clearly stated in an excellent paper by E.

Montgomery in the fifth volume of ' Mind' (1880) : "According to the doctrine of functional indifference, the various qualities—*i.e.*, our well-known sensations—are merely due to differences in the stimulating rhythm, to differences, therefore, of motion communicated from outside to the chemically uniform nerve-substance, and the whole complex make-up of our consciousness is, consequently, thought to result from the coexistence and subsequent combination of such stimulated motions. According to the doctrine of specific energies, the varieties of sensation are due to pre-existing differences in the substratum in which they respectively arise, and all their manifold combinations to higher products are believed to be realised in materially higher — *i.e*, specifically pre-endowed — ranges of nervous substratum " (p. 4).

terminal organ, the connecting fibre or nerve, and the central or percipient organ situated somewhere in the brain. How are these different parts of the combined apparatus anatomically constituted, and what are their respective physiological functions—in particular, where does the specific energy reside? The answer to these questions as regards not only the process of seeing, but likewise that going on in other sense organs, involved an enormous amount of detailed anatomical and physiological, analysing and experimenting work. With this work many great names are connected — first of all, Helmholtz, who in his two great treatises on ' Physiological Optics ' and ' Physiological Acoustics,' [1] has laid the foundation of those two psycho-physical sciences which bring us nearest to an understanding of the interaction of mind and body. Like Young before him, for whom he expresses the greatest admiration, Helmholtz had approached the study of nature from the side of medicine : from this he was, by the peculiarity of his genius, driven to mathematico-physical studies on the one side, to psychological on the other. The exact methods of the mathematical, the experimental methods of the medical sciences ; the mental analysis of Kant and Fichte, as well as the logical methods of J. S. Mill, were equally familiar to him. Inventions of his own, like that of the eye-mirror, or of others, like

14.
Helmholtz.

[1] ' Die Lehre von den Tonempfindungen ; Physiologische Grundlage für die Theorie der Musik,' 1st ed., 1863. ' Handbuch der physiologischen Optik,' 1867, 2nd ed., much enlarged. A succinct and very lucid exposition of the principal contents of those two great treatises, by an authority in the same domain of science, will be found in chaps. x. to xii. of Prof. J. G. M'Kendrick's volume in the "Masters of Medicine" Series on H. von Helmholtz, 1899.

the stereoscope of Wheatstone; pathological cases, like those of colour-blindness; a host of ingeniously devised experiments, as well as the gift of an exceptionally musical ear,—all these factors, and innumerable others, contributed to the production of these two monumental works, which form an epoch in the history of science as well as of philosophy and psychology. They form the first magnificent examples of the comprehensive application of exact methods to phenomena which had before been treated only fragmentarily, and where the influences of taste, fancy, and belief, the vagueness of metaphysics and the difficulties of nomenclature, had created a confusion which to many must have appeared hopeless.   This confusion of language and of terms, of objective observations and subjective fancies, of the data of experience and the prejudices of theory, Helmholtz has done more than any other thinker to unravel.

In his two great treatises on the psycho-physics of the Eye and the Ear, of Vision and of Music, he has drawn two elaborate and detailed charts, which for a long time to come will have to be consulted by those who, in the interests of physics, philosophy, or æsthetics, enter into these mysterious domains.   Many celebrated theories or definite aspects and lines of reasoning invented by others, his forerunners or contemporaries, were adopted, but mostly with important modifications.   It may be of use to enumerate briefly the principal ones, beginning with the most mathematical and exact and ending with the more general and metaphysical.   In the beginning of the century Fourier had shown how any forces of motion in two dimensions—however complicated or irregular that motion might appear to be—could be mathematically represented or calculated by the superposition or addition of a larger or smaller number of simple periodic motions ; as it were analysed and dissected into these simple movements, just as any number can be looked upon as made up by the addition of others—say of prime numbers. Now, it was also known that sounds were produced by wave-like tremors of the air set going by the vibrations of strings or other sounding musical instruments ; further, that definite musical notes were absorbed or transmitted by neighbouring sounding bodies according as these were in or out of tune with the vibrating source of sound. This is the well-known phenomenon of resonance.   Ohm[1] had applied Fourier's mathematical analysis to the explanation of the partial notes, the ground tone and the harmonic overtones (or upper partial tones), of which musical[2] sounds are made up.   Helmholtz invented a

[1] Geo. S. Ohm, the same to whom we are indebted for the well-known law which obtains in electric currents, published in 1843 a paper in Poggendorf's 'Annalen' (reprinted in 'Gesammelte Abhandlungen,' 1892, p. 575), "On the definition of a tone and the theory of the siren," in which he applied the mathematical methods introduced by Fourier in his 'Théorie analytique de la Chaleur' (1822) ; as he had already done in his earlier work on the galvanic current (1827).   In fact, Ohm was one of the first to recognise the value of Fourier's conceptions in contradistinction from Laplace's, which were bound up with certain hypothetical notions as to the molecular constitution of bodies. See the introduction to his treatise on the galvanic current ('Ges. Werke,' p. 63).

[2] Cagniard de la Tour had invented (1819) and Seebeck the younger had improved (1841) the first mechanical counter for the frequencies of musical sounds, the siren ; and the latter as well as Duhamel had studied the composition of such sounds out of their elements or simple notes. A suggestion had been thrown out as to the part played by the upper partial tones which accompanied the ground tone.   Helmholtz treats first of this subject in a lecture (1857), reprinted in 'Vorträge und Reden,' vol. i. p. 79, dealing with "the psychological causes of musical harmony."

series of simple but ingenious apparatus by which these partial notes could be analysed, isolated, and made specially audible, or by which the ground tone could be purified, and thus led up to his conception of the human ear—the different parts of which he analysed anatomically and acoustically——as a most delicate resonator which separately absorbed the different elementary periodic movements that constitute musical sounds, the different nerve-fibres carrying them separately to the central organ of perception.[1]   On the bases of these distinctions, Helmholtz succeeded in giving an accurate definition [2] of that property of musical notes termed " timbre " by the French, " Klangfarbe " by the Germans—that peculiar colouring or texture which characterises the same note [3] if produced by different instruments.   He

15.
"Timbre"
defined.

[1] See 'Die Lehre von den Tonempfindungen,' 1st ed., 1863, pp. 92, 95, 97. "The main result of our description of the ear can be thus stated, that we have found that everywhere the ends of the auditory nerve are connected with special auxiliary apparatus, partly elastic, partly solid, which under the influence of external vibrations are made to vibrate correspondingly and then probably affect and agitate the nerve-substance " (p. 212).

[2] Helmholtz was the first to give a positive definition of "timbre." As he himself says (p. 114), before him it meant all the peculiarities of a musical sound which are not defined by its intensity or its position in the scale—i.e., its "pitch." Of these he eliminates all such as are connected with the beginning, rising, and dying away of sounds, and deals only with sounds which are uniformly maintained (p. 116).

[3] The terminology of acoustics and of music has been considerably changed, especially in this country, through scientific literature, in which the work of Helmholtz forms a kind of epoch. According to Lord Rayleigh ('Sound,' vol. i. § 22, 1st ed.), the word " tone " in the English language has been adopted by Tyndall to denote a musical sound which cannot be further resolved. The word was used before, but in a general sense, not limited only to sounds, and where now " tone " is used in works on acoustics, the word "note" was more usually employed. Sir John Herschel (' Encyclop.   Metrop.,'   article " Sound," 1845) does not consistently use the word "tone" as an equivalent for the German "Ton," but makes use of "sound " or "note" or "tone" promiscuously. Still more uncertain was the terminology by which to express the quality of a musical sound other than loudness and

entered into an analysis of the processes by which vocal
sounds and notes are produced, and showed their importance in musical and linguistic theories.   Combined
with all these deductions and applications, which started
from Fourier's mathematical analysis of compound movements, Helmholtz's anatomical dissection of the organ of
hearing leads him to the conclusion that there "must
exist in the ear different parts which are set in vibration
by notes of different pitch, and which have thus a sensation of these notes." [1]   And here he takes up a different
line of reasoning—that suggested by Johannes Müller's
theory of the specific sense energies.   In his studies
in physiological optics he had already accepted Young's
hypothesis that there exist in the eye three distinct
kinds of nerve-fibres, to which belong distinct modes
of colour-sensation.   Something analogous exists in the
ear.[2]   The differences in notes — namely, pitch and
colour [or character]—are reduced to differences of the
sensitive nerve-fibres, and for each nerve-fibre there exists
only the difference of the intensity of the stimulus."

16.
Analogy
between
sound and
colour.

This brings the action of the sensory nerves into line
with that of motor nerves : everywhere the nerve itself is

pitch, and, to the present day,
the English tongue has no equivalent for the French "timbre" or
the German "Klangfarbe." Everett
used the word character, and so
does Lord Rayleigh. Dr Young,
in his "Essay on Music" (1800,
'Miscell. Works,' vol. i. No. 5),
speaks of the quality of sound,
sometimes called its tone, register,
colour, or timbre (p. 118).   In the
most recent scientific work on
sound in the English language
(Poynting and Thomson's 'Text-

Book of Physics,' Sound, p. 69) we
read, "It is convenient to use the
term note for an ordinary compound sound to which a definite
pitch may be assigned, and the
term tone for each simple harmonic
constituent which goes to form it."
There is an important note on the
terminology by Alex. T. Ellis, the
learned translator of Helmholtz's
'Sensations of Tone' (1875, p. 36).

[1] 'Tonempfindungen,' p. 215.
[2] Ibid., pp. 220, 221.

indifferent to the stimulus, which it carries in or out like a telegraph wire; which, whilst acting in every case in the same way, may, according to its terminal connection,[1] " deliver messages, ring a bell, explode a mine, decompose water, create or move magnets, produce light, &c. The same with the nerves. The state of irritation is, so far as the isolated nerve-fibre is concerned, everywhere the same, but in accordance with the nature of different parts, be it of the brain or of the external portions of the body, it produces motion, secretion, increase or decrease of blood, of heat in different organs, or lastly, sensations of light, sound," &c.

The physiology of hearing had its brilliant application in a clearer understanding of the elements of language, of the formation of the vowel sounds, and in the study of the development of music—that art which, more than any other, seems founded on definite rules.[2]   In analysing

[1] 'Tonempfindungen,' p. 222.

[2] " From the time when Pythagoras is said to have discovered the arrangement of tones in an octave, by observing that the sounds of the blacksmith's hammer in the forge produce a fourth, a fifth, and an octave, and was then led to obtain harmonic proportion between the strings of the heptachord, all who investigate musical tones know that, although these are fleeting sensations, they depend physically on numerical relations between various kinds of movements ; but it was Helmholtz, more than any other philosopher, who examined the whole range of the phenomena, physical as well as physiological, and whose work will for generations remain an enduring monument to his genius" (Prof. M'Kendrick in the Helmholtz volume of the "Masters of Medicine" Series, p. 168).

Since the appearance of the last edition of Helmholtz's great work, of which there exists an excellent English edition with valuable notes, many of the points first investigated by Helmholtz have been taken up by other experimentalists as well as by psychologists. The invention of the phonograph by Edison in 1877 gave a great impetus to exact research in the problems of audition, and various facts and theories have been advanced confirming or modifying the views put forward by Helmholtz. On these see the last chapter of Lord Rayleigh's 'Treatise on Sound,' 2nd ed., 1894. On the psychological side see the 2nd volume of Prof. Wundt's 'Physiologische Psychologie,' pp. 47-96.

these Helmholtz is led into æsthetical and psychological discussions, clearly distinguishing between such principles as are inherent in natural, physical, and physiological relations, and such others as depend on the inventions of genius and the gradual changes brought about by external requirements and ingrained by habit and education.[1]

The physiology of seeing had yet more remarkable consequences for the history of Thought. We may say that through Helmholtz's analysis of the formation of our space perceptions by the eye in connection with the tactile and muscular senses, psychology and metaphysics were brought into immediate contact with physics and physiology. It is here that Helmholtz takes up an entirely different, and, previously, isolated line of reasoning, which centres in Kant's theory of space and time as innate forms of perception—the so-called subjectivity or ideality of time and space. The studies of this subject had been somewhat prepared by the writings of Herbart and Lotze. The teachings of Kant have had an influence in the direction indicated through two distinct channels, —through Johannes Müller's Physiology and through Herbart's Psychology : the latter seems to have had

17.
Helmholtz
and Kant.

[1] See the closing words of the 13th chapter of Helmholtz's work : " As the fundamental principle for the development of the European tonal system, we shall assume that the whole mass of tones and the connection of harmonics must stand in a close and always distinctly perceptible relationship to some arbitrarily selected tonic, and that the mass of tone which forms the whole composition must be developed from this tonic, and must finally return to it. The ancient world developed this principle in homophonic music, the modern world in harmonic music. But it is evident that this is merely an æsthetical principle, not a natural law. The correctness of this principle cannot be established *a priori*. It must be tested by its results. The origin of such æsthetical principles should not be ascribed to a natural necessity. They are the inventions of genius, as we previously endeavoured to illustrate by a reference to the principles of architectural style."

little influence over the Berlin school of physiology, but it has had a considerable influence on several members of the Leipzig school. In this school Lotze was educated.

Locke had taught, and his followers had accepted, the doctrine that the so-called secondary qualities of sensible things, such as colour, sound, hardness, &c., were subjective. Speculative physics had prepared this view by translating such properties into special forms of aggregation or periodic motion, leaving only extension and resistance as the primary properties inherent in things. Kant had gone a step further, and maintained that space and time were likewise only subjective forms of our perceiving sense apparatus. Two problems grew out of this view, which are not clearly stated in Kant's writings. First, How does the perceiving mind arrive at the elaborate and systematic space conception which is peculiar to us human beings ?—i.e., out of what perceptive elements, and by what psychical processes, is it gradually built up ? Secondly—What is it that locates our sensations at definite places in space ? There is a third question which Kant put and answered, that referring to the nature and validity of the geometrical axioms. According to his view the axioms of geometry are innate, expressive of the inborn nature of our space conceptions ; in fact, the truths of geometry formed in his view the only instance of knowledge gained not by experience but *a priori*—before or outside of experience.

18.
The brothers
Weber.

An entirely independent series of psycho-physical investigations was started even before Johannes Müller, by Ernst Heinrich Weber of Leipzig, who, with his two brothers, Wilhelm and Eduard, may be considered as the centre of the Leipzig school of Anatomy, Physiology, and Physics.[1]   After having been among the first to import the exact methods of research into physiology, and having carried on a variety of investigations refer-ring to physiological optics and acoustics,[2] he approached the subjective phenomena of sensation: recording, for example, with what degree of accuracy different parts of the surface of the skin on face, arm, leg, &c., per-ceive the distance between two points which touch the skin — say the two points of a pair of compasses; recording also the relation of the smallest increase of any given sensation to the corresponding increase of stimulus.   In the latter series of experiments, he arrived at what has been termed [3] Weber's Psycho-physical law.   He did not call it so himself; he simply showed by experiment that in a variety of cases the stimulus had to increase in proportion to its own initial intensity in order to produce a just perceptible increase of sensation.   These experiments did not attract much attention till Gustav Theodor Fechner took them up, building upon them his celebrated "Principles of Psycho-physics."   Before referring more in detail to these, I must mention a third line of reasoning which, as stated above, had a considerable influence on the Leipzig school of Psycho-physics, though probably it had as little

19.
Fechner's
Psycho-
physics.

---

[1] On the labours of the brothers Weber, see the references given above, vol. i. p. 196, also the present volume, p. 31, note.

[2] E. H. Weber published in 1817, 'Anatomia comparata nervi sym-pathici;' in 1820, 'De aure et auditu hominis et animalium;' from 1827 onward, 'Annotationes anatomicæ et physiologicæ,' in which, in 1831, there appeared his celebrated treatise "Tastsinn und Gemeingefühl." Joh. Müller's 'Ver-gleichende Anatomie des Gesicht-sinnes' appeared in 1826.

[3] By Fechner in his 'Elemente der Psychophysik' (2 vols., Leipzig, 1860).

influence on E. H. Weber as the earlier philosophy of nature, to which it formed a pronounced opposition.

20.
Influence of
Herbart.

Herbart was not an experimental philosopher; nevertheless a place in a history of scientific Thought belongs to him. Indeed, his philosophy, like that of Kant, and, in quite a different way, of Schelling, has had a marked influence on many thinkers and men of science who have prepared the ground for an exact treatment of the phenomena of Life and Mind. Among exact psychologists I need only name Volkmann, Drobisch, Lotze, and in our time Professor Wundt[1] of Leipzig. It is therefore of interest to mark the precise point where Herbart's influence comes in.

Although an exact school of psychology might aim at studying psychical and psycho-physical phenomena without reference to any general theory of the soul as the supposed centre and substance of these phenomena, the existing ideas and theories as to soul and mind have nevertheless always played a great part in these researches, just as it has been found impossible to free biological research altogether from some theory of life. Older psychologists were consciously or unconsciously governed by the conception of a number of distinct mental faculties. Even Kant's philosophy is still embarrassed by this view, which reigned supreme in the teaching of his predecessor Wolf. The attempt of

[1] This is not the place to speak about the Herbartian school, which is almost entirely confined to Germany. I have referred to Prof. Wundt because, in spite of a running criticism, in the 'Physiologische Psychologie,' of Herbart's special doctrines, the author of that important and comprehensive work himself declares (Preface to the 1st ed., 1874) that for the formation of his own views he is, next to Kant, most indebted to Herbart.

Herbart, therefore, to overthrow the so-called faculty-psychology, and to insist on the essential unity and simplicity of the inner life, must have made a great impression on all who came under the influence of his philosophy.   It did this in two ways.[1]   It first of

21.
His attack on the "faculty-psychology."

[1] Besides Herbart (1776-1841), whose psychological writings date from 1813 to 1825, another German psychologist is usually mentioned as having helped to overthrow the older faculty-psychology. Beneke (1798-1854), a younger contemporary of Herbart, conceived of psychology as a natural science. His principal work, 'Lehrbuch der Psychologie als Naturwissenschaft,' appeared in 1833, and has been several times republished, the fourth edition appearing in 1877. Beneke worked in opposition to Hegel at Berlin, his historical forerunners being the German philosophers, Jacobi, Fries, and Schleiermacher, as well as the English philosophy of the so-called Association - school. An account of his philosophy does not belong to a chapter on psycho-physics except in as much as he introduced into the study of the inner life not indeed the facts and data of physical —i.e., physiological—science, but the physical method. He was the purest representative of the psychology of the "inner sense." Whilst Herbart based his psychology alike on experience, metaphysics, and mathematics, Beneke accepted only the first, and discarded the latter. Standing thus outside the all-powerful school of Hegel and the increasing influence of Herbart, Beneke had during his lifetime only a limited audience, and received due attention in a wider circle, first and principally through Ueberweg, who was greatly impressed by him. In fact, his influence was felt in Germany about the same time as that of the English and Scottish philosophers. Ueberweg, in his well-known 'History of Philosophy,' vol. ii. pp. 281-292 (Engl. transl. by Morris, 1874), gives a full account of Beneke. Prof. Erdmann gives a very full account also in his excellent 'Grundriss der Geschichte der Philosophie' (3te Aufl., 1878, vol. ii. pp. 628-641). The fact that Beneke's method is introspective, brings him not only into contact with the English school, but also with French thought, which has always been characterised by subtle psychological analysis. This explains the fact that M. Marion (in the 'Grande Encyclopédie') calls Beneke "un des principaux philosophes Allemands du siècle,"—a designation which would hardly be echoed either in Germany or in England. The best account of Beneke's position in the development of psychology extant in the English language is that of Dr G. F. Stout, in his article "Herbart compared with English Psychologists and with Beneke," in the 14th volume of the 1st series of 'Mind' (1889). M. Ribot, in his well-known book on 'Modern German Psychology' (Engl. transl. by Baldwin, 1899), does not say much about Beneke, but his account of Herbart and his school, and their position in psycho-physical thought, is concise and much to the point. Dr Stout's articles on Herbart in 'Mind' (vols. 13, 14) are also much to be recommended.

all liberated them from the trammels of an antiquated and misleading terminology ; and secondly, it impressed them with the necessity of giving an answer to the question how the multiplicity of sensations or the flow of ideas was held together in the unity of an inner existence. Thus it is a characteristic of all psycho-physical writers who have come under the influence of Herbart, that however much they may be occupied with detailed description of physiological processes, with the analysis of sensations or the dissection of the data of experience, they never lose sight of the underlying mental unity which is the central phenomenon of psychology and of psycho-physics, just as it must be the central problem of biology to arrive at some definition of life. Had the investigations of psycho-physical phenomena remained where Weber or even Helmholtz left them, we should have brilliant chapters on the phenomena of touch, of seeing, hearing, and other processes where the outer and inner worlds come into contact, but no attempt to sum up these brilliant contributions in a connected view of the inner and higher life—the most remarkable and unique phenomenon in nature. It seems to me that, in Germany at least, it is through Herbart, more than through any other thinker, that we have been preserved from a threatening disintegration of psychological research. It is the more necessary to recognise this, as most of those writers who at one time came greatly under Herbart's influence have found it necessary, after having become thoroughly saturated with this one great truth in his philosophy, to abandon almost the whole of the more detailed expositions con-

22.
Unity of
mental life.

tained in his works.[1]   Herbart was quite as correct
in his ideal of what psychology should be, as he was
unfortunate in the particular manner in which he
elaborated it.

Psychology was to be founded on experience, metaphysics, and mathematics.   Kant had studied the inner
activity of the mind as it is compounded of sensation,
perception, and apperception; of understanding, judgment,
and reasoning.   In opposition to this Herbart went back
to the position taken up by Locke and Hume, looking at
the inner life of a conscious mental being or soul, not as
a complex of mental faculties, but as a flow of ideas or
perceptions.   How is the unity and simplicity of this
mental being preserved in the midst of this continuous
flow of ideas? how is it regained as often as it is in
danger of being lost?   His investigations start at the
point where the inquiries of the association school of
psychologists started in England.   Having, however, the
mechanics and dynamics of physical forces more promin-

[1] Dr Stout has given an account of the Herbartian school
in the 14th volume of ' Mind,' p.
353 *sqq.*   He confines himself to
Drobisch, Waitz, and Volkmann,
the psychologists proper.   M.
Ribot (*loc. cit.*) has dwelt more
on the development of the Herbartian school in the direction of anthropology and ethnology; he
mentions specially Waitz, as well
as Lazarus and Steinthal.   He
contrasts their work and their
positions with those of the great
anthropologists of the English
school, such as Tylor, Lubbock,
and Herbert Spencer, and notes,
in the German school, the absence
of Darwinian ideas.   It is important to observe that both in the case
of Prof. Wundt of Leipzig and of Mr
Spencer in England—that is, in the
case of the latest outcome of the
Kant-Herbartian philosophy on the
one side and of the Association philosophy in England on the other—
and in each case under the influence
of the exact and biological sciences,
philosophy ends in elaborate treatises on Anthropology, which with
Spencer is conceived under the
name of Sociology.   Similarly, the
school of Hegel ended in elaborate
historical treatises.   Hume turned
from abstract philosophy to political economy and history, and
Herder—as we shall see later on
— anticipated much of all this
movement in his History of
Mankind.

ently before his mind than they had, he was tempted
to try how far the conceptions of equilibrium of motion
and of the composition of forces could be applied to the
inner play of ideas which chase, oppose, and displace
each other, preserving all the time a kind of dynamical
equilibrium.   His elaborate mathematical calculations in
the first part of his greater work on psychology do not
specially refer to the purely intellectual process;[1] they
refer rather to all inner processes which oppose each
other, which come into conflict, restraining each other in
proportion to their contrast, creating a tendency towards
reversion to former conditions.   Such a play of opposing forces is to be found likewise in the larger field of
human society; this is accordingly quite as much a case
for the application of those psychical mechanics which
Herbart aimed at establishing.

In a history of scientific Thought, which aims at
showing by what gradual steps the various provinces
of phenomena have been brought under the methods of
exact treatment, the psychology of Herbart has an important as well as a unique and isolated position.   It

23.
Mathe-
matical
psychology.

[1] Herbart himself says of his
mathematical chapter, that the results therein given "do not follow
immediately from the conception
of a thinking being; but they refer to the mutual arrangements of
any things, in so far as they are
opposed and as they collide, restricting each other in proportion
to their contrast, tending to revert
to the previous condition, the
unrestricted portions being fused
into complex forces.   The forces
which are active in society are
doubtless originally psychological
forces.   They meet in so far as they
appear in language and in actions
in a common sensual world.   In
the latter they restrict each other;
this is the universal spectacle of
conflicting interests and social
frictions.   Also the fusion no doubt
exists. . . . We therefore assume
that among men living together
the same conditions appear which
exist, according to our view, among
the ideas in one and the same consciousness.   We examine the result of their mutual restrictive
action" ("Psychologie als Wissenschaft," 'Werke,' ed. Hartenstein,
vol. vi. p. 31, &c.

led psychologists to consider more closely the conditions under which a mathematical treatment is at all possible, and to recognise that exact and accurate measurements must precede all application of an abstract calculus. Herbart's ideal was that of a psychical mechanics; he opposed [1] the idea of a union of physiology and psychology.   And yet this was just the direction in

[1] In a very interesting note at the end of the introduction to the second part of his larger work on psychology, Herbart explains his position with regard to physiological psychology. It refers to certain extracts which he makes from Rudolph's ' Grundriss der Physiologie,' in which that eminent physiologist referred to Herbart's ' Lehrbuch der Psychologie.' " It is not only a metaphysical but also a logical error to confound psychological and physiological research. Psychological phenomena are not in space, but space itself, with all that appears in it, is a psychological phenomenon, and, indeed, one of the first and most difficult facts for psychology, which, in the treatment of it, would behave very improperly if it began by discussing the forces in the nerves ; for the question is not, where sensations come from, but how sensations acquire the form of space.   Now, I maintain further, that the difference between lifeless and living matter — that is, between physics and physiology — cannot be understood until we know mind by means of psychology, for in all the countless elements of the organised body —in plants as well as in animals— there is an analogue of mental development which cannot possibly be found on the surface of phenomena.   We observe internally a fragment of *our own* mental existence.   This fragment is developed into scientific knowledge through speculative psychology based on metaphysics.   This knowledge meets another equally metaphysical science, natural philosophy, with its conception of matter— that is, of such matter as we know through chemistry and dynamics. Then only can the question be put, how such matter must be constituted, so that its separate elements are determined, not only through their original quality, but also through a development analogous to the mental one," &c.   The section closes with the following characteristic passage : " Those who favour empiricism can learn from the present state of physiology how much, or rather how little, mere experience can do. Physiology, as an empirical doctrine, has attained a height which nobody can despise.   Moreover, it proceeds in the light of modern physics.   Nevertheless, it has eagerly sucked up, as the sponge sucks up water, that philosophy of nature which knows nothing, because it began by construing the universe *a priori*.   Towards this error no science has proved so weak, so little capable of resistance, as physiology.   The talk about life has become the Dead Sea in which all spirit of philosophical research is drowned, so that, if a resurrection is at all to be hoped for, it must be born anew in quite unbiassed minds" ('Werke,' vol. vi. p. 65, &c.)

which an exact or scientific treatment of mental phenomena could meet with any success at all. It was in
the schools of physiology, in those of Johannes Müller
and of Weber, that philosophers had to learn how to
attack the borderland of bodily and mental phenomena.

24.
Lotze's
Physiology
of the soul.

The first who approached the subject from this point
of view was Hermann Lotze. He was a disciple of
E. H. Weber, and had been led to psychological researches from two independent starting-points : first from
the study of the medical sciences which, under the hands
of his great master, had largely benefited by the application of the exact methods of the physical, the
measuring, and calculating sciences, but also from an
entirely opposite quarter.[1] "A lively interest in poetry
and art had led him to philosophy." He was attracted
by that great body of ideas which, through the systems
of Fichte, Schelling, and Hegel, had become permanently
domiciled in German culture. In this great realm he
could move "with some freedom," for it had not become crystallised into a definite system of doctrine ;
exact studies had, moreover, easily convinced him "how
absolutely untenable was the form into which Hegel had
cast that valuable possession."

[1] The quotations in the text are
taken from Lotze's polemical pamphlet, 'Streitschriften' (Leipzig,
1857), pp. 6, 7. As already mentioned (supra, p. 407 note), Lotze had
been misunderstood by his critics,
of whom some represented him as
a materialist, others as a follower of
Herbart. In refuting the latter
charge he explains his position towards the idealistic systems of the
first half of the nineteenth century.

He acknowledges two great personal
influences, that of C. H. Weisse,
which, as it were, touches the
kernel of his convictions, and that
of the study of medicine, which,
in his case, was intimately connected with that of the physical
sciences. He admits, as did Herbart, having passed through the
magnificent portal of Leibniz's
Monadology to a general arrangement of his philosophical opinions.

We must bear in mind this twofold source of Lotze's reflections if we want to estimate correctly the value of his early criticisms regarding the then prevalent treatment of such questions as life and mind in the medical sciences. . On the one side he had the object of clearing the way for purely mechanical explanations. We learnt in an earlier chapter how he was one of those who successfully chased out of biology the vague idea of a vital force. And when he approached the problem of mind and body, we find him insisting on the presence of a psycho-physical mechanism which rules [1] the inter-

[1] The opinion of Lotze regarding the relation of soul and body, or rather of psychical and physical phenomena, has been stated by him, variously, as parallelism, occasionalism, pre-established harmony, and was ultimately crystallised in the term psycho-physical mechanism. The question is fully discussed in the articles, "Leben und Lebenskraft," "Instinct," "Seele und Seelenleben," which he contributed to R. Wagner's 'Handwörterbuch der Physiologie.' They are reprinted in Lotze's 'Kleine Schriften,' ed. D. Peipers, 4 vols. (Leipzig, 1885-91). He there says, "The conception of a psycho-physical mechanism can be stated as follows : As ideas, volitions, and other mental states cannot be compared with the quantitative and special properties of matter, but as, nevertheless, the latter seem to follow upon the former, it is evident that two essentially different, totally disparate, series of processes, one bodily and one mental, run parallel to each other. In the intensive quality of a mental process, the extensive definiteness of the material process can never be found ; but if the one is to call forth the other, the proportionality between them must be secured through a connection which appears to be extrinsic to both. There must exist general laws, which ensure that with a modification a of the mental substance a modification b of the bodily substance shall be connected, and it is only in consequence of this independent rule, and not through its own power or impulse, that a change in the soul produces a corresponding one in the body" (vol. i. p. 193). Lotze destroyed the idea of vital force, but he only chased the conception of the soul beyond the limit of the psycho-physical mechanism, and he maintains that natural and medical science have no interest in pursuing the question beyond that limit, "however interesting the further discussion of this subject may be to speculative psychology" (vol. i. p. 197)—"for it is quite indifferent to medicine, wherein the mysterious union of body and soul consists, as this is the constant event which lies equally at the bottom of all phenomena. But it is of the greatest interest to medicine to know what affections of the soul are connected in that mysterious

action of external and internal phenomena, of stimulus and sensation.

There existed indeed another side—that which we may call the philosophical; it does not at present enter into the course of our narrative, which deals only with the extension of scientific or exact thought, and with mental phenomena and the inner life in so far as they form a province—perhaps a very restricted province—of the whole of nature. This province Lotze was among the first to proclaim distinctly to be one which natural science had to conquer and to cultivate. He is careful to explain that it does not cover the whole ground of psychology, and at the end of his long discourse on the "soul and its life," which formed an important contribution to the great physiological encyclopædia published in the middle of the century, he clearly marks out "physiology of the soul as an exposition of the physical and mechanical conditions to which, according to our observation, the life of the soul is attached,"[1] as one of the several problems of psychology. It formed a counterpart to the physiology of the body, of the physical side of our existence, and was, like it, to become a natural —i.e., a mechanical—science. Subsequently he collected the whole of his reflections belonging to these two departments in two treatises on the 'General Physiology of Bodily Life' (1851), and on 'Medical Psychology' or 'The Physiology of the Soul' (1852).

As little as it now enters into our programme to

manner with what affections of the body. Unfortunately, medical science has only too often lost sight of this its proper problem over fruitless speculations referring to that connection itself" (p. 197). Cf. also 'Medicinische Psychologie,' p. 78.

[1] 'Kleine Werke,' vol. ii. p. 204.

follow up the philosophical reasonings of Lotze beyond
the limit of the psycho-physical mechanism, so little
were these at the time of their appearance heeded by
many of his readers, some of whom he seems to have
converted to or confirmed in a purely materialistic conception of the phenomena of the inner or mental world.
Lotze had banished " vital forces " from biology; why
not follow him, and banish all other higher principles,
and revive—as Carl Vogt did [1]—the dictum of Cabanis
about the analogy between the functions of the brain
and the kidneys?   Why should the " anima " of Stahl
not have the same fate as the " vital force " of Bordeu
and Bichat?

This was a misconception of what Lotze had intended.
He had, indeed, banished [2] the principle of life as a
factor useless in physiological explanations; but not the
principle of organisation, which must have presided over
the beginning of all organic forms.   This might be
neglected by physiologists, who had nothing to do with
origins but only with existing relations.   It was quite
different with mental phenomena, which, manifesting
themselves alongside of physical processes, required to be
dealt with and recognised as actually existing and con-
current events.[3]   Herbart's psychical mechanism might

[1] On this, see the account given
in Lange's ' History of Materialism '
(Engl. transl., vol. ii. p. 285) and
Lotze's reference to it in ' Med.
Psychol.,' p. 43.

[2] "There is no doubt that a
legitimate attack upon ' vital force '
has marked in our days that line of
reasoning, which has by the law of
inertia carried many of our contemporaries far beyond the correct

limit on to a negation of the existence of a soul" (ibid., p. 41).

[3] These various points are very
fully discussed in Lotze's earliest
philosophical work, ' Metaphysik '
(Leipzig, 1841), pp. 251, 255, 259 ;
and again in the ' Med. Psychologie '
(1852), p. 78.   Referring to the
last chapter, in which I dealt with
the development of the theories of
life and organisation, two points

be an unrealisable ideal in that it dealt with inner phenomena as unconnected with outer ones : a psycho-physical mechanism was a nearer approach to a true description of reality, and could not be narrowed down to a purely physical occurrence ; moreover, the unity of mental life was a special property which had to be recognised and defined.

26.
The psycho-physics of vision.

Lotze himself, after formulating the conception of a psycho-physical mechanism, and utilising the elaborate and fundamental experiments and observations of Weber as illustrations of what was meant, made an important contribution towards an analysis of a compound physico-psychical process. He took up the problem which Berkeley had attacked, of the formation of our space perception. It had been introduced into German psychology mainly through Herbart with reference to the Kantian doctrine that space is a subjective form. Through Lotze, and subsequently through Helmholtz, it has been shown to have not only a psychological but likewise a physiological importance : it is a problem of psycho-physics.

There exists a peculiar difficulty in bringing home to the popular mind the fact that a special problem is in-

may be noted. First, it is clear that Lotze was an "organicist" before Claude Bernard and other more recent thinkers mentioned above. Secondly, it is very evident that Lotze belongs to the pre-Darwinian school of thought. In fact, he does not relish the genetic aspect. The historical beginnings of ideas are for him no indication of their value and correctness. He says on this point : "The genesis of a conception is no argument for its validity ; in the ever indistinct manner in which language operates in forming its words, it may form the correctest conceptions in just as incorrect a manner as the most erroneous ones. What is important is whether the conception, formed anyhow, can justify itself " ('Med. Psychol.,' p. 41). I shall on another occasion have to refer more fully to this marked absence of the historical sense in Lotze.

volved in the manner in which our senses of sight and touch combine and arrange simple sensations into the whole of a well-ordered perception of space; for we do not become able to appreciate the fact of the slow and gradual growth of this perception, which takes place in the early days of our infancy, till long after we have actually gained full possession of it. Something similar exists with regard to language and thought: we only hear of grammar and logic long after the main difficulties of speech and thinking have been unconsciously mastered, and if it were not for the existence of other languages than our own, and of an erroneous logic as exemplified in errors of calculation and of measurement, it is doubtful whether grammar and logic would have been so early developed. As it is, the physiological problem of the formation of our space perception was actually first forced upon naturalists by the observation of pathological cases, such as the acquisition of sight in later life through couching, the existence of colour blindness, and a variety of optical delusions which still serve as indispensable test cases for the various theories that have been propounded. Only when something turns out to be palpably wrong do we begin to inquire what constitutes the right side of many things.

Thus the cases of Cheselden and Wardrop and the colour blindness of Dalton set physiologists thinking about the genesis of our space and colour perceptions. A very great impetus—perhaps the most valuable of all —was given by Wheatstone's invention of the stereoscope in 1838; an instrument which, as it were through

27.
Wheatstone's stereoscope.

a kind of deception, gave to perfectly flat surfaces the vivid appearance of depth and distance. And here we may note, in passing, how it was almost entirely left to foreign thinkers to utilise this remarkable invention for the benefit of the theory of vision and the science of psycho-physics ; [1] Whewell having characteristically omitted this epoch-making fact, as in his well-known history he omitted to notice many other contemporary British contributions to science.

Philosophers, who are accustomed to find hidden problems where ordinary persons only see common-sense, had already approached the question of the genesis of our space perception from two definite points of view, which we may, for the sake of convenience, identify with the names of Kant and Herbart. The genetic view associated by the physiologists with the name of Kant, and supposed to have been prepared by Locke, Berkeley, and Hume, was this, that what we know of external things depends upon the peculiarities of our own perceiving

[1] Sir Charles Wheatstone (1802-1875), to whom several inventions of equal scientific and practical interest are due, invented the mirror - stereoscope in 1833. A notice of it was given in Mayo's 'Outlines of Human Physiology,' but neither its theoretical nor its practical importance was recognised till Wheatstone published his paper in the 'Phil. Trans.' in 1838. He there refers to Leonardo da Vinci as having been the only one before him to notice the difference of binocular and monocular vision. Since Wheatstone's invention became known and was perfected by Brewster, Moser, and others, and especially since Helmholtz entered the field with his extensive and original researches in optics, it has been found that ancient as well as more recent philosophers had approached the subject very closely ; and many references are given in the new edition of the 'Physiologische Optik' (1896), p. 840. The invention of photography about the same time (1835, by Daguerre, after extensive and prolonged experiments by himself and Niepce, published in 1839 by Arago), which was of great importance to optical theory, was also for some time singularly little appreciated by theorists. See Rosenberger, 'Gesch. d. Physik,' vol. iii. p. 316. See also Helmholtz's lecture "Ueber das Sehen des Menschen" (1855).

and thinking self, on sensations, and on their arrangement or orderly presentation. The sensations themselves are the substance, the spatial arrangement
of them the form, of our perception of external
things. The question was gradually put more and
more clearly, How we come to localise certain of our
sensations at definite places in the totality of a spatial
arrangement? Herbart added another important reflection, which really dated from Leibniz. Impressed with
the unity of all mental existence, and claiming this as
the characteristic property of our inner life, he asked the
question, How can the oneness or simplicity of this inner
existence, as it were, expand itself without losing its
unity, into the orderly variety of a spatial contemplation?
For the purpose of an answer to this question he fixed
on the phenomenon of motion. The conception of an
orderly arrangement of sensations or things in space is
gained in great measure by the aid of definite movements of the sensitive organs, which are accompanied
by definite sensations of motion — *e.g.*, by muscular
sensations.

The first of these two questions may be expressed in
the words, Given the subjective form of a space perception, either complete in its geometrical arrangement (the
nativistic hypothesis) or gradually acquired in the early
moments of our conscious life (the empiric hypothesis),
how do we make ourselves familiar with, and at home in,
this form of perception? And secondly, By what special
properties or local signs do we localise or place each
single sensation in its right and orderly position? The
first is the problem of space construction, the second

that of localisation of things in space. Lotze was one of the first to attempt detailed answers to these questions.

In particular he propounded the theory of " local signs," which with certain modifications has been adopted by subsequent writers on the subject. The combination of physiological, optical, and psychological investigations in Helmholtz's great work on ' Physiological Optics ' has brought definiteness and mathematical precision into many of the questions suggested by philosophers and naturalists before him. Through it and its great companion, the ' Physiological Acoustics,' psycho-physics has to a large extent become an exact science.

A great step in the direction of drawing psychical phenomena into the circle of the exact sciences was taken

independently by Gustav Theodor Fechner ;[1] in fact, it is

[1] G. T. Fechner (1801-1887) was a unique figure in German literature, science, and philosophy. Beyond his own country he is only very imperfectly known and appreciated. He was self-taught, and living all his life somewhat outside the conventional categories of German academic activity, he made a position for himself which has only become intelligible to a larger public through the issue — after his death—of Prof. Wundt's oration, Prof. Kuntze's (his nephew's) charming biography (1892), and Prof. Lasswitz's monograph on Fechner (Stuttgart, 1896), in which for the first time a coherent exposition of his philosophical teaching is attempted. Prof. Wundt has also, in many passages of his work on psychology, and through the second edition of the 'Psychophysik,' contributed largely to a better understanding of Fechner's views and merits. He descended on both sides from ancestors whose position was that of highly esteemed Protestant pastors ; he studied medicine like Lotze, and was the friend and colleague of Lotze's teachers, Weber and Weisse. In his autobiographical record, communicated by Kuntze, he confesses having become almost an atheist under the influence of his medical studies, until he became acquainted with the philosophy of Schelling, Oken, and Steffens, which dazzled him, touched the poetical and mystical side of his nature, and, though he hardly understood it, had a lasting influence on him. The simultaneous occupation with the best scientific literature of the day (he translated French text-books such as those of Biot and Thénard, and verified Ohm's law experimentally), however, forced upon him the sceptical reflection whether, " of all the beautiful orderly connection of optical phenomena, so clearly expounded by Biot, anything could

to him that we are indebted for the term Psycho-physics, which in the present chapter I have used in a more general sense. Fechner worked independently of Lotze and Helmholtz on the lines of E. H. Weber. He does not seem to have been much influenced by either Kant or Herbart. In 1860 he published his 'Elemente der Psychophysik,' which was to be an exact treatise on the relations of "mind and body," founded upon a measurement of psychical quantities.

Herbart's attempt to submit psychical phenomena to the exact methods of calculation had failed through the want of a measure for psychical quantities. Lotze had suggested the idea of a psycho-physical mechanism — *i.e.*, a constant and definite connection between inner and outer phenomena, between sensation and stimulus. E. H. Weber in his important researches on "Touch and Bodily Feeling" had made a variety of measurements of sensations, and shown that in many cases stimuli must be augmented in proportion to their own original intensity in order to produce equal increments of sensation. These observations lent themselves to an easy mathematical generalisation. Fechner was the first to draw

have been found out by Oken-Schelling's method?" This mixture or alteration of exact science and speculation, of faithfulness and loyalty to facts as well as to theory, runs through all Fechner's life, work, and writings. Much of his poetry, of his fanciful and paradoxical effusions, is meant seriously, and is really more coherent than it appeared to his readers, some of whom knew him only under his pseudonym of Dr Mises. He lived, thought, and worked truly on the borderland of nature and mind, of this world and another, of science and poetry, of reality and fiction. Like Lotze, he wanted the genuinely historical sense. Like Lotze, too, he received from others only suggestions which he elaborated independently in his own original fashion. As little as Lotze does he seem ever to have attempted to realise and understand any other philosophical system than his own. To both, the ultimate problem was capable only of a subjective solution. Cf. vol. i. p. 200.

the attention of philosophers to the existence of this relation in a variety of instances, and collected a large
number of facts to prove its general correctness. He
conceived the idea of measuring sensations by their
accompanying stimuli, a mode of measurement based
upon that relation which, under the name of Weber's
law or formula, he introduced as a general psycho-
physical proposition. The intervals in the numerical
scale, the differences in the magnitude of stars, the
facts established by Weber relating to our estimate of
differences of touch, of weight, and of temperature;
lastly, the relation of " fortune physique " and " fortune
morale," known to Euler and Lagrange, could all be
utilised towards proving the general accuracy, within
certain limits, of the psycho - physical formula. The
work gave rise to many discussions [1] as to the meaning of the term quantity applied to psychical phenomena, as to methods of measurement, and as to the
significance to be attached to the new branch of research

[1] In addition to the ' Elemente
der Psychophysik ' (1860), of which
a second edition appeared in 1890,
the author enlarged, discussed, and
defended his special ideas and
theories in three further publications. The year 1877 produced ' In
Sachen der Psychophysik,' the year
1882 the 'Revision der Hauptpunkte
der Psychophysik,' and shortly before his death (1887) there appeared, in the ' Philosophische
Studien ' of Prof. Wundt, his last
contribution, " Ueber die psychi-
schen Maasprincipien und das
Webersche Gesetz," which Prof.
Wundt declares to be " the clearest
and most complete exposition of
the problem which he gave in the
course of the forty years during
which he was occupied with it."
(See the obituary oration, reprinted
in Kuntze's ' Biography,' p. 360.)
The attacks on Fechner came from
many quarters. In the polemical treatise of 1877 he notices
how the views of his critics —
Helmholtz, Aubert, Mach, Bern-
stein, Plateau, Delbœuf, Bren-
tano, Hering, Langer — agree as
little among themselves as with
his own. He sums up with fine
humour : " The tower of Babel was
not finished, because the builders
could not agree how to build it ;
my psycho-physical structure may
remain standing, because the workmen cannot agree how to pull it
down " (' In Sachen,' &c., p. 215).

as well as to the interpretation of the Weber-Fechner law of psycho-physical dependence.

We are indebted to Prof. Wundt of Leipzig for a complete and exhaustive examination of the new province of exact science.[1]   He enlarged its boundaries,

31.
Wundt.

[1] The psychological school, of which Prof. Wundt can be considered the head or centre, has been contrasted by M. Ribot, in his 'Psychologie Allemande Contemporaine' (1st ed., 1879), with the English school, and, in the exposition in the text, I have taken a similar view. It would, however, be unjust not to note that in England, prior to the publication of Prof. Wundt's principal writings, a development of psychology in the same direction had already begun. The principal representative of this development is Prof. Alexander Bain (born 1818), whose two great works, 'The Senses and the Intellect' (1855) and 'The Emotions and the Will' (1859), appeared even before Fechner's 'Psychophysik,' and were characterised by J. S. Mill as "an exposition which deserves to take rank as the foremost of its class, and as marking the most advanced point which the *a posteriori* psychology has reached," being "the most genuinely scientific analytical exposition of the human mind which the *a posteriori* psychology has up till this time produced" ('Edinb. Rev.,' October 1859, reprinted in 'Dissertations and Discussions,' vol. iii. pp. 99, 100). Bain carried out what had been called by Thomas Brown "the physical investigation of the mind," and was probably the first English psychologist who enriched the older associational psychology by an extensive use of the teachings of physiology ; the germ of his theory being contained in a passage cited by him from Johannes Müller : in fact, he appreciated the well-known dictum of the latter, "*psychologus nemo nisi physiologus.*" Shortly after the appearance of Prof. Bain's works, the overmastering influence of the evolutionist school in England, headed by Mr Spencer and supported by Darwin, and the pronounced opposition with which the psycho-physical school started in Germany, cast somewhat into the shade the steady development, in this country, of the exact science of psychology by those who formed the direct succession to the older, purely introspective, school of Scottish thinkers.   As I am not, in the present chapter, treating of psychology and philosophy, but of the attempt to gain, by the methods of the exact sciences, a conception of the phenomena of animation and consciousness, I leave for another occasion the appreciation of the English school of psychology.   The members of this school considered physiology as an aid to psychological research, whereas most of the representatives of the modern German school were, to begin with, physiologists or physicists, and only became subsequently psychologists or philosophers.   Characteristic of this school are two points : the opposition they made from the start to the existing methods, and their prominent use, not only of observation, but of experiment.   The less ostentatious development of English thought would, no doubt, have led in the end, but for the reasons given above, to like results. An opposition similar to that so marked in Germany was, however,

taking in the ground covered by Lotze's medical psychology as well as by Helmholtz's physiology of hearing and seeing; added a large number of measurements of his own, some of them quite original, such as those referring to the time-sense, many of them in confirmation and extension of Fechner's collection of facts; invented new methods and new apparatus; brought the whole subject into connection with general physiology, as also with the more exclusively introspective psychology of the older, notably the English and Scottish, schools; and pointed to the necessary completion which these investigations demand from the several neighbouring fields

32.
Physio-
logical
psychology.

of research. Through his labours "physiological psychology" as an independent science has for the first time become possible. The influence of his great work on this subject, as also of his teaching and demonstrations, has been very stimulating. With its place in the history of philosophical thought I shall have to deal in a later portion of this history. At present I will merely refer to the leading ideas and contributions it contains to our scientific reasoning on the psycho-physical problem.

Wundt approached psychological research from the side of physiology;[1] his earlier writings referred to the

taken up in England in single instances—*e.g.*, by G. H. Lewes and Dr H. Maudsley, the former in favour of Positivism, the latter on the foundation of his 'Physiology and Pathology of Mind' (1st ed., 1867).

[1] The researches of Wundt and the earlier work of Fechner remained practically unknown in this country up to the time of the appearance of the periodical 'Mind,' edited by Prof. Croom

Robertson, in 1876, under the generous patronage of Prof. Bain. Even Lotze and Herbart were hardly known in this country. A similar disregard of English psychology existed in Germany. The foremost writers on the history of modern philosophy, such as Erdmann and Ueberweg, wrote as if modern philosophic—including psychological — thought existed only in Germany. Even the singularly impartial and unbiassed

physiology of the senses, to physiology proper, and to such phenomena of psychical or inner life as can be traced, not only in man, but also in the brute creation. He thus seems to have approached psychology with the true instinct and methods of an exact student of nature. In the course of years his psycho-physical studies took more and more the character of an experimental psychology, and in the latest edition of his great work he describes it as such, maintaining that the designation of physiological psychology has rather a historical meaning.[1]

author of the 'History of Materialism,' Albert Lange, does only scant justice to the labours of the English school, J. S. Mill being, in fact, the only English philosophical writer of the middle of the century who was appreciated in Germany. The last twenty-five years have entirely altered this state of things. French and American writers such as M. Ribot, Prof. M'Cosh, and more recently Prof. James, treat impartially of the rival claims of German and English thinkers. 'Mind' has preserved its fairness in admitting contributions from opposite sides ; and latterly there has been started by the publishing house of Frommann of Stuttgart, under the editorship of Prof. Falckenberg, a series of very useful monographs on recent thinkers, whose voluminous or scattered writings make it difficult to arrive at a comprehensive and just appreciation of the main drift of their doctrine. Ever since some provinces of philosophy were conquered by exact research, unity of plan has been to a great extent sacrificed ; the natural science of mind is becoming split up into fragments like that of life. Prof. Lasswitz has given us for the first time a coherent account of

Fechner's philosophy, and although Prof. Wundt had already put forth in his 'System der Philosophie' (1st ed., 1890) a statement of his systematic views, the monograph by Edmund König (1901) is very helpful in fixing the historical position of Wundt and the genesis of his doctrine. I refer to these volumes for a bibliography of the thinkers discussed.

[1] In the introduction to the 'Physiologische Psychologie' (4te Aufl., vol. i. p. 9) Prof. Wundt says, "The conception of experimental psychology has been expanded beyond its original limits, as we now comprehend under it not only those parts of psychology which are directly accessible to experiment, but the whole of psychology ; as it makes a direct use of the experimental method wherever this is possible, and an indirect use in all other instances through applying the results gained in the former, and through rendering internal observation more acute. . . . The designation of physiological psychology, which originated in the peculiar historical antecedents of our science, is one-sided. . . . The centre of gravity of the experimental method lies in this, that it alone makes reliable inner observation possible."

Whilst his methods are exact and definite, his aim is, nevertheless, wide and comprehensive; for not only is the animal creation studied as a valuable field for enlarged psycho-physical research, but also the psychology of infancy and of human societies (ethnical psychology) are drawn into the circle of a scientific psychology. At the same time his exposition is directed towards the totality [1] of the phenomena of life and mind, it being his ultimate object to arrive at some appropriate conception of the whole of human existence. In this respect his scientific labours form a counterpart to those of naturalists like Humboldt and Darwin, who did so much to direct the attention of natural science to the whole of nature, her history and economy. It seems to me that Prof. Wundt has similarly introduced into the psycho-physical study of nature the prominent consideration of the mental side of life in its totality, starting, as Darwin and Humboldt did, from a large accumulation of detailed observations.

This regard for the whole problem distinguishes Wundt's writings from those of other eminent psycho-physicists, such as Helmholtz, who deals brilliantly and exhaustively with certain special problems, or Fechner, who relegated the discussion of the fundamental questions to a series of half-poetical treatises, which are full of suggestion rather than close scientific reasoning. But

[1] 'Physiologische Psychologie' (4te Aufl., vol. i. p. 2): "Our science has accordingly the task, first, to investigate those vital phenomena which, lying in the middle between outer and inner experience, require the simultaneous application of both methods of observation, outer and inner; and secondly, to throw light from the points thus gained on the totality of the phenomena of life, and, if possible, to gain in this way a comprehensive conception of human existence." See also his essay "Philosophie und Wissenschaft" in a volume of 'Essays' (Leipzig, 1885), p. 1; also 'Die Aufgaben der experimentellen Psychologie,' ibid., p. 127, &c.

Wundt differs quite as much from Lotze, who also strove to arrive at a view of the totality of human life and its significance.   Lotze belonged, in spite of the original and independent view which he took of the psycho-physical problem, to the older school of philosophers. Wundt belongs quite to the modern school.[1]   Fechner forms the transition.   Lotze begins his psychology, and even his physiology of the soul, with a lengthy dissertation on the unity of the soul as a special being, just as Herbart begins his psychology with metaphysics. This metaphysical introduction, these definitions relating to the essence of the soul, its unity, and its location, are absent in the modern psychology.   Instead of founding psychology on experience, metaphysics, and mathematics, Wundt founds it on experience (including experiment), physiology, and mathematics.   In consequence of this altered foundation a new problem has arisen, precisely as a new problem arose for biologists when they discarded vital force as a meaningless and useless encumbrance.   For the older biologists life was the exhibition

33.
Wundt,
Fechner,
and Lotze
compared.

[1] See the preface to the second edition of the 'System der Philosophie' (Leipzig, 1897), p. ix : " I have always tried to co-operate in the endeavour to secure for psychology an independent position as an empirical science outside of philosophy, and to see that she should not lack the support of the scientific method in so far as this could be transferred to her. . . . As I started from natural science and then came to philosophy through occupation with empirical psychology, it would have appeared to me impossible to philosophise in any other way than in correspondence with this sequence of the problems.   But I quite well understand that the position may be different for him who begins with philosophy and then makes occasional excursions into the regions of science or psychology."   Compare with this what Lotze says in the Introduction to his 'Streit-schriften' (1857), or the following passage from one of his last essays ('Contemp. Rev.,' January 1880), " Except in rare cases, a prolonged philosophical labour is nothing else but the attempt to justify, scientifically, a fundamental view of things which has been adopted in early life."

of vital force. This having been dropped, the question arose for modern biology, What is life ? We thus find thinking biologists of the modern, exact school aiming at a mechanical definition of life. Many answers have been attempted, such as that it is the action of a very complex chemical molecule, of dynamical equilibrium, of metabolism, of a special form or organisation, &c. Similarly, when the word soul dropped out of psychology in its older metaphysical meaning as a separate being or entity, when it was used to mean only the sum-total of the inner or psychical phenomena, a new problem arose for the psycho-physicist or experimental psychologist. The problem now was to give some definition of the unity and unified totality of all inner or mental phenomena. The older metaphysical psychology, as also for the most part the so-called empirical psychology, answered this question by placing the conception of an independent entity, the soul, person, or self, at the opening of their discussions. Modern exact psychology cannot do this. For it the unity of the inner life and its unified totality has become a problem. This problem Prof. Wundt faces fully and fairly. He asks himself the question, Wherein consists the unity of consciousness, wherein the totality of all mental life, individual and collective ? Armed with the methods of exact research, he tries to extract from the whole array of mental phenomena an idea of their essence as distinguished from external or natural phenomena, and of their collective meaning and significance. In so doing he enters the domain of philosophy, and his results belong to the realm of philosophical thought. When dealing with that large section of my

34.
The unity of
consciousness.

subject I shall have to take up Wundt's theories where I now leave them.

Through the efforts and widespread influence of Prof. Wundt, the inner or psychical phenomena have been drawn into the circle of exact research; a large portion of psychology has become natural science. It is quite consistent with this that some of the disciples of the modern school should have assumed towards the new branch of natural science the attitude which has become habitual among those who cultivate other natural sciences. All these sciences are based upon observation, aided if possible by experiment; none of them, however, has succeeded in rising to the rank of an exact science without the aid of some generalisation which admitted of clear expression in a few definite conceptions, being the more valuable in the degree that it lent itself to a clothing of mathematical language. In the course of the last centuries, notably the nineteenth, several of these fundamental principles — such as the laws of motion, gravitation, atomism, vibratory motion, the conception of energy, natural selection, metabolism—have attained in various degrees, some almost perfectly, to this state of definiteness, and the sciences built up by their aid have accordingly acquired the character of certainty. Psycho - physics having through Weber, Lotze, Fechner, and Wundt gradually evolved the notion of a partial parallelism of physical and psychical phenomena, the conception of a mathematical dependence or of function could be introduced between the measurable external processes and the hidden internal events which we term mental; the whole of the latter being

looked upon as concomitant occurrences, as "Begleit-
erscheinungen" or "Epi-phenomena" of the more accessible though very complex phenomena of the nervous
system and its centres; whereby it had to be noted,
that whilst the external visible processes exhibit that
continuity in time and space which is characteristic of
all physical phenomena, the epi-phenomena were subject
to discontinuous appearance and disappearance, to sudden
growth and collapse. Having got hold of this partial
formula, which in some cases admits even of a rigorous
mathematical expression, psycho-physics had no pressing
need of investigating its meaning any further, or of inquiring into the supposed independent existence or significance of the "epi-phenomena" as such; similar general
inquiries into the origin of gravitation, of atoms, of the
essence of energy or inertia, having proved to be of little
or no use in furthering astronomy, chemistry, thermo-
dynamics. It cannot be denied that this is a perfectly
tenable scientific attitude. Such an attitude has notably
been taken up by Dr Hugo Münsterberg, and by what
we may term the Freiburg school of psycho-physics.
Also there is no doubt that through a series of very
cleverly contrived experiments—particularly those referring to the muscular sense and the time sense—a
good deal of light has been thrown upon such mental
processes as association of ideas, attention, apperception,
and voluntary effort, which have thus been brought
into closer correspondence with changes taking place in
the nervous system. In fact, a parallelism of neurosis
and of psychosis has been more and more established.

This doctrine of psycho - physical parellelism, also

35.
Doctrine of
parallelism.

called the conscious automaton theory, is the central conception in psychology as a natural science, or, as I have termed it, of the psycho - physical view of nature. It was prepared[1] by earlier thinkers, such as Descartes, and, in a different form, by Spinoza,[2] and by Leibniz's doctrine of pre-established harmony.[3] It has been strengthened by the physiological theory of reflex action,[4] and, independently, by psycho-physics in the narrower sense of the word, as founded by Weber and Fechner. But the possibilities of the automaton theory were not scientifically tested till towards the end of the nineteenth century. In this country, two thinkers

---

[1] The doctrine of psycho-physical parallelism and its historical genesis is given by Huxley in his address before the British Association Meeting at Belfast in 1874, "On the Hypothesis that Animals are Automata, and its History," in which he goes back to Descartes and Charles Bonnet. A good account of the theory is also given by Prof. Wm. James in the 5th chapter of his 'Principles of Psychology'; and it is fully discussed by Prof. James Ward in his Gifford lectures, 'Naturalism and Agnosticism,' vol. ii. pt. iii.

[2] The passage from Spinoza which is constantly quoted, and, as Prof. Ward says, usually in ignorance of the context, is in 'Ethica,' part ii. prop. 7: "Ordo et connexio idearum idem est ac ordo et connexio rerum."

[3] Leibniz, as Huxley (*loc. cit.*) tells us, also invented the term "automate spirituel" and applied it to man.

[4] Du Bois - Reymond, in his "Éloge" of Johannes Müller, has shown that the principle of reflex action dates back to Descartes, who also introduced the term re-

flex. Next in time came Willis ('De motu musculari,' Amsterdam, 1682). The subject seems to have been overlooked to such an extent, that Prochaska (1784) got for a long time the credit of having established the notion of reflex action, and even his work had to be rediscovered by Eduard Weber (1846), after the principle of the transition of a reaction from the afferent to the efferent nerves in the central organs had been prominently put forward by Legallois (1811), Marshall Hall (1835), and Johannes Müller (1835). In more recent times, Prof. Pflüger's "Laws of Reflex Action," and his and G. H. Lewes's theory of the presence of consciousness in the spinal cord, have formed the subject of much discussion and much experimental work. A good historical account will be found in the 13th Leçon of M. Ch. Richet's 'Physiologie des Muscles et des Nerfs' (Paris, 1882), and a discussion of the whole subject in Prof. Wundt's 'Physiologische Psychologie,' ch. xxi., where especially the difference between automatic and reflex movement is brought out.

of eminence, Huxley and Clifford,[1] have made the theory accessible to the popular understanding, without, however, taking a comprehensive view of the study of mental phenomena, inasmuch as they approached the subject from the side of natural science—the former more from that of physiology, the latter from that of the mechanical sciences. Prof. Wundt treats the subject exhaustively in many passages of his works, notably in the last chapter of his great work on 'Physiological Psychology,' in which he broadly defines "the psycho-physical view as that view which starts from the empirically well-established thesis, that nothing takes place in our consciousness which does not find its foundation in definite physical processes. The simple sensation, the connection

---

[1] Although neither Huxley nor Clifford added anything new to the conception of parallelism as contained in the writings of many earlier Continental philosophers, the fact that they were driven from their purely scientific positions to discuss the subject, and were not psychologists and metaphysicians by profession, gave their expositions, which are otherwise as fresh as they are immature, a peculiar charm. Being both masters in style, they at once enriched the vocabulary with new terms which have since become classic. The word "epi-phenomenon," an equivalent for the German 'Begleiterscheinung,' which is of independent origin but expresses Huxley's view, is a real enrichment of thought. It is also the direct way to bring home the absurdity of the whole theory. The things of nature being first considered as "phenomena"—i.e., as "appearing" to some one,—the some one is next looked upon as a secondary phenomenon, an epi-

phenomenon. Clifford actually in his psychological atomism goes the length of saying, "Reason, intelligence, and volition are properties of a complex which is made up of elements, themselves not rational, not intelligent, not conscious" (see 'Mind,' vol. iii. p. 67). In the physical theory of atoms it has been truly said that you cannot get anything out of the atoms that you have not, to begin with, put into them. Clifford's dictum reminds one of Carlyle's definition of the object of political economy, which has to solve the problem, "Given a community consisting of fools and knaves, how to produce efficiency and honesty by their combined action?" Clifford's solution of the psychological deadlock is the "Mindstuff" theory, the theory that all matter is the phenomenal correlate of the elements of mind. Clifford's essay "On the Nature of Things in themselves" is reprinted in 'Lectures and Essays' (1879), vol. ii. p. 71 *sqq.*

of sensations and perceptions, their associations, finally, the processes of apperception and volition, are accompanied by physiological nerve-processes. Other bodily processes, such as the simple and complex reflex actions, do not enter directly into consciousness, but they form important auxiliary processes of the phenomena of consciousness.[1] It is, accordingly, quite consistent, from a purely scientific point of view, to test this central conception of exact psychology, and to refrain from introducing any purely psychical conceptions so long as the possibilities of the conception, that mental phenomena are only concomitant occurrences of changes which take place in the nervous system and centres, have not been exhausted. Investigations, with or without this definite purpose, have been very largely prosecuted in the course of the nineteenth century, and have been in part purely anatomical, in part physiological, the latter again either referring to pathological or to normal cases. Systematic courses of experiments have been begun at Leipzig and taken up, according to a well-defined special programme, by Dr Münsterberg at Freiburg, who in the researches of his laboratory has, more distinctly than any other philosopher, adopted the theory as a working hypothesis.[2]

36.
Münsterberg.

[1] 'Physiologische Psychologie' (4 Aufl.), vol. ii. p. 644.

[2] The principal writings of Dr Münsterberg, in which his psychophysical researches are contained, are : 1, 'Die Willenshandlung,' Freiburg, 1888 ; 2, 'Beiträge zur Experimentellen Psychologie,' 4 parts, 1889-92 ; 3, 'Ueber Aufgaben und Methoden der Psychologie,' being part 2 of the 'Schriften der Gesellschaft für Psychologische Forschung,' 1891. These writings, although starting from the position prepared by the Leipzig school of psycho-physical research, are largely polemical, and directed against some of Prof. Wundt's principal theories. They have received a considerable amount of attention in Germany and America and in this country, and also a good deal

It can hardly be said that this course of study has done more than make a start, and even those who are inclined to consider it a very one-sided attempt are bound to admit that it has a promising future. Thus Prof. Wm. James, whose ' Principles of Psychology ' treat of the subject from many and very different points of view, refers to these experiments in a characteristic passage as follows: " Within a few years, what one may call a microscopic psychology has arisen in Germany, carried on by experimental methods, asking of course every moment for introspective data, but eliminating their uncertainty by operating on a large scale and taking statistical means. . . . Their success has brought into the field an array of experimental psychologists, bent on studying the elements of mental life, dissecting them out from the gross results in which they are embedded, and, as far as possible, reducing them to quantitative scales. . . . The mind must submit to a regular siege, in which minute advantages, gained night and day by the

of opposition. The late editor of ' Mind,' Prof. Croom Robertson, reported pretty fully upon Münsterberg's work in the 15th volume of the first series of ' Mind,' and drew especial attention to the confirmation which certain views contained in the writings of the British Associationist school have received through Dr Münsterberg's expositions. Prof. E. B. Titchener criticised Dr Münsterberg's experiments and theories somewhat severely in the 16th volume of the first series of ' Mind,' p. 521 *sqq.* As the subject is still under discussion, and as in more recent writings of Dr Münsterberg, who is now professor at Harvard University, his studies have shown quite a different side from that exhibited by the above-named earlier writings, it is impossible in this history to do more than refer to them as marking a distinct phase in modern psycho - physical thought. It does not appear that Prof. Wundt agrees with much of the outcome of the important movement he originated ; see his article in ' Philosophische Studien,' vol. vi. p. 382, and a very valuable paper by Prof. J. Ward (' Mind,' 2nd series, vol. ii. p. 54 *sqq.*), entitled "Modern Psychology : a Reflexion." As these discussions refer more to the philosophical value than to the purely scientific aspect of psycho-physics, they would lead us beyond the regions of purely scientific thought.

forces that hem her in, resolve themselves at last into her overthrow.   There is little of the grand style about these new prism, pendulum, and chronograph philosophers.   They mean business, not chivalry.   What generous divination and that superiority in virtue which was thought by Cicero to give a man the best insight into nature have failed to do, their spying and scraping, their deadly tenacity and almost diabolical cunning, will doubtless some day bring about. . . . The experimental method has quite changed the face of the science, so far as the latter is a record of the mere work done."

It is, however, only fair to remark that it has never been the object of any science, and can, therefore, no more be the object of exact psychology, to deal with everything at once, and that psycho-physical science has quite as much right to postpone the question, What is mind ? [1] as biological science has had to postpone, or even to eliminate, the question, What is life ?   But this comparison reveals also the essential difference between the exact science of life and the exact science of mind. Of life we know only through the observation of living beings, but of mind we have not only the apparent knowledge of its unity, which introspection forces upon

[1] " Sensation, Retentiveness, Association by Contiguity,—these are to be our ultimate and sufficient psychological conceptions : the facts of feeling and conation are resolved into facts of sensation ; and all mind-processes held to be not merely conditioned, but explained by brain-processes, which they accompany as epi-phenomena or ' Begleit-erscheinungen.' It is not so long since the world was shocked at Lange's *mot* about a psychology without a soul, but the ' modern ' psychology is a psychology without even consciousness. ' Content of consciousness ' as much as you like, but consciousness itself, consciousness as activity, is not our affair ; we leave that to metaphysics, say our ' modern ' teachers." (Prof. J. Ward, on " Modern Psychology," ' Mind,' 2nd series, vol. ii. p. 55).

us, but we have also a large array of external facts which
have been appropriately defined by the term "the objective mind." There are, in fact, two properties with
which we are familiar through common-sense and ordinary reflection as belonging specially to the phenomena
of our inner self-conscious life, to the so-called "epi-
phenomena" of the higher organic or nervous systems,
and these properties seem to lie quite beyond the sphere
and the possibilities of the ordinary methods of exact
research. The first of these properties is the peculiar
unity exhibited by the higher forms of organic existence,
and still more evident in the phenomena of mental or
inner life. Instead of unity, it might perhaps be better
to call it centralisation. Now, the more we apply mathematical methods, the more we become aware of the impossibility of ever arriving at a comprehensive unity by
adding units or elements together. The sum of atoms or
molecules, however artfully put together, never exhibits
to our reasoning that appearance of concentration which
the higher organisms or our conscious self seem to exhibit.
In this circumstance lies the difficulty of ever arriving at
any really satisfactory definition of life—which definition
eminent physiologists have, as we have seen, felt compelled ultimately to relegate to the realm of the idea.
In the last chapter I showed how modern research into
the phenomena of life has impressed upon our thoughts
the ubiquity, the continuity, and the unique character or
singularity of life, without being able to fix upon any one
satisfactory mechanical definition of life. But as we
ascend in the scale of living things we become aware of
another property : they are centred—*i.e.*, they exhibit a

37.
Phenomenon
of centralisa-
tion.

special kind of unity which cannot be defined, a unity which, even when apparently lost in the periods of unconsciousness, is able to re-establish itself by the wonderful and indefinable property called " memory "—a centre which can only be very imperfectly localised—a together which is more than a mathematical sum ; in fact, we rise to the conception of individuality—that which cannot be divided and put together again out of its parts.

The second property is still more remarkable. The world of the " epi-phenomena," of the inner processes which accompany the highest forms of nervous developments in human beings, is capable of unlimited growth ; and it is capable of this by a process of becoming external : it becomes external, and, as it were, perpetuates itself in language, literature, science and art, legislation, society, and the like. We have no analogue of this in physical nature, where matter and energy are constant quantities, and where the growth and multiplication of living matter is merely a conversion of existing matter and energy into special altered forms without increase or decrease in quantity. But the quantity of the inner thing is continually on the increase ; in fact, this increase is the only thing of interest in the whole world.

38.
Externalisation and growth of mind.

Now, no exact scientific treatment of the phenomena of mind and body, no psycho-physical view of nature, is complete or satisfactory which passes by and leaves undefined these two remarkable properties of the inner life, of the epi-phenomena of nervous action, of consciousness. And it seems to me that Prof. Wundt is the only psycho-physicist who, starting from science and trying to penetrate by scientific methods into the inner or psychic

39.
Wundt's treatment of central problem.

world, has treated the subject comprehensively, and fairly and fully tried to grapple with these two facts peculiar to the inner world—its centralised unity and its capacity of unlimited growth through a process of externalisation. He has done so by his philosophical theory of "apperception and will," and of the "growth of mental values," two conceptions which lead us into the realm of philosophical thought.[1]

But, before closing this chapter, which deals with the study of the phenomena of an inner life and the interaction of body and mind by the methods of exact research, it is well to note that long before psychology existed as a natural science, a large amount of knowledge had been accumulated by a different method. Especially in this country—ever since the time of Locke—there has existed a very large and influential school of thinkers who studied the inner phenomena by what has been appropriately termed the inner sense; every observer recording his own inner experience and leaving it to others, by doing the same, to confirm or correct his statements. Psychology, carried on through self-observation or by the

[1] It would serve no good purpose to string together a list of quotations from Prof. Wundt's voluminous writings in which these two central ideas of his philosophy find expression, especially as there is no one passage to be found in which his highest abstractions and final conclusions find an adequate expression, still less one which could be conveniently rendered in the English language. König has, it seems to me, done much to make Wundt's view more easily understood, and I must content myself at present with referring to his little volume, notably to the extracts given on pp. 134, 141, and 167, which explain more clearly the theory of apperception and will. On the theory of the "growth of mental values," see especially Wundt, 'System der Philosophie' (2 Aufl., pp. 307, 596), "Mental life is, extensively and intensively, governed by a law of growth of values: extensively, inasmuch as the multiplicity of mental developments is always on the increase; intensively, inasmuch as the values which appear in these developments increase in degree" (p. 304).

introspective method, had grown to large dimensions in 40. Introspective method. Scotland and in England, long before Herbart and Beneke in Germany gave it a similar direction. In fact, most of the writings of the introspective school in Germany, which dates from the middle of the century, is concerned with the material accumulated by British psychologists. And even the psycho-physical method itself would carry us only a little way if its results and observations could not continually be checked, supplemented, and interpreted by what we already know by introspection. One of the foremost representatives of the English school of psychology has said, and many will agree with him,[1] "in our desire to know ourselves—to frame some conception of the flow of our feelings and thoughts —we work at first by introspection purely; and if at a later stage we find means of extending and improving our knowledge, introspection is still our main resort— the Alpha and Omega of psychological inquiry: it is alone supreme, everything else subsidiary. Its compass is ten times all the other methods put together, and fifty times the utmost range of psycho-physics alone."

A history of Thought must accordingly contain some account of the view which our century has taken of the introspective method and the value of the inner sense as a means of enlarging our knowledge.[2] This discussion

---

[1] See Prof. Bain's essay in 'Mind,' 2nd series, vol. ii. p. 42: "The respective Spheres and mutual Helps of Introspection and Psycho-physical Experiment in Psychology."

[2] One result of the modern psycho-physical view, or of the doctrine of parallelism of physical and mental states, has been not only to develop a clearer view of physiological psychology, but also to define more clearly the object of psychology proper — that is, of the science which deals with the facts revealed by introspection. When, in the middle of the century, the physiology of the senses attracted the

will, in a future volume, form one of the appropriate links which join science to philosophy—which lead us on from exact to speculative thought. At present I have to refer to another and very extensive field of research, into which the natural as well as the speculative philosopher have been led from opposite sides, and which especially affords a hopeful prospect for an enlargement of the psycho-physical view of nature. If the natural philosopher cannot consistently and fairly enter into the mysteries of an inner consciousness from which his opponent—the speculative philosopher—starts, he may perhaps do so by a roundabout way or a side-door.

As I stated above, the inner world, the psychosis, which intermittently accompanies the neurosis, the epi-

attention of psychologists in all the three countries, it became customary to introduce purely psychological treatises by an exposition of the psycho-physical relations, introducing into psychology chapters from physiology. The consequence of this has been that modern works on psychology have grown to inordinate length, and frequently exhibit a dual aspect and method. Quite recently it has therefore been insisted on that psychology can be written either from the physiological or from the purely psychological point of view. A good example of the latter is Prof. G. F. Stout's 'Analytic Psychology' (2 vols., 1896). "Physiological results," he says (vol. i. p. 37), "are likely to be valuable only in proportion as they are controlled and criticised by psychological analysis. This holds good apart from consideration of such metaphysical questions as whether the brain-process is the sole real agency, and consciousness a mere function, or consequence, or epi-phenomenon; or whether consciousness is the reality of which the correlated brain-process is a phenomenon, or whether they are two aspects of the same fact. Whatever may be our attitude to such questions, the psychologist has still his own work to do on his own lines; and for the sake of physiology itself, so far as it entertains the hope of throwing light on the mechanism of brain-processes, he must attempt to do it. It is idle to require psychology to wait for the progress of physiology. Such a demand is logically parallel to a demand that history or biography, or the practical estimate of character and anticipation of men's actions in ordinary life, shall come to a standstill until they have a sufficient physiological basis. On this view, Carlyle should have abstained from writing his 'French Revolution,' because he did not know what precise configuration and motion of brain particles determined the actions of the mob who stormed the Bastille."

phenomenon which lies on the other side of the phenomenon, is not only characterised by a peculiar unity or
centred connectedness which we look for in vain in the
external and physical world; it has also become external
or objective, it has detached itself from the subjective
and hidden source from which it sprang, and can be
studied as such in the great creations of language, literature, society, science, art, and religion.   Why not study
its nature and its life in these great and undeniable
manifestations, and instead of beginning at the hidden
source, the unknown and indefinable centre, try to reach
this by beginning at the periphery, measuring out the
great circle and learning what it contains?

41.
The "objec-
tive mind."

Ancient philosophy, which found its consummation in
the writings of Aristotle, had already begun this work,
and, in establishing the rules of grammar and logic, had
furnished the material for many modern speculations.
What the ancients had only begun, modern thinkers of
the most opposite schools have been induced to continue
on more methodical lines, and with the more or less
distinct object of learning something definite regarding
that mental life and unity which they have, with little
success, tried long enough to reach by various direct
roads, such as introspection, speculation, physiological
and psycho-physical experiment.   Accordingly we find
springing up almost simultaneously in the three countries, ever since the latter part of the eighteenth century,
the study of mankind or of human culture in all its
historical forms.   Hume and Adam Smith, Montesquieu,
and the French physiocrats, studied society and the great
fabric of industry and commerce; Cabanis and the " Idéo-

logues " pointed to the importance of the philosophical study of language and grammar; the idealistic school in Germany ended by leading to the study of the objective mind in history, art, and philosophy; the school of Herbart in Waitz, Lazarus, and Steinthal led into " Völkerpsychologie " and " Sprachwissenschaft "; and it is well known how in our days the synthetic philosophy of Mr Herbert Spencer in England has entered on the study of sociology on the large scale. We hear on all sides of natural histories of mankind, of society, of religion, &c., and they appear either in the modest attire of the other and older natural histories which we have been accustomed to, preparing the ground by patient and unbiassed collection of facts, or they attach themselves to certain philosophical theories, such as are furnished by the dialectics of Hegel, or by the evolutionary doctrine of Darwin and Spencer, in connection with which we shall meet them in a future section of this work. For it has been found here, as it had been in the older natural histories, that the accumulation of facts and materials was of little use unless some leading idea was at hand by which it became possible to regulate and arrange them.

Thus we see how the psycho-physical problem—the question of the interaction of mind and body, of soul and nature, of the inner and the outer worlds—is being attacked from two entirely different sides,—from the side of the individual and from that of the collective life of the human being : the mental principle is being studied in its inner and hidden existence as the unifying and centralising factor of individual life, or in its external manifestations in history, society, science, art, industry, and religion,—in fact, in the history of culture and civilisation. If Bishop Berkeley has, with some propriety, been called " the historical starting-point " of psycho-physical investigation of the first kind, the importance of that of the second and wider kind is nowhere more clearly and definitely expressed than— over a century ago—in the writings of Johann Gott- fried Herder.[1] His influence in this direction was very

42.
Its study
prepared by
Herder.

[1] The influence of Herder (1744- 1803) on German literature and thought was fully acknowledged by his contemporaries, as is testified by the frequent references to him in the biographies of nearly all the eminent men who lived at the end of the eighteenth and the beginning of the nineteenth centuries, as also in the voluminous correspondence which he carried on with many eminent contemporaries. Had it not been for the overpowering and one-sided influence which the criti- cal, and, later, the transcendental, schools of thought gained, not- ably at the German universities, Herder's ideas would have been more generally acknowledged as forming, to a very great extent, the starting-point of many lines of research which were not exclus- ively controlled by the ruling philosophies, and which gradually and imperceptibly united at a later date to form the more modern current of German thought. Herder was much more allied with the historical studies refer- ring alike to nature, literature, and culture, than with the critical and metaphysical systems, being also well acquainted with con- temporary English thought, as, *inter alia*, with the curious writ- ings of Lord Monboddo. Through Madame de Staël, who was in- timate with Herder, his writings were early known in France, whereas Carlyle's studies in German literature, though most valuable and original in their way, do not give that prominence to Herder's writings which they deserve.   In more recent times, after the indefatigable Düntzer, through the publication of his correspondence, had done much to revive the interest in Her- der, full justice has been done to his great merit by Rudolf Haym, whose great work, ' Herder nach seinem Leben und seinen Werken ' (2 vols., Berlin, 1885), is a perfect mine of informa- tion. The side of Herder's influ- ence which is not sufficiently dwelt on by Haym, but which in- terests us most at present,—what we may call his anthropological view,—had already been exhaust- ively dealt with by Dr Heinrich Boehmer in his little-known ' Geschichte der Entwickelung der Naturwissenschaftlichen Weltan- schauung in Deutschland ' (Gotha, 1872), who especially draws at- tention to the psycho-physical ideas of Herder. It has been truly said that there is hardly any modern idea which has found widespread application that cannot be traced in the writings of Herder ; but Herder had no method, having

great, and would have been greater had he not lived at
a time when the study of the human mind by the purely
introspective or speculative methods had absorbed all
philosophical interest in England and Germany. His
opposition to the (abstract) subjective philosophy of
Kant and Fichte made him unpopular; he was only
half understood at the time; and only towards the end
of our century have his ideas been recognised as containing the clear conception of psycho-physics on the
large scale—*i.e.*, of the natural history of humanity, the
genesis and evolution of the objective mind.

Herder was a pupil of Kant during his pre-critical
period.   He was still more influenced by great
naturalists like Haller, Buffon, Camper, Sömmering,
Forster, and Blumenbach, who through physiology, comparative anatomy, and ethnology, attempted to bring the
study of the human race and its mental development into
connection with that of the brute creation, of the
surrounding plant-life, of the characteristics of climate
and soil, and of the great natural features of sky and
landscape.   He did not believe that we could study
the great forces of nature and mind from inside or in
the abstract—he desired to follow Haller's physiology, to
complete and continue it into psychology.   Irritability,[1]

characteristically maintained that
method is frequently only a convention, and he was deficient in
critical acumen. The German mind
had to go through the severe dis-
cipline of the school of mathematical and critical thought, and to
amass an enormous volume of experimental and historical knowledge, before the brilliant conception
of Herder in his great work 'Ideen

zur Geschichte der Menschheit' (4
pts., 1784-87) could be partially realised by A. von Humboldt in his
'Kosmos' (1841-59), and by Lotze
in his 'Microcosmus' (1856-64).
See especially the preface to the
latter.

[1] See above, p. 471, on a similar
development of Haller's teaching
through Cabanis in France somewhat later in time.

the highest physical phenomenon of matter, was to be the starting-point of this psychology.   In an early essay on understanding and sensation (1778) he wrote: "According to my thinking there is no psychology possible which is not at every step definite physiology. Haller's physiological work once raised to psychology, and, like Pygmalion's statue, enlivened with mind, we shall be able to say something about Thought and Sensation."[1]

But this psycho-physiological view was not limited to the study of the individual: it widened out and embraced the whole of mankind; nature on a large scale had to be observed; historical records had to be collected on all sides; origins had to be studied and the elementary forces followed up in the beginnings of poetry, art, and religion.   Materials were gathered everywhere from historians, chroniclers, travellers, primitive records, and the "voices of the peoples."   All this was to furnish the materials for a "History of Mankind."   "In many

[1] "Vom Erkennen und Empfinden der menschlichen Seele" (1778), in the 9th vol. of the Works of Herder ('Abtheilung zur Philosophie und Geschichte,' 1828). To give an idea of Herder's anticipation of modern views, see p. 10: "We cannot penetrate deeper into the genesis of sensation than to the remarkable phenomenon called by Haller 'Reiz.' The irritated fibre contracts and expands again; perhaps a 'stamen,' the first growing sparklet of sensation, towards which dead matter has purified itself by many steps and stages of mechanism and organisation." Many passages could be quoted from Herder's 'Ideen,' &c., and other writings, anticipating modern Darwinian ideas, such as those of the struggle for existence, and even of automatic selection. See Prof. J. Sully's appreciative article on Herder in the 'Ency. Brit.' (9th ed.), and notably Fr. von Bärenbach, 'Herder als Vorgänger Darwin's' (Berlin, 1877). Haym ('Herder,' vol. ii. p. 209) objects to this extreme view of Herder as a forerunner of Darwin on the ground that, according to the former, no animal in its development ever forsook that adjustment of organic forces peculiar to it, nature having kept each being within the limits of its type. Accordingly, Herder's evolutionism would be more akin to that of K. E. von Baer than to that of Darwin and Haeckel.

parts," he says,[1] "my book shows that one cannot as yet write a philosophy of human history, but that perhaps one may write it at the end of our century or of our chiliad."

And indeed the whole of our own century has been busy in carrying out this prophetic programme of Herder's, consciously as planned by him in Germany—unconsciously and independently in other countries. As a counterpart to the introspective labours of Kant and their followers, a large array of naturalists, historians, philologists, and ethnologists have in the spirit of Herder ransacked every corner of the globe and every monument of history with the distinct object of tracing there the physical basis and the workings of that inner and hidden principle which we call the human mind. In doing this, they or their numerous followers, who belonged to a generation which knew not Herder, have strayed far away from the common starting-point, and have frequently lost themselves in the bewildering details of special research. Above all, in the country to which Herder belonged, a

separation set in early in the century between what have been termed the natural and the mental sciences. The former came more and more under the sway of the mathematical spirit, which, as I showed in an earlier chapter, turned the eyes of its votaries away from their own national scientific literature to that of their neighbours—first to France, latterly to England. The mental sciences, on the other hand,—history, philology, the social sciences,—came under the influence of exactly those philosophical ideas which Herder never understood nor assimi-

---

[1] See the preface to the first part of the ' Ideen,' 1784.

lated:[1] the critical spirit of Kant, and the constructive canons of his successors, each of these distinct and separate movements, supplied exactly what was wanting in the prophetic, not to say dithyrambic, utterances of Herder; they supplied coherence and method. Earlier chapters of this book have shown how the mathematical spirit has permeated and revolutionised the natural sciences, and latterly how it has, in the science of psycho-physics, led philosophers back to the problem which Herder had adumbrated at the end of the previous century. A second large department of my task will consist in showing how what in Germany are called the mental sciences have been developed independently of the natural sciences, how the study of the mind as such—

[1] During the latter part of his life Herder was occupied to a great extent with those publications in which he gave expression to the opposition which he consistently maintained to the critical writings of his master Kant. His two principal works referring to this are 'Eine Metakritik zur Kritik der Reinen Vernunft' (2 parts, 1799) and ' Kalligone' (1800). Kant had reviewed the first volume of Herder's greatest work, the ' Ideen,' anonymously, criticising the absence of logical acumen and clear definitions, and also the attempt towards a genetic as opposed to a critical treatment of the intellect, the former being an enterprise "which transcends the powers of human reason, whether the latter gropes with physiology as a leader, or attempts to soar with metaphysics." In the second part of the ' Ideen ' Herder had taken up a polemical attitude to Kant's teachings, and Kant had again reviewed it, dwelling upon the uncritical manner in which Herder had built up his hypotheses on unsifted material gathered from all sides. In the ' Metakritik ' Herder, irritated by what he considered the arrogance of the Kantian school, undertook to put into systematic form his criticism of Kant's principal work, following to a great extent the suggestions thrown out by a mutual friend of himself and Kant, Johann Georg Hamann (1730-80), and falling back upon the earlier philosophies of Spinoza and Leibniz on the one side, and upon the common-sense philosophy of the Scottish school on the other, seeking for a solution of the problems raised by both, not in abstract reasoning, but in the realism of the concrete and the historical sciences. In the ' Kalligone,' Herder similarly attacks Kant's æsthetical philosophy (' Kritik der Urtheilskraft,' 1790), which had been enthusiastically received in Herder's immediate neighbourhood by Schiller. A full account of these controversies will be found in the 2nd vol. of Haym's work.

in its individual and collective existence—has proceeded when separated from that of nature. This survey will start with exactly that movement of thought which was so distasteful to Herder, the critical inquiry of Kant, and it will follow this up to the point when in our days a junction has again been attempted, not unlike in spirit to that dreamt of by Herder, though very much more accurate and precise in method. There is, moreover, one special problem where this has been markedly the case; one phenomenon stands out pre-eminently; it belongs equally to the realm of nature and of mind. After being independently attacked by philosophers, naturalists, travellers, philologists, and latterly by physicists, it has revealed itself as the psycho-physical problem *par excellence;* and it is exactly that which Herder himself treated with special attention. This phenomenon is that of human speech—the problem of language.[1]

45.
The problem
of language.

[1] The problem of language and the question of its origin independently occupied thinkers in the three countries in the latter half of the eighteenth century. In France the followers of Locke, notably Condillac ('Essai sur l'origine des connaissances humaines,' vol. ii.), wrote on the subject, while Rousseau opposed them ('Sur l'inégalité parmi les hommes,' 1754). In Germany the Pastor Süssmilch, of whom I shall have more to say in the next chapter, wrote an elaborate work to prove the divine origin of language ('Beweis dass der Ursprung der Menschlichen Sprache Göttlich sei,' Berlin, 1776). In order to settle the question the Academy of Berlin offered, in the year 1769, a prize in the following terms : "En supposant les hommes abandonnés à leurs facultés natu- relles, sont-ils en état d'inventer le langage ? et par quels moyens parviendront-ils d'eux-mêmes à cette invention ?" a problem which Herder characterised as a "truly philosophical one, and one eminently suited for me." He had already— following Hamann—thought much about the subject, and he proposes, in his prize essay, which was subsequently crowned by the Academy, "to prove the necessary genesis of language as a firm philosophical truth." A short time after Herder had written his essay (1771), there appeared in England, by James Burnett, Lord Monboddo, a work 'On the Origin and Progress of Language' (1773), in which he refers to the ideas of James Harris in his work 'Hermes ; or a Philosophical Enquiry concerning Language and Universal Grammar'

In no department of knowledge has the scientific spirit worked a greater change than in the science of language. With the exception of suggestions by Leibniz, who clearly saw the necessity of founding the theory of language on a broader basis than the small number of classical and modern tongues then current afforded, and of some glimpses of a correcter view such as those contained in the much ridiculed writings of Lord Monboddo, we find, up to the end of the eighteenth century, hardly any attempt towards a methodical treatment of the great problem. Philosophical theories and vague etymologies, amounting frequently to little more than punning with words, brought the subject into ridicule. Herder has the great merit of having urged the importance of the study of language and literature in primitive forms [1] as the great gateway into anthropology

(1751). The question attracted considerable attention, partly through the eccentricities of Lord Monboddo, of which it has been well said that they appeared more ridiculous to his own than they would to the present age, partly through the controversy which arose shortly after on the publication of Horne Tooke's celebrated 'Ἔπεα πτερόεντα, or the Diversions of Purley' (1786). Herder was acquainted with Monboddo's work, having occasioned a translation of it to be made and written a preface (1787); but he does not seem to have taken any notice of Horne Tooke (1736-1812), who, as the historian of the science of language (Theodor Benfey, 'Geschichte der Sprachwissenschaft,' München, 1869) says, would, for his novel ideas and method, deserve to be put at the entrance of the modern linguistic epoch, had he been able to avail himself of a knowledge of Sanskrit.

[1] This refers to the second greatest work of Herder, his collection of popular songs, published under the significant title of "Voices of the Peoples" ('Stimmen der Völker in Liedern,' 1778), a work which had the greatest influence on German literature as well as on modern philological studies. See Benfey, loc. cit., p. 316, &c. That the publication of the 'Percy Ballads' (1765), of Macpherson's 'Ossian,' and of Lowth's 'Lectures on Hebrew Poetry' (1753), formed a great stimulus to Herder in his historical and poetical studies is shown by Haym in many extracts and passages, also in the prefaces of Herder himself and of his editor, Joh. von Müller (Herder's 'Werke,' 1828, 'Zur schönen Literatur und Kunst,' vols. vii. and viii.)

and the science of humanity.   Through his writings
there rose two distinct views both fruitful for thought,
the philosophico-historical and the strictly scientific. His
immediate successors, or rather those who unconsciously
imbibed the spirit of his writings, took up the former
line.   The great development of classical philology in
the school of Wolf, the discovery of Sanskrit and the
new field of oriental philology, for a time threw the
purely scientific aspect into the background.   Yet at
the same time with Wilhelm von Humboldt and his
philosophical interests in comparative philology, we find
his brother Alexander giving a large share of his attention to the unknown languages of the New World, of
which he has been called " the scientific discoverer."

46.
Its exact
treatment.

But the real beginnings of an exact treatment of the
problem of speech were laid by one who did not come
under the conscious influence of Herder, though he came
under that of Goethe.   By Johannes Müller it was
carried further, and it was completed by some of his
most illustrious pupils and followers—Donders, Brücke,
Helmholtz, and Czermak of Vienna.   Through the
anatomical and physiological labours of these and other
naturalists, joined to the physical analysis of musical
notes and sounds contained in the great work of
Helmholtz on Acoustics, aided by such instruments as
the laryngoscope or throat-mirror, and the wonderful
inventions of the phonograph and phonautograph, the
organ of speech is now known to be a complicated wind
instrument by which pure notes and an almost infinite
variety of nasal, labial, dental, palatal, guttural, and other
sounds can be produced which form the phonetic ele-

ments of speech. Simultaneously the discovery by Broca, in 1861, of the speech centre in the brain marked an epoch on the physiological side.[1] A new science, called Phonetics or Phonology, has sprung up, and is now universally admitted to have created the modern science of language.[2] In addition to this physiological and physical basis, the superstructure of the science of

47.
Phonetics.

[1] This localisation places the speech centre in "a very circumscribed portion of the cerebral hemispheres, and more especially of the left. This portion is situate on the upper edge of the Sylvian Fissure, opposite the island of Reil, and occupies only the posterior half, probably only the posterior third, of the third frontal convolution" (Broca, 'Bulletins de la Société anatomique,' 1861). The discovery resulted from the examination of the brain of patients who had been afflicted with "aphasia," which is accompanied with "a lesion of the posterior half of the third, left or right, frontal convolution, nearly always—nineteen times out of twenty—of the left convolution." The phenomenon of aphasia has ever since been one of the great psycho-physical problems bringing together the most refined and intricate physiological, psychological, and linguistic analyses. To begin with, we have to distinguish *motor* aphasia and *sensory* aphasia. "Our knowledge of this disease has had three stages: we may talk of the period of Broca, the period of Wernicke, and the period of Charcot. Wernicke (1874) was the first to discriminate those cases in which the patient *cannot even understand* speech from those in which he can understand, only not talk; and to ascribe the former condition to lesion of the temporal lobe. The

condition in question is *word-deafness*, and the disease is *auditory aphasia*. . . . The minuter analysis of the facts in the light of individual differences constitute Charcot's contribution towards clearing up the subject" (James, 'Principles of Psychology,' vol. i. p. 54).

[2] In the modern science of language we have one among the many cases where a historical or philosophical science is becoming an exact science by attaching itself to physics and physiology. On the other side we have the great movement initiated by Darwin in the purely natural sciences, which, as was shown above, relies on the historical collection of facts and the judicious critical sifting of evidence. "It is phonology," says Prof. Sayce ('Introduction to the Science of Language,' 2 vols., 1880, chap. iv.), "which has created the modern science of language, and phonology may therefore be forgiven if it has claimed more than rightfully belongs to it or forgotten that it is but one side and one branch of the master science itself. . . . It is when we pass from the outward vesture of speech to the meaning which it clothes, that the science of language becomes a historical one. The inner meaning of speech is the reflection of the human mind, and the development of the human mind must be studied historically."

language has likewise been stated to be no longer a historical or a philosophical, but to have become a physical, science. It is true that, as with other natural sciences, so also in this case, the morphological, genetic, and biological aspects can be specially studied; also analogies can be drawn betweeen geology and glossology as to their mode of inductive reasoning. The great authority who first took up this novel position was the late Prof. August Schleicher of Jena, and the same has to a great extent been simultaneously adopted by Max Müller in his celebrated 'Lectures on the Science of Language.' It is interesting to note that Schleicher wrote on the 'Morphology of Language' in the same year in which the 'Origin of Species' appeared, and that he recognised very early the importance of Darwin's work for the science of language.[1] This became still more evident on the publication, twelve years later, of the 'Descent of Man,' and of 'The Expression of the

[1] On August Schleicher (1821-68) see a very valuable article in the 'Allgemeine Deutsche Biographie' (vol. xxxi. p. 402 *sqq.*) by Johannes Schmidt. Very different currents of modern thought, such as we shall in the sequel frequently have to represent as opposed to each other, the study of the classical and of the modern languages, of critical and comparative philology, the historical and the exact spirit, Hegelianism and Darwinism—*i.e.*, logical and mechanical evolution —the influence of Grimm, Ritschl, and Bopp, of botany and grammar, combined to generate in this remarkable man the conception of linguistic as a natural science in contradistinction from philology as a historical science. The principal works in which he developed his original view were: 'Die deutsche Sprache' (1860); 'Compendium der vergleichenden Grammatik der indogermanischen Sprachen' (1861); 'Die Darwin'sche Theorie und die Sprachwissenschaft' (1863); and 'Ueber die Bedeutung der Sprache für die Naturgeschichte des Menschen' (1865). Schleicher's ideas have been taken up in France, notably by Abel Hovelacque ('La Linguistique,' 4ème ed., 1857), who says of him that "he had completely liberated himself from metaphysical aspirations" (p. 6). On the one-sidedness of the purely physical theory of language see Sayce, 'Introd. to the Science of Language' (1880), vol. i. p. 76, &c.

Emotions in Man and Animals ' a year after.   These writings did more than any others to impress upon philosophers the genetic or historical view, the existence of an unbroken chain or transition from the lower to the higher and the highest forms of animal structures, and culminated in the well-known expression of Darwin, that " in a series of forms graduating insensibly from some ape-like creature to man as he now exists, it would be impossible to fix at any definite point when the term ' man ' ought to be used." [1]   This dictum has been the theme on which endless variations have been played down to the present day—Prof. Ernest Haeckel's address to the Congress of Zoology at Cambridge in 1898 being the latest summary of the physical aspect of the problem. But the problem has also a psycho-physical side, and this aspect is concentrated in the problem of language.   Even those philologists who, like August Schleicher and Max Müller, look upon the science of language as a natural science, bring in at this point the accumulated and weighty evidence of the historical, psychological, and philosophical researches into the growth and development of human speech and human thought, as absolutely negativing the possibility of a gradual transition from the brute to the human creation.   To the latter, language, which he considers to be the union of definite concepts with definite names, is the Rubicon which cannot be crossed,[2] the chasm which divides that portion of the

48.
The dividing
line between
man and
brute.

1 ' Descent of Man,' 1st ed., vol. i. p. 235.
2 See Max Müller, ' The Science of Thought,' *passim*, notably chap. iv. p. 177, where he quotes and maintains his dictum of 1861 (' Lec-

tures on the Science of Language,' vol. i. p. 403): " Language is our Rubicon, and no brute will dare to cross it."   Referring to Schleicher, he says (p. 164):   " Professor Schleicher, though an enthusiastic

living creation which is capable of an unlimited development and an external realisation of its inner life from
that which has no mental history or development: it is
the point of discontinuity in the physical development.
The study of language in its physical and mental aspects
—*i.e.*, in phonetics and in sematology—affords, according to this view, the only means of penetrating from
outside into the inner world of thought: it is the
psycho-physical problem *par excellence*—the "Science of
Thought."

Inasmuch as in this latest development of psycho-
physics the whole of the accumulated material and
most of the arguments have been drawn from the historical and philological researches of such thinkers as
Schlegel, W. von. Humboldt, Bopp, Grimm, and their
followers, who were without exception trained, not in
the mathematical but in the philosophical schools of
Thought which ruled in the earlier part of our century,
the further consideration of their ideas belongs properly
to that portion of this work which will deal specially
with philosophical thought and its application in such
separate branches as are presented, *inter alia*, by the
historical sciences.

admirer of Darwin, observed once
jokingly, but not without a deep
irony, 'If a pig were ever to say to
me, "I am a pig," it would *ipso
facto* cease to be a pig.' This shows
how strongly he felt that language
was out of the reach of any animal,
and constituted the exclusive or
specific property of man. I do not
wonder that Darwin and other
philosophers belonging to his school
should not feel the difficulty of
language as it was felt by Prof.
Schleicher, who, though a Darwinian, was also one of our best
students of the science of language.
But those who know best what
language is, and still more, what
it presupposes, cannot, however
Darwinian they may be on other
points, ignore the veto which, as
yet, that science enters against the
last step in Darwin's philosophy."

It now only remains for me to sum up in a few words the leading conceptions which the psycho-physical view of nature has forced upon us.   In the last chapter I showed how the study of life has in the course of our century more and more brought out the conviction that life is a continuous, a ubiquitous, and a unique phenomenon; an exhaustive or even a working definition of life being so far hardly possible.   In this chapter we have learnt, by following the psycho-physical lines of research, to distinguish another and peculiar side of the higher forms of living matter, that which is commonly called the mental, inner, or self-conscious side.   This appeared, when viewed externally, as a discontinuous epi-phenomenon—"eine Begleiterscheinung"—of some very complex physiological processes and anatomical arrangements of living matter, and as such it exhibits a property with which we are otherwise not familiar in the visible phenomena of nature—namely, discontinuity.   Viewed externally, the inner phenomena, which we comprise under the term "mind," appear and disappear, their continuity being preserved in association with the permanence of the external substratum or basis to which they are attached, and internally regained by the indefinable property of memory.   But inasmuch as we have not only an external but also an internal knowledge of at least some of these epi-phenomena, we have had forced upon us an entirely different view of this inner life, of mind.   To the inner view there exists in self-conscious beings a centre of relatedness—a special kind of unity which we call individuality or personality; and this inner unity is capable of being externalised or made objective in the mental life of mankind, language being the great instrument by which this is accomplished. In this external or objective existence—which, however, is only intelligible to beings which form a part of it—that continuity is regained which in the existence of every individual is continually being interrupted and in danger of being lost. Psycho-physical research reveals to us the existence of a unity different from that visible in merely external or physical nature,—a centred unity which is something else than the sum of parts in a mathematical whole. Through this process of centralisation and externalisation there has been formed in the physical world, or in nature, a new world—the world of mind, which is continually growing in contrast to the former, which only changes without increasing or losing its two constituents, matter and energy.

This new world within the old one, this creation of man, forms indeed a portion of nature—it is the microcosm in the macrocosm. It might be investigated by the usual methods of exact research; and the science of anthropology, with its many branches, proposes to study it in the same way as natural history in modern times has studied the social life of certain animals, such as bees, ants, and beavers. Inasmuch, however, as the exact methods do not lead very far, and have continually to appeal to the interpretations of psychology, gained by personal experience and introspective methods,[1] it seems

---

[1] Prof. E. Hering ('Ueber das Gedächtniss als eine allgemeine Funktion der organischen Materie,' Vienna, 1870) says : "So long as the physiologist is only a physicist he stands in a one-sided position to the organic world. This one-sidedness is extreme but quite

more practical to range the whole of these researches
within that great realm of thought which starts with a
distinct recognition of conscious individual life as its
source and centre. As such, in fact, these researches
have been till quite recently carried on, and the main
lines of their recent development belong accordingly to
philosophic as distinguished from scientific or exact
thought.

The three great facts, however, which even the exact
treatment of mental phenomena has impressed upon us
—namely, the existence of centralised material systems,
termed "individuals," the discontinuity of their inner
life as viewed from outside, and the phenomenon of its
growing external manifestation — have driven natural
philosophers to form some explanation, or at least to
venture upon a definition of this hidden principle,
which shows itself in the highest forms of living matter,
and which, though discontinuous to the external observer,
acquires in the aggregate of human society a continuous
and ever growing reality and development.   Two dis-

50.
The three
facts im-
pressed by
psycho-
physics.

legitimate. As the crystal to
the mineralogist, the vibrating
string to the student of acoustics,
so also the animal, and even man,
is to the physicist only a piece of
matter.   That the animal experiences pleasure and pain—that with
the material life of the human
frame are connected the joys and
sorrows of a soul and the vivid
intellectual life of a consciousness ;
this cannot change the animal and
human body for the physical
student into anything other than
it is — a material complex subject
to the unalterable laws which
govern also the stone and the
substance of the plant, a material
complex whose external and internal movements are causally as
rigidly connected amongst each
other, and with the movements
of the environment, as the working of a machine is with the
revolution of its wheels (p. 4). . . .
Thus the physiologist as physicist.
But he stands behind the scene,
and while he painfully examines
the mechanism and the busy doings
of the actors behind the drop-
scenes, he misses the sense of the
whole which the spectator easily
recognises from the front.   Could
the physiologist not, for once,
change his position ? " (p. 5.

tinct views have been evolved by modern science on this matter.

The one emphasises the fact of the discontinuity of mental—*i.e.*, conscious—life, regards it as an ultimate fact, as a mystery beyond which we cannot travel. This idea presents itself in various forms, and has been notably insisted on—with very varying philosophical inferences—by Du Bois-Reymond in Germany, by Mr A. R. Wallace, and quite recently by the late Prof. St George Mivart in England.

The other takes refuge in the hypothesis of unconscious or subconscious mental life, and again with very different philosophical inferences assumes that all physical existence has an inner side which only under certain favourable conditions rises into the light of self-knowledge or consciousness. The late W. K. Clifford's "mind-stuff" theory, as also the speculations of Fechner and of Prof. Haeckel, are types of this view, which has been consistently and connectedly elaborated in Hartmann's 'Philosophy of the Unconscious.'

These speculations can be summed up under the title "The Creed of Science," and as such will occupy us later on in one of the chapters on the Philosophical Thought of the century.

By many natural philosophers it is felt that the time has not yet come to arrive scientifically at any definite conclusions on these last questions. Sufficient facts have not been collected; or even if collected, they have not yet been classified and tabulated. This is especially the case with the vast materials referring to the collective life of mankind. Leibniz had in his time foretold the

51. Transition to statistics.

necessity of extensive statistical information before building theories.   In one instance, that of language, his advice was followed with signal success.

But even some of the purely physical sciences, like meteorology, are still almost entirely limited to statistical information.

Statistics have thus become a very important department of knowledge, and before taking leave of the exact lines of thought, it will be well to note more precisely the part which these have played in our age, as also the methods by which they proceed.   This will be the object of the next chapter, which will accordingly deal with the Statistical View of Nature.

CHAPTER XII.

ON THE STATISTICAL VIEW OF NATURE.

I HAVE now treated of the several grand and general aspects under which the objects of nature can be scientifically regarded, and have tried to show how these aspects, not unknown to former ages, have nevertheless, in the course of the nineteenth century, become more definite, and accordingly more useful, as means for describing, measuring, and, in many cases, predicting phenomena. It is true that the two last chapters, which dealt with the phenomena of Life and Mind, had to take notice of a principle or of principles which have hardly yet received any scientific definition at all, and which in the progress of the sciences which deal with them have played rather a negative part. It has been mainly by eliminating the conceptions of life and of mind as special agencies, factors, or entities that the scientific study of living and conscious beings has progressed; by showing more and more how an accurate and useful knowledge of much of their nature and behaviour can be gained with the aid of the methods adopted in other scientific inquiries, which we may call mechanical.

1. Life and Mind as limiting conceptions.

Scientific inquiry in biology and psycho-physics has thus advanced on the lines indicated in the earlier chapters, where it was shown how several positive scientific conceptions have been gained, defined, and applied. These conceptions are all generalisations based upon definite observable facts of nature, such as attraction, atomic constitution, motion (rectilinear, periodic, and rotational), energy, form, and change of form,[1] and they have given rise to great branches of science, containing special methods of thought and reasoning. They have all shown themselves accessible, in a greater or less degree, to mathematical treatment, and have consequently been the means of introducing the exact scientific spirit into large fields of research, into ever

---

[1] The statement in the text is not strictly correct ; for of the six definite conceptions mentioned we really, even in single cases, only see two exemplified—viz., motion and form. Neither attraction, nor the atom, nor energy, nor development is, even in single cases, observable, though, with the exception of energy, they are very early and very familiar abstractions. This remark may suggest that motion and form are, at least for the present, the simplest and most obvious conceptions into which we can analyse or resolve all external observations, and that consequently kinetics and morphology may be the fundamental sciences, the first in natural philosophy, the latter in natural history or biology in the widest sense. That a kinetic view will gradually supervene in natural philosophy is, I think, generally admitted. It seems less generally conceded that morphology will supervene in biology ; especially as all the rage is just now for evolution and development. But as development must start from something, it is likely that it will lead back to morphology. As tending in this direction I read the expositions of Lotze, Claude Bernard, and the "Organicists." Organisation must mean a certain arrangement, and arrangement is ultimately the same as order, structure, or form. It may mean something more — viz., unity or centredness ; but this is a conception not capable of a purely mechanical or geometrical definition ; we know of it only through introspection. A great deal has been written on Morphology and Morphogenesis by that very suggestive author, Hans Driesch ; see a list of his writings, *supra*, p. 456 note. I here only refer to them ; for, being myself unable clearly to apprehend his main drift, I hesitate to quote him as confirming the argument of this note. The reader must judge for himself.

widening circles of phenomena and events. This has
been most decidedly the case with the sciences in which
the law or formula of gravitation has become the leading
principle. As we advanced on the other lines of
thought, marked by the conceptions of atomism, of
the various forms of motion and of energy, this subjection to precise formulæ became less perfect, more
complicated and hypothetical, whilst the study of the
typical forms of natural objects, and even more of
their genesis and developments, opened out a field
for much conjecture and fanciful reasoning, amid which
little more than the general outlines of a definite theory
could be established. Lastly, in applying these various
conceptions to the phenomena of the living and self-
conscious creation, we have struck upon the limiting
ideas of life and mind, of which, from a purely external
point of view, little more can be said than that they
indicate to us the existence among natural objects of a
unity of a different kind from that which we can understand mechanically as the sum of many parts. In the
higher forms this unity revealed itself to us through the
analogy of our own inner life as a peculiar kind of
centralisation, discontinuous when viewed from outside,
but possessing, when viewed from another side, a continuity, connectedness, and capacity of unlimited growth
of its own which is the special object of the psychological and historical sciences. These characteristics
belong to the great realm of philosophical as distinguished from exact scientific thought.

2.
Results of
abstract
science.

Before entering on this other great branch of our
subject, we may well pause for a moment and cast

a general and unbiassed glance at the world outside, leaving our study, our observatory, our laboratory, our dissecting- or our measuring-room, and ask ourselves the simple question, By the work carried on in these various secluded places, in the "sapientum templa serena," how much of the world outside have we really learnt to comprehend, or even only to describe and picture to ourselves correctly and completely? The answer is hardly encouraging. The first thing we notice in stepping out of our door is a phenomenon still as incalculable as it has ever been, and yet bound up with the enjoyment of our lives and the success of our work as much as ever—the weather. What do we know of it which is practically reliable and useful? The reply must be, "Next to nothing." Some general astronomical and some more detailed physical and chemical relations permit us to describe a few general meteorological and a few recurring seasonable events, but scarcely with more practical detail and certainty than the unscientific ancients or the untaught children of nature of to-day. We know in general the cause of storms, of changes of temperature, of the seasons, of rain, hail, drought, and cold, but we do not know much more of the exact when and where of these various changes than did our forefathers. The natural atmosphere and climate which surround us are still elements of conjecture and uncertainty.

Assume, however, that we go a step further, and having accustomed ourselves to take the weather, good or bad, as it is, enter into the artificial atmosphere and surroundings of practical life, of industry, trade, and

commerce, of politics and society, in which most of us
have to spend the larger portion of the working hours of
our existence.   We can again put the question, What do
we know with certainty of the changes and vicissitudes
of this artificial atmosphere which surrounds us; what
of the chances of a fall or rise in prices, of increased
or lessened demand, of impending labour troubles, of the
risks even of famine, fire, shipwreck, disease, or war?
Again we may say that in general we know the proximate causes, natural or artificial, which may bring them
about, but the exact when and where of their occurrence
is so slightly known to us that such knowledge is of little,
if of any, practical value, and proceeds, moreover, where
it exists, more from general good sense and practical
experience than from the discoveries of science.   Indeed,
the latter have, through the wonderful applications in
the inventions of arts and crafts, tended to make our
artificial atmosphere more complex, liable to more rapid
and more drastic changes, and accordingly its features
less permanent and less calculable and reliable.

3.
Uncertainty
in the con-
crete.
Thus, in spite of the wonderful increase of scientific
knowledge and the general diffusion of scientific thought
in the course of the century, uncertainty is still the
main and dominant characteristic of our life in nature
and society; the atmosphere and climate of each are as
fickle and changeable, as incalculable and unreliable, as
ever.   Neither the great law of gravitation nor the
fixed proportions of chemistry, neither the intricate
doctrine of undulations nor the conception of energy,
neither the knowledge of typical forms of nature nor that
of their orderly evolution, has, in the hands of those who

govern, regulate, and fashion the practical work of life
and society, become an instrument of personal use and
daily importance.   Statesmen, legislators, organisers of
men, captains of industry, contractors, practical engineers,
colonisers, pioneers, and leaders of all kinds are still
mostly ignorant of these scientific ideas.   They regard
them from a distance, themselves relying mainly on
common-sense, on personal experience, or on the innate
but indefinable impulses of individual genius; professional, scientific knowledge is only one, and hardly the
most important, of the many agencies with which they
deal and which they have to take into account.

And yet, in spite of this fact that the ordinary routine
of life is a very different process from the ways of
science, we must admit that the scientific spirit very
largely pervades the business of to-day.   You cannot
enter any commercial, shipping, or general trading office
without being struck with the number of carefully prepared charts, tables, and statistical registers of all kinds
of curves showing the rise and fall of prices, the production and consumption, the stocks and values of metals,
coal, grain, chemicals, cotton, and produce of every kind;
and in quite recent years, not only material things of all
sorts, but the intangible thing called energy—after
supplanting the older term horse-power—has become the
subject of elaborate tabular and graphical registration.
The streets of even the smaller towns in every civilised
country show, besides the sign-boards of shops, offices,
and banks, an increasing array of insurance firms, whose
whole business depends on elaborate calculations, based
on long tables of births, deaths, marriages, shipwrecks,

4.
Scientific
spirit in
business.

and other casualties.   The daily newspapers bring us
weather charts with isothermic, isobaric, and other lines,
on which they found weather predictions or storm
warnings.   Surely, if counting, measuring, and calculating are the elementary processes of the scientific method,
it must be admitted that the latter has permeated our
practical life to an enormous extent.   Thus the question
can be asked, If the calculating spirit is so general, how
does it come about that in its application to life and
commerce it has led to so much grasp but to so little
certainty; whereas in science itself it has led to so much
actual and reliable knowledge?   How does its application
in practice differ from that in theory?   The answer to
this question is not far to seek, and it will introduce us to
a special branch of science, to a special form of scientific
thought which again is, if not a creation of the nineteenth
century, yet one of its characteristic developments.

That which everywhere oppresses the practical man
is the great number of things and events which pass
ceaselessly before him, and the flow of which he cannot
arrest.   What he requires is the grasp of large numbers.
The successful scientific explorer has always been the man
who could single out some special thing for minute and
detailed investigation, who could retire with one definite
object, with one fixed problem into his study or laboratory and there fathom and unravel its intricacies, rising
by induction or divination to some rapid generalisation
which allowed him to establish what is termed a law
or general aspect from which he could view the whole
or a large part of nature.   The scientific genius can
" stay the moment fleeting "; he can say to the object

of his choice, " Ah, linger still, thou art so fair "; he can fix and keep the star in the focus of his telescope, or protect the delicate fibre and nerve of a decaying organism from succumbing to the rapid disintegration of organic change. The practical man cannot do this; he is always and everywhere met by the crowd of facts, by the relentlessly hurrying stream of events. What he requires is grasp of numbers, leaving to the professional man the knowledge of detail. Thus has arisen the science of large numbers or statistics,[1] and the many methods of which it is possessed. It will form the subject of the present chapter.

5.
The science
of large
numbers.

[1] Gottfried Achenwall (1719-1772) is commonly termed the "father" of statistics. This, however, is hardly correct, either in relation to teaching or to the practical part of the subject, or even so far as the name is concerned. In connection with administration statistics existed in antiquity. They were taught by the celebrated professor, Conring, the elder contemporary and rival of Leibniz, and the name occurs in the seventeenth century in the ' Microscopium statisticum, quo status imperii Romano - Germanici repræsentatur auct. Heleno Politano ' (1672). By Achenwall and his successor, Ludwig August Schlözer (1735-1809), statistics were treated in connection with history. The latter says, " Statistics are history standing still, and history is statistics put in motion." See on this subject, Wegele, ' Geschichte der deutschen Historiographie ' (München, 1885), p. 793 ; also Roscher, ' Geschichte der National-Oekonomik ' (ibid., 1874), p. 466. A very valuable and exhaustive account of the etymology and gradual change of meaning of the words "statist" and statistics will be found in Dr V. John, ' Geschichte der Statistik,' 1. Theil. (Stuttgart, 1884), pp. 3 - 14. He divides the history of the subject down to Quetelet into that of the " German University Statistics," following in the lines of Conring, Achenwall, and Schlözer, also called the " Göttingen School," and that of statistics as an exact, an enumerative science, which he calls the modern science of statistics. It appears that in English also the two meanings of the word are exemplified in the older use of the term "statist" by Shakespeare (" Hamlet," v. 2. ; " Cymbeline," ii. 4.) and Webster, in which sense it meant simply "statesman"; and the modern title ' Statist,' for a statistical and financial periodical. Nor must we forget that England has in her ' Liber judiciarius seu censualis Willelmi I., regis Angliæ,' called ' Domesday - book ' (1083 - 86), as David Hume says, " the most valuable piece of antiquity possessed by any nation " (' Hist. of England,' chap. iv.)

The grasp of large numbers, the methodical array of figures and the registration of events, would in itself be of little use were it not for a fundamental assumption which appeals to common-sense and has been confirmed by science, though it is hardly anywhere expressly stated —namely, the belief in a general order, in a recurrent regularity or a slow but continuous change and orderly development of the things and events of the world. Science, in the different aspects which we have so far passed in review, tries to give a definite expression to this general Order, to this all-pervading rule and regularity. Statistics and the practical use of them limit themselves to the bare fact that such order and regularity do exist, though the formula or reason for them may be unknown or unknowable. It may also be well to note that this belief in a general order is common to all schools of thought, be they ancient or modern, pagan or Christian, religious or scientific, optimist or pessimist.

6.
Belief in
general
order.

The dictum, "est modus in rebus," is the fundamental axiom of all thought and all practice; and the statistical view of nature, which merely puts into form and figure this general axiom or truism, has accordingly been appealed to as much by those who uphold a divine order of things as by others who insist on a natural or mechanical one. In the school of Quetelet, through whose influence statistical knowledge has been so greatly furthered in the course of our century, the regular recurrence of events and the stability of large numbers has been sometimes used as the basis for a fatalistic and pessimistic view, whereas nearly a hundred years before Quetelet, statistics had been elaborated by the Pastor Süssmilch in Prussia, in a celebrated book bearing the title 'On the Divine Order,' with a tendency towards optimism, and as a proof of an overruling Providence.[1]

Although it is generally admitted by writers on statistics that in the narrower sense of the word they have existed ever since the existence of governments which required to know the number of their population, the natural resources of the country, and its means of subsistence or defence, there is a general opinion current that what we now call the statistical methods in science and in practice were introduced, or at least expressly recommended, by Lord Bacon under the name of the "Method of Instances." This method, which consisted in a kind of tabulating of numbers of facts referring to any special subject under investigation, has been criticised

7.
Bacon's "Method of Instances."

---

[1] The difference seems to narrow itself down to this, that one class of writers refers everything to a physical, the other to a moral, order. M. Maurice Block, an eminent writer on statistics, discusses this question, passing a number of modern authors under review in the fifth chapter, § 3, of his excellent 'Traité théorique et pratique de Statistique' (2me éd., Paris, 1886). Referring to the theological statistician, A. von Oettingen, and comparing him with Quetelet, he says (p. 146): "Sous certains rapports, l'opinion de M. le professeur de théologie Alexandre d'Œttingen, pourra paraître l'opposée de celle de Quetelet, mais elle nous semble en différer beaucoup moins que le savant professeur ne le croit. . . . Nous pouvons caractériser en peu de mots ce que MM. d'Œttingen et Quetelet ont de commun et comment ils diffèrent : ils ont de commun le fond de la science ; ils constatent l'un et l'autre la régularité du mouvement des faits ; ils ne diffèrent que par l'interprétation : Quetelet voit des lois naturelles là où M. le professeur d'Œttingen voit des lois morales instituées par Dieu. Aussi l'un nomme-t-il son livre Physique sociale, et l'autre Éthique sociale. M. d'Œttingen est un croyant qui aime à s'appuyer sur la science. Il dit, page 13 de la première édition : ' Dans les sciences comme dans la religion, ce que l'homme invente ne peut être que faux, tandis que les vérités qu'il découvre, sont uniquement des faits ou des lois qui rayonnent du Créateur.'" The reconciliation of either physical or moral order with the existence of freewill is not a statistical but a philosophical problem.

by writers like Whewell, von Liebig, Stanley Jevons, and many others, and shown to be of very doubtful value; the example given by Bacon himself—the research into the nature of heat—being especially unfortunate and badly chosen. In spite of this, it is noteworthy that, up to quite recent times, the Baconian method is continually referred to, mainly by writers who are desirous of introducing what they call the exact methods of research into other sciences than those of external nature. A good example of this kind is given by Walter Bagehot, and as it serves to make an important point more intelligible than a general statement would, I will here give it in full. He speaks of the Enumerative, or, as he calls it, the "All-case method," and then continues: "A very able German writer [1] has said of a great economical topic—banking—' I venture to suggest that there is but one way of arriving at such knowledge and truth, namely, a thorough investigation of the facts of the case: by the facts I mean not merely such facts as present themselves to so-called practical men in the common routine of business, but the facts which a complete historical and statistical inquiry would develop. When such a work shall have been accomplished, German economists may boast of having restored the principle of banking—that is to say, of German banking, but not even then of banking in general. To set forth principles of banking in general, it will be necessary to master in the same way the facts of English, Scottish, French, and American banking — in short of every

[1] Prof. Cohn in 'Fortnightly Review,' Sept. 1873.

country where banking exists. . . . The only, but let us add also the safe, ground of hope for political economy, is following Bacon's exhortation to recommence afresh the whole work of economic inquiry. In what condition would chemistry, physics, geology, zoology be, and other branches of natural science which have yielded such prodigious results, if their students had been linked to their chains of deduction from the assumptions and speculations of the last century?'" To this Bagehot replies: "The method which Mr Cohn suggests was tried in physical science and failed. And it is very remarkable that he should not have remembered it as he speaks of Lord Bacon, for the method which he suggests is exactly that which Lord Bacon himself followed, and owing to the mistaken nature of which he discovered nothing. The investigation into the nature of heat in the 'Novum Organum' is exactly such a collection of facts as Mr Cohn suggests, but nothing comes of it. As Mr Jevons well says, Lord Bacon's notion of scientific method was that of a kind of scientific book-keeping. Facts were to be indiscriminately gathered from every source and posted in a kind of ledger, from which would emerge in time a clear balance of truth. It is difficult to imagine a less likely way of arriving at discoveries." [1]

[1] 'The Postulates of English Political Economy' (1885), p. 17, &c. He further remarks: "If we wait to reason till the 'facts' are complete, we shall wait till the human race has expired. I think that Mr Cohn, and those who think with him, are too 'bookish' in this matter. They mean by having all the 'facts' before them, having all the printed facts, all the statistical tables. But what has been said of nature is true of commerce. 'Nature,' says Sir Charles Lyell, 'has made it no part of her concern to provide a record of her operations for the use of men'; nor does trade either — only the

In fact, the eight chapters of this work which have dealt with the various abstract views from which natural phenomena have been considered in recent times, form an elaborate refutation of the so-called Baconian, of the enumerative or "all case," method. It was the light of the idea which brought life and order into the "rudis indigestaque moles" of badly collected facts, and in many cases even led for the first time to their useful and intelligent enumeration. But now we come to a further important question. Allowing that in certain large but nevertheless secluded spheres of science a few general ideas have been found to apply and work wonders of calculation, prediction, and useful application, how about those complicated phenomena which form our natural and social environment, and where so far no scientific formula has proved powerful or comprehensive enough? Are all these elaborate enumerations and graphical representations in meteorology, in sociology, commerce, industry, and finance, to which we have instinctively and increasingly had recourse during the whole of the century, of no value? Is no useful

smallest of fractions of actual transactions is set down so that investigation can use it. Literature has been called the 'fragment of fragments,' and in the same way statistics are the 'scrap of scraps.' In real life scarcely any one knows more than a small part of what his neighbour is doing, and he scarcely makes public any of that little, or of what he does himself. A complete record of commercial facts, or even of one kind of such facts, is the completest of dreams. You might as well hope for an entire record of human conversation."

Stanley Jevons ('Principles of Science,' Preface, p. vii), says: "Within the last century a reaction has been setting in against the purely empirical procedure of Francis Bacon, and physicists have learnt to advocate the use of hypotheses. I take the extreme view of holding that Francis Bacon, although he correctly insisted upon constant reference to experience, had no correct notions as to the logical method by which, from particular facts, we educe laws of nature."

result to spring from them ? Had they been conducted under the influence of no useful general idea, our answer would indeed have to be in the negative. But if, as practice shows, they have been of use, if, in fact, they prove to be in many cases quite indispensable, we may ask, What is the idea, the abstract thought, which dominates them ? I will give the answer at once and then fix the aspect with which the present chapter has to deal. It is the conception and doctrine of averages.

8.
General idea underlying enumeration.

Although to the general reader nothing may seem to be simpler than a process of counting and of registration, the science of statistics, the systematic collection of large numbers, and the fixing of averages, is comparatively young : it dates from the beginning of the seventeenth century, when Sully in France, followed by Richelieu and Colbert, had organised what may be called the first statistical bureau.[1] It emanated from the same spirit which called into existence the Paris Academy of Sciences. Characteristically for the two other nations with which we are mainly concerned in this history, the

9.
Doctrine of averages.

[1] M. Block (*loc. cit.*, p. 25) says : "En France Sully avait déjà organisé, vers 1602, un *cabinet complet de politique et de finances*, qui peut être considéré comme le premier bureau de statistique. Les rapports que Sully demandait embrassaient l'armée, la marine, les finances et un grand nombre de branches de l'administration, et le résultat de ses investigations se trouve exposé dans l'ouvrage qui a été souvent réimprimé sous le titre de 'Mémoires de Sully.' Richelieu et Colbert se sont également fait adresser des rapports, auxquels on a puisé, dans ces derniers temps, bien des éléments utiles à l'histoire et que la statistique pourrait également utiliser." The Romans, who in antiquity may be regarded as the forerunners of the French in administrative ability and business-like conduct of State affairs, seem also to have developed an extensive system of registration. The question has been fully treated by the late Prof. Hildebrand of Jena in the 'Jahrbuch für Nationale Ökonomie und Statistik' (1866), in an article entitled "Die Amtliche Bevölkerungs - statistik im alten Rom."

10.
Statistics in
France, Ger-
many, and
England.
labour of statistics was taken up in Germany by the
Universities, whereas in England it fell to the lot chiefly
of a single person—the celebrated Sir William Petty,
the creator of the term " Political Arithmetic." Thus, as
in science generally, so in statistics, France marched
ahead with her systematic and administrative genius;
Germany followed in the person of Professor Conring,[1]
who introduced the matter as a subject of university
teaching; whilst Sir William Petty[2] wrote his essay
with the practical object of disproving an opinion then
much current in England, and which has periodically
cropped up in the writings of journalists at home and
abroad—the threatened decline of the English nation.

[1] Hermann Conring (1606-81),
Professor of Medicine and Philosophy at Helmstädt, lectured on
"Staatskunde, Notitia Rerum Pub-
licarum," from about 1660.

[2] About the same time when
lectures on "The Science of the
State" were begun in Germany by
Conring, Sir William Petty (1623-
87) in England, one of the founders
of the Royal Society, occupied himself for practical reasons with similar
subjects, collecting his views in a
tract called ' Political Arithmetic '
about the year 1677, besides con-
tributing various papers to the
' Philosophical Transactions ' and
publishing several ' Essays' (1681-
86). The ' Political Arithmetic '
would have been printed, but for
the French policy of Charles II., to
whom it was presented in manuscript. It was not published till
1690, after the author's death, on a
permission "given at the Court
of Whitehall on the seventh day
of November," by Lord Shel-
burne, the son of the author.
In the preface, he characteristically says: "I have thought fit to
examine the following Persuasions;
which I find too current in the
world, and too much to have
affected the minds of some, to the
prejudice of all—viz., That *the
rents of land are generally fallen;*
that therefore, and for many other
reasons, *the whole kingdom grows
every day poorer and poorer.* That
formerly it abounded with gold;
but now, *there is a great scarcity,
both of gold and silver.* That *there
is no trade, nor employment for the
people;* and yet that *the land is
under-peopled.* That *taxes have
been many and great.* That *Ireland and the Plantations in
America, and other additions to
the Crown, are a burden to England.* That *Scotland is of no advantage.* That trade, *in general,
doth lamentably decay.* That *the
Hollanders are at our heels, in the
race for naval power; the French
grow too fast upon both; and appear
so rich and potent, that it is but their
clemency that they do not devour
their neighbours.*"

And as in science, so also in statistics, Germany in time followed the example of France by introducing organisations similar to that of the " Cabinet complet de politique et de finances " of Sully. It was notably during the reign of Frederick the Great that the population statistics were regularly and systematically collected in Prussia, this enterprise being greatly stimulated by the publication of J. P. Süssmilch's [1] ' Treatise on the Divine Order.' In England—with a notable exception to be mentioned immediately—the line of research opened out by Sir William Petty was not followed up, and Mac-Culloch, when publishing, at the beginning of our cen-

[1] Johann Peter Süssmilch (1707-67) published, in the year 1741, a book with the following title : ' Die göttliche Ordnung in den Veränderungen des menschlichen Geschlechts, aus der Geburt, dem Tode und der Fortpflanzung desselben erwiesen von Johann Peter Süssmilch, Prediger beym hochlöblichen Kalcksteinischen Regiment. Nebst einer Vorrede Herrn Christian Wolffens.' The book, as well as the author, was for a long time but little appreciated ; for although the former was dedicated to Frederick the Great, and must presumably, to judge from the several editions which appeared, have been made use of in the statistical labours of the Prussian administration, the author, not having been connected with any university, had, for a long time, little influence on the so-called "university school" of statistics. In the course of the last fifty years, all prominent writers on statistics, such as Wappäus, Roscher, von Oettingen, Knapp, and V. John, in Germany, M. Block and others in France, as also Italian writers on statistics, have taken increased interest in the book. Dr V. John ('Geschichte der Statistik,' vol. i. p. 241, &c.) gives an exhaustive analysis of the work. He calls the author "the first statistician in the modern sense," the precursor of Quetelet, and says, moreover, "It is easily explained how the philosopher Süssmilch would vanish into the background as soon as the conception of the encyclopædists, that only matter in motion exists and no mind, came to be generally accepted, and that the politician Süssmilch should utterly disappear in the turmoil of the French Revolution." Von Oettingen, who, on the other side, agrees in accepting with Süssmilch the existence of a Divine or moral order, says of the latter, that "he has become, through his magnificent labours, the founder of the science which we now call moral statistics," inasmuch as he, "for the first time, recognised the intrinsic regularity in the apparently most accidental human phenomena and actions, and tried to establish it by inductive methods " (' Moralstatistik,' 3rd ed., 1882, p. 21). That he was known to Herder and appreciated by him, we saw supra, p. 536 note.

tury, his 'Statistical Account of the British Empire,' had hardly any similar work to refer to during the whole of the eighteenth century.

The exception just referred to was "The Tables of Mortality," which date back to the middle of the sixteenth century, and in a more regular form to 1603.

They were analysed by John Graunt, captain, in 1661, in a tract with the title 'Natural and Political Observations upon the Bills of Mortality.'[1] Of Graunt's[2] work, M. Maurice Block says that the difficulties of preparing such a table at that time were so great that it might wellnigh be considered a performance of genius.   The invention once made, improvement

[1] The tract was presented to the Royal Society in 1662, and printed by order of the latter in 1665, the author becoming a fellow at the request of the king. V. John gives a full account of the book, and as much of the author as he could collect from the scanty records of him which exist (loc. cit., pp. 161-178). He was born in 1620, was a man of business, and latterly became connected with the Gresham College and with sundry matters pertaining to the administration of the City. He died in 1674. In 1676 a new, sixth, edition of the tract was published by Sir W. Petty, whom both Halley and Evelyn erroneously referred to as the author.

[2] 'Statistique,' p. 194. Süssmilch, a century after Graunt, says that the material for the determination of the 'Divine Order' existed in the parish registers since the time of the Reformation. "But who," he exclaims, "made use of it for this purpose before Graunt? The discovery was just as easy as that of America, but the Columbus was

lacking" (quoted by V. John, loc. cit., p. 177). The author, however, who suggested to Süssmilch the researches which led to the celebrated 'Divine Order,' was not John Graunt, but Dr William Derham (1657-1735), an eminent divine and natural philosopher, who published in 1713 his ' Physico-Theology ; or a Demonstration of the Being and Attributes of God from His Works of Creation,' a book which ran through six editions in ten years, being translated into French and several times into German. This book contained, as Süssmilch himself says, besides numerous notes, a collection of the observations of other English authors on the lists of births, deaths, and marriages. On following up the clue given by it he arrived ultimately at Graunt and Petty, of whom the former had, as he says, broken the ice, whereas Petty had mainly discussed the influence of the changes of population in politics (V. John, 'Statistik,' p. 243).

was easy; the invention was the difficulty. The next great name connected with this subject was the astronomer and mathematician Edmund Halley,[1] who had before him, in addition to John Graunt's work, the figures of birth and mortality during the five years 1686 to 1691 collected by Kaspar Neumann for the city of Breslau, capital of the province of Silesia. Tables of mortality, based upon several thousands of life annuities, were prepared in Holland by order of the Grand Pensioner, John de Witt, and used in 1671 as the basis for a loan in the form of annuities.[2] The growing practice of life insurance, as is well known, attaches a great interest to these tables of mortality, which have been slowly perfected in the course of the last hundred and fifty years; it having been reserved for the labours

[1] For a long time is was not known how Halley came into possession of Kaspar Neumann's mortality-tables; but, in recent times, mainly through examination of the local records of the city of Breslau by Bergius and others, and notably by the aid of S. Grätzer ('Edmund Halley und Kaspar Neumann,' Breslau, 1883), it has become almost certain that Neumann's registers were communicated to the Royal Society by no less a person than Leibniz, who corresponded with Neumann on the one side as well as with the secretaries of the Royal Society on the other. Some of the original documents have been traced in the archives of the Society by Dr Bond and Prof. Burdon Sanderson. It is well known that Leibniz himself attached great importance to accurate statistical knowledge of all kinds, and considered the collection of such to be one of the main duties of the various academies which he planned or founded.

[2] "Le grand pensionnaire de Hollande, Jean de Witt, se fondant sur les calculs de probabilités enseignés par Chrétien Huygens, se servit, comme éléments d'observation, des résultats constatés sur quelques milliers de rentiers viagers. Il présenta sa table aux états généraux le 25 avril 1671, pour servir de base à un emprunt fait sous la forme d'annuités viagères. Cette table citée par M. de Baumhauer, se trouve dans les registres des états de Hollande, année 1671" (Block, loc. cit., p. 196). A translation of this document appeared in 'Contributions to the History of Insurance' by F. Hendriks, 'Ass. Mag.,' vol. ii., 1852.

of quite recent writers [1] to place the whole matter upon a thoroughly scientific basis. But it is not these necessary technical refinements that interest us most at present; rather let us take note how the needs of governments, as well as the uncertainty and risks of life, have automatically led to the definition and study of three distinct statistical conceptions, which in our age govern a very large part of all our practical enterprises. These three conceptions are the probability of future events based upon long series of past experiences, the idea of reducing or averaging risks by "amicable" co-operation, and the "equitable" distribution of the burdens of such co-operation according to the individual units who co-operate. [2]   It will at

12.
Probability,
Co-opera-
tion, Equit-
able Distri-
bution.

[1] It is generally admitted that Prof. G. F. Knapp created a kind of era in the more rigorous mathematical treatment of the subject by his various publications, dating from the year 1868 with his tract 'Ueber die Ermittelung der Sterblichkeit aus den Aufzeichnungen der Bevölkerungs - statistik.' M. Block (loc. cit., p. 232) says : "Ce livre a fait une véritable sensation parmi les hommes spéciaux ; non que l'auteur ait apporté beaucoup de nouvelles pierres à l'édifice, mais il a donné à ces pierres une ordonnance, une disposition qui les constituent un monument." In the year 1874 he published his 'Theorie des Bevölkerungswechsels.' Many other writers have followed in the new track, among whom I will only mention Becker, Zeuner, and Lexis. The graphical method is largely employed by these authors, amongst whom Zeuner resorts to a representation in three dimensions with some very elegant results. See his 'Abhandlungen zur mathematischen

Statistik' (Leipzig, 1869). A historical and critical review of these and older writings is given in the last-named work of Knapp, p. 53, &c. See also Prof. Lexis's ' Einleitung in die Theorie der Bevölkerungs-statistik' (Strasburg, 1875).

[2] This is not the place to discuss the social and moral aspects of co-operation, which by future historians will possibly be looked upon as one of the very few novel political ideas which our century has evolved or at least elaborated in a practical form ; the older co-operative attempts, such as were made under the influence of the ideals of the great Revolution by Fourier, Saint Simon, and Babeuf in France, and by Robert Owen in this country, not having contained the elements of permanent success. These elements seem to belong almost exclusively to the line of development started by the "Rochdale Pioneers."

once be seen how all arrangements which are based upon these three conceptions — viz., probability, co-operation, and equitable distribution — lead us away from the study of individual cases to that of totals and averages; how they merge the interests of single persons and the peculiarities of single cases in those of the aggregate of a large number and the properties of the average event or the "mean" man. Their value and success depend on the consideration and participation of large numbers, and they have accordingly only arisen during the latter days which have witnessed the steady growth of modern populations and the bewildering complication of modern business. The moral or social aspect which has simultaneously been evolved during our period does not for the moment concern us. We are concerned at present only with the fact that statistics as the science of large numbers and of averages has been increasingly drawn into use. In fact, we might call our century —in distinction from former centuries—the statistical century.

The necessity of having recourse to elaborate countings, to registrations of births, deaths, and marriages, to lists of exports and imports, to records of consumption and production of food-stuffs and many other items, forced upon those who were entrusted with the gathering and using of these data the observation that all such knowledge is incomplete and inaccurate. Owing to the variability, within certain limits, of recurring events and the errors of counting and registration, we have to content ourselves always with approximation instead of certainty. Error bulks very largely in all statistics, and vitiates them; and as regards coming events, our minds are in a state of expectation rather than of assurance. But events can be more or less probable, errors can be greater or smaller, cumulative or compensatory, and our expectations may be well- or ill-founded. And so there has arisen the

science of Probabilities and of Chances, and the Theory of Error, two subjects intimately interwoven. The former arose in the seventeenth century out of the frivolous or vicious practice of betting and gambling,[1] whilst the latter was founded when astronomical observations accumulated, and the question presented itself how to combine them so as to arrive at the most reliable result. The greatest mathematicians and philosophers, such as Pascal, Huygens, and Leibniz, the Bernoullis, De Moivre, Laplace, Gauss and Poisson, have bestowed much thought on the subject,[2] which has nevertheless been very differently judged—praised beyond measure by some, and ridiculed by others; sometimes pronounced to be merely common-sense put in figures, and then again wrapped up

[1] See *supra*, vol. i. p. 120 *sqq.*

[2] In addition to the references given in vol. i., the following are of importance. The history of the Theory of Probabilities, as stated above, has been written by Isaac Todhunter. This history brings the subject down to the writings of Laplace, whose two works mentioned in the text still remain the two standard works on the science. In quite recent times the history has been written and brought up to date by Prof. Emanuel Czuber in his ' Entwickelung der Wahrscheinlichkeits-Theorie und ihre Anwendungen,' contained in the seventh volume of the ' Jahresbericht der Deutschen Mathematiker Vereinigung' (Leipzig, 1899). The latter work is written on a different principle from that of Todhunter. Whereas Todhunter deals in separate chapters with the work of the foremost mathematicians on this subject, Prof. Czuber gives an independent historical and critical analysis of the different developments of the theory and its applications. Quite recently the same author has published an independent treatise on the subject (Leipzig, 1902).

in appalling mystery.[1] There is, however, no doubt that
the Theory of Probability increasingly pervades scientific
as well as statistical work in our age, and that in the

[1] In spite of the encomium on
the theory of probabilities quoted
in vol. i. p. 123, Sir John Herschel
gave only a qualified adherence to
one of its principal applications
(see 'Brit. Assoc. Rep.,' vol. i. p.
165). The two foremost adverse
critics of the theory were Auguste
Comte in France and John Stuart
Mill in England. In the second
volume of the 'Philosophie Positive' (1st ed., 1835, p. 371) the
former explains why he omitted
to deal with so important a subject
in his mathematical philosophy.
"Le calcul des probabilités ne me
semble avoir été réellement, pour
ses illustres inventeurs, qu'un texte
commode à d'ingénieux et difficiles
problèmes numériques, qui n'en conservent pas moins toute leur valeur
abstraite, comme les théories analytiques dont il a été ensuite l'occasion, ou, si l'on veut, l'origine.
Quant à la conception philosophique sur laquelle repose une telle
doctrine, je la crois radicalement
fausse et susceptible de conduire
aux plus absurdes conséquences.
Je ne parle pas seulement de
l'application évidemment illusoire
qu'on a souvent tenté d'en faire
au prétendu perfectionnement des
sciences sociales : ces essais, nécessairement chimériques, seront car-
actérisés dans la dernière partie de
cet ouvrage" : and in the fourth
volume (1839, p. 512), "La seule
aberration de ce genre . . . c'est
la vaine prétention d'un grand
nombre de géomètres a rendre
positives les études sociales d'après
une subordination chimérique à
l'illusoire théorie mathématique
des chances. . . . Quelque grossière que soit évidemment une
telle illusion, elle était néanmoins

essentiellement excusable, quand
l'esprit éminemment philosophique
de l'illustre Jacques Bernoulli
conçut, le premier, cette pensée
générale, dont la production, à une
telle époque, constituait réellement
le précieux et irrécusable symptôme
du besoin prématuré pour ce temps,
mais qui n'y pouvait être éprouvé
même ainsi que par une intelligence
vraiment supérieure." John Stuart
Mill, in the second volume of his
' Logic,' has devoted a whole chapter
to the subject, in which he corrects
a statement made by him in the
first edition of his book, attributing
a "fundamental fallacy" to the
arguments of Laplace and other
mathematicians, but nevertheless
takes an unfavourable view of the
usefulness of the calculus. In
more recent times the subject has
been exhaustively treated from a
logical point of view by Mr John
Venn in his work, 'The Logic of
Chance' (3rd ed., London, 1888),
and by Stanley Jevons in 'The
Principles of Science' (vol. i. ch. x.)
The doubts with which Mill, and
still more Comte, regarded the
subject, seem to have been dispelled in works on Logic ; and the
increasing use to which the methods
for the correction of error have
been put in many branches of
science have convinced mathematicians of its applicability. The
ninth edition of the ' Ency. Brit.'
contains an excellent article on
"Probabilities" by M. W. Crofton.
Among the clearest and safest
guides in this intricate subject
must be counted the late Prof.
Augustus de Morgan, whose profound treatise in the ' Ency.
Metrop.' (vol. ii.), as well as his
' Essay on Probabilities ' (London,

course of the last hundred years much has been done to
make it more easily understood.

James Bernoulli had already in his celebrated book
which bears the title, 'De arte conjectandi,' promised
to show the application of the mathematical doctrine
of probability to political, moral, and economical subjects,[1] but the fourth and last part of the book which
was to give this, remained unfinished.   It was left to
his successors, notably to Daniel Bernoulli, to take up
this side of the question.   But the first practical statesman who — as we are told by Condorcet[2]—held the

14.
Condorcet.

1838), still rank with the best
that has been written.   Stanley
Jevons sums up his opinion in the
words : "This theory appears to me
the noblest creation of the human
intellect, and it passes my conception how two men possessing such
high intelligence as Auguste Comte
and J. S. Mill could have been
found depreciating it, or even
vainly attempting to question its
validity.   To eulogise the theory
is as needless as to eulogise reason
itself" ('Principles of Science,'
vol. i. p. 227).

[1] James Bernoulli (1654 - 1705)
was the eldest of the celebrated
family of mathematicians.   Daniel,
his nephew, lived half a century
later (1700-82).   The 'Ars Conjectandi' was published posthumously in 1713 by Nicholas, another
nephew of the author.   In a letter
to Leibniz the author says : "Ab-
solvi jam maximam libri partem,
sed deest adhuc præcipua, qua
artis conjectandi principia etiam
ad civilia, moralia, et œconomica
applicare doceo."   Daniel Bernoulli,
as we saw above (vol. i., chap. v. p.
434), was the father of the kinetic
theory of gases, of which more
hereafter.   He was also the first
to make a distinction between

mathematical and moral expectation, — a difference which led
Laplace to distinguish between
"fortune physique" and "fortune
morale," to which reference was
made in connection with Fechner's
psycho-physical measurements.

[2] 'Essai sur l'application de
l'Analyse à la Probabilité des Dé-
cisions, Rendues à la pluralité
des voix' (Paris, 1785) : "Un
grand homme, dont je regretterai
toujours les leçons, les exemples,
et surtout l'amitié, était persuadé
que les vérités des sciences morales
et politiques, sont susceptibles de
la même certitude que celles qui
forment le système des sciences
physiques, et même que les
branches de ces sciences qui, comme
l'astronomie, paroissent approcher
de la certitude mathématique.
Cette opinion lui était chère, parce
qu'elle conduit à l'espérance con-
solante que l'espèce humaine fera
nécessairement des progrès vers le
bonheur et la perfection, comme
elle en a fait dans la connois-
sance de la vérité."   It is evident
from this extract that Condorcet
(1743-94) thought that his friend
Turgot shared his own well-known
opinions as to the unlimited per-
fectibility of the human race.

view that morals and politics might derive the same benefit from the science of calculation as the physical sciences had already experienced, seems to have been Turgot. To show the importance of this view, Condorcet wrote his much quoted but little read essay on the application of analysis to decisions based on the plurality of votes. In his Introduction the author laments that his friend, on whose suggestions he had commenced his work, did not live to see it finished.[1] It would have been interesting to know whether so eminent a practical philosopher as Turgot is considered to have been, would have been encouraged by his friend's specimen of political algebra, or whether he would have held the opinion of Mill, who saw in these " applications of the calculus of probabilities . . . the real opprobrium of mathematics." [2]

[1] (Loc. cit., p. i.) " Si l'humanité n'eût pas eu le malheur, longtemps irréparable, de le perdre trop tôt, cet ouvrage eût été moins imparfait: éclairé par ses conseils, j'aurois vu mieux ou plus loin, et j'aurois avancé avec plus de confiance des principes qui auroient été les siens. Privé d'un tel guide, il ne me reste qu'à faire à sa mémoire l'hommage de mon travail, en faisant tous mes efforts pour le rendre moins indigne de l'amitié dont il m'honoroit."

[2] There is no doubt that the writings of Condorcet, through the useless accumulation of formulæ with very little substance behind them, contributed to bring the whole theory into discredit. Another still more eminent contemporary mathematician, D'Alembert, after having occupied himself at considerable length with problems in probabilities, formed an unfavourable opinion of the usefulness of the calculus. Gouraud (quoted by Todhunter, p. 293) says: "Quant au reste des mathématiciens, ce ne fut que par le silence ou le dédaint qu'il répondit aux doutes que d'Alembert s'était permis d'émettre. Mépris injuste et malhabile où tout le monde avait à perdre et qu'une postérité moins prévenue ne devait point sanctionner." It is interesting to note that Laplace, in his historical account at the end of his ' Essai Philosophique,' does not refer either to Condorcet or to D'Alembert. J. S. Mill (' Logic,' vol. ii. p. 66) says : " It is obvious, too, that even when the probabilities are derived from observation and experiment, a very slight improvement in the data, by better observations, or by taking into fuller consideration the special circumstances of the case, is of more use than the most elaborate application of the calculus to probabil-

So far as the formal part of the subject was concerned, it was left to Laplace to place it on the foundation upon which it has ever since rested. He brought together the ideas of his predecessors, notably of De Moivre, the two Bernoullis, Stirling, Bayes, and Lagrange, as well as his own extensive researches, in his great analytical theory of Probability, which appeared in 1812, and, with several editions and an elaborate introduction, in two subsequent editions during his lifetime. This work has been justly considered a monument of human genius, and stands worthily beside the great 'Mécanique Céleste' of its author. The

ities founded on the data in their previous state of inferiority. The neglect of this obvious reflection has given rise to misapplications of the calculus of probabilities which have made it the real opprobrium of mathematics. It is sufficient to refer to the applications made of it to the credibility of witnesses, and to the correctness of the verdicts of juries." I have already referred to the position which Comte took up. De Morgan, with his usual clearness and wisdom, at the end of his "Theory of Probabilities" (' Ency. Metrop.,' vol. ii. p. 470), whilst reducing to a very narrow province these applications of the calculus of probabilities, says : "There are circumstances connected with the mathematical theory of independent evidence which it may be useful to examine. In this, as in several other preceding investigations, it is not so much our wish to deduce and impose results, as to inquire whether these results really coincide with the methods of judging which our reason, unassisted by exact comparison, has already made us adopt. The use of the process is, that both our theory and our pre-conceptions thus either assist or destroy each other : in the former case we feel able to trust this science for *further directions ;* in the latter, a useful new inquiry is opened. For when we consider the very imposing character of the first principles of the science of probabilities, and the mathematical necessity which connects those simple first principles with their results, we feel convinced that, even on the supposition that the main conclusions of the present treatise are altogether fallacious, there must arise a necessity for investigating the reason why a *methodical* treatment of certain notions should lead to results inconsistent with the *vague* application of them on which we are accustomed to rely. For it must not be imagined that opposition to the principles laid down in this treatise is always conducted on other principles : on the contrary, it frequently happens that it is only a result of themselves obtained without calculation, which is arrayed against arithemetical deduction."

labours of mathematicians since Laplace in the field of probabilities have consisted mainly in commentaries on and simplifications of his expositions, and in a great improvement in the formal methods, due mostly to English workers.[1]   At present we are not interested in the purely mathematical side of the subject, which for some minds has a great fascination, but rather in the question : To what extent have the anticipations of such men as Condorcet, Turgot, and Laplace, as to the practical value of these researches, been realised ? in how far have they proved to be " the happiest supplement to the ignorance and weakness of the human mind " ? [2] This idea, though ridiculed by some, has as often cropped

[1] The problems suggested by the calculus of probabilities gave rise, collaterally, to several important mathematical developments, notably the combinatorial analysis, the calculus of finite differences, and, in the hands of Laplace, the theory of generating function and the recurrent series. A large part of Laplace's great work is taken up with this purely mathematical device.   It has in more recent times been supplanted, especially under the hands of English mathematicians, by the calculus of operations, of which the germ is to be found, according to Laplace. in a suggestion of Leibniz (see ' Essai Philosophique sur les Probabilités,' p. 65).

[2] " La théorie des probabilités n'est, au fond, que le bon sens réduit au calcul : elle fait apprécier avec exactitude ce que les esprits justes sentent par une sorte d'instinct, sans qu'ils puissent souvent s'en rendre compte.   Elle ne laisse rien d'arbitraire dans le choix des opinions et des partis à prendre, toutes les fois que l'on peut, à son moyen, déterminer le choix le plus avantageux. Par là, elle devient le supplément le plus heureux à l'ignorance et à la faiblesse de l'esprit humain. Si l'on considère les méthodes analytiques auxquelles cette théorie a donné naissance, la vérité des principes qui lui servent de base, la logique fine et délicate qu'exige leur emploi dans la solution des problèmes, les établissemens d'utilité publique qui s'appuient sur elle, et l'extension qu'elle a reçue et qu'elle peut recevoir encore, par son application aux questions les plus importantes de la Philosophie naturelle et des sciences morales ; si l'on observe ensuite que dans les choses mêmes qui ne peuvent être soumises au calcul, elle donne les aperçus les plus sûrs qui puissent nous guider dans nos jugemens, et qu'elle apprend à se garantir des illusions qui souvent nous égarent, on verra qu'il n'est point de science plus digne de nos méditations, et qu'il soit plus utile de faire entrer dans le système de l'instruction publique " (loc. cit., p. 273 et seq.)

up again in the course of the century, and is at present occupying the attention of distinguished thinkers. It will be interesting to give some account of these practical applications.

16.
Four applications.

Of these, four notably attract our attention. First, the theory of error, prominently associated with the name of Gauss. Secondly, the writings of Adolphe Quetelet, and the great impetus given by him to statistical research. Thirdly, the peculiar development of the Atomic theory known as the Kinetic theory of gases, which gave to many scientific investigations what Clerk - Maxwell termed the statistical, in opposition to the historical or descriptive, character. Lastly, the Darwinian ideas which deal with the great and increasing numbers of living things, and the changes inherent in their growth and development. These have led to statistical enumerations and registrations which, beginning with Mr Francis Galton's researches into the phenomena of heredity, are at the present moment being continued on special lines by Prof. Karl Pearson.

17.
Theory of
Error.

That Error is subject to law, or, to express it mathematically, to regularity, is a reflection which forced itself upon the attention of thinkers who occupied themselves with the doctrine of chances, and of statisticians who collected registers of large numbers of events. Let special known sources of error be eliminated or allowed for in every instance, there still remains a very large, practically an infinite, number of unknown sources of error which—where we have to do with simple magnitude—may increase or reduce our result by mutually destroying or augmenting each other. The repeated measurement of a physical quantity, of the position of a fixed star; the arrangement of the bullet marks on a target; the grouping of the impressions made on the sand by a stone let fall vertically from the same point at a considerable height; even the countings by a large number of skilled persons of the same number or the estimates of the same distance or height of an object, of the weight of a heap of materials: all these statements will show a certain regularity around the mean number which we consider to be the most probable or correct one. Small errors will be more frequent than large ones; very large ones will be practically absent; and the mean will be the result of a mutual destruction or compensation of many small sources of error acting both ways. Mathematicians, from the time of Lagrange and Bernoulli, have tried to put into a mathematical formula this regularity in the distribution of error; and, since Laplace and Gauss approached the subject from different points of view, they have arrived at a definite analytical expression [1] for the distribution of errors of increasing magnitude around a fictitious centre or mean which is considered in every instance to be the most probable quantity. Practical trials on a very large scale have been made by Bessel, Encke, Quetelet, Faye, and others, and they have in every case yielded a satisfactory approximation to the figure given by the theoretical formula; so that at present little doubt as to its usefulness exists in the minds of those who employ it for the purposes of

This is the well-known " curve of Error."

elaborate calculations in astronomy, geodesy, and in various physical and statistical researches.

Bound up with the theory of Error is the celebrated method of least Squares, first used by Gauss in 1795, published by Legendre in 1805 in his memoir 'On a New Method of Determining the Orbit of a Comet,' and elaborately discussed by Laplace, Gauss, and many subsequent writers to this day.[1] It may be looked upon as an extension or generalisation of the common-sense

[1] In addition to the references given in the notes to pp. 120 and 183 of vol. i., I can now recommend two excellent summary accounts of the history and theory of the method of least squares—the one in Prof. Czuber's 'Bericht,' quoted above (pp. 150 to 224); the other in Prof. Edgeworth's article on "The Law of Error" in the Supplement to the last edition of the 'Ency. Brit.' (vol. xxviii., 1902, p. 280, &c.) Prof. Cleveland Abbe, in a "historical note on the method of least squares" ('American Journal of Mathematics,' 1871), has drawn attention to the fact, that already in 1808 Prof. R. Adrain of New Brunswick had arrived at an expression for the law of error identical with the formula now generally accepted, without knowing of Gauss's and Legendre's researches. See a paper by Prof. Glaisher in the 39th vol., p. 75, of the 'Transactions of the Royal Astronomical Society.' The logical and mathematical assumptions upon which the method is based have been submitted to repeated and very searching criticisms, many rigid proofs having been attempted, and every subsequent writer having, seemingly, succeeded in discovering flaws in the logic of his predecessors. In connection with another subject, I may have occasion to point out how nearly all complicated logical arguments have shown similar weakness, and how, in many cases, the conviction of the correctness or usefulness of the argument comes back to the self-evidence of some common-sense assumption, which cannot be proved, though it may be universally accepted. Many analysts have tried to prove the correctness of the everyday process of taking the arithmetical mean, but have failed. Prof. Czuber says, inter alia (loc. cit., p. 159): "The fact that Gauss, in his first demonstration of the method of least squares, conceded to the arithmetical mean a definite theoretical value, has been the occasion for a long series of investigations concerning the subject, which frequently showed the great acumen of their authors. The purpose aimed at— viz., to show that the arithmetical mean is the only result which ought to be selected as possessing cogent necessity, hereby giving a firm support to the intended proofs, has not been attained, because it cannot be attained. Nevertheless, these investigations have their worth because they afford clear insight into the nature of all average values and into the position which the arithmetical average occupies among them."

method of taking the arithmetical mean in determining
what figure to accept in a number of slightly differing
computations.   Where more than one quantity is to be
determined—for instance, where from a series of observations dotted on a chart the continuous curve which
marks the course of a planet or comet is to be deduced
—the simple method of averaging cannot be applied.
Every set of three complete observations suffices, as
Gauss has shown, to determine the elements or constants of an elliptical orbit.   But astronomers try to
get as many observations as possible, and none of these
is a repetition of the same observation—as, for instance, are the repeated weighings of a substance in
chemistry, of the measurings of a length in surveying,
or the counting of a number in statistics: on the contrary, each is the independent ascertainment of definite
positions in a moving object.   It is clear that the
method of averaging must be more general than the
common-sense method of taking the arithmetical mean,
but must — where the latter is applicable — coincide
with it.   It has been shown that the following rule
answers this purpose.   Fix the average constants or
elements so that the sum of the squares of the differences between the observed and calculated positions is a
minimum.   In mathematical language this results in the
algebraical determination of the constants in an equation.

Whereas the labours of Gauss and the school of
astronomers which he headed in Germany were mostly
occupied in the mathematical proof of this rule, and
in its applications in astronomical and geodetic computations, the doctrine of probabilities acquired a larger

meaning and attracted much popular attention in France
and Belgium through the dominating influence of Laplace.   He had not only collected in his abstract and
very difficult 'Analytical Theory of Probabilities' all
that himself and others had done in this line of research,
but he had in a similar manner to that adopted in his
'Celestial Mechanics' tried to bring the substance of
the theory home to the non-mathematical student in
his 'Essai Philosophique sur les Probabilités.'

The analytical formulæ of probabilities can, he maintained, " be regarded as the necessary complement of the
sciences which are founded on a mass of observations
which are subject to error.   They are indeed indispensable for solving a large number of questions in the
natural and moral sciences.   The regular causes of
events are mostly either unknown or too complicated to
be submitted to calculation : frequently also their effect
is disturbed by accidental and irregular causes, but it
always remains impressed on the events produced by
all these causes, and it brings about changes which
a long series of observations can determine.   The
analysis of probabilities shows these modifications : it
assigns the probability of their causes, and it indicates
the means of increasing their probability more and
more." [1]   Then, referring to the phenomena of the
weather, Laplace proceeds : " Moreover, the succession
of historical events similarly shows us the constant
action of the great moral principles in the midst of
the diverse passions and interests which agitate society
in every direction.   It is remarkable how a science

[1] 'Essai Philosophique,' p. 271.

which began with the consideration of play has risen to the most important objects of human knowledge."

In 1823, soon after the appearance of the works of Laplace and other French writers, this application of the theory of probabilities was taken up by Adolphe Quetelet, who collected his researches in his celebrated work, ' Sur l'Homme et le Développement de ses Facultés, ou Essai de Physique sociale.'[1]   Quetelet

20.
Quetelet.

---

[1] In addition to this work, which was published at Brussels in 1836 in two small volumes, and which Quetelet (1796-1874) describes as a 'résumé de tous mes travaux antérieurs sur la statistique,' he published, besides a great number of memoirs, a series of ' Lettres sur la Théorie des Probabilités' (begun in 1837, pub. 1845, Eng. trans. by O. G. Downes, 1849), and as a continuation of the former work in 1848, ' Du Système social et des Lois qui le régissent.' Less known than those of Quetelet, but about the same time, and independently, there appeared in France the writings of A. M. Guerry, beginning with the publication in 1829—in collaboration with A. Balbi—of ' Statistique comparée, et l'état de l'instruction et du nombre des crimes,' and in 1833, ' Essai sur la statistique morale de la France.' The term "moral statistics" appears here for the first time. Quetelet was the inventor of the term "Social Physics." Guerry employed graphical methods, and published in 1864 ' Statistique morale de l'Angleterre comparée avec la statistique morale de la France.' M. Block (' Statistique,' p. 43) attributes to Guerry and Charles Dupin the general introduction of the graphical method in statistics; geometrical representation having been adopted at the end of the eighteenth century by Wm. Playfair in England, and, before him, by Crome, professor at Giessen, in 1782, and tabular synoptical statements going back to the Danish writer J. P. Anchersen, in his ' Descriptio Statuum Cultiorum in Tabulis' (Copenhagen and Leipzig, 1741); see V. John, ' Geschichte der Statistik,' p. 88. Referring to Guerry, V. John (p. 367) says : "Quetelet is incontestably to be regarded as the founder of the new science (viz., moral statistics), for the rival works of the French lawyer Guerry appeared only partly before Quetelet's, and are excelled by the latter in the use made of the material. Independently of this formal difference, the two authors have quite different conceptions of the new science. Guerry regards its object as consisting mainly in collecting data in order to gain an opinion of the moral status of a country. Thus he looked upon moral statistics as auxiliary to the history of civilisation. Quetelet went beyond this, inasmuch as he was the first to inquire into the cause of the moral level of a population, and in as much as in his criminal statistics of Belgium, 1833, he had already given expression to the fundamental idea, ' Society bears the germs of crime in itself.' "

was astronomer-royal of Belgium and the founder of the Observatory at Brussels. Having opened his career by some memoirs on geometrical subjects, he directed his attention to questions of meteorology and statistics, which he was probably the first to extend into the region not only of the physical but also of the moral attributes of man, studying the phenomena of crime, suicide, and disease as revealed by the criminal courts in France, the Netherlands, and other countries.

Subsequently it was mainly through his influence that a series of international statistical congresses was held in the principal cities of Europe, and a greater uniformity in the methods of research and registration attempted and partially attained.

21.
The "mean man."

Quetelet's statistical inquiries centre in the conception of the average or mean man who, in a very geometrical fashion, is looked upon as an analogue of the centre of gravity[1] of a body, being the mean around which the social elements oscillate. "If one tries," he says, "to

[1] Quetelet defines the object of his work as follows ('Sur l'Homme,' vol. i. p. 21): "L'objet de cet ouvrage est d'étudier, dans leurs effets, les causes, soit naturelles, soit perturbatrices qui agissent sur le développement de l'homme; de chercher à mesurer l'influence de ces causes, et le mode d'après lequel elles se modifient mutuellement. Je n'ai point en vue de faire une théorie de l'homme, mais seulement de constater les faits et les phénomènes qui le concernent, et d'essayer de saisir, par l'observation, les lois qui lient ces phénomènes ensemble. L'homme que je considère ici est, dans la société, l'analogue du centre de gravité dans les corps; il est la moyenne autour de laquelle oscillent les élémens sociaux : ce sera, si l'on veut, un être fictif pour qui toutes les choses se passeront conformément aux résultats moyens obtenus pour la société. Si l'on cherche à établir, en quelque sorte, les bases d'une *physique sociale*, c'est lui qu'on doit considérer, sans s'arrêter aux cas particuliers ni aux anomalies, et sans rechercher si tel individu peut prendre un développement plus ou moins grand dans l'une de ses facultés."

establish in some way the foundation of Social Physics, it is the mean man whom one must consider without stopping at particular and anomalous cases and without investigating whether some individual can take a development more or less great in one of his faculties.[1] . . . After having considered man at different epochs and among different peoples, after having successively determined the different elements of his physical and moral condition, . . . we shall be able to fix the laws to which he has been subjected in different nations since their birth—that is to say, we shall be able to follow the course of the centres of gravity of every part of the system." [2] In an astronomical fashion Quetelet speaks of the perturbing forces and variations, and of the "stability of the social system," [3] and compares the new science of society to the mechanics of the Heavens.[4] The influence of Laplace and his school is evident in every page of Quetelet's work. Whilst speaking of the "variability of the human type and the mean man among different peoples and in different centuries," he

[1] 'Sur l'Homme,' vol. i. p. 22.

[2] Ibid., p. 23.

[3] Ibid., p. 26.

[4] Vol. ii. p. 338. Quetelet speaks of the annual and diurnal periods, and continues : "Les causes régulières et *périodiques*, qui dépendent ou de la période annuelle ou de la période diurne, exercent sur la société des effets plus prononcés et qui varient dans des limites plus larges, que les effets combinés *non périodiques*, produits annuellement par le concours de toutes les autres causes qui agissent sur la société ; en d'autres termes, le système social, dans sa manière d'être, paraît être plus dissemblable à lui - même pendant le cours d'une année ou même pendant l'espace d'un jour, que pendant deux années consécutives, si l'on a égard à l'accroissement de la population. La période *diurne* semble exercer une influence un peu plus prononcée que la période *annuelle*, du moins en ce qui concerne les naissances. La période annuelle produit des effets plus sensibles dans les *campagnes* que dans les *villes*, et il paraît en être de même des causes en général qui tendent à modifier les faits relatifs à l'homme."

anticipates discussions which came fifty years later.[1]
His aim is to arrive at a precise knowledge of things
hitherto vaguely known and merely sketched by artists
and literary persons; but he evidently looks beyond the
study of the average man to that of individual departures,
as of special interest to the physician,[2] for instance,
in the case of disease, and he significantly recommends
what he calls the "study of maxima."[3]　He regards the
"mean man in the circumstances in which he is placed
as the type of all that is beautiful and all that is

[1] Vol. ii. p. 270 : "Les anciens ont représenté avec un art infini l'homme physique et moral, tel qu'il existait alors ; et la plupart des modernes, frappés de la perfection de leurs ouvrages, ont cru qu'ils n'avaient rien de mieux à faire que de les imiter servilement ; ils n'ont pas compris que le type avait changé ; et que, tout en les imitant pour la perfection de l'art, ils avaient une autre nature à étudier.　De là, ce cri universel, 'Qui nous délivrera des Grecs et des Romains !'　De là cette scission violente entre les classiques et les romantiques ; de là enfin, le besoin d'avoir une littérature qui fût véritablement *l'expression de la société*. Cette grande révolution s'est accomplie, et elle fournit la preuve la plus irrécusable de la variabilité du type humain ou de l'homme moyen chez les différens peuples et dans les différens siècles."　It is interesting to see from this quotation that the opposition to a one-sided classical education emanated at that time from the romantic movement, whereas in our days it is the scientific movement which forms the opposition.

[2] Vol. ii. p. 281 : "Comme dans le plus grand nombre de cas, le malade ne peut présenter aucune observation satisfaisante faite sur sa propre personne, ni aucune des élémens qui lui sont particuliers, le médecin se trouve forcé de la ramener à l'échelle commune, et de l'assimiler à l'homme moyen ; ce qui au fond semble présenter le moins de difficultés et d'inconveniens ; mais peut causer aussi de graves méprises dans quelques circoustances ; car c'est encore le cas de faire observer ici que les lois générales relatives aux masses sont essentiellement fausses étant appliquées à des individus : ce qui ne veut pas dire cependant qu'on ne peut les consulter avec fruit : et les écarts sont toujours considérables."

[3] Vol. ii. p. 284 : "Il ne faut pas confondre les lois de développement de l'homme moyen à telle ou telle époque, avec les lois de développement de l'humanité. 'Elles n'ont en général que peu de rapport entre elles : ainsi je serais très disposé à croire que les lois de développement de l'homme moyen restent à peu près les mêmes aux différens siècles, et qu'elles ne varient que par la grandeur des *maxima*. Or, ce sont justement ces *maxima*, relatifs à l'homme développé, qui donnent, dans chaque siècle, la mesure du développement de l'humanité."

good."[1] And further, "one of the principal things accomplished by civilisation is to draw closer and closer the limits within which the different elements oscillate which are characteristic of man."[2]

There was, however, another idea besides that of the mean man which followed in the course of this mathematical or astronomical treatment of social statistics — namely, the seeming negation of the scope of freewill and of moral responsibility, which seemed inconsistent with the regularity of the statistical records. In his treatise, 'Sur l'Homme,' Quetelet had drawn attention to the regular recurrence of crime —of the tendency to crime—as one of the most remarkable features in society; which, through its physical and moral constitution, "prepares crime, the guilty being only the instrument which carries it

22.
Social statistics and freewill.

[1] Vol. ii. p. 287 : "J'ai dit précédemment que l'homme moyen de chaque époque représente le type du développement de l'humanité pour cette époque ; j'ai dit encore que l'homme moyen était toujours tel que le comportait et qu'exigeaient les temps et les lieux ; que ses qualités se développaient dans un juste équilibre, dans une parfaite harmonie, également éloignée des excès et des défectuosités de toute espèce ; de sorte que, dans les circonstances où il se trouve, on doit le considérer comme le type de tout ce qui est beau, de tout ce qui est bien." P. 289 : "Un individu qui résumerait en lui-même, à une époque donnée, toutes les qualités de l'homme moyen, représenterait à la fois tout ce qu'il y a de grand, de beau et de bien."
[2] Vol. ii. p. 342 : "Un des principaux faits de la civilisation est de resserrer, de plus en plus, les limites dans lesquelles oscillent les différens élémens relatifs à l'homme. Plus les lumières se répandent, plus les écarts de la moyenne vont en diminuant ; plus, par conséquent, nous tendons à nous rapprocher de ce qui est beau et de ce qui est bien. La perfectibilité de l'espèce humaine résulte comme une conséquence nécessaire de toutes nos recherches. Les défectuosités, les monstruosités disparaissent de plus en plus au physique ; la fréquence et la gravité des maladies se trouvent combattues avec plus d'avantage par les progrès des sciences médicales ; les qualités morales de l'homme n'éprouvent pas de perfectionnemens moins sensibles ; et plus nous avancerons, moins les grands bouleversemens politiques et les guerres, ces fléaux de l'humanité, seront à craindre dans leurs effets et dans leurs conséquences."

out ";[1] society, as it were, exacting a certain proportion
of crime, as it does of suicide, poverty, physical and
mental disease, for the maintenance of its equilibrium
and as an "alarming"[2] tribute to its stability. The
extreme consequences which seemed to flow from this
doctrine were not drawn by Quetelet, who believed in a
gradual though slow development of human society, and
in moral as well as physical causes and influences. They
were drawn, however, by what we may term the mathematical school of social philosophers, who relied greatly
upon the figures collected by Quetelet and confirmed by
others.   In this country the statistical labours of Quetelet
were made known by Sir John Herschel in a brilliant
article[3] in the 'Edinburgh Review' on the "Translation
of Quetelet's Letters to Prince Albert on the Theory of
Probabilities." They do not seem to have been regarded
as detrimental to the moral aspect of human history till
Henry Thomas Buckle, in his celebrated 'History of
Civilisation,'[4] made use of Quetelet's statistics in sup-

23.
Buckle.

[1] 'Sur l'Homme,' vol. ii. p. 241.
[2] Cf. vol. ii. p. 262; also
'Système Social' (1848), p. 95,
and the 'Mémoire sur la Statistique
Morale' (1848).
[3] Vol. xcii. p. 18.
[4] The 'History of Civilisation,'
vol. i., appeared in 1857, and was
very soon translated in Germany,
running in a short time through
five editions. There the statistical
theories of Quetelet had not made
that impression which they made
in some other countries. This is
explained by the fact that the
philosophy of Kant, to which
Buckle himself referred in a long
passage in his "Introduction," had
long before Quetelet accustomed

thinkers to abandon the popular
conception of freewill, which sees
in it merely the absence of causal
determinateness, in favour of the
causal connection of so-called free
actions with the motives and the
moral character. The subject has
been very fully discussed by F. A.
Lange in his well-known 'History
of Materialism' (Eng. trans. by
Thomas, vol. iii. p. 196, &c.)
Lange refers to a remark of the
well-known political economist,
Prof. Adolph Wagner, who, in his
work 'Die Gesetzmässigkeit in den
scheinbar willkührlichen menschlichen Handlungen' (Hamburg,
1864, p. xiii, &c.), mentions the
fact that Quetelet's writings had

port of one of his favourite theses — viz., that the course of historical progress depends on the combined action of the external physical surroundings and of the intellectual side of human nature. Apart from intellectual modifications the moral side is a constant. In the course of the discussions following the appearance of Buckle's History, especially in Germany, it was conclusively shown that statistical figures prove neither one view nor the other: indeed, one of the most complete and exhaustive treatises on moral statistics comes from the orthodox pen of Alexander von Oettingen, a Professor of Theology, just as we saw that the first great work on political arithmetic in Germany came from the pastor Süssmilch a century earlier. Philosophical writers like Lotze [1]

not received the attention merited : "This reproach does not quite hit the right point. . . . Wagner might, in fact, have been led by Buckle . . . to see that German philosophy in the doctrine of the freedom of the will has for once an advantage which permits it to regard these new studies with equanimity ; for Buckle supports himself above all upon Kant, adducing his testimony for the empirical necessity of human actions, and leaving aside the transcendental theory of freedom. Although all that materialism can draw from moral statistics . . . for the practical value of a materialistic tendency of the age as against idealism has thus been conceded by Kant, it is by no means indifferent whether moral statistics, and, as we may put it, the whole of statistics, is placed in the foreground of anthropological study or not ; for moral statistics direct the view outwards upon the real measurable facts of life, while the German philosophy, despite its clearness as to the nullity of the old doctrine of freewill, still always prefers to direct its view inwards upon the facts of consciousness."

[1] Lotze's deliverances on this subject will be found in the third chapter of the seventh book of the 'Microcosmus' (Eng. trans. by Hamilton and Jones, vol. ii. p. 200, &c.), and also in the 'Logik' of 1874 (Book II. chap. 8). In the former passage he says : "The dislike with which we hear of laws of psychic life, whilst we do not hesitate to regard bodily life as subordinate to it own laws, arises partly because we require too much from our own freedom of will, partly because we let ourselves be too much imposed upon by those laws. If we do not find ourselves involved in the declared struggle between freedom and necessity, we are by no means averse to regarding the actions of

24.
Criticism of
pretension
of statistics. and Drobisch[1] have long ago reduced to their proper measure the pretensions of statistics, and it is now generally admitted that in the sciences dealing with human nature and society, as in those which investigate purely physical phenomena, observations, figures and measurements rarely if ever suffice to establish a valid generalisation; but that, if such be suggested by other processes of thought, notably through attentive reflection on, and analysis of, single and accessible cases, statistics supply the indispensable material by which

men as determined by circumstances : in fact, all expectation of good from education and all the work of history are based upon the conviction that the will may be influenced by growth of insight, by ennoblement of feeling, and by improvement of the external conditions of life. On the other side, a consideration of freedom itself would teach us that the very notion is repugnant to commonsense if it does not include susceptibility to the worth of motives, and that the freedom of willing can by no means signify absolute capacity of carrying out what is willed." And, further, he remarks on "the extreme overhastiness with which the statistical myth has been built up from deductions which cannot be relied upon. We have yet to obtain from exacter investigations the true material for more trustworthy conclusions —material which should take the place of the statistical myth above referred to."

[1] Before Lotze, and as early as 1849, M. W. Drobisch, the Herbartian, had reviewed Quetelet's Memoir, 'Sur la Statistique morale,' &c. ; and later (1867), after the publication of A. Wagner's work, he came back to the subject in an important tract, 'Die moralische Statistik und die menschliche Willensfreiheit,' which should be read by every one who desires to form just views on the subject. "In all such facts," says Drobisch, "there are reflected not natural laws pure and simple, to which man must submit as to destiny, but at the same time the moral conditions of society, which are determined by the mighty influences of family life, of the school, the Church, of legislation, and are, therefore, quite capable of improvement by the will of man" (Zeitsch. für exacte Philos.,' vol. iv. p. 329). After all that has been said by Quetelet, Buckle, and others, the words of Schiller ('Wallenstein's Tod,' ii. 3) still remain the best statement of the problem :—

"Des Menschen Thaten und Gedanken, wisst !
Sind nicht wie Meeres blind bewegte Wellen.
Die innre Welt, sein Microcosmus, ist
Der tiefe Schacht, aus dem sie ewig quellen.
Sie sind nothwendig, wie des Baumes Frucht ;
Sie kann der Zufall gaukelnd nicht verwandeln,
Hab'ich des Menschen Kern erst untersucht,
So weiss ich auch sein Wollen und sein Hendeln."

these generalisations can be tested, elevated to the rank of leading canons of thought and research, and in rare cases to that of the expression of a law of nature. So far, therefore, as the complicated phenomena presented in meteorology, agriculture, and economics are concerned, the suggestions leading to so-called laws have in every case been got elsewhere—from astronomy, chemistry, psychology, history, &c.; and the work of science has subsequently consisted largely in gathering the necessary statistical materials by which to prove, amplify, curtail, or refute them. In many cases it has been found that even elaborate series of observations had not been performed in such a manner[1] as would permit of the necessary inferences being drawn from them. Similarly biologists after Darwin have had to rearrange the collections made by those who came before the epoch marked by that great name.

[1] This refers as much to statistical figures as to the knowledge accumulated in many of the natural sciences. Especially it refers to the statistical material upon which Quetelet based his startling and epoch-making assertions: the earlier critics had, as V. John observes ('Geschichte der Statistik,' p. 364), dealt with the deductions which Quetelet had drawn, without dealing with the empirical material itself. It was therefore of great importance that Prof. Rehnisch of Göttingen for the first time submitted the figures themselves to a searching analysis. He did this in the years 1875-76, in his articles in the 'Zeitschrift für Philosophie und Philosophische Kritik,' through which it became evident that the inferences were, as Lotze had already suggested, to say the least, premature. "In the memoir 'Sur le Penchant au Crime' (1831), only four years, and in the work 'Sur l'Homme,' only six years 1826-31) of the 'compte général,' furnished the data upon which the astounding regularity with which crime repeats itself was maintained" (V. John, p. 365). Rehnisch adds many other examples of the extreme incompleteness of the records upon which the theory of Quetelet is built up. More recent labours have therefore been to a large extent directed towards gathering more complete statistical data, as well as towards improving the mathematical methods themselves to which not only these but also the population and mortality statistics have been submitted, for the purpose of arriving at average figures.

With the scientific treatment of the phenomena of human society, the name of Adolphe Quetelet will always be associated; yet the mathematical or exact school was not the only one which in the course of the first half of the century had approached the subject.

25.
Historical
criticism.
Notably in Germany, under the ruling influence of philosophical, historical, and critical studies, a school of research had grown up calling itself the historical. If the centre of gravity of the mathematical view lies in the conception of a certain uniformity and stability of social phenomena, the other school looked more to historical changes and developments, opposing the doctrine of the movement or of the dynamics to that of the statics of society. Its inspiration came from a different quarter, and will occupy us in a later portion of this work. For the moment it suffices to remark how here also, in the study of economics and social phenomena, the developmental or genetic view has gradually dispelled the earlier search for recurrent forms and regularities, which we may term the morphological aspect: the physiology has succeeded the anatomy of society.

But statistical methods, with the accompanying doctrines of probability and averages and the theory of error, have not only been extensively and usefully employed where large numbers of similar facts and events crowd in upon our observation, and, as it were, overwhelm us by their multitudes, as in astronomy, meteorology, economics, and political arithmetic: they have also shown themselves applicable by what we may term the inverse method. Quetelet, when deal-

ing with long columns of human statistics, felt a
relief in studying the average or mean man. Is it
not possible that in many instances what nature and
experience show us is only the average itself — our
senses and our intellect being too coarse to penetrate
to the numberless individual cases out of which the
sum or the average is made up ? May not even the
simplest phenomenon or thing in nature be in fact
an aggregate, a total, and its apparent behaviour and
properties merely a collective effect ? Both the kinetic
and the atomic view of natural objects and phenomena
seem to favour this way of regarding things,— the
former showing us in many cases motion and unrest
where at the first glance we saw only rest, and the
latter dissolving apparently continuous and homogeneous structures into crowds or assemblages of many
particles.

26.
Application
in physics.

Thus the apparently steady pressure of gases is now
known to be in reality the violent bombardment of
the wall of the containing vessel by their molecules ; and the most homogeneous and transparent
crystal is revealed, by its optical properties, as an
assemblage of very minute particles, held together by
forces which may be overcome by mechanical or
chemical agencies. Regarded from this point of view,
our knowledge of natural objects is merely statistical :
it deals with aggregates ; it is a collective knowledge.
And if we further consider that the sameness of the
numberless constituent particles is by no means proved,
this collective knowledge turns out to be merely concerned with averages : it is statistical, not individual,

information that we seem to possess ; it resembles the knowledge which an economist may possess of the statistics of a society or of the properties of the 'mean" man. If such be the case, the theory of large numbers and the calculus of probabilities must be applicable and useful in dealing with those phenomena which, through their minuteness and great number, elude our detailed examination.

The first to introduce this conception of treating a very large assemblage of moving things by the method of averages was Joule,[1] who, adopting Daniel Bernoulli's conception, calculated the average velocity which a particle of hydrogen gas must possess in order to explain the total effect which shows itself as a definite gas pressure at a definite temperature. His result was that this average speed must be 6055 feet per second in order to be equal to the pressure of one atmosphere at the zero temperature of the Centigrade scale. The speed of the particles, however, cannot be assumed to be equal, owing to continual encounters ; and we are indebted to Clausius and Clerk-Maxwell for introducing the more refined statistical methods of the theory of probabilities. They calculated the mean free path, and showed that former calculations of the average speed were in the main correct. The kinetic theory of gases afforded an opportunity of brilliantly applying the conceptions of averages or means and of the differences of frequencies as the measure of the probability of certain occurrences. In this case—as was first shown by Joule's figures—we

27.
Clausius
and Clerk
Maxwell.

[1] See *supra*, vol. i. p. 434, and vol. ii. p. 110.

have to do with billions and trillions of particles, moving with velocities varying from zero to many thousands of miles per second: we have therefore to do with numbers which practically mean infinity — that is to say, we have to do with that condition of things where alone the laws of probability become strictly correct.[1]

In this case, any deductions which can be made as to the average condition or collective behaviour of an infinitely large assemblage of particles, whose individual members move about with infinitely varying velocities at infinitely varying speeds in infinitely varying directions, must be realised in the well-known laws of gaseous bodies referring to pressure, volume, expansion, molecular structure, and heat, assuming the latter to be merely the sensible effect on our nerves of very numerous impingements of infinitesimally small particles. It is one of the greatest triumphs of the mathematical methods applied in one of the most difficult instances, that the average behaviour and collective properties of

---

[1] P. G. Tait ('Heat,' 1884, p. 355) says: "It is to Clausius that we are indebted for the earliest approach to an adequate treatment of this question. He was the first to take into account the collisions between the particles, and to show that these did not alter the previously obtained results. He has also the great credit of introducing the statistical methods of the theory of probabilities, and of thus giving at least approximate ideas as to the probable length of the *mean free path*—i.e., the average distance travelled over by a particle before it impinges on another, and thus has its course changed. He thus explains also the slowness of diffusion of gases, and their very small conductivity of heat. Clerk-Maxwell shortly afterwards improved the theory by introducing, also from the statistical point of view, the consideration of the variety of speed at which the different particles are moving; Clausius having expressly limited his investigations by assuming for simplicity that all move with equal speed. Clerk-Maxwell explained gaseous friction, and gave a more definite determination of the length of the mean free path."

28.
Mathe-
matical rep-
resentation
of experi-
mental laws.

such moving crowds turn out to be exactly those laws which Boyle, Charles, Gay-Lussac, Dalton, and Avogadro had found out by direct experiments with gaseous bodies. James Clerk - Maxwell was the first to recognise the great importance of the statistical methods, and to apply them in an exhaustive manner.[1] And we witness here the same spectacle which presented itself in the history of the theory of probabilities. Problems which are to be solved by the mere application of a few rules dictated by common-sense and an exercise of common logic, present in their complexity such a multitude of traps, snares, and pitfalls, that it required the successive application of the highest intellects to free the reasoning from insidious errors, and put the results on

[1] The manner in which Joule dealt with the problem of a large crowd of moving particles in his memoir of 1851 was not strictly statistical, inasmuch as he dealt with an average velocity of the molecules, and assumed that all the molecules of a gas moved with the same velocity. Clausius, in his memoir of 1857, made use of assumptions which were more in conformity with nature : he had, accordingly, to employ the calculus of probabilities. Clerk - Maxwell's occupation with the subject dates from the year 1859, when he read his paper, "Illustrations of the Dynamic Theory of Gases," Part I. (published in the 'Phil. Mag.,' 4th series, vol. xix. p. 19, reprinted in 'Scientific Papers,' vol. i.) He showed that "the velocities are distributed among the particles according to the same law as errors are distributed among the observations in the theory of the method of least squares. The velocities range from 0 to ∞, but the number of those having great velocities is comparatively small." If we leave out Joule's imperfect attempt to employ the statistical method, one of the first applications of the method of averages to a physical problem is to be found in Sir G. G. Stokes's paper " On the Composition of Streams of Polarised Light from different Sources " (' Camb. Phil. Trans.,' 1853), where he shows "what will be the average effect of a very great number of special sources of light : thus giving one of the earliest illustrations of the use, in physics, of the statistical methods of probabilities. . . . From this point of view the uniformity of optical phenomena becomes quite analogous to the statistical species of uniformity, which is now found to account for the behaviour of the practically infinite group of particles forming a cubic inch of gas " (P. G. Tait, 'Light,' 2nd ed., 1889, p. 237).

undisputed and indisputable bases.[1] In proportion as this has been done the calculated results have proved to be in closer and closer accord with observed facts. I will here mention only one of the latest achievements in this line of research and reasoning. Assuming— as the atomic and kinetic theories do—that all external phenomena of bodies can be reduced to the collective or mean effect of a practically infinite variety of turbulent movements of a very large number of particles, it must be possible to give a mechanical explanation of that remarkable property of all phenomena of nature, first noticed by Lord Kelvin, that they are essentially irreversible—*i.e.*, that, with very rare exceptions, they take place in a certain direction which we may define as an equalisation of existing differences of level, temperature, electric pressure, and similar inequalities. In order to fix this remarkable property of all natural phenomena, physicists found themselves obliged to introduce, alongside of energy and mass (which are both assumed to conserve or maintain their total quantity), a third something which is the measure of the degree in which an existing distribution of mass and energy can be considered to be capable of external, visible, finite activity

29. Irreversibility of natural processes.

[1] Those who are interested in seeing how difficult it is to link together the common-sense arguments of the theory of probabilities in a consistent chain of unimpeachable logic, should read the report on the various attempts to prove Clerk-Maxwell's law (mentioned in the foregoing note) contained in Prof. O. E. Meyer's ' Kinetische Theorie der Gase ' (2nd ed., Breslau, 1899), especially p. 46, &c., and 'Mathematical Appendix,' p. 17; and the great number of memoirs referred to on p. 60 of that book. Nevertheless Tait speaks of the still remaining difficulties in the kinetic theory of gases as having been " greatly enhanced by an apparently unwarranted application of the theory of probabilities on which the statistical method is based." ('Properties of Matter,' 2nd ed., 1890, p. 291.)

—*i.e.*, of its availability to do work.[1] The infinitesimally small motions of an immense crowd may be exerted in such a way as to total up to a finite movement perceptible to our senses and accessible to our handling, or they may so mutually annul each other as to present in their finite sum and aggregate the appearance of rest and inaction, however turbulent their behaviour might appear to an observer gifted with powers of perception millions of times more delicate than ours.   Lord Kelvin introduced the conception of the availability of energy,[2] Clausius that of entropy (or energy which is hidden away), to measure this condition of any natural system. Has the statistical view any conception to put at the base of this remarkable property of natural phenomena ? It has, and we must assign to Clerk - Maxwell [3] the

30.
Lord
Kelvin.

---

[1] See *supra*, chap. vii. p. 128, &c.

[2] Or of "motivity" (*i.e.*, "energy for motive power"), this being "the possession, the waste of which is called dissipation." See *supra*, chap. vii. p. 168; also Thomson (Lord Kelvin), . ' Popular Addresses,' vol. i. p. 141.

[3] The contributions of Clerk-Maxwell to this topic are notably two, independently of the larger view which he took of statistical, as compared with historical, knowledge, of which I treat farther on in this chapter.   First, in the concluding remarks of his treatise on the 'Theory of Heat' ("On the Limitation of the Second Law of Thermodynamics") he introduced his famous conception of a "sorting demon," the meaning of which fanciful device was, to impress upon the student of the dynamical theory of heat, first, the fact that the

loss of availability of the energy of molecular motion is owing to the coarseness of our senses ; and second, that the restoration of differences of temperature, or of availability of energy, is simply a matter of arrangement or order, not of an increase of the intrinsic energy of the system.   The subject has been frequently referred to, notably by Lord Kelvin, who says ("On the Sorting Demon of Clerk-Maxwell," Royal Institution, February 1879. Reprinted in 'Popular Lectures and Addresses,' vol. i. p. 137, &c.) : "Dissipation of energy follows in nature from the fortuitous concourse of atoms.   The lost motivity is essentially not restorable otherwise than by an agency dealing with individual atoms ; and the mode of dealing with the atoms to restore motivity is essentially a process of assortment, sending this way all of one kind or class, that way all of another kind or class "

credit of having first indicated, and to Prof. Boltzmann [1]
—aided by many other eminent natural philosophers
—that of having definitely established, this highly
suggestive explanation or illustration. The doctrine
of chances, to which artifice the statistical view of

(p. 139). "The conception of the 'sorting demon' is merely mechanical, and is of great value in purely physical science. It was not invented to help us to deal with questions regarding the influence of life and mind on the motions of matter, questions essentially beyond the range of mere dynamics" (p. 141). The other contribution through which Clerk - Maxwell's name has become celebrated in this connection is to be found in the so-called Maxwell-Boltzmann law of the distribution of kinetic energy in a mass of moving particles. The discussion of the subject dates from the first memoir of Clerk-Maxwell, quoted above ; and, after Prof. Boltzmann had treated of the same subject in 1868, and Mr Watson in 1876, Clerk-Maxwell returned to it in a paper "On Energy in a System of Material Points" ('Camb. Phil. Soc.,' vol. xii.) In the year 1894 Prof. Bryan presented the 2nd part of his Report on "Our Knowledge of Thermodynamics" ('Brit. Assoc. Rep.,' 1894, p. 64, &c.), in which he gives an account of all the different investigations referring to this subject, up to that date. This was followed by a long discussion of the subject in the pages of 'Nature' (vol. li.), in which Messrs Bryan, Boltzmann, Burbury, Culverwell, Larmor, and H. W. Watson took part, and which gave Prof. Boltzmann the opportunity of giving a final expression of his opinion (p. 415).

[1] Prof. Boltzmann's investigations connected with the second law of thermodynamics and the kinetic theory of gases cover the last thirty - five years. He has succeeded in putting the whole problem more and more into a strictly accurate, as also into a popularly intelligible, form. Unfortunately his very numerous contributions are scattered in various periodical publications, and have not yet appeared in a collected edition. Most of them appeared in the Proceedings and Transactions of the Vienna Academy, among which the Address delivered on the 29th May 1886 can be specially recommended. Since then, and after the correspondence in 'Nature' referred to in the last note, he has published his lectures 'Vorlesungen über Gas-Theorie' (2 vols., Leipzig, 1896-98). He there (vol. ii. p. 260, note) gives a list of the most important literature on the subject, and also a general summary regarding the application of the theory of probabilities to the distribution of the kinetic energy of a crowd of moving particles. In this connection he also deals with the consequences of the atomic hypothesis, the irreversibility of all natural processes, and the application of the second law to the history of the universe. He there says (p. 253) : "The fact that the closed system of a finite number of molecules, if it had originally an orderly condition, and has then lapsed into a disorderly one, must finally, after the lapse of an inconceivably long period, assume again orderly conditions, is

phenomena reduces us, distinguishes between probable and improbable events or arrangements of a crowd of elements—*i.e.*, between such as are of an average and such as are of an exceptional character. Any highly improbable arrangement—though possible—will be followed by a gradual settling down to more probable or average arrangements. And as in nature you are forced to introduce the conception of availability, so in the calculus of chances you can introduce a certain mathematical quantity which is the measure of the probability. The more improbable, *i.e.*, exceptional, the begin-

not a refutation, but a confirmation, of our theory. But one must not consider the matter thus : as if two gases . . . which were initially unmixed, then became mixed, after a few days again unmixed, then again mixed, &c. We find, rather, that . . . only after a period which, even compared with $10^{10^{10}}$ years, is enormously great, a perceptible unmixing would take place. That this is practically equivalent to never, we see, if we consider that in this period there would be, according to the laws of probability, many years in which, by mere chance, all the inhabitants of a large city would, on the same day, commit suicide, or fire break out in all its buildings; whereas the insurance companies are in so good an agreement with facts that they do not consider such cases at all. If even a much smaller improbability were not practically identical with impossibility, nobody could rely upon the present day being followed by night and the latter again by day." And further (p. 255) : "If we, therefore, represent the world under the figure of an enormously large mechanical system, composed of enormously numerous atoms, which started from a very perfectly ordered condition, and exist still mainly in an orderly condition, we arrive at consequences which actually stand in perfect harmony with observed facts"; and (p. 258), "That in nature the transition from a probable to an improbable condition does not happen as frequently as the reverse, can be explained by the assumption of a very improbable initial state of the whole surrounding universe, in consequence of which any arbitrary system of interacting bodies is, in general, in an improbable condition to begin with. But one might say, that here and there the transition from probable to improbable conditions must, after all, be observable. . . . From the numbers regarding the inconceivably great rarity of a transition from probable to improbable conditions, happening in observable dimensions and during an observable period, it is explained how such a process within what we, cosmologically, call a single world, or, specially, our world, is so extremely rare that any experience of it is excluded."

ning you choose, the greater your distance from the average or most probable condition into which, in the long-run, things must settle down ; the more play for the equalising and levelling down of coming events. The world—or at least that part of the world accessible to our observation, and the playground of our activity— shows a large amount of available energy, or, expressed in a purely statistical manner, it started from a highly improbable condition, and it is descending or running down into a more probable or average condition. The doctrine of availability or of its reverse, of entropy —*i.e.*, of the loss of availability—turns out to be a theorem of probabilities; and the refined mathematical researches of Prof. Boltzmann and others show that these two conceptions can be made to cover each other. Moreover, we can bring home to the popular under- standing the difference between the exceptional con- dition, with its large amount of available energy, and the average condition, with its large amount of self- destructive and wasted energy (or entropy), by the simile of order and disorder.   For every arrangement of a crowd of things or beings which is orderly, there are innumerable arrangements which are disorderly ; every one knows how easily the orderly arrangement lapses into disorder, and nobody expects by mere haphazard or chance movements to produce order out of disorder. There are thousands of ways by which a stone can fall from the peak of a mountain to the lower levels, but only one direction which would take it up again to the top.   A tree has been suggested as the picture of the course that natural movements take : for the one position

31.
" Avail- ability " a theorem in probability.

in the trunk, where all branches and all roots meet, there are in both directions numberless ways of ramification or dissipation into the twigs or the root-fibres. The statistical view measures the chances of an orderly arrangement compared with disorder, of a commanding unique position compared with the average or mean position, by saying the odds are infinity to one against it. The orderly exceptional position and arrangement of a crowd does not possess more actual energy, but its energy is directed, arranged, it has become available— get-at-able.

32.
"Selection" as conceived by Maxwell.

And what is it that changes disorder into order? It is a process of selection. Maxwell imagined a sorting demon endowed with powers of perceiving and dividing the immeasurably small movements of a gaseous body— i.e., of a crowd of particles in turbulent to and fro movement. Such a being could, by mere selection and separation of the slow and fast moving particles, bring order into disorder, converting the unavailable energy into available energy. It would be a process of mere sifting and arranging, such as is apparently carried out in the living creation and by organic structures.[1] And Maxwell went a step further, and conceived the idea

[1] See *supra*, chap. x. p. 437, note, where the selective action of certain organisms is referred to in connection with Prof. Japp's Address to the Brit. Assoc. in 1898. Lord Kelvin says ("On the Dissipation of Energy," 1892, 'Popular Lectures and Addresses,' vol. ii. p. 463, &c.): "It is conceivable that animal life might have the attribute of using the heat of surrounding matter, at its natural temperature, as a source of energy for mechanical effect. . . . The influence of animal or vegetable life on matter is infinitely beyond the range of any scientific inquiry hitherto entered on. Its power of directing the motions of moving particles, in the demonstrated daily miracle of our human free-will, and in the growth of generation after generation of plants from a single seed, are infinitely different from any possible result of the fortuitous concourse of atoms."

that, after all, the whole of our knowledge of natural phenomena and natural things may be only statistical, not historical or individual. "In dealing," he says,[1] "with masses of matter, while we do not perceive the individual molecules, we are compelled to adopt the statistical method of calculation, and to abandon the strict dynamical method in which we follow every motion by the calculus. It would be interesting to inquire how far those ideas about the nature and the methods of science which have been derived from examples of scientific investigation in which the dynamical method is followed, are applicable to our actual knowledge of concrete things, which, as we have seen, is of an essentially statistical nature, because no one has yet discovered any practical method of tracing the path of a molecule, or of identifying it at different times." And elsewhere [2] he says: "The statistical method of investigating social questions has Laplace for its most scientific and Buckle for its most popular

[1] 'Theory of Heat,' 8th ed., p. 329.

[2] 'Life of Clerk - Maxwell by Campbell and Garnett.' Chap. xiv. contains a paper with the title, "Does the progress of Physical Science tend to give any advantage to the opinion of Necessity (or Determinism) over that of the Contingency of Events and the Freedom of the Will?" In it (p. 435) there occurs the following passage: "The doctrine of the conservation of energy, when applied to living beings, leads to the conclusion that the soul of an animal is not, like the mainspring of a watch, the motive power of the body, but that its function is rather that of a steersman of a vessel — not to produce, but to regulate and direct, the animal powers." He then speaks of the "powerful effect on the world of thought" which the developments of molecular science are likely to have, considering the "most important effect on our way of thinking to be that it forces on our attention the distinction between two kinds of knowledge, which we may call for convenience the Dynamical and Statistical." The paper from which the extracts in the text are taken is dated 1873. Clerk-Maxwell was then forty-one years of age.

expounder. Persons are grouped according to some characteristic, and the number of persons forming the group is set down under that characteristic. This is the raw material from which the statist endeavours to deduce general theorems in sociology. Other students of human nature proceed on a different plan. They observe individual men, ascertain their history, analyse their motives, and compare their expectation of what they will do with their actual conduct. . . . However imperfect this study of man may be in practice, it is evidently the only perfect method in principle. . . . If we betake ourselves to the statistical method, we do so confessing that we are unable to follow the details of each individual case, and expecting that the effects of widespread causes, though very different in each individual, will produce an average result on the whole nation, from the study of which we may estimate the character and propensities of an imaginary being called the Mean Man. Now, if the molecular theory of the constitution of bodies is true, all our knowledge of matter is of a statistical kind. A constituent molecule of a body has properties very different from those of the body to which it belongs. The smallest portion of a body which we can discern consists of a vast number of molecules, and all we can learn about the group of molecules is statistical information. . . . Hence those uniformities which we observe in our experiments with quantities of matter containing millions of millions of molecules are uniformities of the same kind as those explained by Laplace and wondered at by Buckle, arising from the slumping to-

33.
Statistical
knowledge
of nature.

gether of multitudes of cases, each of which is by no
means uniform with the others. . . . Much light may
be thrown on some of these questions by the consideration of stability and instability.   When the state of
things is such that an infinitely small variation of the
present state will alter only by an infinitely small
quantity the state at some future time, the condition
of the system, whether at rest or in motion, is said to be
stable; but when an infinitely small variation in the
present state may bring about a finite difference in the
state of the system in a finite time, the condition of the
system is said to be unstable.   It is manifest that the
existence of unstable conditions renders impossible the
prediction of future events, if our knowledge of the
present state is only approximate and not accurate.   It
has been well pointed out by Prof. Balfour Stewart that
physical stability is the characteristic of those systems
from the contemplation of which determinists draw their
arguments, and physical instability that of those living
bodies, and moral instability [1] that of those developable
souls which furnish to consciousness the conviction of
free-will." [2]

[1] There is an awkward misprint
in the first edition of 'The Life,'
which is corrected in the second
edition.

[2] Clerk - Maxwell frequently reverts to this subject.   In an article
on "Molecules," contributed to the
ninth edition of the 'Ency. Brit.'
(reprinted in 'Scientific Papers,'
vol. ii.), he contrasts historical and
statistical knowledge as follows (p.
373): "The modern atomists have
adopted a method which is, I
believe, new in the department of

mathematical physics, though it
has long been in use in the section
of statistics.   When the working
members of Section F (of the Brit.
Assoc.) get hold of a report of the
census, or any other document containing the numerical data of
economic and social science, they
begin by distributing the whole
population into groups according to
age, income-tax, education, religious
belief, or criminal convictions.   The
number of individuals is far too
great to allow of their tracing the

The conceptions involved in the atomic and kinetic views of natural processes, and the statistical manner of dealing with these crowds of moving particles, have thus introduced into natural philosophy two distinct and novel considerations not known to former ages: first, the consideration that our knowledge of things and phenomena in nature is not historical, but that it is that of the mean or average and of the total effects produced by an immensely large number of singly imperceptible events upon our senses which are too coarse to receive or deal with individual occurrences; secondly, the consideration that our knowledge is not purely mechanical, inasmuch

history of each separately, so that, in order to reduce their labour within human limits, they concentrate their attention on a small number of artificial groups. The varying number of individuals in each group, and not the varying state of each individual, is the primary datum from which they work. This, of course, is not the only method of studying human nature. We may observe the conduct of individual men and compare it with that conduct which their previous character and their present circumstances, according to the best existing theory, would lead us to expect. Those who practise this method endeavour to improve their knowledge of the elements of human nature in much the same way as an astronomer corrects the elements of a planet by comparing its actual position with that deduced from the received elements. The study of human nature by parents and schoolmasters, by historians and statesmen, is, therefore, to be distinguished from that carried on by registrars and tabulators, and by those statesmen who put their faith in figures. The one may be called the historical and the other the statistical method. The equations of dynamics completely express the laws of the historical method as applied to matter, but the application of these equations implies a perfect knowledge of all the data. But the smallest portion of matter which we can subject to experiment consists of millions of molecules, not one of which ever becomes sensible to us. We cannot, therefore, ascertain the actual motion of any one of these molecules; so that we are obliged to abandon the strict historical method of dealing with large groups of molecules. The data of the statistical method, as applied to molecular science, are the sums of large numbers of molecular quantities. In studying the relations between quantities of this kind, we meet with a new kind of regularity, the regularity of averages, which we can depend upon quite sufficiently for all practical purposes, but which can make no claim to that character of absolute precision which belongs to the laws of abstract dynamics."

as besides the purely mechanical movements and their summation, it must contain a reference to the nature of our own faculties—a principle which indicates to what extent the elementary movements come under our control or escape it. There must be a principle which measures the availability and usefulness—for our powers—of natural processes, marking off what is orderly for our senses and accessible to our powers, from what is disorderly and inaccessible. This principle the founders of the science of Thermodynamics—Rankine, Clausius, and Thomson—had empirically established; Thomson having foreseen its far-reaching importance in the economy of nature and the applications of industry. The statistical view of natural phenomena forced upon us by atomism and kinetics has shown us that it is not a purely mechanical [1] principle. It is one belonging to the theory of averages and probability. The scientific view of nature is thus, as Clerk-Maxwell says, neither purely historical nor purely mechanical—it is statistical.[2]

34.
As opposed to historical and mechanical knowledge.

To this view of the scientific treatment of natural phenomena Clerk-Maxwell has attached a further con-

---

[1] Clerk-Maxwell, in a review of Tait's "Thermodynamics" ('Scientific Papers,' vol. ii. p. 670): "The truth of the second law is therefore a statistical, not a mathematical, truth, for it depends on the fact that the bodies we deal with consist of millions of molecules, and that we never can get hold of single molecules."

[2] Any one who has had occasion to observe the internal work of any large industrial or manufacturing organisation, will have noticed the twofold way in which important occurrences are looked at by the commercial and the technical chiefs. As regularity is in many instances the condition of success, any break of its routine is carefully examined and criticised. In such cases the technical man will look to the proximate mechanical causes for an explanation, whereas the commercial man, unable to reflect on the technical and mechanical conditions of the special case, will always refer to his statistics of the past as a guide in judging the immediate difficulty that is before him.

sideration, which is interesting inasmuch as it shows that that which I called above the inverse method of statistics does not involve ideas identical with those which the direct method — as applied in ordinary economic and social statistics—involves. In the direct processes of statistics, which we may class under the all-case or enumerative method, we rise, from a large number of individual facts and data which are all different, to the conception of certain uniform averages, to recurring, or continuously and slowly changing, totals, such as we handle daily in sciences like meteorology, in moral, economic, and industrial statistics. The averages are nowhere represented by the individuals, and the regularity of the totals does not appear in dealing with single instances, or with such restricted numbers as come under the personal control of any of us; hence the general uselessness of statistics in handling individual cases or predicting special occurrences. But the statistical view of natural phenomena, as applied to the atomic constitution of bodies, leads us ultimately to the conception that the smallest constituents of matter, the atoms, exhibit a regularity and recurrent uniformity of structure which reminded Sir John Herschel of manufactured articles. The attempt to reduce the somewhat numerous types of these ultimate elements to purely geometrical configurations of the homogeneous elements of one substance has indeed failed, though it is being continually revived. But allowing that there exist some sixty or seventy distinct forms of matter or atomic structures, these structures seem to be alike and stable wherever we meet with them; our observations ranging over very large distances in space and time, from the particles immediately before us in artificial flames to the vibrations of atoms of distant stars, which must have taken millions of years to reach us. "I do not think," says Clerk-Maxwell,[1] "that the perfect identity which we observe between different portions of the same kind of matter can be explained on the statistical principle of the stability of the averages of large numbers of quantities, each of which may differ from the mean. . . . For if the molecules of some substance, such as hydrogen, were of sensibly greater mass than others, we have the means of producing a separation between molecules of different masses, and in this way we should be able to produce two kinds of hydrogen, one of which would be somewhat denser than the other. As this cannot be done, we must admit that the equality which we assert to exist between the molecules of hydro-

---

[1] 'Theory of Heat,' p. 329, &c. Cf. also many passages in the articles on "Atom," "Molecule," "Constitution of Bodies," &c., reprinted in the second volume of 'Scientific Papers'; *inter alia*, p. 483: "But the equality of the constants of the molecules is a fact of a very different order. It arises from a particular distribution of matter, a *collocation*, to use the expression of Dr Chalmers, of things which we have no difficulty in imagining to have been arranged otherwise. But many of the ordinary instances of collocation are adjustments of constants, which are not only arbitrary in their own nature, but in which variations actually occur; and when it is pointed out that these adjustments are beneficial to living beings, and are therefore instances of benevolent design, it is replied that those variations which are not conducive to the growth and multiplication of living beings tend to their destruction, and to the removal thereby of the evidence of any adjustment not beneficial. The constitution of an atom, however, is such as to render it, so far as we can judge, independent of all the dangers arising from the struggle for existence. Plausible reasons may, no doubt, be assigned for believing that if the constants had varied from atom to atom through any sensible range, the bodies formed by aggregates of such atoms would not have been so well fitted for the construction of the world as the bodies which actually exist. But as we have no experience of bodies formed of such variable atoms, this must remain a bare conjecture."

gen applies to each individual molecule, and not merely to the average of groups of millions of molecules." And Clerk-Maxwell goes on to show how the fact that the molecules [1] " all fall into a limited number of classes or species with no intermediate links . . . to connect one species with another by uniform gradation, produces that kind of speculation with which we have become so familiar under the name of theories of evolution, it being quite inapplicable to the case of the molecules. The individuals of each species [2] of molecules are like tuning-forks all tuned to concert pitch, or like watches regulated to solar time." [3]

[1] 'Theory of Heat,' p. 330.

[2] Ibid., p. 331.

[3] The passages quoted from Clerk-Maxwell's writings, and the inferences drawn by him, were criticised by Clifford in a lecture delivered in 1874 with the title, "The First and the Last Catastrophe. A Criticism of some recent Speculations about the Duration of the Universe" (reprinted in 'Lectures and Essays,' vol. i. p. 191 sqq.); and, quite recently, Prof. Ward has, in his Gifford lectures, reviewed both Maxwell's and Clifford's arguments ('Naturalism and Agnosticism,' vol. i. p. 99, &c.) As Prof. Ward says, the ideas of Herschel and Clerk-Maxwell "are far more due to theological zeal than to the bare logic of the facts." It is, therefore, out of place to discuss here the philosophical consequences of the ideas of the immutability or of the gradual evolution of the ultimate elements of matter. In a former chapter (see pp. 360 sqq. and 369, note, of this volume) I referred to the theories of the evolution of the different chemical elements as they have been put forward by various scientific authorities. The interest which attaches to the passages quoted from Clerk-Maxwell is, that in them, for the first time, an instance was given of the application of statistical methods in the domain of abstract science. The reader may gather from a perusal of the writings mentioned above, as also of the present and foregoing chapters of this history, that there is an inherent contradiction (or as Kant would say, antinomy) between the logical methods and the highest objects of scientific reasoning. The methods all tend in the direction of reducing existing differences in the things and phenomena of nature to a small number of data which are easily grasped and calculated, whereas the observation of things natural forces increasingly upon us the existence of ever greater differences, changes, and varieties. The question presents itself, Is it likely that a process the principle of which is unification and simplification, will ever lead to a comprehension of that which increasingly reveals itself to be infinitely complex and varying? Dr Larmor has some remarks which bear on this subject

The progress of modern science has, however, given a great impetus to the development of statistical or enumerative methods, and notably to the graphical registration of these results, through the importance which the phenomena of variation attained in all theories of evolution, and chiefly in those based upon natural selection. Quetelet had already pointed to the study of the maxima of the possible deviations from the mean and average, as of special interest and value. Nevertheless, the centre of gravity of the aspect unfolded in the writings of Quetelet and his followers was the idea of uniformity and average sameness. The conception of change and development did not fit naturally and logically into their scheme.[1] It was not till after the

35.
Sameness and variation.

('Æther and Matter,' p. 288): "The processes by which our conception of the uniformity of Nature is obtained essentially involve averaging of effects, and lose their efficacy long before the individual molecule is reached. Mechanical determinateness thus need not involve molecular determinateness; then why should either of them involve determination in the entirely distinct province of vital activity? . . . Every vital process may conceivably be correlated with a mechanical process, as to its progress, just to that extent to which it is possible experimentally to follow it, without lending any countenance to a theory that would place its initiation under the control of any such system of mechanical relations. In other terms, there is room for complete mechanical co-ordination of all the functions of an organism, treated as an existing material system, without requiring any admission that similar principles are supreme in the more remote and infinitely complex phenomena concerned in growth and decay of structure."

[1] A fate overtook the theories and writings of Quetelet and Buckle similar to that which I had occasion to notice above in referring to the great work of A. von Humboldt. Through the influence of the evolutionist movement, prepared by Lamarck, von Baer, Spencer, and others, centring in Darwin, the statical or morphological view had in every department of science to give way to the kinetic or genetic view. This explains why some names, once celebrated, like Humboldt and Buckle, sank rapidly into oblivion. Grant Allen, in his somewhat one-sided but spirited monograph on Darwin ('English Worthies,' 1888), has drawn attention to this. I give here the striking passage, reserving for the sequel of this work the liberty to differ in detail from much in it that is too drastically expressed: "There is no department of human

publication of the ' Origin of Species ' that the phenomena of variation—*i.e.*, of deviation from the existing type or average—forced themselves upon naturalists and statisticians as requiring to be specially observed, described, and accounted for. Since that time a new branch of science has sprung up, unknown before even by name—the study of variation in nature. This, as we have seen in a former chapter, is one of the great and important aspects of nature brought prominently before the thinking naturalist by Darwin's and Wallace's discoveries, and strongly urged forward by the independent arguments of Mr Herbert Spencer. It involves the great problems of Inheritance and Adaptation. What are the facts, and what the causes of variation, of the moving and propelling principle in natural selection and evolution ? The latter is a physiological problem—the former is one of statistics.

thought or human action which evolutionism leaves exactly where it stood before the advent of the Darwinian conception. In nothing is this fact more conspicuously seen than in the immediate obsolescence (so to speak) of all the statical pre-Darwinian philosophies which ignored development, as soon as ever the new progressive evolutionary theories had fairly burst upon an astonished world. Dogmatic Comte was left forthwith to his little band of devoted adherents ; shadowy Hegel was relegated with a bow to the cool shades of the common-rooms of Oxford ; Buckle was exploded like an inflated windbag ; even Mill himself,—*magnum et venerabile nomen*,—with all his mighty steam - hammer force of logical directness, was felt instinctively to be lacking in full appreci-ation of the dynamic and kinetic element in universal nature. Spencer and Hartmann, Haeckel and Clifford, had the field to themselves for the establishment of their essentially evolutionary systems. Great thinkers of the elder generation, like Bain and Lyell, felt bound to remodel their earlier conceptions by the light of the new Darwinian hypotheses. Those who failed by congenital constitution to do so, like Carlyle and Carpenter, were, philosophically speaking, left hopelessly behind and utterly extinguished. Those who only half succeeded in thus reading themselves into the new ideas, like Lewes and Max Müller, lost ground immediately before the eager onslaught of their younger competitors " (*loc. cit.*, p. 197).

The first who seems to have fully grasped the Darwinian problem from this point of view is Mr Francis Galton,[1] who in a series of papers, and notably in his well-known works on 'Hereditary Genius' (1869) and on 'Inheritance' (1889), made a beginning in the statistical treatment of the phenomena of Variation. The novel point of view which was thus introduced into natural science was perhaps somewhat obscured by its immediate application to a most difficult and unique problem, which can hardly be discussed without importing what may be called a sentimental bias. This was the question of the connection through descent of those rare occurrences in human nature which we term genius. Mental phenomena had been almost entirely passed over[2] by Darwin. The results which Mr Galton arrives at, so far as the phenomena of genius are concerned, are of minor importance compared with the general methods which he introduced or suggested for dealing with statistics of heredity. In these he combined the ideas of Quetelet with that remarkable

[1] Mr Francis Galton (born 1822, a grandson of Erasmus Darwin) had, like his celebrated cousin, begun his career as a medical student, and then become a well-known traveller and explorer. Subsequently he devoted himself to meteorology, where he drew attention to the existence and theory of anti-cyclones. His first publication, referring not to physical but to human statistics, appeared in 'Macmillan's Magazine' in 1865, in the shape of two articles on "Hereditary Talent and Character." Here he introduced the "theory of hereditary genius," which was "usually scouted." He rightly claims "to be the first to treat the subject in a statistical manner, to arrive at numerical results, and to introduce the 'law of deviation from an average' into discussions on heredity" (Preface to 'Hereditary Genius,' published one year after Darwin's great work in which was put forward the hypothesis of Pangenesis).

[2] As stated by Darwin himself. See 'Animals and Plants under Domestication' (1868), vol. ii. p. 353.

speculation of Darwin's which he put forward at the end of his work on 'The Variation of Animals and Plants under Domestication' (1868)—the theory of "Pangenesis." "This hypothesis implies that the whole organisation, in the sense of every separate atom or unit, reproduces itself. Hence ovules and pollen-grains, the fertilised seed or egg as well as buds, include and consist of a multitude of germs thrown off from each separate atom of the organism."[1] These germs he calls gem-mules, and admits that they agree to some extent with Buffon's organic molecules, only that neither in these nor in Spencer's physiological units does it seem clear that each "independent or autonomous" organic unit, say each cell, throws off or contributes its free gemmule (or gemmules), which is capable of reproducing a similar cell.[2]

The theory of Pangenesis has not found much favour with biologists.[3] For their purposes it would be neces-

[1] *Loc. cit.*, vol. ii. p. 358.

[2] "Physiologists agree that the whole organism consists of a multitude of elemental parts, which are to a great extent independent of each other" (*loc. cit.*, vol. ii. p. 368). Darwin then quotes Claude Bernard (1866) and Virchow (1860) on the doctrine of the "autonomy" of cells : "I assume that the gem-mules in their dormant state have a mutual affinity for each other, leading to their aggregation either into buds or into the sexual ele-ments" (p. 374). "Physiologists maintain, as we have seen, that each cell, though to a large extent dependent on others, is likewise, to a certain extent, independent or autonomous. I go one small step farther, and assume that each cell casts off a free gemmule, which is capable of reproducing a similar cell" (p. 377). "As each unit, or group of similar units throughout the body, casts off its gemmules, and as all are contained within the smallest egg or seed, and within each spermatozoon or pollen-grain, their number and minuteness must be something inconceivable" (p. 378).

[3] Grant Allen dismisses the whole speculation in the fol-lowing words : "The volume on the variation of animals and plants contained also Darwin's one solitary contribution to the pure speculative philosophy of life—his 'Provisional Hypothesis of Pan-genesis,' by which he strove to account, on philosophical principles,

sary to define somewhat more clearly what those units
or gemmules are. This has accordingly been attempted
in several other hypotheses put forward about the
same time or somewhat later; each thinker having
elaborated, when so inclined, his own fanciful picture,
following consciously or unconsciously in the line of
Spencer's physiological units. We have in Germany
Nägeli's micellar theory, Haeckel's kinetic hypothesis,
Prof. Weismann's idioplasma theory, and Prof. Pflüger's
theory of the compound organic molecule. All these
theories attempt to bring biological phenomena into
closer connection with the firmly established conceptions current in physics and chemistry, where atomism
and kinetics have been so successfully used in analysing
and, to a smaller extent, in putting together the complex processes of nature. Of this I treated in former
chapters. But the hypothesis of Darwin is capable of
another treatment. Wherever we have to deal with a
large, an immense number of single elements or units,
which in their totality form certain phenomena, there

39.
Lends itself
to statistical
treatment.

for the general facts of physical
and mental heredity. Not to
mince matters, it was his one
conspicuous failure, and is now
pretty universally admitted as
such. Let not the love of the
biographer deceive us; Darwin
was here attempting a task *ultra
vires*. As already observed, his
mind, vast as it was, leaned rather
to the concrete than to the
abstract side: he lacked the
distinctively metaphysical and
speculative twist. Strange to say,
too, his abortive theory appeared
some years later than Herbert
Spencer's magnificent all-sided conception of 'Physiological Units,'
put forth expressly to meet the
self-same difficulty. But while
Darwin's hypothesis is rudely
materialistic, Herbert Spencer's
is built up by an acute and
subtle analytical perception of all
the analogous facts in universal
nature. It is a singular instance
of a crude and essentially un-
philosophic conception endeavouring to replace a finished and
delicate philosophical idea" (*loc.
cit.*, p. 126). See also many
references to the unfavourable
criticisms of Pangenesis in the
third volume of the 'Life of
Charles Darwin.'

is room for the statistical treatment. This treatment
entirely ignores the definite nature of the component
units, and merely investigates those properties which
depend upon aggregation in large numbers, the average
or mean results, and the chances of deviations or variations. Now, if organic beings are supposed to be made
up of immeasurably large numbers of units transmitted
to them by inheritance, and capable of self-multiplication,
they must be subject to certain regularities, to regular
deviations or recurrent changes; and, under the influence of selection, be it artificial or automatic, to
certain developments which can be studied without a
precise knowledge of the biological, chemical, or physical nature of these units themselves, or of the mechanism of their movements. Economics, meteorology, the
kinetic theory of gases, deal in this way with complex
phenomena, the exact individual history of which they
are quite incapable of narrating. As in the case of the
kinetic theory of gases we had to translate into statistical language the phenomena of pressure, temperature,
volume, available or hidden energy, &c., so in dealing
statistically with biological phenomena, such as inheritance, on the basis of the theory of Pangenesis, we have
to translate into statistical language such phenomena as
"types, sports of nature, stability, variation and individuality." "The word man," as Mr Galton says,[1]
"when rightly understood, becomes a noun of multitude,
because he is composed of millions, perhaps billions, of
cells, each of which possesses in some sort an independent life, and is parent of other cells. He is a conscious

[1] 'Hereditary Genius' (1892), pp. 349, 350.

whole, formed by the joint agencies of a host of what appear to us to be unconscious or barely conscious elements. . . . The doctrine of Pangenesis gives excellent materials for mathematical formulas, the constants of which might be supplied through averages of facts." [1] Mr Galton does "not see any serious difficulty in the way of mathematicians in framing a compact formula, based on the theory of Pangenesis, to express the composition of organic beings in terms of their inherited and individual peculiarities, and to give us, after certain constants had been determined, the means of foretelling the average distribution of characteristics among a large multidude of offspring whose parentage was known.[2] . . . In short, the theory of Pangenesis brings all the influences that bear on heredity into a form that is appropriate for the grasp of mathematical analysis."

Evidently in the mind of Mr Galton the problem of heredity divides itself into two distinct problems ; and he has himself laboured at the solution of both. We may call the one the " historical " or the " mechanical " problem, the other the " statistical " problem, following the distinction which Maxwell drew when dealing with the kinetics of gases. The historical problem would involve a more detailed account of the nature of those organic units which the theory of Pangenesis, in common with other similar theories, like those of Buffon and Nägeli, assumes, and of the mechanism by which they unite and are transmitted. If this is impossible, or at all events highly hypothetical, the actual following up— by observation and experiment—of the phenomena of

40.
Problem of
Heredity.

[1] 'Hereditary Genius' (1892), p. 356.   [2] Ibid.- p. 358.

variation in special instances would at least allow us to accumulate many interesting life-histories of families of living creatures, and might some day lead to important generalisations. Mr Galton has himself made an attempt to modify and further elaborate the hypothesis of Pangenesis; [1] and Mr William Bateson has given us,

[1] Mr Galton in 1871 advanced certain objections to the theory of Pangenesis, based upon experiments made with the transfusion of blood, and tending to show that blood cannot be the carrier of the germs or gemmules. See a paper read before the Royal Society, March 30, 1871. Darwin did not think Pangenesis had "received its deathblow, though from presenting so many vulnerable points, its life is always in jeopardy" ('Life of Darwin,' vol. iii. p. 195). In 1875 Mr Galton published an article in the 'Contemporary Review,' vol. xxvii. p. 80, entitled "A Theory of Heredity," in which he put what may be termed the atomic theory of life and its propagation into a form in which it might serve as a working formula for statistical research. It is a mistake to look upon any such theory as a biological, mechanical, or historical explanation. For statistical purposes only the scantiest data need be borrowed from biology. There is, however, one very important biological conception which Galton introduced, which is not contained in Darwin's "provisional hypothesis," and which somewhat later became celebrated mainly through the writings of Prof. Weismann. This is the distinction between the germ-plasma and the body-plasma, the former preserving the continuity of life and inheritance, whereas the latter forms the character of the individual, and is probably sterile. In fact, Galton, from a purely statis- tical point of view, anticipated—as several other naturalists did, from various other aspects—the theory of the differentiation of the germinal from the personal portions or aggregates of life units in the "stirp" or sum-total of organic units of some kind which are to be found in the newly fertilised ovum. Prof. J. A. Thomson ('The Science of Life,' p. 147) gives the following succinct statement of the conception of "stirps": "First. Only some of the germs within the stirp attain development in the cells of the 'body.' It is the dominant germs which so develop. Second. The residual germs and their progeny form the sexual elements or buds. The part of the stirp developed into the 'body' is almost sterile. . . . The continuity is kept up by the undeveloped residual portion. Third. The direct descent is not between body and body, but between stirp and stirp. The stirp of the child may be considered to have descended directly from a part of the stirps of each of its parents; but then the personal structure of the child is no more than an imperfect representation of his own stirp, and the personal structure of each of the parents is no more than an imperfect representation of each of their own stirps. This is a definite expression of the notion that the germinal cells of the offspring are in direct continuity with those of the parents. The antithesis between the 'soma' and the chain of sex-cells is emphasised."

in his 'Materials for the Study of Variation,' a remarkable specimen of the historical treatment of the problem. But the aspect we are at present specially interested in is the other one which, in the course of Mr Galton's studies, has presented itself to him with increasing clearness, namely, the bearing which the general laws of averages and statistics have on the facts of inheritance. Thus, in his second main contribution to the subject, which appeared in 1889, twenty years after the earlier work, the statistical problem comes out much more clearly, and quite separated from the mechanical or the historical one.   The hypothesis of Pangenesis is retained only as a general scheme which suggested "the idea though not the phrase of particulate inheritance." It was felt to be no longer necessary, for the purpose of the problem, "to embarrass ourselves with any details of theories of heredity beyond the fact that descent either was particulate or acted as if it were so."[1]   And what is meant by "particulate" (i.e., "bit by bit") is illustrated in the following expressive manner:[2] "Many of the modern buildings in Italy are historically known to have been built out of the pillaged structures of older days.   Here we may observe a column or a lintel serving the same purpose for a second time, and perhaps bearing an inscription that testifies to its origin; while as to the other stones, though the mason may have chipped them here and there and altered their shape a little, few if any came direct from the quarry."   "This simile gives a rude though true idea of the exact meaning of Particulate Inheritance—namely, that each piece of the new structure

41.
Mr Bateson's historical treatment.

42.
"Particulate" descent.

<hr>

[1] 'Natural Inheritance,' p. 193.   [2] Ibid., p. 8.

is derived from a corresponding piece of some older one, as a lintel was derived from a lintel, a column from a column, a piece of wall from a piece of wall. . . . We appear to be severally built up out of a host of minute particles of whose nature we know nothing, any one of which may be derived from any one progenitor, but which are usually transmitted in aggregates, considerable groups being derived from the same progenitor. It would seem that while the embryo is developing itself, the particles more or less qualified for each new post wait, as it were, in competition to obtain it. Also that the particle that succeeds must owe its success partly to accident of position and partly to being better qualified than any equally well-placed competitor to gain a lodgment. Thus the step-by-step development of the embryo cannot fail to be influenced by an incalculable number of small and mostly unknown circumstances."[1]

Now, wherever we have to do with a very large number of unknown elements which combine to produce a result, we are introduced to those conditions with which the theory of averages and probability deals. The curve of error discovered by Laplace and Gauss to picture the distribution of a large number of observations around the average or mean position, which is taken as the most probable or correct one, comes in as a valuable aid, not in studying the errors of natural growth, but as the graphical illustration of the deviations or variations which cluster around what we call the normal, or with Quetelet the mean, figure. Only the interest is now attached not so much to specifying and defining the

[1] 'Natural Inheritance,' p. 9.

homme moyen as to studying the deviations from this ideal standard. " How little," says Mr Galton,[1] " is conveyed by the bald statement that the average income of English families is £100 a-year, compared with what we should learn if we were told how English incomes were distributed." A crowd of data furnish for the astronomer the material out of which he has to choose the most probable, the correct figure; a crowd of observations furnish for the naturalist the material from which he has to learn how nature deviates from her types and exhibits variations which are the factors of change and development. Thus, under the hands of Mr Galton, the Law of Error becomes a Law of Distribution, and the whole machinery of the doctrine of probabilities, " excogitated for the use of astronomers and others who are concerned with extreme accuracy of measurement, and without the slightest idea, until the time of Quetelet, that they might be applicable to human measures,[2] become the only tools by which an opening can be cut through the formidable thicket of difficulties that bars the path of those who pursue 'the science of man.'"

Hence while most people regard statistics as dull, they become for the naturalist and student of human nature " full of beauty and interest ";[3] there is scarcely anything so apt to impress the imagination as the wonderful form of cosmic order expressed by the " law of frequency of error." " It would have been personified by the Greeks, and deified if they had known of it."[4]

---

[1] 'Natural Inheritance,' p. 35.
[2] Ibid., pp. 55, 62.
[3] Ibid., p. 62.
[4] Ibid., p. 66.

43.
Application
of theory of
error.

Every mathematical instrument, when applied to a novel purpose for which it was not originally invented, "derives as much benefit in its development as it confers through being made use of." Thus Mr Galton's application of the theory of error to the facts of distribution and variation not only enabled him to bring method and order into such questions raised by the Darwinian theory [1] as natural selection,

[1] It is perhaps premature to speak with great confidence of the actual results which have been gained by this novel branch of scientific inquiry, or of the practical importance which these results may have in the future with regard to some of the great social questions. Still, in a history of thought it is of importance to note how, through Mr Galton's writings, the problem of Inheritance has acquired quite a new aspect. This finds expression in his famous so-called "law of filial regression," which goes against "the current belief that the child tends to resemble its parents" (p. 104). In fact, all opinions and theories which had been propounded before Galton, either popularly or scientifically, were based upon a one-sided regard to the more visible portion of the ancestry—viz., the parents ; whereas, if any general theory like that of "pangenesis," or of "stirps," or of the "differentiation of the germ-plasma and the body-plasma" be made the basis of discussion, the whole ancestral tree must be considered to contribute to the formation of the characters of any individual. In fact, we have before us not one pair, but an endless line of pairs which are, as the terms of a series, connected by the powers of the number two ; and it is then easily seen, without going into refinements (which, however, in the further elaboration of the problem, may become very important), that the first term of the series, which represents the parents, contributes only one-half of the whole, that is, each parent one quarter. It is also evident, if each parent only contributes on the average one quarter, that an exceptional bias in any direction communicated by them would be balanced in the long-run by the opposite action of the remaining ancestry, and that, contrary to ordinary belief, inheritance would operate in the direction of bringing each individual back to the average of the whole lineage. Mr Galton first observed this law of regression to the average by definite countings with seeds and "a comparatively small number of observations of human stature "; and he remarks that if it was only by these experiments and observations that the law of regression had been established, it could not have been expected that the truth of the apparent paradox would be recognised. When, however, the rule was once expressed, it was "easily shown that we ought to expect filial regression, . . . two different reasons for its occurrence " existing—" the one connected with our notions of stability of type, the other as follows : the child inherits

regression, reversion to ancestral types, extinction of families, effect of bias in marriage, mixture of inheritance, latent elements, and generally to prepare the ground for the combined labours of the naturalist and the statistician; he was also able to put novel problems to the mathematician.

To understand this latter point we must realise the

partly from his parents, partly from his ancestry. In every population that intermarries freely, when the genealogy of any man is traced far backwards, his ancestry will be found to consist of such varied elements that they are indistinguishable from a sample taken at haphazard from the general population." As to the mathematical problem referred to, it was submitted by Mr Galton in a definite form to Mr J. D. H. Dickson, whose solution is given in the appendix to 'Natural Inheritance.' On this solution Mr Galton remarks: "The problem may not be difficult to an accomplished mathematician, but I certainly never felt such a glow of loyalty and respect towards the sovereignty and wide sway of mathematical analysis as when his answer arrived, confirming, by pure mathematical reasoning, my various and laborious statistical conclusions with far more minuteness than I had dared to hope, because the data ran somewhat roughly, and I had to smooth them with tender caution. . . . It is obvious from this close accord of calculation with observation, that the law of Error holds throughout with sufficient precision to be of real service, and that the various results of my statistics are not casual and disconnected determinations, but strictly interdependent" (p. 202). Another passage indicating how much the inferences from the law of regression run contrary to popular opinions on inheritance is the following: "The law of Regression tells heavily against the full hereditary transmission of any gift. Only a few out of many children would be likely to differ from mediocrity so widely as their mid-parent, and still fewer would differ as widely as the more exceptional of the two parents. The more bountifully the parent is gifted by nature, the more rare will be his good fortune if he begets a son who is as richly endowed as himself, and still more so if he has a son who is endowed yet more largely. But the law is even-handed; it levies an equal succession-tax on the transmission of badness as of goodness. If it discourages the extravagant hopes of a gifted parent that his children will inherit all his powers, it no less discountenances extravagant fears that they will inherit all his weakness and disease" (p. 106). Prof. Karl Pearson ('The Grammar of Science,' 2nd ed., p. 479) says of the law of ancestral inheritance: "If Darwinism be the true view of evolution—*i.e.*, if we are to describe evolution by natural selection combined with heredity—then the law which gives us definitely and concisely the type of the offspring in terms of the ancestral peculiarities, is at once the foundation-stone of biology and the basis upon which heredity becomes an exact branch of science."

great difference which exists between dealing with a vast number of lifeless and of living units. This difference becomes evident if we consider that in the former case the number of units is unalterable and the units are indestructible; in the latter the elements or units are subject to enormous increase and corresponding destruction, generally with a preponderance of the first. In the kinetic theory of gases we have to consider, in every finite system, the conservation or persistence of mass and motion, the two units we deal with. To these two properties of an immensely large crowd we have to reduce the various phenomena of pressure, temperature, volume, available or unavailable energy. In the vast crowd of gemmules which build up a new organism or regenerate an existing one, we have to deal with a continual influx or creation of new units and a continual extinction and ejection of old or dead ones. Without venturing on any theory as to how this state of things has come about, we may see that the mathematics and statistics of such crowds must be different from those referring to stable, lifeless assemblages. The twofold task arises of formulating the new problems and solving them. To the extent that this is possible we shall be able to deal mathematically with the great problem of variability; and for the practical application of these mathematical formulæ we shall have to collect long series of facts and data of measurements—the material which has to be statistically arranged and sifted, and which is to confirm the conclusions and test the results which calculation has brought out.

Mr Galton found ready, or instituted himself, various countings of large numbers, which formed valuable material for his mathematical schemes, and which confirmed them in a surprising degree. Some very elaborate series of measurements of the varying dimensions of individual members in large crowds of animals were published by Prof. Weldon, whose monograph on Crabs will always remain an historical document.[1] It was noticed about the same time that the attempt to bring the measured deviations from the average into a symmetrical arrangement on the sides of more or less was impossible, and the fact had to be realised and mathematically expressed that special influences tending towards change on the intermixing of different varieties produced an asymmetrical distribution or frequency:[2] in fact, nature works with loaded dice, producing a bias in certain directions; this is the favour which, according to Darwin, Wallace, and Lamarck's ideas, must meet the better fitted individuals and exact from them a smaller tribute in the inevitable process of destruction and removal.

We owe it to Prof. Karl Pearson to have first grasped clearly and comprehensively the mathematical problem involved, and to have solved it in a manner useful for

45.
Prof. Pearson. The mathematical problem.

[1] See the 'Proceedings of the Royal Society' since 1890, notably vol. lvii., 1895, p. 360 *sqq.*

[2] "An asymmetrical frequency curve may arise from two quite distinct classes of causes. In the first place the material measured may be heterogeneous, and may consist of a mixture of two or more homogeneous materials. . . .

The second class of frequency curves arises in the case of homogeneous material when the tendency to deviation on one side of the mean is unequal to the tendency to deviation on the other side" (Karl Pearson, "On the Mathematical Theory of Evolution," 'Trans. Roy. Soc.,' 1895, p. 344).

biological research.[1]   He has thus put into the hands of
naturalists an instrument wherewith to describe graphically the observed facts of variation and other allied

[1] A considerable literature has already accumulated in this novel branch of exact inquiry. The complete list of it is given in a pamphlet by Georg Duncker, entitled ' Die Methode der Variations-statistik' (Leipzig, 1899). From this list (p. 60) it will be seen that one of the earliest workers in the field of biological statistics was the botanist F. Ludwig, whose 'Abschnitte der Mathematischen Botanik' have appeared in various periodicals abroad since the year 1883. The philosopher, however, to whom we are most indebted for the mathematical foundations of the whole theory, is, as noted above, Prof. Karl Pearson, whose "Contributions to the Mathematical Theory of Evolution" have been appearing since the year 1893 in the Trans. of the Royal Society. Very helpful abstracts of these contributions, covering a large field of mathematical theory, and containing elaborate discussions of many of the terms recently introduced into biological science, such as regression, reversion, inheritance, panmixia, selection, &c., will be found in the Proceedings of the Royal Society (1893, onwards). Also in his collected essays, 'The Chances of Death and other Studies in Evolution' (2 vols., 1897) ; and, lastly, in the later chapters of the second edition of his 'Grammar of Science'(1890). From the latter it will be seen what far-reaching inferences may eventually be drawn from the quantitative treatment and mathematical discussion of biological data ; notably the results so far gained "lead us to consider variation as a permanent attribute of living forms, which can hardly

have been substantially modified since the beginnings of life. In the same manner we find heredity intimately associated with variation in the individual, and not differing very substantially as we pass from one character to a second, or from one to another form of life. We conclude that variation and inheritance rather precede than follow evolution ; they are, at present, *one* fundamental mystery of the vital unit" (p. 502). Prof. Pearson, whose training was that of a mathematician and a lawyer, approached the problems of biology from the exact point of view, and it is interesting to see how, in many ways, he comes to results similar to those arrived at by one of the other great representatives of modern biological research, Mr Wm. Bateson. See his 'Materials for the Study of Variation, treated with especial regard to the discontinuity in the Origin of Species' (1894). If I understand him rightly, his researches have led him to the conclusion that variation cannot be the work of natural selection, since he has given " such evidence as to certain selected forms of variations " as to afford "a presumption that the discontinuity of which species is an expression has its origin, not in the environment, nor in any phenomenon of adaptation, but in the intrinsic nature of organisms themselves, manifested in the original discontinuity of variations" (p. 567). This " disposes, once and for all, of the attempt to interpret all perfection and definiteness of form as the work of selection. . . . It suggests, in brief, that the discontinuity of species results from the discontinu-

phenomena, such as correlation, heredity, regression and panmixia, and he has shown how to analyse these graphical tracings so as to indicate the several possible elements out of which they are compounded, representing separate agencies which are at work in nature. The mathematical inventions of Fourier had similarly enabled physicists to analyse the complicated periodicity of tidal curves into their elements, and, under the hands of Ohm and Helmholtz, to resolve the harmonies of music.

We have here arrived at the last stage of the development of the statistical view of nature. It has been variously judged by biologists according to the special views they take of their problems, and also according

ity of variation" (p. 568). Mr Bateson expects great assistance from the statistical methods. "There is," he says, "no common shell or butterfly of whose variations something would not be learnt, were some hundreds of the same species collected from a few places and statistically examined in respect of some varying character. Any one can take part in this class of work, though few do" (p. 574). Notwithstanding the general resemblance noted above between the ideas of Mr Bateson and of Prof. Pearson, they differ so much in detail as to be led to confess that they do not understand one another's languages. Cf. W. Bateson, "Heredity, Differentiation, and other Conceptions of Biology," 'Roy. Soc. Proc.,' vol. lxix. pp. 193-205 ; K. Pearson, "On the Fundamental Conceptions of Biology," 'Biometrika,' vol. i. pp. 320-344. Prof. Pearson's view is that, for the working out of the theory of evolution, "biological conceptions can be accurately defined, and so defined measured with quantita-tive exactness" (loc. cit., p. 324). Mr Bateson, on the other hand, regards them as to some extent out of the reach of mathematical definition and measurement. "Discontinuous variation" in Mr Bateson's special sense—by which we may perhaps understand great as distinguished from small but numerous deviations from the average —Prof. Pearson regards as "statistically negligible for the purpose of vital statistics" (pp. 333, 334). He, in fact, holds closer to Darwinism as understood by Darwin, who never looked with much favour on Huxley's view, for example, that "sports," as distinguished from the sum of small differences in individuals, might furnish an appreciable part of the materials for natural selection. Mr Bateson's view found favour with Huxley, as may be observed in the 'Life and Letters.' On the novelty and value of Prof. Pearson's methods, see also the Address by Prof. Weldon to the Zoological Section of the British Association in 1898.

to the degree in which they appreciate and are able to grasp mathematical methods. The subject is still under discussion, and will belong to the History of Thought of a coming age. It is enough to have indicated the latest lines of reasoning which our century has marked out, and to notice how they form a new and remarkable instance of the growth and diffusion of the exact or mathematical spirit in a department of research hitherto almost untouched by it, prepared though it has been for such treatment by one among whose great endowments a grasp of mathematical reasoning hardly formed a distinctive feature. In former chapters I have had occasion to show how Charles Darwin introduced into the science of nature two novel points of view—the genetic view and the process of judicial sifting of evidence. We may now add that he has indirectly, more than directly, furthered quite as much the statistical view of natural phenomena through which we have learned to find and trace law and order in great realms of phenomena and events usually supposed to be governed by what is termed blind chance. The study of this blind chance in theory and practice is one of the greatest scientific performances of the nineteenth century.

46.
Statistical
knowledge
one-sided.

But whilst acknowledging the great importance which the statistical treatment of phenomena has acquired in our age, and the value of the statistical view of many large departments of natural processes which escape almost every other mode of dealing with them, we must not forget that it is essentially one-sided.

Clerk-Maxwell has suggestively opposed it alike to the mechanical and the historical views, of which the former tries to describe the general mechanism *under* which, the latter the individual steps and incidents *by* which, special events or phenomena proceed and are characterised. Earlier chapters of this narrative attempted to give an account of the former, whilst the essentially historical treatment belongs to another portion of the work. The word history has generally been reserved for records which deal with those events in which human consciousness has played a large, if not an overwhelming, part, and has been able to assist the observer by its own accounts and representations. What should we know of human life and human interests without them, and how helpless—in spite of minutest observation—do we still appear to be in understanding the life of the brute and mute creation, even of the domestic animals, our daily friends and companions? But if history, as opposed to statistics, really seems only possible where the living voice or the surviving narrative of those who have departed helps us to a true understanding of its incidents and its meaning, it also imposes upon us the task of sifting its value and trustworthiness critically. Mathematics, logic, and statistics may do something to exclude the actually impossible or the highly improbable from a vast mass of material; but more delicate criteria are required in dealing with the accumulated testimony of bygone ages. With an unerring instinct of what, in addition to mathematical measurements, may be required in order to accomplish this task, the nineteenth century has not only nursed the scientific spirit and cultivated its methods, but with equal diligence and originality those other methods which lie at the foundation of

47.
Critical
methods.

all recent philosophical thought — the methods of criticism.

And yet, before taking leave of science and entering on a comprehensive appreciation of the workings of the Critical Spirit with which all our thought seems to be permeated, I owe to my readers the attempt to answer one remaining question. If it be true, as the foregoing narrative has abundantly insisted, that through the increasing application of mathematical methods of measuring and calculating, our thought has become truly scientific and our knowledge accurate and useful for describing and predicting phenomena, as also for manifold practical applications, we may be curious to know whether the refined instrument, mathematical thought itself, has been subject to such change and development as has been undergone by the various branches of science to which it has been applied. In fact, we have to ask the question, How has mathematical thought itself fared in the course of the nineteenth century? The concluding chapter of the present volume will try to give a reply to this question.

48.
The instru-
ment of
exact re-
search.

CHAPTER XIII.

ON THE DEVELOPMENT OF MATHEMATICAL THOUGHT DURING THE NINETEENTH CENTURY.

IN venturing upon the last and most abstract portion of the great domain of Scientific Thought of the century, it may be well to remind the reader that it is not a history of science but a history of thought that I am writing. When dealing in the foregoing chapters with manifold discoveries, drawn promiscuously from the various natural sciences, I have done so only to show how the scientific mind has, in the course of the period, come to regard the things of nature from different points of view, and to think and reason on them differently. Such changes have frequently been brought about by the discovery of novel facts, but this alone has not generally sufficed to mark also a change in the manner of reasoning on and thinking about them. The increase in the number of natural species, of the chemical elements or of the smaller planets, has not necessarily made us think differently about these things in themselves: the theory and point of view may change without any change in the object towards which they are directed,

1.
History of thought.

for they mark more the attitude of the beholder than the things which he regards. It is true that a very small addition to our actual knowledge of facts, like the sudden appearance of some characteristic feature in a landscape, may sometimes entirely alter the whole aspect, induce us to abandon our accustomed views, and call up suddenly an unforeseen train of ideas; in such a case, perhaps, this insignificant discovery becomes historically interesting, although it is mainly by the altered trains of thought which it has evoked that it has become important to us.

2.
Difference between thought and knowledge.

The difference of scientific knowledge and scientific thought is thus owing to the two factors which are involved—the facts of science or nature on the one side and the scientifically thinking mind on the other. Now it might appear as if this difference vanished when we approach the abstract science of mathematics, or at least that of number; for in numbering and counting we have really only to do with a process of thought, and it would seem as if the science of number were itself the science of thought, or at least a portion of it. In fact, the question arises, Is there any difference between mathematical science and mathematical thought? Some considerations might induce us to think that there is not. On the other side, I shall try to show in this chapter that there is, and that the development of mathematics during our period has brought this out very clearly and prominently.

3.
Popular prejudices regarding mathematics.

There is an opinion current among many thinking persons who have not occupied themselves with mathematical science, though they may be very efficient in calculating and measuring, that there is really nothing new in mathematics, that two and two always make four, that the sum of the angles in a triangle always make two right angles, and that all progress in mathematics is merely a question of intricacy, a never-ending process of increased complication by which you can puzzle even the cleverest calculator.   To them the history of mathematics would be something analogous to the history of games like whist or chess, the resources and complications of which seem to be inexhaustible.   So they think [1] that the intricacies and refinements of elementary and higher mathematics will supply endless material for training the minds of schoolboys or trying the ingenuity

[1] "Some people have been found to regard all mathematics, after the 47th proposition of Euclid, as a sort of morbid secretion, to be compared only with the pearl said to be generated in the diseased oyster, or, as I have heard it described, 'une excroissance maladive de l'esprit humain.'   Others find its justification, its *raison d'être*, in its being either the torch-bearer leading the way, or the handmaiden holding up the train of Physical Science ; and a very clever writer in a recent magazine article expresses his doubts whether it is, in itself, a more serious pursuit, or more worthly of interesting an intellectual human being, than the study of chess problems or Chinese puzzles.   What is it to us, they say, if the three angles of a triangle are equal to two right angles, or if every even number is, or may be, the sum of two primes, or if every equation of an odd degree must have a real root ?   How dull, stale, flat, and unprofitable are such and such like announcements !   Much more interesting to read an account of a marriage in high life, or the details of an international boat-race.   But this is like judging of architecture from being shown some bricks and mortar, or even a quarried stone of a public building, or of painting from the colours mixed on the palette, or of music by listening to the thin and screech sounds produced by a bow passed haphazard over the strings of a violin.   The world of ideas which it discloses or illuminates, the contemplation of divine beauty and order which it induces, the harmonious connexion of its parts, the infinite hierarchy and absolute evidence of the truths with which it is concerned, these, and such like, are the surest grounds of the title of mathematics to human regard, and would remain unimpeached and unimpaired were the plan of the universe unrolled like a map at our feet, and the mind of man qualified to take in the whole scheme of creation at a glance " (Prof. J. J. Sylvester, Address before Brit. Assoc., see 'Report,' 1869, p. 7).

of senate-house examiners and examinees, without for a
moment considering the question whether mathematical
thought as distinguished from mathematical problems is
capable of and has undergone any radical. and fundamental change or development.

Closely allied with this is the further question as to
the use of mathematics.   Two extreme views have always
existed on this point.[1]   To some, mathematics is only a
measuring and calculating instrument,[2] and their interest

[1] Of the two greatest mathematicians of modern times, Newton and
Gauss, the former can be considered
as a representative of the first, the
latter of the second class ; neither of
them was exclusively so, and Newton's inventions in the pure science
of mathematics were probably equal
to Gauss's work in applied mathematics.   Newton's reluctance to
publish the method of fluxions invented and used by him may perhaps be attributed to the fact that
he was not satisfied with the logical
foundations of the calculus ; and
Gauss is known to have abandoned
his electro-dynamic speculations, as
he could not find a satisfactory
physical basis (see *supra*, p. 67).
Others who were not troubled by
similar logical or practical scruples
stepped in and did the work, to the
great benefit of scientific progress.
Newton's greatest work, the 'Principia,' laid the foundation of mathematical physics ; Gauss's greatest
work, the 'Disquisitiones Arithmeticæ,' that of higher arithmetic
as distinguished from algebra.
Both works, written in the synthetic style of the ancients, are
difficult, if not deterrent, in their
form, neither of them leading the
reader by easy steps to the
results.   It took twenty or more
years before either of these works
received due recognition ; neither

found favour at once before that
great tribunal of mathematical
thought, the Paris Academy of
Sciences.   Newton's early reputation was established by other
researches and inventions, notably
in optics ; Gauss became known
through his theoretical rediscovery
of Ceres, the first of the minor
planets (see above, vol. i. p. 182).
The country of Newton is still pre-
eminent for its culture of mathematical physics, that of Gauss for
the most abstract work in mathematics.   Not to speak of living
authorities, I need only mention
Stokes and Clerk-Maxwell on the
one side, Grassmann, Weierstrass,
and Georg Cantor on the other.

[2] Huxley said : " Mathematics
may be compared to a mill of
exquisite workmanship which grinds
you stuff of any degree of fineness :
but, nevertheless, what you get out
depends on what you put in ; and
as the grandest mill in the world
will not extract wheat-flour from
peas-cods, so pages of formulæ will
not get a definite result out of
loose data " ; and on another occasion he said that mathematics " is
that study which knows nothing of
observation, nothing of induction,
nothing of experiment, nothing of
causation. "   The former statement
was endorsed by Lord Kelvin
('Pop. Lectures,' &c., vol. ii. p.

ceases as soon as discussions arise which cannot benefit those who use the instrument for the purposes of application in mechanics, astronomy, physics, statistics, and other sciences. At the other extreme we have those who are animated exclusively by the love of pure science. To them pure mathematics, with the theory of numbers[1] at the head, is the one real and genuine science, and the applications have only an interest in so far as they contain or suggest problems in pure mathematics. They are mainly occupied with examining and strengthening the foundations of mathematical reasoning and purifying its methods, inventing rigorous proofs, and testing the validity and range of applicability of current conceptions. We may say that the former are led by practical, the latter by philosophical, interests, and these latter may be either logical or ontological,[2]

102); the latter was energetically repudiated by Sylvester in his famous Address to the first section of the British Assoc. at Exeter (1869, 'Report,' &c., p. 1, &c.)

[1] Gauss considered mathematics to be "the Queen of the Sciences, and arithmetic the Queen of Mathematics. She frequently condescends to do service for astronomy and other natural sciences, but to her belongs, under all circumstances, the foremost place" (see 'Gauss zum Gedächtniss,' by Sartorius von Waltershausen, Leipzig, 1856, p. 79). Cayley's presidential Address to the British Association, 1883, has been frequently quoted: "Mathematics connect themselves on one side with common life and the physical sciences; on the other side with philosophy in regard to our notions of space and time and the questions which have arisen as to the universality and necessity of the truths of mathematics, and the foundation of our knowledge of them. I would remark here that the connection (if it exists) of arithmetic and algebra with the notion of time is far less obvious than that of geometry with the notion of space" ('Mathematical Papers,' vol. xi. p. 130). In addition to founding higher arithmetic, Gauss occupied himself with the foundations of geometry, and, as he expected much from the development of the theory of numbers, so he placed "great hopes on the cultivation of the *geometria situs*, in which he saw large undeveloped tracts which could not be conquered by the existing calculus" (Sartorius, *loc. cit.*, p. 88).

[2] To this might be added the psychological interest which attaches to mathematical conceptions. The late Prof. Paul Du Bois - Reymond occupied himself

inasmuch as number and form are considered to be
the highest categories of human thought, or likewise as
the ultimate elements of all reality. These two interests
existed already in antiquity,[1] as the word "geometry"

much with the question. See the
following works : 'Die Allgemeine
Functionentheorie,' part i., Tübingen, 1882 ; 'Ueber die Grundlagen der Erkenntniss in den exacten Wissenschaften,' Tübingen,
1890 ; and his paper "Ueber die
Paradoxien des Infinitärcalcüls"
('Mathematische Annalen,' vol. ix.
p. 149). In addition to the two
main interests which attach to
mathematical research, and which
I distinguish as the practical and
the philosophical, a third point of
view has sprung up in modern
times which can be called the
purely logical. It proposes to
treat any special development of
mathematical research with the
aid of a definite, logically connected complex of ideas, and not
to be satisfied to solve definite
problems with the help of any
methods which may casually present themselves, however ingenious
they may be. In this way the
great geometrician, Jacob Steiner,
e.g., refused the assistance of analysis in the solution of geometrical
problems, conceiving geometry as
a complete organism which should
solve its problems by its own
means. This view has been much
strengthened by the development
in modern times of the theory of
Groups ; a group of operations
being defined as a sequence of such
operations as always lead back
again to operations of the same
kind. Mathematical rigorists in
this sense would look upon the
use of mixed methods or operations not belonging to the same
group with that kind of disfavour
with which we should regard an

essayist who could not express his
ideas in pure English, but was
obliged to import foreign words
and expressions. It is interesting
to see that the country which has
offended most by the importation
of foreign words — namely, Germany—is that in which this purism
in mathematical taste has found
the most definite expression. (See,
inter alia, Prof. Friedrich Engel's
Inaugural Lecture, "Der Gesch-
mack in der neueren Mathematik,"
Leipzig, 1890, as also Prof. F.
Klein's suggestive tract, 'Ver-
gleichende Betrachtungen über
neuere Geometrische Forschungen,'
Erlangen, 1872.)

[1] The literature of this subject
is considerable. I confine myself
to two works. The late eminent
mathematician, Hermann Hankel,
of whom more in the sequel of
this chapter, besides showing much
originality in the higher branches
of the science, took great interest
in its philosophical foundations
and historical beginnings. In 1870
he published a small but highly
interesting volume, 'Zur Geschichte der Mathematik in Alter-
thum und Mittelalter' (Leipzig,
Teubner). We have, besides, the
great work of Prof. Moritz Cantor,
'Vorlesungen über Geschichte der
Mathematik,' in three large volumes
(Leipzig, Teubner). It brings the
history down to 1758. Referring
to the two interests which led to
mathematical investigations, Hankel
says (p. 88) : "From the moment
that Greek philosophers begin to
attract our attention through their
mathematical researches, the aspect which mathematics present

and the well - known references to mathematical ideas in the schools of Pythagoras and Plato indicate. An ancient fragment[1] which enumerates briefly the Grecian mathematicians, says of Pythagoras, " He changed the occupation with this branch of knowledge into a real science, inasmuch as he contemplated its foundation from a higher point of view, and investigated the theorems less materially and more intellectually ; "[2] and of Plato it says that " He filled his writings with mathematical discussions, showing everywhere how much of geometry attaches itself to philosophy."[3]

This twofold connection of mathematical with other pursuits has, after the lapse of many centuries, come prominently forward again in the nineteenth century. We have already had to record a powerful stimulus to mathematical thought in almost every chapter in which we dealt with the fruitful ideas which governed scientific work, and we have now no less to draw attention to the philosophical treatment which has been bestowed upon the foundations of science and the inroad of mathemati-

changes radically. Whilst among the earlier civilised nations we only meet with routine and practice, with empirical rules which served practical purposes in an isolated manner, the Grecian mind on the other side recognised, from the first moment when it became acquainted with this matter, that it contained something which transcended all those practical ends, but which was worthy of special attention, and which could be expressed in a general form, being, in fact, an object of science. This is the high merit of the Greek mathematicians ; nor need one fear that this merit should be diminished by admitting that they borrowed the new material from the ancient Egyptian civilisation."

[1] The fragment referred to is preserved by Proclus, and is given in full in Cantor's work (vol. i. p. 124 *sqq.*) He calls it an ancient catalogue of mathematicians. It is generally attributed to Eudemus of Rhodes, who belonged to the peripatetic school of philosophy, and was the author of several historical treatises on geometry and astronomy (Cantor, vol. i. p. 108).

[2] Cantor, vol. i. p. 137.

[3] Ibid., p. 213.

cal into philosophical thought;[1] so much so that this
closing chapter on the development of mathematical
thought forms a fitting link with the next great department of our subject—the Philosophy of the Century.

6.
Origin of
mathe-
matics.

We are told that mathematics among the Greeks had
its origin in the Geometry invented by the ancient
Egyptians for practical surveying purposes. The first
mathematical problems arose in the practice of mensuration. Modern mathematical thought received in
an analogous manner its greatest stimulus through the
Uranometry of Kepler, Newton, and Laplace: through
the mechanics and the survey of the heavens new
methods for solving astronomical problems were invented in the seventeenth and eighteenth centuries,
and the nineteenth century can be said to have attempted to perform towards this new body of doctrine
the same task that Euclid, three hundred years before
the Christian era, performed towards the then existing
mathematics. As Proclus tells us, " putting together
the elements, arranging much from Eudoxus, furnishing
much from Theætetus, he, moreover, subjected to rigorous
proofs what had been negligently demonstrated by his
predecessors."[2] What one man, so far as we know, did
for the Grecian science, a number of great thinkers in

---

[1] Thus, for instance, the recent
investigations and theories of the
"manifold," as they have been
set forth by Prof. Georg Cantor
of Halle, constitute, as it were,
a new chapter in mathematical
science, whereas they were formerly a subject merely of philosophical interest. See a remark to
this effect by B. Kerry at the end
of his very interesting article on
Cantor's doctrine in the 9th
vol. of Avenarius's 'Zeitschrift
für wissenschaftliche Philosophie'
(1885), p. 231, where he refers to
Kant's comparison of philosophy
to a Hecuba "tot generis natisque
potens."

[2] Quoted by Cantor, vol. i. p.
247. See also Hankel, *loc. cit.*,
p. 381 *sqq.*

our century, among whom I only mention Gauss, Cauchy, and Weierstrass, attempted to do for the new science which was created during the two preceding centuries. As Prof. Klein says, "We are living in a critical period, similar to that of Euclid." [1]

[1] See 'The Evanston Colloquium, Lectures on Mathematics delivered in August and September 1893,' by Felix Klein, notably Lecture vi. In this lecture Prof. Klein explains his view (to which he had given utterance in his address before the Congress of Mathematics at Chicago: 'Papers published by the American Mathematical Society,' vol. i. p. 133. New York, 1896) on the relation of pure mathematics to applied science. This view is based upon the distinction between what he calls the "naïve and the refined intuition." . . . "It is the latter that we find in Euclid; he carefully develops his system on the basis of well-formulated axioms, is fully conscious of the necessity of exact proofs, clearly distinguishes between the commensurable and the incommensurable, and so forth. . . . The naïve intuition, on the other hand, was especially active during the period of the genesis of the differential and integral calculus. Thus we see that Newton assumes without hesitation the existence, in every case, of a velocity in a moving point, without troubling himself with the inquiry whether there might not be continuous functions having no derivative."

In the opinion of Prof. Klein "the root of the matter lies in the fact that the naïve intuition is not exact, while the refined intuition is not properly intuition at all, but arises through the logical development from axioms considered as perfectly exact."

In the sequel Prof. Klein shows that the naïve intuition imports into the elementary conceptions elements which are left out in the purely logical development, and that this again leads to conclusions which are not capable of being verified by intuition, no mental image being possible. Thus, for instance, the abstract geometry of Lobatchevsky and Riemann led Beltrami to the logical conception of the pseudosphere of which we cannot form any mental image. Similar views to those of Prof. Klein have been latterly expressed by H. Poincaré in his suggestive volume 'La Science et l'Hypothèse' (Paris, 1893). He there says (p. 90): ". . . L'expérience joue un rôle indispensable dans la genèse de la géométrie ; mais ce serait une erreur d'en conclure que la géométrie est une science expérimentale, même en partie. . . . La géométrie ne serait que l'étude des mouvements des solides ; mais elle ne s'occupe pas en réalité des solides naturels, elle a pour objet certains solides idéaux, absolument invariables, qui n'en sont qu'une image simplifiée et bien lointaine. . . . Ce qui est l'objet de la géométrie c'est l'étude d'un 'groupe' particulier ; mais le concept général de groupe préexiste dans notre esprit au moins en puissance. . . . Seulement, parmi tous les groupes possibles, il faut choisir celui qui sera pour ainsi dire l'étalon auquel nous rapporterons les phénomènes naturels." This distinction between the mathematics of intuition and the mathematics of logic has also been forced upon us from quite a different quarter. The complica-

It is right to place the name of Gauss at the head, for his investigations regarding several fundamental and critical questions in arithmetic and geometry date from the last years of the eighteenth century, long before Cauchy's influence made itself felt. This is now abundantly clear through the publication of Gauss's works, and from much of his correspondence with personal friends, notably with the astronomer Bessel. We can now understand how those who knew him regarded him as a kind of mathematical oracle to whom "nothing in theory existed that he had not looked at from all sides,"[1] and who anticipated in his own mind the development which mathematical thought was to take for a long time after him. And yet it was not to him primarily that the great change was due which came over mathematical reasoning during the first half of the century. Gauss was not a great teacher. In fact, there existed in the first quarter of the period only one great training school in advanced mathematics, and that was Paris.

There it was that Augustin Cauchy—first as lecturer,

tion of modern mathematics and the refinement of the modern theories have brought about the desire "to create an abridged system of mathematics adapted to the needs of the applied sciences, without passing through the whole realm of abstract mathematics" (Klein, *loc. cit.*, p. 48). In this country Prof. Perry has made a beginning by publishing his well-known work, 'Calculus for Engineers,' which has been welcomed by Prof. Klein in Germany, and which has led to an extensive correspondence in the pages of 'Nature'; it being recognised by many that a quicker road must be

made from the elements to the higher applications of mathematics in the natural sciences than the present school system, beginning with Euclid, admits of. The separation of the logical and practical treatment of any science, as likewise the independent development in Germany of the polytechnic school alongside of the university, has, however, its dangers, as is recognised by Prof. Klein ('Chicago Mathematical Papers,' p. 136).

[1] See Bessel's letter to Gauss, 27th December 1810, in 'Briefwechsel zwischen G. and B., Leipzig, 1880, p. 132.

then as professor—exerted his great influence in the famous École Polytechnique, in the Sorbonne, in the Collége de France.[1] In contrast with Gauss—who was self-contained, proud, and unapproachable, whose finished and perfect mathematical tracts were, even to those who worshipped him, an abomination,[2] owing to their unintelligible and novel enunciation, who hated lecturing —Cauchy possessed the enthusiasm and patience of the teacher,[3] spent hours with his pupils, and published his lectures on the foundations of the Calculus for the benefit of the rising mathematical generation. Thus he has the merit of having created a new school of mathematical thought—not only in France but also abroad, where the greatest intellects, such as that of Abel,[4] expressed themselves indebted to him for having pointed out the only right road of progress. It will be useful to define somewhat more closely wherein this new school differed from that preceding it, which culminated in the great names of Euler, Lagrange, and Laplace.

The great development of modern as compared with ancient mathematics may be stated as consisting in the in-

[1] See Valson, 'La Vie et les Travaux du Baron Cauchy,' Paris, 1868, vol. i. p. 60 sqq.

[2] " On disait que sa manière d'exposer était mauvaise, ou encore qu'il faisait comme le renard, qui efface avec sa queue les traces de ses pas sur le sable. Crelle dit, selon Abel, que tout ce qu'écrit Gauss n'est qu'abomination (Gräuel), car c'est si obscur qu'il est presque impossible d'y rien comprendre " (Bjerknes, ' Niels Henrik Abel,' Trad. française, Paris, 1885, p. 92).

[3] " C'est que Cauchy alliait au génie des Euler, des Lagrange, des Laplace, des Gauss, des Jacobi, l'amour de l'enseignement porté jusqu'à l'enthousiasme, une rare bonté, une simplicité, une chaleur de cœur qu'il a conservées jusqu'à la fin de sa vie " (Combes, quoted by Valson, vol. i. p. 63).

[4] See Bjerknes, ' N.-H. Abel,' p. 48 sqq. ; p. 300. Cauchy's ' Cours d'Analyse' appeared in 1821 ; the 'Résumé des leçons sur le calcul infinitésimal,' to which Abel refers in a letter to Holmboe, dated 1826, appeared in 1823.

troduction of algebra or general arithmetic, in the application of this to geometry and dynamics, and in the invention of the infinitesimal methods, through which the rigorous theorems of the older geometricians which referred to the simpler figures—such as straight lines, circles, spheres, cones, &c.—became applicable to the infinite variety of curves and surfaces in which the objects and phenomena of nature present themselves to our observation. Logically speaking, it was a grand process of generalisation, based mostly on inference and induction, sometimes merely on intuition.[1] Such a process of generalisation has a twofold effect on the progress of science.

9.
Process of
generalisa-
tion.

The first and more prominent result was the greatly increased power of dealing with special problems which the generalised method affords, and the largely increased field of research which it opened out. We may say that the century which followed the inventions of Descartes, Newton, and Leibniz, was mainly occupied in exploring the new field which had been disclosed, in formulating and solving the numberless problems which presented themselves on all sides; also, where complete and rigorous solutions seemed unattainable, in inventing methods of approximation which were useful for practical purposes. In this direction so much had to be done, so much work lay ready to hand, that the second and apparently less practical effect of the new generalisations receded for a time into the background. We may term

[1] "On se reportait inconsciemment au modèle qui nous est fourni par les fonctions considérées en mécanique et on rejetait tout ce qui s'écartait de ce modèle ; on n'était pas guidé par une définition claire et rigoureuse, mais par une sorte d'intuition et d'obscur instinct" (Poincaré, "L'œuvre math. de Weierstrass," 'Acta Mathematica,' vol. xxii. p. 4).

this second and more hidden line of research the logical side of the new development. It corresponds to the work which Euclid performed in ancient geometry, the framing of clear definitions and of unambiguous axioms; proceeding from these by rigorous reasoning to the theorems of the new science.[1] But the translation of geometrical and mechanical conceptions into those of generalised arithmetic or algebra brought with it a logical problem of quite a novel kind which has given to modern mathematics quite a new aspect. This new problem is the retranslation of algebraical— i.e., of general—formulæ into geometrical conceptions—the geometrical construction of algebraical expressions. It is the inverse operation of the former. In this inversion of any given operation lies the soul and principle of all mathematical progress, both in theory and in application.[2] The invention of

10.
Inverse
operations.

---

[1] Referring specially to the definition of a "function" or mathematical dependence, a conception introduced by Euler, but not rigorously defined by him, M. Poincaré says, loc. cit.: "Au commencement du siècle, l'idée de fonction était une notion à la fois trop restreinte et trop vague. . . . Cette définition, il fallait la donner : car l'analyse ne pouvait qu'à ce prix acquérir la parfaite rigueur." In its generality this task was performed in the last third of the century by Weierstrass, but the necessity of this criticism of the formulæ invented by modern mathematics dates from the appearance of Cauchy's ' Mémoire sur la théorie des intégrales définies' of 1814, which Legendre reported on in this sense, but which was not published till 1825.

[2] The operations referred to are generally of two kinds : first, there is the operation of translating geometrical relations, intuitively given, into algebraical relations ; and, secondly, the operation of extending algebraical relations by going forward or backward in the order of numbers, usually given by indices. In each case the new relations arrived at require to be interpreted, and this interpretation leads nearly always to an extension of knowledge or to novel conceptions. A simple example of the first kind presents itself in the geometrical construction of the higher powers of quantity. Having agreed to define by a the length of a line, by a^2 an area, what is the meaning of a^3 a^4 . . . a^n ? Can any geometrical meaning be attached to these symbols ? An example of the

the seventeenth century afforded two grand occasions
for such progress, and the creation through it of novel
mathematical ideas.   The translation of geometrical con-

second class is the following :
having defined the symbols
$$\frac{dy}{dx}, \ \frac{d^2y}{dx^2} \cdots \frac{d^ny}{dx^n},$$
an operation suggests itself in the
inverse order, the indices or their
reciprocals (inversions) being taken
negatively.   Can any meaning be
attached to these latter symbols?
Further, if the operation denoted
by going on from one of these
symbols to the next is known and
feasible, how can the inverse operation be carried out ?   In the first
class of problems we proceed from
an intuitively given order to a
purely logical order, and have in
the sequel to go back from the
purely logical order to an intuitive
order of ideas.   In the second
case, having followed a certain
logical order, we desire to know
what the inversion of this order will
produce and how it can be carried
out.   The view that the direct and
indirect processes of thought form
the basis of all mathematical
reasoning, and an alternation of
the two the principle of progress,
has been for the first time consistently expounded by Hermann
Hankel in his 'Theorie der Com-
plexen Zahlen - Systeme,' Leipzig,
1867.   But it had already been
insisted on by George Peacock in
his "Report," &c., contained in
the 3rd vol. of the 'Reports of
the Brit. Assoc.,' 1833, where he
says (p. 223): "There are two
distinct processes in Algebra, the
direct and the inverse, presenting
generally very different degrees of
difficulty.   In the first case, we
proceed from defined operations,
and by various processes of de-
monstrative reasoning we arrive
at results which are general in

form though particular in value,
and which are subsequently generalised in value likewise ; in the
second, we, commence from the
general result, and we are either
required to discover from its form
and composition some equivalent
result, or, if defined operations
have produced it, to discover the
primitive quantity from which those
operations have commenced.   Of
all these processes we have already
given examples, and nearly the
whole business of analysis will
consist in their discussion and
development, under the infinitely
varied forms in which they will
present themselves."
    It is extraordinary how little in-
fluence this very interesting, comprehensive, and up-to-date report on Continental mathematics,
including the works of Gauss,
Cauchy, and Abel, seems to have
had on the development of English
mathematics.   But the latter have
through an independent movement
—viz., the invention of the
Calculus of Operations — led on
to the radical change which has
taken place in recent mathematical
thought.   This change, which can
be explained by saying that the
science of Magnitude must be
preceded by the doctrine of Forms
or Relations, and that the science
of Magnitude is only a special
application of the science of Forms,
was independently prepared by
Hermann Grassman, of whom
Hankel says (loc. cit., p. 16) : "The
idea of a doctrine of Forms which
should precede a doctrine of Magnitude, and of considering the
latter from the point of view
of the former, . . . remained of
little value for the development

ceptions into algebraical language suggested the inverse operation of interpreting algebraical terms by geometrical conceptions, and led to an enormous extension of geometrical knowledge.[1] Further, the infinitesimal methods through which curves and curved surfaces were conceived as being made up of an infinite number of infinitesimally small, straight—*i.e.*, measurable—lines, led to the inverse problem; given any algebraical operations which obtain only in infinitesimally small dimensions—*i.e.*, at the limit—how do they sum up to finite quantities and

of mathematics, so long as it was only used to prove theorems which besides being already known, were sufficiently though merely empirically proved. It was H. Grassmann who took up this idea for the first time in a truly philosophical spirit and treated it from a comprehensive point of view." Hankel also refers to Peacock as well as to De Morgan, whose writings, however, he was insufficiently acquainted with (ibid., p. 15). In quite recent times Mr A. N. Whitehead has conceived "mathematics in the widest signification to be the development of all types of formal, necessary, deductive reasoning," and has given a first instalment of this development in his 'Treatise on Universal Algebra' (vol. i., Cambridge, 1898). See the preface to this work (pp. 6, 7).

[1] A good example of the use of the alternating employment of the intuitive (inductive) and the logical (deductive) methods is to be found in the modern doctrine of curves. The invention of Descartes, by which a curve was represented by an equation, led to the introduction of the conception of the "degree" or "order" of a curve and its geometrical equivalent;

whereas the geometrical conception of the tangent to a curve led to the distinction of curves according to their "class," which was not immediately evident from the equation of the curve but which led to other analytical methods of representation where the tangential properties of curves became more evident. A third method of studying curves was introduced by Plücker (1832), who started from "the singularities" which curves present, defined them, and established his well-known equations. A further study of these "singularities" led to the notion of the "genus" or "deficiency" (Cayley) of a curve. The gradual development of these and further ideas relating to curves is concisely given in an article by Cayley on "Curve" in the 6th vol. of the 'Encyclopædia Britannica,' reprinted in Cayley's collected papers, vol. xi. This article furnishes also a good example of the historical treatment of a purely mathematical subject by showing, not so much the progress of mathematical knowledge of special things, as the development of the manner in which such things are looked at —*i.e.*, of mathematical thought.

figures ?   What are the properties of these finite figures as inferred from the properties of their infinitesimally small parts ?   The infinitesimal methods evidently corresponded with the atomistic view of natural objects, according to which the great variety of observable phenomena, the endlessly complicated properties of natural objects, could be reduced to a small number of conceivable properties and relations of their smallest parts, and could then be made intelligible and calculable.

The general reader who is unacquainted with the numberless problems and intricate operations of higher mathematics can scarcely realise how in these few words lie really hidden the great questions of all the modern sciences of number and measurement; the trained mathematical student will recognise in a process of inversion not only the rationale of such extensive doctrines as the integral calculus, the calculus of variations, the doctrine of series, the methods of approximation and interpolation, but also the application of analysis to geometry, the theory of curves of higher order, the solution of equations, &c.   All these various branches were diligently cultivated by the great mathematicians of the eighteenth century, mostly, however, with the object of solving definite problems which were suggested by the applied sciences,[1]

[1] In general it can be stated that the impetus given to mathematical research by the problems set by the applied sciences has been immeasurably greater than that which can be traced to the abstract treatment of any purely mathematical subject.   We have a good example of this at the beginning of the nineteenth century in the great work of Laplace as summed up, for the most part, in the 'Mécanique Celeste' and the 'Théorie des Probabilités,' which contain the beginnings and the development of a great number of purely mathematical theories suggested by problems in astronomy, physics, and statistics.   On the other side we have at the same time the so-called "Combinational School" in Germany, whose members and

notably astronomy—not infrequently also as objects of mere curiosity without any practical purpose whatever. In the latter part of the eighteenth century the need was felt of putting the new science into a comprehensive system. The attempts to do this—notably the great text-books of Leonhard Euler in Germany and of Lacroix in France—revealed how uncertain were the foundations and how paradoxical some of the apparent conclusions of the reasoning which, in the hands of the great inventors and masters, had led to such remarkable results.

As in other cases which we dealt with in former chapters of this work, so also in the present instance we may find a guide through the labyrinth of modern mathematical thought in the terms of language around which cluster the more recent doctrines. Two terms present themselves which were rare or altogether absent in older treatises : these terms are the "complex quantity" and the "continuous." To these we can add a third term which we meet with on every page of the writings of mathematicians since Newton and Leibniz, but which has only very recently been subjected to careful analysis and rigorous definition,—the term "infinite." Accordingly we may say that the range of mathematical thought during

11. Modern terms indicative of modern thought.

their labours are almost forgotten, although in their elaborate treatises there are to be found many formulæ which had to be rediscovered when, fifty years later, the general theory of forms and substitutions began to be systematically developed, and proved to be an indispensable instrument in dealing with many advanced mathematical problems.   See on the latter subject an article by Major MacMahon on "Combinational Analysis" ('Proc., London Math. Soc.,' vol. xxviii. p. 5, &c.), as also the chapters on this subject and on "Determinants" in the first vol. of the 'Encyclopädie der Mathematischen Wissenschaften' (Leipzig, 1898).   Also, *inter alia*, a note by J. Muir in 'Nature,' vol. lxvii., 1903, p. 512.

the last hundred years has grown in proportion to the methodical study and stricter definition of the notions of the complex quantity, of the continuous, and of the infinite. And these conceptions indicate three important logical developments which characterise modern mathematical reasoning. The conception of the complex quantity or the complex unit introduces us to the possible extension of our system of counting and measuring, retaining or modifying, the fundamental rules on which it is based. The conception of the continuous and its opposite, the discontinuous, introduces us to the difference of numbers and quantity, numbers forming a discontinuous series, whilst we conceive all natural changes to be made up of gradual—*i.e.*, of imperceptibly small—changes, called by Newton fluxions. The discussion, therefore, of the continuous leads us ultimately to the question how our system of counting can be made useful for dealing with continuously variable quantities—the processes of nature. The conception of the infinite underlies not only the infinitesimal methods properly so called, but also all the methods of approximation by which—in the absence of rigorous methods—mathematical, notably astronomical, calculations are carried out.

12.
Complex quantities.

13.
The continuous.

14.
The infinite.

Problems involving one or more of these conceptions presented themselves in large number to the analysts of the eighteenth century : there were notably two great doctrines in which they continually occur— the general solution of equations,[1] and the theory of

[1] As it may not be immediately evident how the ideas of continuity have to do with the general solution of equations, I refer to the first publication by Gauss, in 1799, containing a proof of the fundamental theorem of algebra, and its republication fifty years later (see Gauss,

infinite series.   The solution of an equation being called
finding its roots, it was for a long time assumed that
every equation has as may roots as are indicated by
its degree.   A proof of this fundamental theorem of
algebra was repeatedly attempted, but was only completed by Gauss in three remarkable memoirs, which
prove to us how much importance he attached to rigorous
proofs and to solid groundwork of science.   The second
great doctrine in which the conceptions of the continuous
and the infinite presented themselves was the expansion
of mathematical expressions into series.   In arithmetic,
decimal fractions [1] taken to any number of terms were
quite familiar; the infinite series presented itself as a
generalisation of this device.   A very general formula

15.
Doctrine
of series.
Gauss.

'Werke,' vol. iii. pp. 1 and 71).   A
very good summary of this proof
is given by Hankel ('Complexe
Zahlen-Systeme,' p. 87).   A purely
algebraical demonstration of the
same theorem, not involving considerations of continuity and approximations, was also given by
Gauss in the year 1816, and reproduced by others, including
George Peacock, in his 'Report,'
quoted above, p. 297.   Hankel
(*loc. cit.*, p. 97) shows to what
extent Gauss's proof supplemented
the similar proofs given by others
before and after.

[1] Decimal fractions seem to have
been introduced in the sixteenth
century.   Series of other numbers,
formed not according to the decimal
but to the dyadic, duodecimal, or
other systems, were known to the
ancients, and continued in use to
the middle ages.   The dyadic system was much favoured by Leibniz.
It was also known that every
rational fraction could be developed into a periodical decimal

fraction.   Prominent in the re-
commendation of the use of decimal fractions was the celebrated
Simon Stevin, who, in a tract
entitled 'La Disme' attached to
his 'Arithmétique' (1590, translated into English, 1608), described
the decimal system as "enseignant
facilement expédier par nombres
entiers sans rompus tous comptes
se rencontrans aux affaires des
hommes."   Prof. Cantor ('Gesch.
der Math.,' vol. ii. p. 616) says,
"We know to-day that this prediction could really be ventured
on—that indeed decimal fractions
perform what Stevin promised."
At the end of his tract he doubts
the speedy adoption of this device,
connecting with it the suggestion
of the universal adoption of the
decimal system.   The best account
of the gradual introduction of decimal fractions is still to be found in
George Peacock's 'History of Arithmetic' ('Ency. Metrop.,' vol. i. p.
439, &c.)

of this kind was given by Brook Taylor, and somewhat
modified by Maclaurin. It embraced all then known and
many new series, and was employed without hesitation
by Euler and other great analysts. In the beginning of
the century, Poisson, Gauss, and Abel drew attention to
the necessity of investigating systematically what is
termed the convergency [1] of a series. As a specimen
of this kind of research, Gauss published, in 1812, an
investigation of a series of very great generality and
importance.[2] We can say that through these two isolated
memoirs of Gauss, the first of the three on equations,
published in 1799, and the memoir on the series of
1812, a new and more rigorous treatment of the infinite and the continuous as mathematical conceptions
was introduced into analysis, and that in both he showed
the necessity of extending the system of numbering and
measuring by the conception of the complex quantity.
But it cannot be maintained that Gauss succeeded in
impressing the new line of thought upon the science of

[1] A very good account of the gradual evolution of the idea of the convergency of a series will be found in Dr R. Reiff's 'Geschichte der unendlichen Reihen' (Tübingen, 1899, p. 118, &c.) Also in the preface to Joseph Bertrand's 'Traité de Calcul Différentiel' (Paris, 1864, p. xxix, &c.) According to the latter Leibniz seems to have been the first to demand definite rules for the convergency of Infinite Series, for he wrote to Hermann in 1705 as follows: "Je ne demande pas que l'on trouve la valeur d'une série quelconque sous forme finie ; un tel problème surpasserait les forces des géomètres. Je voudrais seulement que l'on trouvât moyen de décider si la valeur exprimée par une série est possible, c'est-à-dire convergente, et cela sans connaître l'origine de la série. Il est nécessaire, pour qu'une série indéfinie représente une quantité finie, que l'on puisse démontrer sa convergence, et que l'on s'assure qu'en la prolongeant suffisamment l'erreur devient aussi petite que l'on veut." In spite of this, Leibniz, through his treatment of the series of Grandi, $1-1+1-1$, &c., the sum of which he declared to be $\frac{1}{2}$, seems to have exerted a baneful influence on his successors, including Euler (see Reiff, *loc. cit.*, pp. 118, 158).

[2] The memoir on the Hypergeometrical series.

mathematics in general.   This was done about fifteen or
twenty years after Gauss had begun to publish his
isolated memoirs, in a comprehensive treatment of the
subject by Cauchy, who, before 1820, delivered lectures
on Analysis at the École Polytechnique and in other
colleges, and commenced their publication in 1821.   In
this course of lectures the discussion of the notions of the
infinite, of the continuous, of the convergence of series,
and of the extension of our conception of quantity
beyond the ordinary or real quantities of algebra, is
put in the foreground, and the illicit habit of using the
generalisations of algebra without defining the conditions
of their validity severely criticised.[1]   It is also evident,
from the extensive notes which Cauchy added to the
"cours" of 1821, that he felt the necessity of a revision
of the fundamental notions of algebra.   The publication
of 1821 was followed by others on the Calculus, and it
is through these treatises mainly that a new spirit was
infused into general mathematical literature, first in

16.
Cauchy's
Analysis.

[1] The earliest labours of Cauchy
were geometrical, and he evidently
acquired through them an insight
into the contrast between the
rigour of the older geometrical
and the looseness of the modern
algebraical methods.   In this regard he says : " J'ai cherché à leur
donner toute la rigueur qu'on
exige en géometrie, de manière à
ne jamais recourir aux raisons
tirées de la généralité de l'algèbre.
Les raisons de cette espèce, quoique
assez communément admises, surtout dans le passage des séries con-
vergentes aux séries divergentes,
et des quantités réelles aux expressions imaginaires ne peuvent
être considérés, ce me semble, que
comme des inductions propres à
faire pressentir quelque fois la
vérité, mais qui s'accordent peu
avec l'exactitude si vantée des
sciences mathématiques.   On doit
même observer qu'elles tendent à
faire attribuer aux formules algébriques une étendue indéfinie,
tandis que, dans la réalité, la plupart de ces formules subsistent
uniquement sous certaines conditions, et pour certaines valeurs des
quantités qu'elles renferment.   En
déterminant ces conditions et ces
valeurs, et en fixant d'une manière
précise le sens des notations dont
je me sers, je fais disparaître toute
incertitude " ('Cours d'Analyse,'
1821, Introd., p. ii).

France, somewhat later also in England and Germany. In the latter country, the highly original writings of Abel, and the independent labours of Jacobi, opened out an entirely new branch of higher mathematics, beginning with the discovery of the property of double periodicity of certain functions.[1] This extensive and fruitful province of analysis for a time retarded the revision and extension of the groundwork of mathematical reasoning which Cauchy had begun, and upon which Gauss evidently desired to make the extension of higher mathematics proceed.[2]

[1] Before the discovery of the functions with a double period, functions with one period were known : the circular and exponential functions—the former possessing a real, the latter an imaginary, period. The elliptic functions turned out to "share simultaneously the properties of the circular functions and exponential functions, and whilst the former were periodical only for real, the latter only for imaginary, values of the argument, the elliptic functions possessed both kinds of periodicity." This great step became clear when it occurred to Abel and Jacobi independently to form functions by inversion of Legendre's elliptic integral of the first kind. The two fundamental principles involved in this new departure were thus the process of inversion and the use of the imaginary, as a necessary complement to the real, scale of numbers. The share which belongs independently to Abel and Jacobi has been clearly determined since the publication of the correspondence of Jacobi with Legendre during the years 1827-32 (reprinted in Jacobi's 'Gesammelte Werke,' ed. Borchardt, vol. i., Berlin, 1881), and of the complete documents referring to Abel, which are now accessible in the memorial volume published in 1902. A very lucid account is contained in a pamphlet by Prof. Königsberger, entitled 'Zur Geschichte der Theorie der Elliptischen Transcendenten in den Jahren 1826-29' (Leipzig, 1879).

[2] Of the four great mathematicians who for sixty years did the principal work in connection with elliptic functions — viz., Legendre (1752 - 1833), Gauss (1777 - 1855), Abel (1802-29), and Jacobi (1804-51), each occupied an independent position with regard to the subject, —suggested originally by Euler, and important for the practical applications which it promised. Legendre during forty years, from 1786 onward, worked almost alone : he brought the theory of elliptic integrals, which had occurred originally in connection with the computation of an arc of the ellipse, into a system, and to a point beyond which the then existing methods seemed to promise no further advance. This advance was, however, secured by the labours of Jacobi through the introduction of the novel principles referred to in the last note. Two years before Jacobi's publication commenced, Abel had already approached the subject from an entirely different and much more

That such a revision had become necessary was seen, slowly if in many quarters, but it did not become generally recognised till late in the century, when thinkers of

17.
Revision
of funda-
mentals.

general point of view. "Abel," as Monsieur L. Sylow says ('Mémorial des études d'Abel,' p. 14), "était avant tout algébriste. Il a dit lui-même que la théorie des équations était son sujet favori, ce qui d'ailleurs apparaît clairement dans ses œuvres. Dans ses travaux sur les fonctions elliptiques, le traitement des diverses équations algébriques dont cette théorie abonde est mis fortement en évidence, et dans le premier de ces travaux, la résolution de ces équations est même indiquée comme étant le sujet principal. Qui plus est, la théorie des équations était entre se mains l'instrument le plus éfficace. Ce fut ainsi sans aucun doute la résolution de l'équation de division des fonctions elliptiques qui tout d'abord le conduisit à la théorie de la transformation. Elle joue encore un rôle capitale dans sa démonstration du théorème dit théorème d'Abel, et dans les recherches générales sur les intégrales des différentielles algébriques qui se trouvent dans son dernier mémoire le 'Précis d'une Théorie des fonctions elliptiques.'" But whilst Abel certainly took a much more general view than either Legendre or Jacobi, both of whom came to a kind of deadlock on the roads they had chosen (Jacobi, when he attempted to extend the theory of the periodicity of functions), it is now quite clear that Gauss viewed the whole subject almost thirty years before Abel and Jacobi entered the field from a still more general point of view. Already, in 1798, when he was only twenty-one, he must have recognised the necessity of enlarging and defining the fundamental conceptions of algebra and of functionality or mathematical dependence; and it is very likely that the magnitude of the

undertaking, for which his astronomical labours left him no time, debarred him from publishing the important results which he had already attained, and which covered to a great extent the field cultivated in the meantime by Abel and Jacobi, leaving only the celebrated theorem of the former (referring to the algebraical comparison of the higher non - algebraical functions) and the discovery of a new function on the part of Jacobi (his Theta function) as the two great additions which we owe to them in this line of research (see Königsberger, loc. cit., p. 104). In this recognition of the fundamental change which mathematical science demanded, and its bearing upon these special problems here referred to, Gauss must have for a long time stood alone; for his great rival Cauchy, to whom we are mainly indebted for taking the first steps in this direction, did not for many years apply his fundamental and novel ideas to the theory of elliptic functions, which up to the year 1844, when Hermite entered the field, were almost exclusively cultivated by German and Scandinavian writers (see R. L. Ellis, "Report on the recent Progress of Analysis," Brit. Assoc., 1846; reprinted in 'Mathematical and other Writings,' p. 311). Nor could it otherwise be explained how Cauchy could keep the manuscript of Abel's great memoir without ever occupying himself with it, and thus delay its publication for fifteen years after it had been presented to the Academy. (See the above - mentioned correspondence between Legendre and Jacobi, 1829; also Sylow, p. 31.)

the highest rank, who for some time had lived apart in the secluded regions of sublime analysis, descended again into the region of elementary science, both pure and applied, where they speedily remodelled the entire mode of teaching. England possessed very early a writer of great eminence who represented this tendency, and whose merits were only partially recognised in his day— Augustus de Morgan.

18.
Extension of
conception
of number.

It will now be necessary to explain more definitely what is meant by the extension of our conception of number and quantity through the introduction of complex numbers or complex quantities. This extension first forced itself on analysts in the theory of equations, then in the algebraical treatment of trigonometrical quantities — i.e., in the measurement of angles, or, as it is now called, of direction in geometry. The first extension of the conception of number lay in the introduction of negative numbers. These admitted of comparatively easy representation arithmetically by counting backward as well as forward from a given datum ; practically in the conception of negative possessions, such as debts, geometrically by the two opposite directions of any line in space. In algebra, where the simple operations on quantities are usually preserved in the result and not lost in the simple numerical value of the result as in arithmetic, compound quantities were looked upon as generated by the processes of addition, resulting in the binomial (of which the polynomial was an easy extension), and further by the multiplication with each other of different binomials or polynomials, through which process expressions of higher order or degree were arrived at. The forward or direct process was easy enough, though even here assumptions or arbitrary rules were included which escaped notice for a long time; but the real labour of the analysts only began with the inverse problem—viz., given any compound quantity, similar in structure to those directly produced by multiplication of binomials, to find the factors or binomials out of which it can be compounded. Now it was found that as in the arithmetical process of division, the invention of fractional quantities; as in that of extraction of roots, the irrational quantities had to be introduced: so in the analysis of compound algebraical expressions into binomial factors, a new quantity or algebraical conception presented itself. It was easily seen that this analysis could be carried out in every case only by the introduction of a new unit, algebraically expressed by the square root of the negative unity. There was no difficulty in algebraically indicating the new quantity as we indicate fractions and irrational quantities; the difficulty lay in its interpretation as a number. Since the time of Descartes geometrical representations of algebraical formulæ had become the custom, and it was therefore natural when once the new, or so-called imaginary, unit was formally admitted, that a geometrical meaning should be attached to it.

Out of the scattered beginnings of these researches two definite problems gradually crystallised: the one, a purely formal or mechanical one — viz., the geometrical representation of the extended conception of quantity, of the complex quantity; the other, a logical

19.
The geometrical and the logical problems.

or philosophical one—viz., the clearer definition of the assumptions or principles which underlie arithmetical and algebraical reasoning. And if algebraical, then also geometrical reasoning. Both problems seem to have presented themselves to the youthful mind of Gauss, as is evident from his correspondence with Bessel [1] and Schumacher, and from his direct influence on Bolyai,[2] Möbius, and Von Staudt, perhaps also indirectly on Lobatchevsky.[3]   It does not, however, appear as if he

[1] See especially the letters of Gauss to Bessel, dated November and December 1811 and May 1812 ('Briefwechsel,' Leipzig, 1880, p. 151 *sqq.*)

[2] Bolyai, the elder (1775-1856), was a student friend of Gauss in the years 1797 to 1799, and kept up a correspondence with him during half a century. This correspondence has now been published by F. Schmidt and P. Stäckel, Leipzig, 1899, with a supplement containing some information about this extraordinary man. His son, Johann Bolyai (1802-60), is the author of the celebrated "Appendix, scientiam spatii absolute veram exhibens," which was attached to his father's 'Tentamen, juventutem . . . in elementa matheseos puræ . . . introducendi,' 1832. The tract seems to have been written in 1823. A translation, with introduction, has been published by Dr G. Bruce Halsted ('Neomonic Series,' vol. iii. 4th ed., Austin, Texas, 1896). When the elder Bolyai sent to Gauss in the year 1831 to 1832 a copy of his son's tract and of his own work on Geometry, Gauss expressed great surprise at the contents of the former. (See his letter of March 6, 1832.) His remarks that the younger Bolyai had anticipated some of his own ideas on the

subject, remind one of a similar remark which he made, May 30, 1828, to Schumacher with reference to Abel's "Memoir on Elliptic Functions" in vol. ii. of Crelle's 'Journal' (see Gauss, 'Werke,' vol. iii. p. 495). In both cases he felt himself relieved from the necessity of publishing his own results, though, so far as those referring to the foundations of geometry are concerned, it does not appear that his ideas had arrived at that state of maturity which the publication of his posthumous papers has proved to have been attained in his treatment of the higher functions. Indeed little or nothing of prime importance has been found among his papers referring to the principles of geometry ; and he stated to Bolyai that though he had intended to commit his views to paper, so that they should not be lost, he had not intended to publish anything during his lifetime.

[3] It is doubtful whether Gauss's speculations had any influence on the younger Bolyai's theory, and still more so as regards Lobatchevsky, whose first tract appeared in the 'Kazan Messenger,' 1829 to 1830, but dates back probably to 1826. Inasmuch, however, as the younger Bolyai must have become acquainted

had arrived at any finality in his speculations, and, beyond occasional hints which have only subsequently become intelligible, the love of finish exhibited in all his published writings prevented him from giving to the world the suggestive ideas which evidently formed the groundwork of his mathematical labours.   There is no doubt that—like Goethe in a very different sphere— Gauss anticipated individually the developments in the sphere of mathematical thought down to the end of the century.   The interpretation of the complex quantity had been given by Wessel, Buée, and Argand [1] in the early years of the century; but it remained unnoticed till it received the sanction of Gauss in a celebrated memoir referring to the theory of numbers, and until in

through his father with the speculations of the youthful Gauss, and as Lobatchevsky was a pupil of another student friend of Gauss in the person of Prof. Bartels, it is not unlikely that the interest which these thinkers took in the subject can be originally traced to the same source. (See Dr Halsted's address on Lobatchevsky, 'Neomonic Series,' vol. i., 1894.) A complete bibliography of the earlier papers, referring to the so-called "non-Euclidean" literature down to 1878, is given by Dr Halsted in the first two vols. of the 'American Journal of Mathematics': the most recent publications are those of the Hon. B. A. W. Russell in his work, 'The Foundations of Geometry' (1897) and his excellent article on "Non-Euclidean Geometry" in the 28th vol. of the 'Ency. Brit.' See also Klein's lithographed lectures on 'Nicht-Euklidische Geometrie,' Göttingen, 1893.

[1] The first somewhat exhaustive historical statement as to the geometrical representation of the complex or imaginary quantity was given by Hankel in the above-mentioned work (see above, note, p. 645), p. 82. He there says, after discussing the claims of others,— notably of Gauss, — that Argand in his 'Essai' of the year 1806 (re-edited by Hoüel, 1874) "had so fully treated of the whole theory that later nothing essentially new was added, and that, except a publication of still earlier date were found, Argand must be considered the true founder of the representation of complex quantities in the plane." Such an earlier publication has indeed been met with in a tract by Caspar Wessel, which was presented to the Danish Academy in 1797, and published in 1799. Having been overlooked, like Argand's 'Essai,' it has now been republished at Copenhagen, 1897, with the title 'Essai sur la représentation de la direction' (see 'Encyk. Math. Wissenschaften,' vol. i. p. 155).

this country the labours of De Morgan and of Sir William
Rowan Hamilton gave the matter a further and very
important extension.[1] It was also in this country that
the second problem, the critical examination of the
principles which underlie the process of legitimate
generalisation of algebra, received distinct attention. To
George Peacock, and to the school of algebraists which
followed him, is due the merit of having brought out
clearly the three fundamental laws of symbolical reasoning
now generally admitted in text-books on the subject—
the associative, distributive, and commutative principles.
That these principles were to a great extent conventional,
or empirically adopted from ordinary arithmetic, and in
consequence not necessarily indispensable for a consistent
system of symbolical reasoning, has been generally admitted ever since Sir William Rowan Hamilton, after
ten years of labour, succeeded in establishing a new
calculus—the method of quaternions, in which the commutative principle of multiplication is dropped. This

20.
Quater-
nions.

[1] Far more important than the
suggestions or artifices mentioned
in the foregoing note, and which
since the time of Argand and
Gauss have been variously modified,
is the conception that our common numbers do not form a
complete system without the addition of the imaginary unit, but
that with the introduction of a
second unit "numbers form a
universe complete in itself, such
that, starting in it, we are never
led out of it. There may very well
be, and perhaps are, numbers in a
more general sense of the term;
but in order to have to do with
such numbers (if any) we must
start with them" (Cayley in art.
"Equation," 'Ency. Brit.'; 'Coll.
Works,' vol. xi. p. 503). There
seems little doubt that this conception was first clearly established
in the mind of Gauss, and that
none of the contemporary writers
can be shown to have had a
similarly clear insight. Since this
has become generally recognised—
and we owe this recognition probably to the independent labours
of Grassmann and Riemann —
the discussion of the whole subject has been raised to a much
higher level, as may be seen by
comparing the Report of Peacock,
quoted above, with the discussion
of Hankel (*loc. cit.*), and still more
with the exhaustive article by Prof.
E. Study in vol. i., 'Encyk. Math.
Wiss.,' pp. 147-184.

calculus was shown to be of special use in expressing the relations of spherical trigonometry. Two terms expressing definite notions special to geometry, by which science has been enriched and practical application greatly simplified, are an outcome of this line of research. These are the terms " vector," to express the notion of directed magnitude—*i.e.*, of direction and magnitude combined as distinguished from magnitude and position alone; and the notion of an " operator " which changes direction and magnitude as an ordinary multiplier changes magnitude only.[1] It was shown by Argand and others that the

[1] These two notions, which have their origin in the writings of Hamilton on the one side and the Calculus of Operations on the other, belong to this country and to a period during which mathematical researches were carried on in a fragmentary manner, and much out of contact with the contemporary mathematics of the Continent. Both the Calculus of Quaternions of Hamilton and the Calculus of Operations were looked upon for a long time as curiosities (as was also the Barycentric Calculus of Möbius in Germany). Gradually, however, the valuable ideas which were contained in them became recognised as much from the practical as from the theoretical point of view. In the former interest the application of Vector Analysis or the Algebra of Directed Quantities received a great impetus when the need was felt of having an algebra of "physical quantities." This found expression in the writings of Clerk-Maxwell. (See his 'Treatise on Electricity and Magnetism,' vol. i. p. 8, 2nd ed., as also his paper on "The Mathematical Classification of Physical Quantities," 1871. ' Coll. Papers,' vol. ii. p. 257.) In the practical application of electrical theories

these notions have since become indispensable, and the subject has received increasing attention, notably in America, which holds a foremost place in the development of electrical science and its application. Mathematicians of the first order, such as J. Willard Gibbs, have published text-books on the subject, whilst other electricians of eminence, such as Mr Oliver Heaviside, have elaborated special forms of the Directional Calculus to serve their purposes. In Dynamics the Dublin School, represented after the death of Hamilton by Sir Robert S. Ball (in his 'Theory of Screws,' 1876), has had an important influence in the introduction of novel and more appropriate methods which have gradually permeated the general treatment of the subject. Whilst there is no doubt that for a long time the Calculus of Quaternions was the only methodical elaboration of these novel and useful ideas, it was overlooked that simultaneously and quite independently H. Grassmann of Stettin (see above, vol. i. p. 243) had worked out a much more comprehensive and fundamental calculus, of which the method of quaternions and all the different forms of Vector Analysis can be

arithmetic based upon two units instead of one—*i.e.*, the arithmetic of couples or complex quantities—could be completely and consistently represented by choosing as axes whereon the separate units were counted, the two perpendicular axes of Cartesian geometry. An attempt to extend this geometrical representation into space led Hamilton to the invention of his method, Gauss having very early satisfied himself that within the limits of ordinary algebra no further extension was necessary or possible.

The examination into fundamental principles was not limited in the mind of Gauss to those of algebra: he early applied himself likewise to those of geometry and of dynamics. The great French mathematicians, such as Legendre and Lagrange, were also occupied with such speculations. They have been carried on all through the century, but have only towards the end of the period been brought into connection and shown to be of importance for the general progress of mathematics. The secluded, and for a long time unappreciated, labours of isolated but highly original thinkers have accordingly

21.
Foundations
of geometry.

considered as merely special instances. This has now been abundantly proved through the writings of mathematicians in all countries, among whom I will only mention Hankel and Dr V. Schlegel in Germany, Clifford, Prof. Henrici, and latterly Mr Whitehead in England, Prof. Peano in Italy, and M. Burali Forti in France. See on the whole subject, on the fate of Grassmann and of his great work, V. Schlegel, 'Die Grassmann'sche Ausdehnungslehre,' Leipzig, 1896; also, by the same author, a short biography of Grassmann (Leipzig, Brockhaus, 1878). A complete edition of Grassmann's works is being published by Teubner. Those who are interested in seeing how the notions underlying the directional calculus are gradually becoming clarified, and the terminology and notation settled, may read with profit the controversy carried on in the pages of 'Nature,' vols. xlvii. and xlviii., between Prof. Macfarlane, Willard Gibbs, Mr O. Heaviside, Mr A. M'Aulay, and Dr Knott; also Dr Larmor's review of Hayward's 'Algebra of Coplanar Vectors' (vol. xlvii. p. 266), and Sir R. S. Ball's reference to the 'Ausdehnungslehre' of Grassmann (vol. xlviii. p. 391, 1893).

received tardy recognition. Such speculations can be carried on either as fascinating exercises of mere ingenuity, or for practical purposes to improve the refined instruments of mathematical calculation, or in the philosophical interest of arriving at the fundamental processes of human thought and intuition.[1] Many persons think that only the second of these three in-

[1] Already Euler had remarked on the different interests that prompted mathematical research. Referring to the writings of Count Fagnano, he says in the introduction to the first of his memoirs on Elliptic Integrals (1761, quoted by Brill & Nöther in 'Bericht der Deutschen Mathematiker-Vereinigung,' vol. iii. p. 206): " If one looks at mathematical speculations from the point of view of utility, they can be divided into two classes : first, those which are of advantage to ordinary life and other sciences, and the value of which is accordingly measured by the amount of that advantage. The other class comprises speculations which, without any direct advantage, are nevertheless valuable because they tend to enlarge the boundaries of analysis and to exercise the powers of the mind. Inasmuch as many researches which promise to be of great use have to be given up owing to the inadequacy of analysis, those speculations are of no little value which promise to extend the province of analysis. Such seems to be the nature of observations which are usually made or found a posteriori, but which have little or no chance of being discovered a priori. Having once been established as correct, methods more easily present themselves which lead up to them, and there is no doubt that through the search for such methods the domain of analysis may be considerably ex-

tended." The school of mathematicians headed by Abel and Jacobi pursued mathematics from purely scientific interest, and was criticised on this ground by eminent contemporary mathematicians in France : see a letter of Jacobi to Legendre, dated July 2, 1830, in which he refers to a Report of Poisson on his great work, but adds : " M. Poisson n'aurait pas dû reproduire dans son rapport une phrase peu adroite de feu M. Fourier où ce dernier nous fait des reproches, à Abel et à moi, de ne pas nous être occupés de préférence du mouvement de la chaleur. Il est vrai que M. Fourier avait l'opinion que le but principal des mathématiques était l'utilité publique et l'explication des phénomènes naturels ; mais un philosophe comme lui aurait dû savoir que le but unique de la science, c'est l'honneur de l'esprit humain et que sous ce titre, une question de nombres vaut autant qu'une question du système du monde." In the sequel he adds : " Je crois entrevoir que toutes ces transcendantes " (i.e., the elliptic and Abelian functions) "jouissent des propriétés admirables et inattendues auxquelles on peut être conduit par le thèoréme d'Abel. . . . J'ai réfléchi aussi de temps en temps sur une méthode nouvelle de traiter les perturbations célestes, méthode dans laquelle doivent entrer les théories nouvelles des fonctions elliptiques."

ducements is likely to prove fruitful for the progress of science; they look upon the first as an amusing pastime, and upon the third as empty and not devoid of danger. In recognition of the partial correctness of this view, I will follow up the practical stimulus in its fruitful influence upon the development of the lines of mathematical research.

This stimulus came in the closing years of the preceding century through the lectures of Gaspard Monge at the École Normale, and has become popularly known through his invention of Descriptive Geometry, the first modern systematic application of purely graphical methods in the solution of mathematical problems. As Cauchy was the founder of the modern school of analysts, so Monge, together with Carnot, founded the modern school of geometricians; Dupin, Poncelet, and Chasles being among his most illustrious pupils. The aim of this school was to give to geometrical methods, such as had been practised by the ancients,[1] the same generality and systematic unity which characterised the analytical methods introduced by Descartes.

Not long after the introduction of the latter, Leibniz

22. Descriptive Geometry.

---

[1] These methods had been largely used in this country by Newton, Robert Simson, and Stewart. They were systematised by L. N. M. Carnot. Chasles ("Discours d'inauguration, &c.," 1846, 'Géométrie Supérieure,' p. lxxvii) says: "Dans le siècle dernier, R. Simson et Stewart donnaient, à l'instar des Anciens, autant de démonstrations d'une proposition, que la figure à laquelle elle se rapportait présentait de formes différentes, à raison des positions relatives de ses diverses parties. Carnot s'attacha à prouver qu'une seule démonstration appliquée à un état assez général de la figure devait suffire pour tous les autres cas; et il montre comment, par des changements de signes de termes, dans les formules démontrées par une figure, ces formules s'appliquaient à une autre figure ne différant de la première, commes nous l'avons dit, que par les positions relatives de certaines parties. C'est ce qu'il appela le 'Principe de corrélation des figures.'"

had foretold [1] the possibility and necessity of such an independent development of pure geometry, in which the relations of position in space, as opposed to those of measure, magnitude, or quantity, would be placed in the foreground. Projection, as practised in the drawing of maps, and perspective, as practised in the fine and descriptive arts, had already revealed a number of remarkable properties of figures in the plane and in space. By continuous motion of points or lines, by artifices like throwing of shadows, by sections of solids with lines and surfaces, a vast number of problems had been solved and isolated theorems established. The method here practised was that of construction, as in analysis the method was that of calculation with subsequent interpretation. All this purely constructive work was to be brought together and systematically combined in a whole. It was evidently a distinct line of research, based upon intellectual processes other than the purely analytical method — a line which, as it seemed to its followers, had been unduly neglected and pushed into the background. Although Monge became the founder of this purely descriptive or constructive branch of geometry, he was himself equally great as an analyst; in fact, the fusion in his mind of the two methods was the origin of much of his greatest work. In attempting to carry out more thoroughly the separation or independent development of the constructive or descriptive method, his great pupil, J. V. Poncelet—whilst deprived of all literary resources

23.
Poncelet.

---

[1] See the quotations from his letters to Huygens and others given above, vol. i. p. 103 note.

in the prisons of Russia—meditated on the real cause of the power which algebraical analysis possessed, on the reason why geometry proper was deprived of it, and what might be done to give it a similar generality. In pursuing this line of thought he was led to discover the cause of the existing limitation of purely geometrical reasoning in its rigidity, inasmuch as it was arrested as soon as its objects ceased to have a positive or absolute, that is a physical, existence.[1] Opposed to this limitation was the freedom of the analytical method, which, operating with indeterminate symbols, could, by letting them change gradually, include not only what was explicitly given, but also that which was merely implied; not only the finite, but likewise the infinite; not only the real, but likewise the fictitious or imaginary. In order to gain a similar generality in purely geometrical or descriptive science, a similar flexibility would have to be introduced. Poncelet was thus led to the enunciation of his celebrated and much-criticised "principle or law of continuity."[2]

[1] See the "Introduction" to the 1st volume of the 'Traité des Propriétés projectives des figures,' pp. xi, xii. I quote from the 2nd edition of 1865. The 1st was published in 1822. The researches date from 1813, the year of Poncelet's imprisonment. See "Préface de la première édition."

[2] Ibid., Introduction, p. xiv. On the principle of continuity in geometry, see an article in vol. xxviii. "Ency. Brit.' by the Rev. Charles Taylor, and the references given therein; also Prof. E. Kötter's Report on the "Development of Synthetic Geometry" in vol. v. of the 'Jahresbericht der Deutschen Mathematiker Vereinigung,' p.

122, &c.: "Originally the expositions referring to the principle of continuity were intended to occupy much greater space. . . . In consequence of correspondence with Terquem, Servois, and Brianchon, Poncelet desisted from the publication of it. . . . However cautiously Poncelet advanced his principle"—in the 'Essai sur les propriétés projectives des sections coniques' (presented to the Academy in 1820)—"it nevertheless aroused the doubts of Cauchy, who in his report on Poncelet's paper warns against the too hasty application of the principle. Gergonne accompanied the reprint of this report with notes, in which he characterised

Analytical geometry, by substituting an algebraical expression for a geometrical figure—say a curve,—could apply to it all the artifices of abstract analysis. By varying the co-ordinates you can proceed along the whole extent of the curve and examine its behaviour as it vanishes into infinity, or discover its singular points at which there occurs a break of continuity : you can vary its constants or parameters, and gradually proceed from one curve to another belonging to the same family, as is done in grouping together all curves of the second order, or—as was done in the calculus of variation, invented by Euler and Lagrange—you can vary the form of the equation, proceeding from one class of curve to another. Now clearly all this operating on equations and symbolic expressions was originally abstracted from geometry, including the mechanical conception of motion ; in particular the ideas which underlie the method of fluxions were suggested by the motion of a point in space. The conception of continuous motion in space—

the principle as a valuable instrument for the discovery of new truths, which nevertheless did not make stringent proofs superfluous." Cauchy's report seems to have aroused Poncelet's indignation. Hankel ('Elemente der Projectivischen Geometrie,' 1875, p. 9) says : "This principle, which was termed by Poncelet the 'Principle of Continuity,' inasmuch as it brings the various concrete cases into connection, could not be geometrically proved, because the imaginary could not be represented. It was rather a present which pure geometry received from analysis, where imaginary quantities behave in all calculations like real ones. Only the habit of considering real and imaginary quantities as equally legitimate led to that principle which, without analytical geometry, could never have been discovered. Thus pure geometry was compensated for the fact that analysis had for a long time absorbed the exclusive interest of mathematicians ; indeed it was perhaps an advantage that geometry, for a time, had to lie fallow." Kötter continues : "Von Staudt was the first who succeeded in subjecting the imaginary elements to the fundamental theorem of projective geometry, thus returning to analytical geometry the present which, in the hands of geometricians, had led to the most beautiful results."

of motion of points, lines, planes—corresponded accordingly to the notion of variability in analysis. The introduction of motion, gradual and continuous, would give to purely geometrical or descriptive reasoning the same flexibility which analysis had acquired in the calculus of fluxions and of variations. Figures would lose their rigidity and isolation and limited nature and become movable, related to each other, filling the whole of space instead of a restricted and confined area or region. It is the peculiarity of the modern as opposed to the older geometry, never to let figures become motionless or rigid,[1] never to consider them in their isolation, but always in their mutual relations; never to have regard only to a finite portion of a line or surface, but to conceive of it in its infinite extension. By a reaction of analysis and geometry on each other, freedom and generality have been gradually acquired.

24.
Character
of modern
geometry.

But this moving about of figures in space in order to learn their properties and mutual relations must be according to some method; otherwise it will not lead to scientific and exact knowledge. Poncelet, in considering how the two successful methods in geometry — the Cartesian and the Descriptive—had attained to their perfection, discovers a general principle which underlies their proceedings, and which is capable of great extension: this is the principle of projection.[2]

[1] See, inter alia, what Geiser says of Jacob Steiner's method in his pamphlet 'Zur Erinnerung an Jacob Steiner,' Schaffhausen, 1874, p. 27.

[2] 'Traité des Propriétés projectives,' vol. i. p. xviii: "En réfléchissant attentivement à ce qui fait le principal avantage de la Géométrie descriptive et de la méthode des coordonnées, à ce qui fait que ces branches des Mathématiques offrent le caractère d'une véritable doctrine, dont les principes, peu nombreux, sont liés et enchaînés d'une manière nécessaire

Of this principle of projection, which Poncelet at once introduces in the more general form as conical or central projection, two signal applications existed in the treatises on Conic Sections handed down from antiquity, and in the practical methods and Rules of Perspective invented by Lionardo da Vinci and further developed by various geometricians. The results, which lay scattered in many books and memoirs, Poncelet collected in a systematic form, bringing them, by the application of the law of continuity, under a few general and eminently useful points of view or principles. By the method of projection or perspective he " transformed figures which are very general into others which are particular, and *vice versâ.*" He established the principle of "homology" in figures, and by showing how figures apparently very different could be described by the process of projection from the same original figure, he showed that there existed a peculiar relation among figures—viz., their "reciprocity." [1]

25.
Method of
projection.

et par une marche uniforme, on ne tarde pas à reconnaître que cela tient uniquement à l'usage qu'elles font de la projection."

[1] The properties of figures, called by Poncelet "homology" and "reciprocity," refer to the correspondence of certain elements of one figure to those of another figure. In the case of "homology," we have to do with corresponding points or corresponding lines—*i.e.*, with the correspondence of the same elements. In the case of "reciprocity," we have to do with correspondence of points or lines in the one figure, with lines or points in the other—*i.e.*, with the correspondence of different elements. The idea of placing figures in an homologous relation was got by the device of making two planes, which contained figures in perspective, fall together into one plane; upon which the section of the two original planes became the "axis," and the eye-point the "centre" of homology—all situated in one and the same plane. Poncelet had already conceived of the possibility of reducing the two planes in Monge's 'Descriptive Geometry,' which represent the plan and elevation of a figure in one plane, on which the elevations were marked by what are now called "contour lines." The idea of the correspondence of figures by what is called "reciprocity" was sug-

26.
Law of
continuity.

By the law of continuity he showed how in pure geometry it became necessary to introduce the consideration of points and lines which vanish into infinity or which become imaginary, establishing by their invisible elements the continuous transition from one geometric form to another; just as in algebra these conceptions had forced themselves on the attention of analysts. Ideal elements were thus made use of to lead to the discovery of real properties.

The consideration of lines and points which vanish or lie at infinity was familiar to students of perspective from the conception of the "vanishing line"; but the inclusion of ideal points and lines was, as Hankel says, a gift which pure geometry received from analysis, where imaginary (i.e., ideal or complex) quantities behave

27.
Ideal
elements.

in the same way as real ones. Without the inclusion of these ideal or invisible elements the generality or continuity of purely geometrical reasoning was impossible.

The geometrical reasoning of Monge, Carnot, and Poncelet was thus largely admixed with algebraical or analytic elements. It is true that Monge's descriptive geometry was a purely graphical method, and that

gested to Poncelet by the property, known already to De la Hire ("Sectiones Conicæ," 1685), that in the plane of a conic section every point corresponds to a straight line called its "polar," that to every straight line corresponds a point called its "pole," that the "polars" corresponding to all the points of a straight line meet in one and the same point, and vice versa that the "poles" corresponding to all lines going through one and the same point lie on a straight line; the line and point in question standing in both cases in the relation of pole and polar to each other. Poncelet uses "this transformation of one figure into its reciprocal polar systematically as a method for finding new theorems: to every theorem of geometry there corresponds in this way another one which is its 'polar,' and the whole of geometry was thus split up into a series of truths which run parallel and frequently overlap each other" (Hankel, loc. cit., p. 20).

Poncelet's method of central projection attacked geometrical problems from a purely constructive point of view.
Nevertheless the frequently expressed object of the later
writings of Monge, as well as those of Carnot and
Poncelet, was to introduce into geometrical reasoning
the generality and continuity which analysis possessed,
and this was largely attained by the interpretation of
nations taken over from analysis.   Their endeavours
were, however, in the sequel crowned by the discovery
of a purely geometrical property, the understanding of
which has ever since formed the basis of what may be
termed modern geometry.

This remarkable property, which may be regarded
as revealing the very essence of extension in space or
of the "space-manifold,"—inasmuch as it brings the
different elements of space into mutual relation,—is the
so-called principle of "duality" or of "reciprocity."   The
principle of duality is now usually defined to mean that
in geometry on the plane or in space, "figures coexist in
pairs, two such coexisting figures having the same genesis
and only differing from one another in the nature of the
generating element."[1]   The elements of plane geometry
are the point and the line ; the elements of solid geometry
are the point and the plane.   By interchanging these
correlative terms, correlative propositions may be written
down referring to plane and to space geometry.   In projective geometry there are two processes which are correlative or complementary to each other—the process of
projection and the process of section.   We can project

28.
Principle of
duality.

[1] Cremona, 'Elements of Projective Geometry,' transl. by Leudesdorf.
Oxford, 1885, p. 26.

from a point drawing lines or rays on the plane and in space, and we can cut these by lines in a plane or by planes in space. And it can be shown that "if one geometric form has been derived from another by means of one of these operations, we can conversely, by means of the complementary operation, derive the second from the first."[1]

The projective geometry of Poncelet contains the two-fold origin of the principle of duality in his method of projection and section, and in his theory of the reciprocity of certain points and lines in the doctrine of conic sections, called the theory of reciprocal polars. But the mathematician who first expressed the principle of duality in a general—though not in the most general—form was Gergonne, who also recognised that it was not a mere geometrical device but a general philosophical principle, destined to impart to geometrical reasoning a great simplification. He sees in its enunciation the dawn of a new era in geometry.[2]

29.
Reciprocity.

[1] Cremona, *loc. cit.*, p. 33.

[2] The principle of Duality seems to have been first put forward in its full generality by Gergonne, inspired probably by the theory of Reciprocal Polars (see note, p. 663) enunciated by Poncelet, who many years afterwards carried on a voluminous polemic as to the priority of the discovery. "Gergonne saw that the parallelism (referred to above) is not an accidental consequence of the property of conic sections, but that it constitutes a fundamental principle which he termed the 'principle of duality.' The geometry which is usually taught, and in which a line is considered to be generated by the motion of a point, is opposed by another geometry equally legitimate in which a point is generated by the rotation of a line. Whereas in the first case the line is the locus of the moving point, in the latter case the point is the geometrical intersection of the rotating line. In this generality the principle of duality has been incorporated into modern geometry" (Hankel, *loc. cit.*, p. 21). Gergonne says of the new principle (1827, see Supplement to vol. ii. 2nd ed. of Poncelet's 'Traité,' p. 390) : "Il ne s'agit pas moins que de commencer pour la géométrie, mal connue depuis près de deux mille ans qu'on s'en occupe, une ère tout-à-fait nouvelle ; il s'agit d'en mettre tous les anciens traités à peu près au

It must, however, in all fairness be stated that about
the period from 1822 to 1830 this great simplification
and unification of geometric science was as it were in the
air—that it had presented itself to various great thinkers
independently, being suggested from different points of
view. The beginnings can no doubt be traced in the
beautiful theorems of older French mathematicians, such
as Pascal and De la Hire, and more generally in the
suggestive methods of Monge and Poncelet; its first
formal enunciation is in the memoirs of Gergonne: but
the comprehensive use of it—the rewriting of geometry
from this point of view—was the idea of Jacob Steiner,
who, in his great but unfinished work on the "Systematic
Development of the Dependence of Geometric Forms"
(1830), set himself the great task "of uncovering the
organism by which the most different forms in the world
of space are connected with each other."   "There are,"
he says, "a small number of very simple fundamental
relations in which the scheme reveals itself, by which
the whole body of theorems can be logically and easily
developed."   "Through it we come, as it were, into possession of the elements which Nature employs with the
greatest economy and in the simplest manner in order to
invest figures with an infinite array of properties."[1]

30.
Steiner.

rebut, de leur substituer des traités
d'une forme tout-à-fait différente,
des traités vraiment philosophiques
qui nous montrent enfin cette étendue, réceptacle universel de tout ce
qui existe, sous sa véritable physionomie, que la mauvaise méthode
d'enseignement adoptée jusqu'à ce
jour ne nous avait pas permis de
remarquer ; il s'agit, en un mot,
d'opérer dans la science une révolution aussi impérieusement nécessaire qu'elle a été jusqu'ici peu
prévue."

[1] See the Preface to the 'Systematische   Entwickelung,   &c.,'
in Jacob Steiner's 'Gesammelte
Werke' (ed. Weierstrass), vol. i.
p. 229. "In the beautiful theorem
that a conic section can be generated by the intersection of two
projective pencils (and the dually

The labours of Poncelet and Steiner introduced into geometry a twofold aspect, and accordingly, about the middle of the century, we read a good deal of the two kinds of geometry which for some time seemed to develop independently of each other. The difference has been defined by the terms "analytic or synthetic," "calculative or constructive," "metrical or projective." The one operated with formulæ, the other with figures; the one studied the properties of quantity (size, magnitude), distances, and angles, the other those of position.

The projective method seemed to alter the magnitude of lines and angles and retain only some of those of position and mutual relation, such as contact and intersection. The calculating or algebraical method seemed to isolate figures and hide their properties of mutual interdependence and relation.

31.
Mutual influence of metrical and projective geometry.

These apparent defects stimulated the representatives of the two methods to investigate more minutely their hidden causes and to perfect both. The algebraical formula had to be made more pliable, to express more naturally and easily geometrical relations; the geometrical method had to show itself capable of dealing with quantitative problems and of interpreting geometrically those modern notions of the infinite and the complex which the analytic aspect had put promi-

correlated theorem referring to projected ranges), Steiner recognised the fundamental principle out of which the innumerable properties of these remarkable curves follow, as it were, automatically with playful ease. Nothing is wanted but the combination of the simplest theorems and a vivid geometrical imagination capable of looking at the same figure from the most different sides in order to multiply the number of properties of these curves indefinitely" (Hankel, *loc. cit.*, p. 26; see also Cremona, 'Projective Geometry,' p. 119).

nently into the foreground. The latter was done by the geometric genius of Von Staudt, who succeeded in giving a purely geometrical interpretation of the imaginary or invisible elements [1] which algebra had introduced, whilst Steiner astonished the mathematical world by the fertility of the methods by which he solved the so-called isoperimetrical problems—*i.e.*, problems referring to largest or smallest contents contained in a given perimeter or *vice versâ*, problems for which Euler and Lagrange had invented a special calculus.[2] In spite of

[1] The geometrical interpretation of the imaginary elements is given by Von Staudt in a sequel to his 'Geometrie der Lage' (1847), entitled 'Beiträge zur Geometrie der Lage' (1856-60); and after having been looked upon for a long time as a curiosity or a "hair-splitting abstraction," it has latterly, through the labours of Prof. Reye ('Geometrie der Lage,' 1866-68) and Prof. Lüroth ('Math. Annalen,' vol. xiii. p. 145), become more accessible, and is systematically introduced into many excellent text-books published abroad. The simplest exposition I am acquainted with is to be found in the later editions of Dr Fiedler's German edition of Salmon's 'Conic Sections' (6th Aufl., vol. i. p. 23, &c., and p. 176, &c.) In 1875, before the great change which has brought unity and connection into many isolated and fragmentary contributions had been recognised, Hankel wrote with regard to Von Staudt's work, and in comparison with that of Chasles, as follows: "The work of Von Staudt, classical in its originality, is one of those attempts to force the manifoldness of nature with its thousand threads running hither and thither into an abstract scheme and an artificial system : an attempt such as is only possible in

our Fatherland, a country of strict scholastic method, and, we may add, of scientific pedantry. The French certainly do as much in the exact sciences as the Germans, but they take the instruments wherever they find them, do not sacrifice intuitive evidence to a love of system nor the facility of method to its purity. In the quiet town of Erlangen, Von Staudt might well develop for himself in seclusion his scientific system, which he would only now and then explain at his desk to one or two pupils. In Paris, in vivid intercourse with colleagues and numerous pupils, the elaboration of the system would have been impossible " (*loc. cit.*, p. 30).

[2] See the lecture delivered by Steiner in the Berlin Academy, December 1, 1836, and the two memoirs on 'Maximum and Minimum' (1841), reprinted in 'Gesammelte Werke,' vol. ii. p. 75 *sqq.*, and 177 *sqq.*, especially the interesting Introductions to both, in which he refers to his forerunner Lhuilier (1782), deploring that others had needlessly forsaken the simple synthetical methods adopted by him. Some of Steiner's expositions in these matters were apparently so easy that non - mathematical listeners

these marvellous works of genius, science is probably indebted for its greatest advances to those mathematicians who, like Plücker in Germany, Chasles in France, and Cayley in England, employed the analytic and constructive methods alternately and with equal mastery.

It is impossible—and it is not my object—to allot to each of these original thinkers the special ideas introduced by him into modern science; but for the purpose

like Johannes Müller could not understand how such simple things could be brought before the Academy of Sciences, whereas the great mathematician Dirichlet was full of praise of the ingenuity of the method by which problems were solved which the Calculus of Variations attacked long after Steiner, and then only in ways which the synthetical method had indicated (see Geiser, 'Zur Erinnerung an Jacob Steiner,' p. 28). It must not be supposed, however, that Steiner was an extreme purist so far as geometrical methods were concerned, for he says himself "that of the two methods neither is entitled to exclude the other; rather both of them will, for a long time, have plenty to do in order to master the subject to some extent, and then only can an opinion as to their respective merits be formed" ('Ges. Werke,' vol. ii. p. 180). An instance of a celebrated problem being treated alternately by synthetic and analytic methods is that of the Attraction of Ellipsoids, in which the Theorem of Maclaurin had created quite a sensation. In spite of the admiration which it evoked, both Legendre and Poisson expressed the opinion that the resources of the synthetic method are easily exhausted. The latter, whilst admitting "que la synthèse ait d'abord devancé l'analyse," never-theless concludes that "la question n'a été enfin résolue complètement que par des transformations analytiques. . . auxquelles la synthèse n'aurait pu suppléer." This expression of opinion was falsified when Chasles presented to the Academy, in the year 1837, a memoir in which, through the study of confocal surfaces, the Theory of Maclaurin was synthetically proved in its full generality. Poinsot, who reported on this memoir, attached the following remarks : "Ce mémoire remarquable nous offre un nouvel exemple de l'élégance et de la clarté que la géométrie peut répandre sur les questions les plus obscures et les plus difficiles. . . . Il est certain qu'on ne doit négliger ni l'une ni l'autre ; elles sont au fond presque toujours unies dans nos ouvrages, et forment ensemble comme l'instrument le plus complet de l'esprit humain. Car notre esprit ne marche guère qu'à l'aide des signes et des images ; et quand il cherche à pénétrer pour la première fois dans les questions difficiles, il n'a pas trop de ces deux moyens et de cette force particulière qu'il ne tire souvent que de leur concours. C'est ce que tout le monde peut sentir, et ce qu'on peut reconnaître dans le Mémoire même." (Chasles, 'Rapport sur les progrès de la géométrie,' 1870, p. 105, &c.)

of bringing some order into the tangled web of mathematical speculation, mainly represented by these, I shall identify the name of Plücker with the great advance which has taken place in geometry through the change in our ideas as to the elements of space construction and the generalisation of our ideas of co-ordinates: with Chasles I shall specially connect the modern habit in geometry of combining figures in finite space with their infinitely distant elements, and with Cayley the application to geometrical science of the novel and comprehensive methods of modern algebra. Let us dwell for a moment on each of these three great departures.

32.
Plücker,
Chasles,
Cayley.

The elements of any science are a very different thing from the elements of the special object with which that science is concerned. The èlements of chemistry are not the chemical elements. The latter are, we suppose, something existing in nature, something fixed and unalterable, which science aims at finding out; the former are certain conceptions from which we find it convenient to start in teaching, expounding, and building up the science of chemistry. The latter are artificial, the former are natural. The same remark obtains in geometrical science. The elements of geometry have an historical, a practical beginning: the elements of space form a conception which gradually emerges in the progress of geometrical science. In every science there is a tendency to replace the casual and artificial elements by the natural or real elements, and to build up the historical traditional body of doctrine anew, using the very elements which Nature herself, as it were, employs in producing her actual forms and objects. As the pass-

33.
Historical
and logical
foundations.

age quoted above shows, such an idea must have been
before the mind of Jacob Steiner when he wrote the
' Systematische Entwickelung.'   Through Euclid geometricians had learnt to begin with the straight line of
definite—not indefinite—length, the triangle, the circle,
advancing to more complicated figures; practice had
made geometry a science of mensuration, involving
number; the convenience of practice in astronomy,
geodesy, and geography had introduced the artifice of
referring points and figures in space to certain arbitrarily chosen data—points and lines.   The terms "right
ascension" and "declination," "altitude" and "azi-
muth," "latitude" and "longitude," led to the co-
ordinates of Descartes and to analytical geometry.   In
this older and modern geometry, the beginnings were
arbitrary, and many conceptions were introduced which
were foreign to the object of research.   It was through
a slow process that in quite recent times—notably during the nineteenth century — mathematicians became
aware how artificial were their methods, and with how
many foreign elements they had encumbered the objects
of their study.   To replace the artificial by natural conceptions, and to open the eyes of geometricians to the
advantage of not confining themselves to the point (its
motion and distances) as the element in their space
construction, no one did more than Julius Plücker of
Bonn.   We have now not only a point - geometry,
but likewise a line - geometry — i.e., we have a geometry in which the line is the primary element, the
point being the secondary element, defined by the
intersection of two lines.   This conception, which

can be applied also to geometry in space, the point being conceived as generating a plane by its motion, or three planes defining a point by their intersection, leads us to the same idea of dual correspondence or reciprocity which Poncelet and Gergonne had arrived at by entirely different considerations. Plücker's was an analytical mind, and with him the principle of duality at once assumes an analytical form. He saw that the same equation lent itself to a twofold interpretation, accordingly, as we adopt point co-ordinates or line co-ordinates —*i.e.*, according as we refer our geometrical figure to the point or the line as the moving and generating space element. Through this step the idea of co-ordinates was generalised, and the dualistic conception of figures in space received an analytical expression. It was the junction of analytical and descriptive methods on a higher level, from which an entirely novel and fertile development of geometry became possible.

34. Generalised co-ordinates.

Whilst the labours of Plücker lay in the direction of making analytical formulæ more natural, better adapted to the expression of geometrical forms and relations, and of reading out of these remodelled formulæ novel geometrical properties, the French school, with Michel Chasles [1]

---

[1] In addition to numerous valuable memoirs, Chasles published, among others, two works of paramount importance, inasmuch as they for a long time dominated purely geometrical research, not only in France but also in Germany and England,—the 'Aperçu historique sur l'origine et le développement des méthodes en géométrie' (1837), and the 'Traité de géométrie supérieure' (1852). These works, through their brilliant style, not only threw into the shade for a time the labours of contemporary German mathematicians, such as Möbius, Steiner, Plücker, and Von Staudt, but also obscured some of the single discoveries of the author himself. The 'Aperçu' was early translated into German; whereas in this country it was the Dublin school, notably Townsend and Dr Salmon, who spread a knowledge of Chasles's work.

as its leader and centre, laboured at the introduction into pure geometry of those ideas which were
peculiar to the analytical method, and which gave to
that method its unity, generality, and comprehensiveness.
Two ideas presented themselves as requiring to be geometrically dealt with : the infinite and the imaginary—
i.e., the elements of a figure which lie at infinity and those
which are ideal or invisible, which cannot be construed.
It is usually supposed that the consideration in geometry
of imaginary or invisible elements in connection with real
figures in space or on the plane has been imported from
algebra; but the necessity of dealing with them must
have presented itself when constructive geometry ceased
to consider isolated figures rigidly fixed, when it adopted
the method of referring figures to each other, of looking
at systems of lines and surfaces, and of moving figures
about or changing them by the processes of projection
and perspective. The analytical manipulations applied
to an equation, which according to some system or other
expressed a geometrical figure, found its counterpart
in projective geometry, where, by perspective methods,—
changing the centre or plane of projection,—certain
elements were made to move away into infinity, or when
a line that cut a circle moved away outside of it, seemingly losing its connection with it. By such devices,
implying continuous motion in space, Poncelet introduced
and defined points, lines, and other space elements at
infinity, and brought in the geometrical conception of
ideal and imaginary elements. "Such definitions," he
says, "have the advantage of applying themselves at
once to all points, lines, and surfaces whatsoever; they

35.
Ideal
elements.

are, besides, neither indifferent nor useless, they help to shorten the text and to extend the object of geometrical conceptions; lastly, they establish a point of contact, if not always real, at least imaginary, between figures which appear—*prima vista*—to have no mutual relation, and enable us to discover without trouble relations and properties which are common to them." [1] It was the principle of geometrical continuity which led Poncelet to the consideration of infinite and imaginary elements.

As we saw above, the projective methods of Poncelet had introduced into geometrical reasoning a remarkable distinction among the properties of figures. In general it was recognised that, in the methods of central and parallel projection or in drawing in perspective, certain properties or relations of the parts of a figure remain unaltered, whereas others change, become contorted or out of shape. Poncelet called the former projective or descriptive, the latter metrical, properties. This distinction introduced into all geometry since his time several most important and fundamental points of view; it divided geometrical research into two branches, which we may term positional and metrical geometry—the geometry of position and that of measurement. We know that ancient geometry started from problems of mensuration: modern geometry started, with Monge, from problems of representation or graphical description. It has thus become a habit to call ancient geometry metrical, modern geometry projective. This habit has led to an unnecessary separation of views, but in the further course of development also

[1] 'Traité des Propriétés projectives,' vol. i. p. 28.

to a unification on a higher level. But the distinction mentioned above led to another most remarkable line of thought and research which tends more and more to govern mathematical doctrine. The methods of projection are based upon the motion or upon the transformation of figures. Under such a process some relations remain unaltered or invariant, others change. As analytical methods in the hands of Plücker and others began to accommodate themselves more closely to geometrical forms, as an intimate correspondence was introduced between the figure and the formula, it became natural to study the unalterable properties of the figure in the invariant elements of the formula. This is the origin and meaning of the doctrine of Invariants.[1] It is the great merit of the English school of mathematicians, headed by Boole, Cayley, and Sylvester, both to have first conceived the idea of a doctrine of invariant

36.
Invariants.

[1] " In any subject of inquiry there are certain entities, the mutual relations of which, under various conditions, it is desirable to ascertain. A certain combination of these entities may be found to have an unalterable value when the entities are submitted to certain processes or are made the subjects of certain operations. The theory of invariants in its widest scientific meaning determines these combinations, elucidates their properties, and expresses results when possible in terms of them. Many of the general principles of political science and economics can be expressed by means of invariantive relations connecting the factors which enter as entities into the special problems. The great principle of chemical science which asserts that when elementary or compound bodies combine with one another the total weight of the materials is unchanged, is another case in point. Again, in physics, a given mass of gas under the operation of varying pressure and temperature has the well-known invariant, pressure multiplied by volume and divided by absolute temperature. Examples might be multiplied. In mathematics the entities under examination may be arithmetical, algebraical, or geometrical; the processes to which they are subjected may be any of those which are met with in mathematical work. It is the principle which is valuable. It is the idea of invariance that pervades to-day all branches of mathematics " (Major P. A. MacMahon, Address, Brit. Assoc., 1901, p. 526).

forms, and to have foreseen its importance and corresponding significance when applied to a great variety of scientific problems, notably to the projective processes in geometry. These were known to them mainly through the classical treatises of Poncelet and Chasles, the leading ideas of which had been introduced to British students by the labours of the Dublin school.[1]

The investigations referred to mark the junction of two important lines of mathematical research, which had been carried on independently in earlier times, or only united for special purposes or for the solution of special problems. The history of the progress of geometry during the nineteenth century has already shown us the use and interest which belong to two different aspects of the common object, of which the one relies mainly on processes of measurement, including number, the other mainly on processes of description, in-

[1] The history of the doctrine of invariants has been written by Dr Franz Meyer, and is published in the first volume of the 'Jahresbericht der Deutschen Mathematiker Vereinigung' (p. 79 *sqq.*) The fact that this formed the first of the several Reports which the German Mathematical Society has undertaken to publish, testifies to the great importance which belongs to this doctrine in the history of recent mathematics. A concise summary with copious references is given by the same author in the first volume of the 'Encyklopädie der Math. Wissenschaften,' p. 320 *sqq.* How necessary the form and perfection of algebraic operations was for the development of the geometrical conceptions which are laid down, *e.g.*, in the works of Plücker, can be seen in the work of Otto Hesse, who introduced ele-gance and conciseness into many of the expositions which, for want of this formal development, appear cumbrous in the writings of Plücker. "The analytical form in which Plücker's Researches present themselves is frequently wanting in that elegant form to which we have become accustomed, specially through Hesse. Plücker's calculations frequently bear the stamp of mere aids for representing geometrical relations. That algebraical connections possess an interest in themselves, and require an adequate representation, was realised only by a generation which habitually employed methods that had been largely devised by Plücker himself" (A. Clebsch, 'Zum Gedächtniss an Julius Plücker,' 1872, p. 8. See also Gustav Bauer, 'Gedächtnissrede auf Otto Hesse,' München, 1882).

cluding arrangement. The same difference of views can be established with regard to many other things which form the objects of other sciences. In geometry this difference obtrudes itself, as it were, in its naked form. Thus in all the natural, and even the social, sciences we have become accustomed to look first at the constituent elements or parts of things, to count and measure them, then afterwards to look at their possible arrangement, or existence together in the actual world of nature or society. Astronomy, crystallography, chemistry, geology, the natural history sciences, economics and statistics, the doctrine of chances,—all furnish, especially in their systematic development during the last hundred or hundred and fifty years, examples of the twofold aspect just referred to. The progress of these sciences, as we have abundantly seen, has depended largely upon the application of mathematical methods. As the analysis into elements or parts, and the possible synthesis of such elements in complicated structures, has become everywhere the order of study, so there must exist in the abstract science of mathematics—*i.e.*, in the framework of our scientific reasoning —not only the theory of measurement and number, but also that of combination, form or arrangement, and order.

37.
Theory of
forms.
The doctrine of forms in the well-known problems of permutations and combinations begins with modern mathematics in the seventeenth century, and received scientific recognition mainly in connection with the doctrine of chances at the hands of James Bernoulli abroad, and of De Moivre in this country. The process of multiplication of binomials and polynomials leads to the formation of combinations, and

where the factors are the same, as in Newton's binomial theorem, to combinations with permutation; and consequently the doctrine of chances and of arrangements in triangular, pyramidal, or other figures is closely connected with the doctrine of series and algebraical expressions. In this country the interest in the subject has been stimulated and kept alive by isolated problems and puzzles in older popular periodicals, such as the ' Gentleman's Magazine ' and the ' Ladies' Diary'; in Germany—as we noticed before—a school of mathematicians arose who attempted a systematic treatment of the whole subject, which, owing to its barrenness in practical results, brought this line of research somewhat into disrepute. What was wanted was a problem of real scientific interest and a method of abbreviation and condensation. Both were supplied from unexpected [1]

[1] The theory of arrangement or of order, also called the "Ars Combinatoria," has exerted a great fascination on some master minds, as it has also given endless opportunities for the practical ingenuity of smaller talents; among the former we must count in the first place Leibniz, and in recent times J. J. Sylvester, who conceived the "sole proper business of mathematics to be the development of the three germinal ideas—of which continuity is one, and order and number the other two" ('Philosophical Transactions,' vol. clix. p. 613). This idea has been dwelt on by Major MacMahon in his address (Brit. Assoc., 1901, p. 526), who says: "The combinatorial analysis may be described as occupying an extensive region between the algebras of discontinuous and continuous quantity. It is to a certain extent a science of enumeration, of measurement by means of integers as opposed to measurement of quantities which vary by infinitesimal increments. It is also concerned with arrangements in which differences of quality and relative position in one, two, or three dimensions are factors. Its chief problem is the formation of connecting roads between the sciences of discontinuous and continuous quantity. To enable, on the one hand, the treatment of quantities which vary *per saltum,* either in magnitude or position, by the methods of the science of continuously varying quantity and position, and, on the other hand, to reduce problems of continuity to the resources available for the management of discontinuity. These two roads of research should be regarded as penetrating deeply into the domains which they connect."

quarters—the one purely theoretical, the other practical. Accordingly the doctrine of forms and arrangements has during the last century been developed by mathematicians in two distinct interests, which only quite lately seem to approach and assist each other.

38.
Theory of
numbers.

The purely abstract or theoretical interest came from the side of the theory of numbers, a branch of research which was revived by Legendre in France and by the youthful genius of Gauss in Germany; the more practical one came from the theory of equations, notably in its application to problems of geometry. The methods by which these subjects were treated had in the early part of the nineteenth century undergone a great change. The older inductive method in both branches—namely, in the solution of equations and in the investigation of the properties of numbers—relied mainly on ingenious devices which were mostly of special, not of general, value. Theorems were found by induction, and had afterwards to be proved by rigorous logical deduction. Success depended on the degree of care with which the mind operated with mathematical symbols, and rested frequently on the intuition, if not the inspiration, of genius. Two of the greatest mathematical minds— Fermat[1] in France and Newton[2] in England — stood

---

[1] Pierre Fermat (1601-65) prepared an edition of the Treatise of Diophantus, and his marginal notes contain many theorems referring to the properties of numbers which have been the subject of much comment and examination by mathematicians of the first rank down to the present day. In letters to contemporaries he referred to many of these discoveries, and to his proofs, which he did not communicate. Some

of these proofs seem not to have satisfied him, being deficient in rigour. In spite of the labours of Euler, Lagrange, Cauchy, Dirichlet, Kummer, and others, one of these theorems still awaits proof. A full account of Fermat's theorems is given in Cantor's 'Geschichte der Mathematik,' vol. ii. 2nd ed., p. 773 *sqq.* Also in W. Rouse Ball's 'History of Mathematics,' p. 260 *sqq.*

[2] Newton, in his 'Universal

foremost in having with unrivalled fertility propounded theorems which were as difficult to prove as the manner in which they had been arrived at was mysterious. The great analytical genius of Euler, who possessed unequalled resources in the solution of single problems, spent much time and power in unravelling the riddles of Fermat. In the theory of equations the general solution beyond the fourth degree baffled the greatest thinkers. The time had come when in both branches a systematic study of the properties had to be attempted. This was done for the theory of numbers by Gauss, for that of equations by Abel. Every great step in advance of this kind in mathematics is accompanied by, and dependent on, skilful abbreviations, and an easy algorithm or mathematical language. An assemblage of elements held together by the simplest operations or signs of arithmetic — namely, those of addition and multiplication — is much easier to deal with if it can be arranged with some regularity, and accordingly methods were invented by which algebraical expressions or forms were made symmetrical and homogeneous;[1] the latter property signifying that each term

39. Symmetry.

Arithmetic,' gave an interesting theorem by which the number of imaginary roots of an equation can be determined ; he left no proof, and the theorem was discussed by Euler and many other writers, till at last Sylvester in 1866 found the proof of it in a more general theorem. In more recent times Jacob Steiner published a great number of theorems referring to algebraical curves (see Crelle's 'Journal,' vol. xlvii.) which have been compared by Hesse with the "riddles of Fermat." Luigi Cremona succeeded at last in proving them by a general synthetical method.

[1] The introduction of homogeneous expressions marks a great formal advance in algebra and analytical geometry. The first instance of homogeneous co-ordinates is to be found in Möbius's "Barycentric Calculus" (1826), in which he defined the position of any point in a plane by reference to three fundamental points, considering each point as the centre of gravity of those points when weighted. "The idea of co-ordinates appears here for the first time in a new

contained the same number of factors. Such forms
could be written down on the pattern or model of
one of their terms by simple methods of exchange or
permutation of the elements. It would then not be
necessary to write down all the terms but only to indicate
them by their elements, these also being abbreviated by
the use of indices. Rows and columns or arrangements
in squares suggested themselves as easy and otherwise
well-known artifices by which great masses of statistics
and figures are marshalled and controlled. Out of these
manifold but simple devices there grew an algebra of
algebra, a symbol for denoting in a very general way
symmetrical and homogeneous algebraical expressions.[1]

40.
Determin-
ants.

Gauss termed such expressions Determinants: they
turned up in his ' Disquisitiones Arithmeticæ ' as they had
done half a century before in Cramer's 'Analyse des lignes
courbes algébriques.'   Just as common fractions can be

garb, which soon led to a more
general conception. The Barycentric co-ordinates were the first
instance of homogeneous co-ordinates, . . . and already with Möbius
the advantages become evident
through the symmetry and ele-
gance of his formulæ" (Hankel,
'Project. Geom.,' p. 22).

[1] Determinants were first used
by Leibniz for the purpose of
elimination, and described by him
in a letter to the Marquis de
l'Hospital (1693). The importance
of his remarks was not recognised
and the matter was forgotten, to
be rediscovered by Cramer in the
above - named work (1750, p.
657). It is interesting to note
that the same difficulty of the
process of elimination induced
Plücker to resort to geometrical

interpretation of analytical expressions, and that whilst he "saw
the main advantage of his method
in avoiding algebraical elimination
through a geometrical consideration, Hesse showed how, through
the use of Determinants, algebraical
operations could receive that pliabil-
ity the absence of which was the
reason for Plücker to discard it."
(See the account of Clebsch's work
in 'Math. Ann.,' vol. vii. p. 13.)
Through this invention the combinatorial analysis, which, in the
hands of the school in Germany,
had led into a desert, was raised
again into importance. It has become still more important since the
general theory of forms and of
groups began to play an increasing
part in modern analysis.

dealt with as if they were special things having special properties, though the latter depend only on the properties of the numbers they are made up of and their mode of connection; as powers and surds are separately examined; so the arrangements called determinants can be subjected to a special treatment, their properties ascertained, and themselves subjected to the ordinary operations of arithmetic. This doctrine, which constitutes the beginning and centre of the theory of algebraical forms or "quantics" and of algebraical operations or "tactics," was pretty fully worked out and first introduced into the course of teaching by Cauchy in France; then largely adopted by Jacobi in Germany, where Otto Hesse, trained in the ideas of Plücker, first showed its usefulness in his elegant applications to geometry. In France it was further developed by Hermite, who, together with Cayley and Sylvester in England, proclaimed the great importance of it as an instrument and as a line of mathematical thought.[1] In the latter country the idea of abbreviating and summarising algebraical operations had become quite familiar through another device which has not found equal favour abroad — namely, the Calculus of

[1] "For what is the theory of determinants? It is an algebra upon algebra; a calculus which enables us to combine and foretell the results of algebraical operations, in the same way as algebra enables us to dispense with the performance of the special operations of arithmetic. All analysis must ultimately clothe itself under this form." In this connection Sylvester ('Phil. Mag.,' 1851, Apl., p. 301) refers to Otto Hesse's "problem of reducing a cubic function of three letters to another consisting only of four terms by linear substitutions — a problem which appears to set at defiance all the processes and artifices of common algebra," as "perhaps the most remarkable indirect question to which the method of determinants has been hitherto applied."

Operations, the idea of treating algebraical operations and their symbols as quantities, and of subjecting them to arithmetical treatment separately from the material operated on. The genius of Arthur Cayley was specially fertile in this direction, as was that of Sylvester in the nomenclature or language of the doctrine of forms.[1] The merit, however, of having brought together the new ideas which emanated from the schools of Poncelet and Chasles in France, of Cayley and Sylvester in England, into a connected doctrine, and of having given the impetus to the fundamental re-

[1] The theory of invariants was gradually evolved from many independent beginnings. In 1864 Sylvester wrote ('Phil. Trans.,' p. 579), "As all roads are said to lead to Rome, so I find, in my own case at least, that all algebraical inquiries, sooner or later, end at the Capitol of Modern Algebra, over whose shining portal is inscribed the Theory of Invariants." About the same time (1863) Aronhold developed the principal ideas which lay at the foundation of the theory in organic connection and in complete generality, hereby domiciling in Germany the doctrine which had previously owed its development mainly to English, French, and Italian mathematicians (see Meyer, 'Bericht,' &c., p. 95). The different roads which Sylvester refers to can be traced, first, in the love of symbolic reasoning of Boole, who was "one of the most eminent of those who perceived that the symbols of operation could be separated from those of quantity and treated as distinct objects of calculation, his principal characteristic being perfect confidence in any result obtained by the treatment of symbols in accordance with their primary laws and conditions, and an almost unrivalled skill and power in tracing out these results" (Stanley Jevons in article "Boole," 'Ency. Brit.'); secondly, in the independent geometrical labours of Hesse in Germany (whose mathematical training combined Plücker's and Jacobi's teaching) and Dr Salmon in Dublin (who, after having transplanted Poncelet and Chasles to British soil, recognised the importance of Cayley's and Sylvester's work, and introduced in the later editions of his text-book modern algebraical methods); thirdly, in the independent investigations belonging to the theory of numbers of Eisenstein in Germany and Hermite in France. In full generality the subject was taken up and worked out by Sylvester in the 'Cambridge and Dublin Mathematical Journal' (1851-54), and by Cayley in the first seven memoirs upon Quantics (1854-61), which "in their manysidedness, together with the exhaustive treatment of single cases, remain to the present day, for the algebraist as well as for the geometrician, a rich source of discovery" (Meyer, loc. cit., p. 90).

modelling of the text-books and school-books of algebra
and geometry in this country and in Germany, belongs
undeniably to Dr Salmon of Dublin.[1]   The conception of
a form—be this geometrical or algebraic—suggests the
investigation of the change, the recurrence of forms.
How do forms under the process of geometrical or
algebraical manipulation alter or preserve their various
properties ?   The processes of projection practised by
Monge, Poncelet, and Chasles in France had already
led to a distinction between descriptive and metrical
properties of geometrical figures.   A corresponding examination of algebraical forms, which are all capable of
geometrical representation or interpretation, would lead
to the extensive and fundamental doctrine of the invariants of these forms—i.e., of such arrangements of
the elements as remain absolutely or proportionally unaltered during the processes of change and combination.
Notably instead of the geometrical process of projection
by central perspective we may employ in our algebraic
formulæ a corresponding process, that which is known as
linear substitution.   And at the time when it was
recognised that geometrical transformation had its

---

[1] Of Dr Salmon, whose 'Lessons introductory to the Modern
Higher Algebra' appeared in 1859
(4th ed., 1855 ; 1st German ed. by
Fiedler, 1863), Meyer says : "Recognising how the special results
in this domain gradually acquired
a considerable bulk, we must the
more gratefully acknowledge the
work of Salmon—who had already,
in the direction of algebra as well as
of geometry, furnished valuable contributions of his own—in undertaking the labour of collecting the
widely-scattered material in a concise monograph. For the promulga-
tion in Germany we have to thank
Fiedler both for his edition. of
Salmon, and for having already
given an independent introduction
to the subject, in which especially he
made Cayley's applications to projective geometry generally accessible. About the same time (1862)
there appeared likewise an edition
by Brioschi, which gained many adherents for the theory of Invariants
in Italy."

counterpart in the transformation of algebraical forms
by the processes of substitution, these latter had
already been extensively studied for their own sakes in
the theory of algebraical equations, which in the first
quarter of the century had undergone a great development under the hands of two brilliant mathematical
talents both lost to science at an early age—the
Norwegian Abel and the Frenchman Évariste Galois.[1]

Like all algebraical expressions, those termed equations were originally invented and commanded attention

[1] Évariste Galois is held to have
been one of the greatest mathematical geniuses of modern times, who,
if he had lived, might have been a
rival of Abel : he was born in 1811,
and died before he was twenty-one,
in consequence of a duel. For a
long time his writings remained unpublished and unknown, till Liouville published them in the 11th vol.
of his 'Journal' (1846). Liouville
was also the first to recognise the
importance and absolute correctness
of Galois's method, which, when submitted to the Academy in the year
1831, and reported on by Lacroix
and Poisson, had appeared almost
unintelligible. On the eve of his
death Galois addressed a letter to
his friend Auguste Chevalier, which
is a unique document in mathematical literature, forming a kind of
mathematical testament. He desires this letter to be published
in the 'Revue Encyclopédique,'
referring publicly the "importance," not the "correctness," of his
discoveries to the judgment of
Jacobi and Gauss, and expressing
the hope that some persons would
be found who would take the
trouble to unravel his hieroglyphics.
The first attempt to make Galois's
ideas generally accessible is to be
found in Serret's 'Algèbre Supérieure' (3rd ed., 1866), but it was

not till after the publication of
Camille Jordan's 'Théorie des
Substitutions' (1870) that the
short papers of Galois were recognised as containing the germs and
beginnings of an entirely novel and
comprehensive mathematical theory
—viz., the "Theory of Groups."
The relation between the writings
of Abel and Galois is exhaustively
treated in Prof. Sylow's Paper on
Abel's work, contained in the 'Memorial Volume,' 1892, p. 24. He
there says : "Le mérite de Galois
ne consiste pas essentiellement dans
ses propositions, mais dans la généralité de la méthode qu'il appliqua.
C'est son admirable théorème fondamental qui a donné à la théorie
des équations sa forme définitive,
et d'où est sortie, en outre, la théorie
des groupes généralisée, qui est
d'une si grande importance, on peut
le dire, pour toutes les branches des
mathématiques, et qui déjà, entre
les mains de Jordan, de Klein, de
Lie, de Poincaré et d'autres, a en-
richi la science d'une longue suite
de découvertes importantes." The
memoirs of Abel and Galois referring to the Theory of Equations
have been conveniently edited, in a
German translation, by H. Maser,
1889. See also Cayley's article on
"Equation" in the 'Ency. Brit.,'
§ 32.

as instruments or devices for the solution of definite problems in arithmetic, geometry, and mechanics. The solution of the equation—*i.e.*, the expression of the unknown quantity in terms of the known quantities—served a practical end. Gradually as such solutions became more and more difficult, owing to the complexity of the formulæ, the doctrine divided itself into two distinct branches, serving two distinct interests. The first, and practically the more important one, was to devise methods by which in every single case the equations which presented themselves could be solved with sufficient accuracy or approximation; this is the doctrine of the numerical solution of equations. The other more scientific branch looked upon equations as algebraical arrangements of quantities and operations which possessed definite properties, and proposed to investigate these properties for their own sake. The question arose, How many solutions or roots an equation would admit of, and whether the expression of the unknown quantity in terms of the known quantities was or was not possible by using merely such operations as were indicated by the equation itself—*i.e.*, the common operations and the ordinary numbers of arithmetic? This doctrine of the general properties of equations received increasing attention as it became empirically known that equations beyond the fourth degree could not be solved in the most general form.[1] Why could they not be solved,

43. General solution of equations.

---

[1] Since the researches regarding the solubility of Equations have led on, through Galois and the French analysts, to the same line of reasoning as other researches mentioned before—viz., toward the development of the theory of groups—the history of the whole subject has aroused special interest. The earlier beginnings and the labours of forgotten analysts have been un-

and what were the conditions—*i.e.*, the special properties—of an equation which rendered it soluble ? These were some of the questions which the great mathematicians, such as Gauss, Abel, and Galois, placed before themselves during the earlier part of the century. There are other unsolved problems which the nineteenth century inherited from preceding ones, where the same line of reasoning was adopted—*i.e.*, where the question was similarly reversed. Instead of trying to solve problems as yet unsolved, it was proposed to prove their general insolubility, and to show the reason of this; also to define the conditions which make a solution possible.

earthed and placed in their correct historical perspective. Prof. Burkhardt of Göttingen, to whom we also owe the chapter on this subject in the first volume of the 'Encyklopädie,' &c., contributed in the year 1892 a most interesting historical paper, "Die Anfänge der Gruppentheorie und Paolo Ruffini" ('Abhandl. zur Gesch. der Math.,' 6 Heft). In this paper he also goes back to other earlier analysts, among them Prof. Waring of Cambridge, who during his lifetime used to complain that he knew of no one who read his mathematical tracts. It appears that during nearly the last thirty years of the eighteenth century nothing had been added regarding the general theory of equations, and that Ruffini was the first to begin a new epoch in the year 1799, with the distinct assertion that a general solution of algebraic equations beyond the fourth degree, by means of radicals, was impossible, and with an attempt to prove this. His researches were therefore contemporaneous with those of Gauss, who published his 'Dissertation' (see note p. 644) in the same year, and his great arithmetical work

in 1801. Although Gauss seems to have arrived at the same conclusion, and perhaps even to have anticipated much later attempts to solve the general equation of the fifth degree by other than algebraical operations (see Sylow, *loc. cit.*, p. 16), his published researches rather took the line of the study of a definite class of soluble equations which were connected with the celebrated problem of the division of the circle ; a satisfactory proof of Ruffini's statement being withheld till Abel published his celebrated memoir in the year 1825 in the first volume of Crelle's 'Journal.' With this memoir the theory of equations entered a new phase, towards which the labours of Ruffini were preparatory. As in so many other cases, so also in this, the solution of the problem depended upon stricter definitions of what was meant by the solution of an equation, and by "algebraical" and other ("transcendental") functions and operations. We know that both Abel and Galois began their research by futile attempts to find a solution of the general equation of the fifth degree.

In following this altered course of investigation, an enormous amount of mathematical knowledge was gained, and problems were solved which had previously never been thought of. Especially through the theory of equations the abstract doctrine of algebraical forms was created and greatly advanced long before it was generally recognised that it had peculiar importance through the correspondence or parallelism which existed between algebraical expressions and geometrical configurations.

Out of these earlier algebraical and later combined algebraical and geometrical investigations, a novel and very useful point of view has been gradually gained which represents the most general conception of mathematical tactics.   This centres in the notion of a group of elements.   These elements may be quantities or operations, so that the theory of Groups embraces not only the doctrines which deal with quantities but also those which deal with arrangements and their possible changes. The older combinatorial analysis dealt mainly with assemblages of a quantity of separate elements, their number, their variety : the modern theory of groups deals rather with the processes and operations by which different arrangements can be transformed one into the other.   It is an algebra of operations.   The methods of transformation which presented themselves first of all were the methods known in algebra as substitution. Accordingly the first comprehensive treatise on the theory was the ' Treatise on Substitutions,' published in 1870 by M. Camille Jordan.   This book forms a landmark in modern mathematics ; it brought into a system

44.
Theory of
groups.

the beginnings of the new and comprehensive calculus of operations which were contained in the writings of Lagrange, Abel, Cauchy, and Galois, and established the terminology and the algorithm. A group of substitutions is defined as having the property that each two or more operations belonging to it and successively applied can be replaced by another single operation contained in the same group. Succeeding operations are symbolically represented by the product of two or more letters. This product has certain algebraical properties, and in analogy with common products it has factors, a degree, an index; the substitution may be cyclical and symmetric, and may have many other remarkable properties which the theory [1]

[1] The "Theory of Groups" has now grown into a very extensive doctrine which, according to the late Prof. Marius Sophus Lie (1842-99), is destined to occupy a leading and central position in the mathematical science of the future. "The conception of Group and Invariant was for him not only a methodical aspect from which he intended to review the entire older region of mathematics, but also the element which was destined to permeate and unify the whole of mathematical science" (M. Nöther, 'Math. Ann.,' vol. liii. p. 39). But though it is an undoubted fact that the largest systematic works on the subject emanate from that great Norwegian mathematician, and that his ideas have won gradual recognition, especially on the part of prominent French mathematicians, notably M. Picard ('Traité d'Analyse,' 1896, vol. iii.) and M. Poincaré, the epoch-making tract which pushed the novel conception into the foreground was Prof. F. Klein's 'Erlangen Programme' (1872), entitled "Vergleichende Betrachtungen über neuere geometrische Forschungen." To those who read and re-read this short but weighty treatise, it must indeed have been like a revelation, opening out entirely new avenues of thought into which mathematical research has been more and more guided during the last generation. The tract, which has now been translated into all the important modern languages, remained for a long time comparatively unnoticed, and, twenty years after its publication, was reprinted by the author in the 43rd volume of the 'Math. Annalen,' with some introductory remarks which indicate the changes that had taken place in the interval as regards the scope of the idea. The main result of the dissertation is this : That, primarily, for all geometrical investigations, the characteristic properties of any manifold (or arrangement) is not the element out of which it is composed, but the group, the transformations of which reveal its invariantive properties. There are, accordingly, as many different ways of

of groups investigates. Its immediate application, and the purpose for which it was elaborated, was the theory of Equations. Every equation constitutes an arrangement in which a finite number of independent elements, called constants or coefficients, is presented under a certain algebraical form. The solution of the equation means the finding of such an arrangement as when substituted in the equation for the unknown quantity, will satisfy the equation.

The conception of a group of operations standing in the defined relations is, however, capable of a great and fundamental extension into that region of mathematics which deals, not with fixed or constant, but with variable or flowing quantities; not with elements which are disconnected or discontinuous, but with such as are continuous. To understand the development of modern mathematical thought, it is accordingly necessary to go back somewhat and review the progress which the

45. Continuo and discontinuous groups.

studying any manifold (*e.g.*, such as projective geometry, line geometry, geometry of reciprocal radii, Lie's sphere geometry, analysis situs, &c.) as there are continuous groups of transformations that can be established ; and there are as many invariant theories (see ' Ency. Math. Wiss.,' vol. ii. p. 402 ; Nöther, *loc. cit.*, p. 22). From that date onward the different kinds of groups have been defined and systematically studied, notably by Klein and Lie and their pupils. In this country, although many of the relevant ideas were contained in the writings notably of Cayley and of Sylvester, the systematic treatment of the subject was little attended to before the publication (1897) of Prof. Burn-side's ' Theory of Groups of Finite Order,' and latterly of his article on the whole Theory of Groups in the 29th volume of the ' Ency. Brit.' It has been remarked by those who have studied most profoundly the development of the two great branches of mathematical tactics —viz., " The Theory of Invariants " and the " Theory of Groups "—that the progress of science would have been more rapid if the English school had taken more notice of the general comprehensive treatment by Lie, and if Lie himself had not refrained from entering more fully into the special theories of that school (see Dr F. Meyer, ' Bericht,' &c., p. 231).

conception of the variable [1] has undergone in the course of the last hundred years. Here we come upon a term which was introduced into mathematical language mainly through the writings of Euler—the term function. It is used to denote the mathematical dependence of two or more variable quantities on each

[1] To the theory of equations in algebra there corresponds the theory of differential equations in analysis; and as the theory of algebraical equations had gradually emerged in a complete form out of investigations of special equations, or sets of equations, so likewise in analysis a general theory of differential equations is gradually being evolved out of the scattered and very extensive investigations of special differential equations which presented themselves notably in the application of analysis to astronomical and physical problems. It is claimed by those who have grasped the abstract ideas of Sophus Lie, that he has taken a great step forward in the direction of a general theory of differential equations, by applying methods which suggested themselves to him through the general theory of algebraic forms and its connection with geometry. Accordingly, the theories of Lie can be termed an algebraical theory of differential equations, depending upon transformations analogous to those which had been established in the general theory of forms or quantities of which I treated above. Prof. Engel, in his obituary notice of Sophus Lie ('Deutsche Math. Ver.,' vol. viii. p. 35), tells us that in the year 1869-70, when Lie met Prof. Klein in Berlin, the former was occupied with certain partial differential equations which exhibited, under certain transformations, invariantive properties, and that Klein then pointed out "that his procedure had a certain analogy with the methods of Abel. The suggestion of this analogy became important for Lie, as he was generally intent upon following up more closely the analogies with the theory of algebraical equations." Dr H. F. Baker, in his recent article on Differential Equations in the 'Ency. Brit.' (vol. xxvii. p. 448), roughly distinguishes two methods of studying differential equations, which he names respectively "transformation theories" and "function theories," "the former concerned to reduce the algebraical relation to the fewest and simplest forms, eventually with the hope of obtaining explicit expressions of the dependent in terms of the independent variables; the latter concerned to determine what general descriptive relations among the quantities are involved by the differential equations, with as little use of algebraical calculations as may be possible." For the history of thought and connection of ideas, it is interesting to learn, through Prof. Engel, that it was not purely algebraical work,—such as is represented by Galois and Jordan, to which Lie was early introduced by Prof. Sylow,—but the study of Poncelet's and Plücker's methods which led Lie to his original conceptions, and that he was fond of calling himself a pupil of Plücker, whom he had never seen (Engel, *loc. cit.*, p. 34).

other. The question arises, What are we to understand under this term? What is a mathematical function or dependence? The question was approached by the great analysts of the second half of the eighteenth century. A preliminary answer which served the requirements of a very wide field of practical application was given by Fourier at the beginning of the nineteenth century. Since that time the question has been independently treated by two schools of Continental mathematicians. Of these the first was founded by Cauchy in France, and is mainly represented by Bernhard Riemann and his numerous pupils in Germany; the other centres in the Berlin school, headed by Weierstrass, and goes back to the work of Lagrange.

The interests which have led to this modern branch of mathematical research [1] are various, but we can

46. Theory of Functions.

The literature suitable for introducing the student of mathematics to the modern theory of functions —which plays in analysis, *i.e.*, the doctrine of variable quantity, a part of similar importance to that which the theory of forms plays in algebra—is so enormous, the subject being approached from so many sides by different writers, that it seems worth while to refer to two expositions which may be read with profit, and which do not require extensive mathematical knowledge. First and foremost I would recommend Cayley's article on "Functions" in vol ix. of the 'Ency. Brit.' Then there is the chapter on "Foundations of the General Theory of Functions," contained in the 2nd volume of the German 'Mathematical Encyclopedia,' written by Prof. Prings-

heim. Cayley's article introduces the general theory after giving a short summary of the more important "known" functions, including those which presented themselves in the first half of the nineteenth century, and which I referred to in dealing with the work of Abel and Gauss (see note, p. 648). The treatment of these latter functions, which had been brought to a certain degree of perfection by Jacobi, had made it evident that more general aspects had to be gained and broader foundations laid. But ever since the middle of the eighteenth century another development of mathematical ideas had been soing on which started from the solution of a problem in mathematical physics—namely, that of vibrating strings, which led in the sequel to

distinguish two which are very prominent, and are roughly represented by the two schools just referred to. In the first place, a function can be formally defined as an assemblage of mathematical symbols, each of which denotes a definite operation on one or more quantities. These operations are partly direct, like addition, multiplication, &c.; partly indirect or inverse, like subtraction, division, &c. Now, so far as the latter are concerned, they are not generally and necessarily practicable, and the question arises, When are they practicable, and if they are not, what meaning can we connect with the mathematical symbol? In this way we arrive at definitions for mathematical functions which cannot immediately be reduced to the primary operations of arithmetic, but which form special expressions that become objects of research as to their properties and as to the relation they bear to those fundamental operations upon which all our methods of calculation depend. The inverse operations, represented by negative, irrational, and imaginary quantities; further, the operations of integration in its definition as the

a certain finality when Fourier introduced his well-known series and integrals, by which any kind of functionality or mathematical dependence, such as physical processes seem to indicate, could be expressed. The work of Fourier, which thus gave, as it were, a sort of preliminary specification under which a large number of problems in physical mathematics could be attacked and practically solved, together with the stricter definitions introduced by Lejeune Dirichlet, settled for a time and for practical purposes the lengthy discussions which had begun with Euler, Daniel Bernoulli, d'Alembert, and Lagrange. The above-named chapter, written by Prof. Pringsheim, gives an introduction to the subject showing the historical genesis of the conception of function and the various changes it was subjected to, and then proceeds to expositions and definitions mostly taken from the lectures of Weierstrass (see p. 8), whereas Cayley's article introduces us to the elements of the general theory of functions as they were first laid down by Riemann in the manner now commonly accepted.

inverse of differentiation,—led early to investigations of the kind just mentioned.   The experience that ordinary fractions might be expressed by decimal fractions—*i.e.*, by finite or infinite series—led to the inverse problem of finding the sum of such series and many other answerable and apparently unanswerable problems.   The older method of research consisted in treating these problems when and as they arose : new chapters were accordingly added to the existing chapters of the text-books, dealing with special functions or mathematical expressions.   It was only towards the end of the eighteenth century, and at the beginning of the nineteenth, that Lagrange, Gauss, and Cauchy felt and proclaimed the necessity of attacking the question generally and systematically ; the labours of Euler having accumulated an enormous mass of analytical knowledge, a great array of useful formulæ, and amongst them not a few paradoxes which demanded special attention.   I have already had occasion to refer to the problem of the general solution of equations as an instance where, in the hands of Abel, the tentative and highly ingenious attempts of earlier analysts were replaced by a methodical and general treatment of the whole question. Another chapter of higher mathematics, the investigation of expressions which presented themselves in the problems of finding the length of the arc of an ellipse, and which opened the view into the large province of the so-called higher transcendents, gave Abel further occasion of laying new foundations and of creating a general theory of equations or of forms.

But yet another interest operated powerfully in the

direction of promoting these seemingly abstract researches. Nature herself exhibits to us measurable
and observable quantities in definite mathematical dependence;[1] the conception of a function is suggested by
all the processes of nature where we observe natural
phenomena varying according to distance or to time.

47.
Physical
analogies.

[1] Nearly all the "known" functions have presented themselves in
the attempt to solve geometrical,
mechanical, or physical problems,
such as finding the length of the
arc of the ellipse (elliptic functions); or answering questions in
the theory of attraction (the potential function and other functions,
such as the functions of Legendre,
Laplace, and Bessel, all comprised
under the general term of "harmonic functions"). These functions, being of special importance in mathematical physics, were
treated independently before a
general theory of functions was
thought of. Many important properties were established, and
methods for the numerical evalu-
ation were devised. In the course
of these researches other functions
occurred, such as Euler's "Gam-
ma" function and Jacobi's "Theta"
function, which possessed interesting analytical properties. These
functions, suggested directly or
indirectly by applications of analysis, did not always present themselves in a form which indicated
definite analytical processes, such
as processes of integration or the
summation of series. Very frequently they presented themselves,
not in an "explicit" but in an
"implicit" form; their properties
being expressed by certain conditions which they had to fulfil. It
then remained a question whether
a definite symbol, indicating a
set of analytical operations, could
be found. This arises from the

fact that the solution of most problems in mechanics and physics
starts from the assumption that,
though the finite observable phenomena of nature are extremely intricate, they are, nevertheless,
compounded out of comparatively
simple elementary processes, which
take place between the discrete
atoms, or the elementary but continuous portions of matter. Mathematically expressed, this means that
the relations in question present
themselves in the form of differential equations, and that the solution
of them consists in finding functions of finite (observable) quantities which satisfy the special conditions. A comparatively small
number of differential equations
has thus been found empirically
to embrace very large and apparently widely separated classes of
physical phenomena, suggesting
physical relations between those
phenomena which might otherwise
have remained unnoticed. The
physicist or astronomer thus hands
over his problems to the mathematician, who has either to in-
tegrate the differential equations,
or, where this is not possible, at
least to infer the properties of the
functions which would satisfy them
—in fact, the differential equation
becomes a definition of the function
or mathematical relation. In consequence of this the theory of
differential equations is, as Sophus
Lie has said, by far the most
important branch of mathematics.

The attraction of the heavenly bodies varies with the distance, the velocity of a falling stone or the cooling of a hot body varies with the interval of time which has lapsed or flown.   We are now so much accustomed to represent such dependence by curves drawn on paper, that we hardly realise the great step in advance towards definiteness and intelligibility that this device marks in all natural sciences and in many practical pursuits.   But the representation of the natural connections of varying quantities by curves also forms the connecting link with the other class of researches just mentioned.   Descartes had shown how to represent algebraical formulæ by curves in the plane and in space ; and at the beginning of the nineteenth century this method was modified by Gauss and Cauchy so as to deal also with the extended conception of number which embraced the imaginary unit.   Two questions arise, Is it possible to represent every arbitrary dependence such as we meet with in the graphical description of natural phenomena by a mathematical formula— *i.e.*, by a formula denoting several specified mathematical operations in well-defined connections ? and the inverse question, Is it possible to represent every well-defined arrangement of symbols denoting special mathematical operations graphically by curves in the plane or in space ?   The former question is one of vital importance in the progress of astronomy, physics, chemistry, and many other sciences, and has accordingly occupied many eminent analysts ever since Fourier gave the first approximative answer in his well-known series : the latter question can only be answered by much stricter definitions of all the more advanced and of some even of the elementary operations which analysts had become accustomed to use without a previous knowledge of the range of their validity. All applications of mathematics consist in extending the empiricial knowledge which we possess of a limited number or region of accessible phenomena into the region of the unknown and inaccessible; and much of the progress of pure analysis consists in inventing definite conceptions, marked by symbols, of complicated operations; in ascertaining their properties as independent objects of research; and in extending their meaning beyond the limits they were originally invented for,—thus opening out new and larger regions of thought.

48.
The
potential.

A brilliant and most suggestive example of this kind of reasoning was afforded by a novel mode of treating a large class of physical problems by means of the introduction of a special mathematical function, termed by George Green, and later by Gauss, the " Potential " or " Potential function." [1] All the problems of Newtonian attraction were concentrated in the study of this formula: and when the experiments of Coulomb and Ampère showed the analogy that existed between electric and magnetic forces on the

[1] See vol. i. p. 231 of this work. The history of the subject has been written by Todhunter ('History of the Theories of Attraction and the Figure of the Earth,' 2 vols., 1873) for the earlier period down to 1832. For the later period see Bacharach's 'Abriss der Geschichte der Potentialtheorie,' Göttingen, 1883; for the connection of the theory with Riemann's mathematical methods, especially Prof. F. Klein's tract, 'Ueber Riemann's Theorie der algebraischen Functionen' (Leipzig, 1882, trans. by F. Hardcastle, Cambridge, 1893); Prof. Carl Neumann's 'Untersuchungen über das Logarithmische und Newtonische Potential' (Leipzig, 1877); Dr Burkhardt's 'Memorial Lecture on Riemann' (Göttingen, 1892); and jointly with Dr Franz Meyer, the same author's chapter on "Potentialtheorie" in the 2nd volume (p. 464) of the 'Encyclopädie der Math. Wiss.,' 1900.

one side, and Newtonian forces on the other; still more when Fourier, Lamé, and Thomson (Lord Kelvin) pointed to the further analogy which existed between the distribution of temperature in the stationary flow of heat and that of statical electricity on a conductor, and extended the analogy to hydrostatics and hydrodynamics, —it became evident that nature herself pointed here to a mathematical dependence of the highest interest and value. Many eminent thinkers devoted themselves to the study of this subject, but it was reserved for Bernhard Riemann to generalise the mode of reasoning peculiar to these researches into a fundamentally novel method for the explanation and definition of mathematical function or dependence.[1]

[1] Although Riemann's original method of dealing in a general way with algebraical functions is here introduced as a generalisation of certain ideas suggested by mathematical physics, it was not in this way that they were introduced to the mathematical world. This was done in his very abstract and difficult memoir, ' Theorie der Abel'schen Functionen ' (published in 1857 in vol. liv. of Crelle's ' Journal '). In this memoir the connection which existed with mathematical physics was not patent, and it took a long time before his methods, which seemed to be a development of Cauchy's earlier researches, were understood and fully appreciated. It was only after he had lectured repeatedly on the subject, and initiated a number of younger mathematicians, who now occupy many of the chairs at the German universities, that the discoveries and inventions of Riemann received their deserved appreciation.   Even in his own lectures on mathematical physics— notably on partial differential equations (including harmonics) and the theory of the potential— he did not lead up to the fundamental ideas which he developed in his lectures on the theory of the Abelian functions. Some light is thrown on the subject of the genesis of Riemann's ideas by his dissertation written in the year 1851, though even the biographical notice attached to the 1st edition of his works (1876) did not deal with the origins of his theory. It seems, therefore, correct to date the adequate recognition of Riemann's work in wider circles from the publication in 1882 of Prof. F. Klein's tract mentioned above. Like several other short treatises of this eminent living mathematician, it must have thrown quite a new light upon the subject; and, like several of his other writings, it revealed connections between regions of thought which to many students must have appeared isolated. "Through the treatment initiated by Klein, the theory of

The peculiarity of such dependence, as exemplified in the phenomena of the steady flow of heat or of electric distribution, consisted in this, that if at certain points or in certain regions of space the thermal or electrical conditions were defined and known by actual observation, then the whole distribution in other points and regions was completely determined. Those boundary conditions could therefore be regarded as the necessary and sufficient definition of the whole existing distribution. Translated into mathematical language, this means that functions exist which are completely defined by boundary values and singularities—*i.e.*, values at single points. Nature herself had shown the way to define and calculate measured relations when through their intricacy they evaded the grasp of the ordinary operations of algebra.[1] Plücker had already in geometry (following in the lines of Newton), when attacking the problem of the infinite variety of higher curves, suggested the method of classifying them according to their characteristic properties or singularities. What had been done by geometers and physicists in isolated cases with the expenditure of much ingenuity and skill, Riemann and his school elevated to the rank of a general method and doctrine.

functions acquires a great degree of clearness and connectedness, which is mainly gained by conceptions derived from the (physical) theory of the potential, and thus exhibits the intimate relationship of these theories" (Bacharach, 'Geschichte der Potentialtheorie,' Göttingen, 1883, p. 71).

[1] On this subject see Burkhardt's 'Memorial Lecture on Riemann' (Göttingen, 1892), p. 5, &c. ; Bacharach (*loc. cit.*), p. 30, &c. The latter especially with reference to the theorem called by Clerk-Maxwell "Thomson's theorem" ('Cambridge and Dublin Mathematical Journal,' 1848, or 'Reprint of Papers on Electro-statics,' &c., p. 139) ; and abroad 'Dirichlet's Principle,' after Riemann (1857). Further, Brill and Nöther's "Bericht" ('Math. Ver.,' vol. iii. p. 247) ; and lastly, a very suggestive address by Prof. Klein ("On Riemann's Influence on Modern Mathematics") to the meeting of the German Association in Vienna in 1804 (' Report,' p. 61).

It is a process of generalisation and simplification. Moreover, Riemann's manner of proceeding brought with it the gain that he could at once make the various theorems of the doctrine of the potential useful for purely mathematical purposes : the equation which defined the potential in physics became the definition of a function in mathematics.[1]

[1] " One may define Riemann's developments briefly thus : that, beginning with certain differential equations which the functions of the complex variable satisfy, he is enabled to apply the principles of the potential theory. His starting-point, accordingly, lies in the province of mathematical physics " (Klein, ' Vienna Report,' *loc. cit.*, p. 60). By starting with physical analogies Prof. Klein evades certain difficulties which the purely mathematical treatment had to encounter. In the preface to his tract of the year 1882, quoted above,—in introducing his method of explaining Riemann's theory,— he says : " I have not hesitated to make exactly these physical conceptions the starting-point of my exposition. Instead of them, Riemannn, as is well known, makes use in his writings of Dirichlet's principle. But I cannot doubt that he started from those physical problems, and only afterwards substituted Dirichlet's principle in order to support the physical evidence by mathematical reasoning. Whoever understands clearly the surroundings among which Riemann worked at Göttingen, whoever follows up Riemann's speculations as they have been handed down to us, partly in fragments, will, I think, share my opinion." And elsewhere he says : " We regard as a specific performance of Riemann in this connection the tendency to give to the theory of the potential a fundamental importance for the whole of mathematics, and further a series of geometrical constructions or, as I would rather say, of geometrical inventions " ('Vienna Report,' p. 61). Klein then refers to the representation on the so-called " Riemann surface," which is historically connected, as Riemann himself points out, with the problem which Gauss first attacked in a general way—viz., the representation of one surface on another in such a manner that the smallest portions of the one surface are similar to those of the other : a problem which is of importance in the drawing of maps, and of which we possess two well-known examples in the stereographic projection of Ptolemy and the projection of Mercator. This method of representation was called by Gauss the "Conformal Image or Representation." His investigations on this matter were suggested by the Geodetic Survey of the kingdom of Hanover, with which he was occupied during the years 1818 to 1830. (See Gauss, ' Werke,' vol. iv., also his correspondence with Schumacher and Bessel.) A very complete treatise on this aspect of Riemann's inventions is that by Dr J. Holtzmüller, ' Theorie der Isogonalen Verwandschaften ' (Leipzig, 1882). On the historical antecedents of Riemann's conception, which for a long time appeared somewhat strange, not to say artificial, see Brill and Nöther's frequently quoted "Report" ('Bericht der Math. Verein.,' vol. iii.), p. 256 *sqq.*

In the investigation of those higher functions which the purely analytical methods of Abel and his followers had forced upon the attention of mathematicians, the methods of Riemann proved to be eminently useful and suggestive. But these novel methods themselves had been imported into the pure science from the side of its application in physics. The value of such ideas has always been questioned by another class of thinkers who aim at building up the edifice of the science by rigorous logic, without making use of practical devices which could only be legitimately employed when once their validity had been thoroughly proved and its limits defined. The merit of having done this in the whole domain of those conceptions which, since the age of Descartes, Newton, and Leibniz, had been introduced as it were from the outside into analysis, belongs to the school of mathematicians headed in Germany by Karl Weierstrass.

50.
Weierstrass.

Riemann had grown up in the traditions of the school of mathematical thought which was inspired by Gauss and Weber in Göttingen. Geometrical representation and physical application, including the immediate evidence of the senses, formed a large and important factor in the body of arguments by which scientific discovery and invention was carried on in that school; though Gauss himself made logical rigour the final test of maturity in all his published writings, abstaining in many cases from communicating his results when they had not satisfactorily passed that test in his own mind. Through this self-imposed restriction he had permitted important discoveries, which led to large increase of mathematical knowledge, to be anticipated by others.

The cases of Cauchy, Abel, and Jacobi are the best-known instances. Through their labours an entirely new field had been prospected and partially cultivated. It was to this that Weierstrass, the other great leader in modern theory, was attracted. He made the clear definition and logical coherence of the novel conceptions which it involved his principal aim. Gauss had laboured without assistance at similar problems, making many beginnings which even his colossal intellect could not adequately develop. Weierstrass early gathered around him a circle of ardent and receptive pupils and admirers,[1] to whose care and detailed elaboration he

[1] The researches of Weierstrass (1815 to 1897) began somewhat earlier than those of Riemann, but only became generally known and appreciated in their fundamental originality through his pupils—his academic influence dating from the year 1861. Some account of Weierstrass's activity is given by Emil Lampe in the 6th volume (1899) of the 'Bericht der Math. Verein.,' p. 27, &c. The genesis of his ideas is traced by Brill and Nöther in the Report quoted in the last note, and by M. Poincaré in 'Acta Math.,' vol. xxii. The former divides his Researches roughly into two periods, during the first of which (1848 - 56) he dealt with what Cayley would call "known" functions; progress during this period depending not so much upon fundamentally new ideas as upon an investigation of special problems and great analytical skill. The second period begins in the year 1869, and is devoted to nothing less than the building up of the entire structure of mathematical thought from the very beginning upon altered definitions, through which the dilemmas and paradoxes would be obviated that had shown themselves ever since the middle of the eighteenth century in consequence of a too confident application and extension of conventional ideas suggested mainly by practical problems. The elements of this grand edifice are now largely accepted, not only in Germany, but also in France, Italy, and England. In Germany Prof. O. Stolz, through his works on General Arithmetic, 2 vols. (1885 and 1886), and the Calculus, 3 vols. (1893 to 1899), has probably done more than any other academic teacher to utilise the new system of mathematical thought for the elementary course of teaching. It seems of importance to state, however, that outside of the circle of Weierstrass's influence, and quite within the precincts of Riemann's school, the necessity was felt of strengthening the foundations on which research in higher mathematics was carried on, by going back to the fundamental ideas of arithmetic. The principal representative of this line of research was Hermann Hankel (1839-73), a pupil of Riemann's, who, in the

confided many separate and lengthy investigations.   It was through one of these that a test-case, in which existing mathematical definitions broke down, was published in 1872.   It forms a kind of era in the history of

middle of the sixties, delivered lectures at the University of Leipsic upon "Complex numbers and their functions," starting in a characteristic manner with that extended algebra which Cauchy and Riemann had used to such good purpose.   The first part of these lectures was published in 1867. In the preface Hankel says: "In the natural sciences we witness in recent times the distinct tendency to ascend from the world of empirical detail to the great principles which govern everything special and connect it into a whole—*i.e.*, the desire for a philosophy of nature, not forced upon us from outside, but naturally evolved out of the subject itself.   Also in the domain of mathematics a similar want seems to make itself generally felt —a want which has always been alive in England."   Had the author not been prematurely taken away, there is no doubt that he would have still more largely contributed to the revolution of mathematical ideas now in progress.   As it is, he made one further important contribution, of which more hereafter.   In Italy Prof. Ulisse Dini began to lecture in the year 1871 to 1872 on the theory of functions, and published his lectures in 1878.   A translation was brought out in Germany (1892) by Prof. Lüroth and Mr A. Schepp, in which many of the modern developments are utilised.   In France we owe to M. Jules Tannery a valuable introduction to the theory of functions of one variable, based upon a series of lectures delivered in the École Normale in 1883, in which, as he says

(Preface, p. vii), he collected the labours of Cauchy, Abel, Lejeune Dirichlet, Riemann, Ossian Bonnet, Heine, Weierstrass, and others ; after which he considers that nothing essential need be added in the way of elucidation of the foundations of the theory. M. Émil Borel published in 1898 'Lectures on the Theory of Functions,' the first of a series of text-books dealing with various aspects of the theory of functions, in which he largely refers to the labours of Weierstrass.   Before Weierstrass's theory had become known, however, M. Méray had already entered upon an exposition of the foundations of analysis on lines which had much analogy with those adopted by Weierstrass.   In England the late Prof. Clifford had occupied himself in various memoirs with the theories of Riemann ; but we owe the first comprehensive treatise, embracing the work of Riemann as well as that of Weierstrass, to Prof. Forsyth ('Theory of Functions of a Complex Variable,' Cambridge, 1893).   Almost simultaneously Professors Harkness and Morley published a 'Treatise on the Theory of Functions,' and in 1898 an 'Introduction to the Theory of Analytic Functions,' in which they in the main adopted the point of view of Weierstrass.   A very original thinker, whose independent researches reach back to the year 1872, and who played an important part in the investigation of many obscure points, was the late Prof. Paul Du Bois-Reymond, who published in 1882 the first part of his 'Allgemeine Functionentheorie,'   containing   the

mathematical thought. Up to that time "one would have said that a continuous function is essentially capable of being represented by a curve, and that a curve has always a tangent. Such reasoning has no mathematical value whatever; it is founded on intuition, or rather on a visible representation. But such representation is crude and misleading. We think we can figure to ourselves a curve without thickness; but we only figure a stroke of small thickness. In like manner we see the tangent as a straight band of small thickness, and when we say that it touches the curve, we wish merely to say that these two bands coincide without crossing. If that is what we call a curve and a tangent, it is clear that every curve has a tangent; but this has nothing to do with the theory of functions. We see to what error we are led by a foolish confidence in what we take to be visual evidence. By the discovery of this striking example Weierstrass has accordingly given us a useful reminder, and has taught us better to appreciate the faultless and purely arithmetical methods with which he more than any one has enriched our science." [1]

"metaphysics and theory of the fundamental conceptions in mathematics : quantity, limit, argument, and function" (Tübingen). This work touches the borderland of mathematics and philosophy, as does the same author's posthumous work, 'Über die Grundlagen der Erkenntniss in den exacten Wissenschaften' (Tübingen, 1890), and will occupy us in another place.

[1] M. Poincaré in the 'Acta Mathematica,' vol. xxii., "L'œuvre mathématique de Weierstrass," p. 5. The "test-case" referred to in the text consisted in the publication by Weierstrass (in the year 1872, 'Trans. Berlin Academy,' reprinted in Weierstrass's 'Math. Werke,' vol. ii. p. 71) of the proof of the existence of a continuous function which nowhere possessed a definite (finite or infinite) differential coefficient. This example cleared up a point brought into prominence by Riemann in his posthumously (1867) published Inaugural Dissertation of 1854 ('Werke,' p. 213). The question had already, following on Riemann's suggestions, been discussed by Hermann Hankel in a

Before Weierstrass, Cauchy and Riemann had attempted to define the vague term "function" or mathematical dependence. Both clung to the graphical representation so common and so helpful in analysis since Descartes invented it. We have, of course, in abstract science, a right to begin with any definition we choose. Only the definition must be such that it

remarkable tract on "Oscillating functions," in which he drew attention to the existence of functions which admit of an integral, but where the existence of a differential coefficient remains doubtful. In fact, it appears that the question as to the latter had never been raised; the only attempt in this direction being that of Ampère in 1806, which failed (Hankel, p. 7). Hankel in his original investigation showed that a continuous curve might be supposed to be generated by the motion of a point which oscillated to and fro, these oscillations at the limit becoming infinitely numerous and infinitely small : a curve thus generated would present what he called "a condensation of singularities" at every point, but would possess no definite direction, hence also no differential coefficient. The arguments and illustrations of Hankel have been criticised and found fault with. He nevertheless deserves the credit of having among the first attempted "to gain a firm footing on a slippery road which had only been rarely trodden" (p. 8). In this tract (which is reprinted in 'Math. Ann.,' vol. xx.), as well as in his valuable article on "Limit" (Ersch und Gruber, 'Encyk.,' vol. xc. p. 185, art. "Grenze"), Hankel did much to establish clearly the essential point on which depends the entire modern revolution in our ideas regarding the foundations

of the so-called infinitesimal calculus ; reverting to the idea of a "limit," both in the definition of the derived function (limit of a ratio) and of the integral (limit of a sum) as contained in the writings both of Newton and Leibniz, but obscured by the method of "Fluxions" of the former and the method of "Infinitesimals" of the latter. Lagrange and Cauchy had begun this revolution, but it was not consistently and generally carried through till the researches of Riemann, Hankel, Weierstrass, and others made rigorous definitions necessary and generally accepted. It is, however, well to note that in this country A. de Morgan very early expressed clear views on this subject. Prof. Voss, in his excellent chapter on the Differential and Integral Calculus ('Encyk. Math. Wiss.,' vol. ii. i. p. 54, &c.), calls the later period the period of the purely arithmetical examination of infinitesimal conceptions, and says (p. 60), "The purely arithmetical definition of the infinitesimal operations which is characteristic of the present critical period of mathematics has shown that most of the theorems established by older researches, which aimed at a formal extension of method, only possess a validity limited by very definite assumptions." Such assumptions were tacitly made by earlier writers, but not explicitly stated.

corresponds with conditions which we meet with in reality, say in geometry and physics, otherwise our science becomes useless : further, our definitions must be consistent, and follow logically from the fundamental principles of arithmetic, otherwise we run the risk of sooner or later committing mistakes and encountering paradoxes. We have two interests to serve : the extension of our knowledge of functions and the rigorous proof of our theorems. The methods of Riemann and of Weierstrass are complementary. " By the instrument of Riemann we see at a glance the general aspect of things—like a traveller who is examining from the peak of a mountain the topography of the plain which he is going to visit, and is finding his bearings. By the instruments of Weierstrass analysis will, in due course, throw light into every corner, and make absolute clearness shine forth." [1] The complementary character of

51.
Riemann
and
Weierstrass
compared.

[1] Poincaré, *loc. cit.*, p. 7. Similarly Prof. Klein (*loc. cit.*, ' Vienna Report,' p. 60) : " The founder of the theory [viz., of functions] is the great French mathematician Cauchy, but only in Germany has it received that modern stamp through which it has, so to speak, been pushed into the centre of our mathematical convictions. This is the result of the simultaneous exertions of two workers—Riemann on the one side and Weierstrass on the other. Although directed to the same end, the methods of these two mathematicians are in detail as different as possible : they almost seem to contradict each other, which contradiction, viewed from a higher aspect, naturally leads to this—that they mutually supplement each other. Weierstrass defines the functions of a complex variable analytically by a common formula—viz., the ' Infinite Power Series ' ; in the sequel he avoids geometrical means as much as possible, and sees his specific aim in the rigour of proof. Riemann, on the other side, begins with certain differential equations. The subject then immediately acquires a physical aspect. . . . His starting - point lies in the region of mathematical physics." We now know from the biographical notice of Riemann, attached to his collected works (1st ed., p. 520), that he was pressed (in 1856) by his mathematical friends to publish a *résumé* of his Researches on Abelian functions—" be it ever so crude." The reason was that Weierstrass was already at work on the same subject. In consequence of Riemann's

the labours of the two great analysts is nowhere better shown than in the special manner in which Weierstrass succeeded in strengthening the foundations [1] on which much of Riemann's work rests.

The labours of the great analysts—Gauss, Cauchy, Riemann, and Weierstrass—all tended to increase our

publication Weierstrass withdrew from the press an extensive memoir which he had presented in the year 1857 to the Berlin Academy, because, as he himself says (Weierstrass, 'Math. Werke,' vol. iv. p. 10): "Riemann published a memoir on the same problem which rested on entirely different foundations from mine, and did not immediately reveal that in its results it agreed completely with my own. The proof of this required investigations which were not quite easy, and took much time; after this difficulty had been removed a radical remodelling of my dissertation seemed necessary," &c. &c. The mutual influence of Riemann's and Weierstrass's work is also referred to by Weierstrass in a letter to Prof. Schwarz, dated 1875, in which he utters what he calls his confession of faith: "The more I ponder over the principles of the theory of functions—and I do this incessantly—the stronger grows my conviction that it must be built up on the foundation of algebraical truths, and that, therefore, to employ for the proof of simple and fundamental algebraical theorems the 'transcendental,' if I may say so, is not the correct way, however enticing *prima vista* the considerations may be by which Riemann has discovered many of the most important properties of algebraical functions. It is a matter of course that every road must be open to the searcher as long as he seeks; it is only a question of

the systematic demonstration" (Weierstrass, 'Werke,' vol. ii. p. 235).

[1] This refers mainly to Weierstrass's investigation of the principle called by Riemann "Dirichlet's principle," but which had been stated already with great generality by Thomson (Lord Kelvin) in the year 1847. The validity of this method depended on a certain minimum theorem. Weierstrass has shown that the existence of such a minimum is not evident, and that the argument used is not conclusive. He laid before the Berlin Academy, in the year 1870, a communication giving a test-case to prove that Dirichlet's method not generally valid ('Werke,' vol. ii. p. 49). "Through this," Prof. Klein says (*loc. cit.*, p. 67), "a great part of Riemann's developments become invalidated. Nevertheless the far-reaching results which Riemann bases upon the principle are all correct, as was shown later on exhaustively and with all rigour by Carl Neumann and H. A. Schwarz. Indeed we must come to the conclusion that Riemann himself arrived at these theorems by a physical intuition, and only afterwards resorted to the principle referred to in order to have a consistent mathematical line of reasoning" (*loc. cit.*, p. 67). See on this also Poincaré (*loc. cit.*, pp. 10 and 15), who gives other instances where the work of Weierstrass supported that of Riemann.

knowledge of the higher mathematical relations, but also to reveal the uncertainty and absence of rigorous definition of the foundations of arithmetic and of geometry. Accordingly we find these great thinkers continually interrupting their more advanced researches by examinations of the principles. This feeling of uncertainty had led, ever since the end of the eighteenth century, to many isolated attacks and half-philosophical discussions by various writers in this country and abroad. Many of them remained long unrecognised; such were the suggestive writings of Hamilton, De Morgan, Peacock in England, Bolzano [1] in Bohemia,

52.
Examination of foundations.

[1] The merits of Bernhard Bolzano (1781-1848) as one of the earliest representatives of the critical period of mathematics were recognised after a long interval of neglect by Hankel in his article on "Limit" mentioned above. This philosophical mathematician published many years before Cauchy a tract on the Binomial Theorem (Prague, 1816), in which he gives, in Hankel's opinion, the first rigid deduction of various algebraical series. "Bolzano's notions as to convergency of series are eminently clear and correct, and no fault can be found with his development of those series for a *real* argument (which he everywhere presupposes); in the preface he gives a pertinent criticism of earlier developments of the Binomial Theorem, and of the unrestricted use of infinite series, which was then common. In fact, he has everything that can place him in this respect on the same level with Cauchy, only not the art peculiar to the French of refining their ideas and communicating them in the most appropriate and taking manner. So it came about that Bolzano remained unknown and was soon forgotten; Cauchy was the happy one who was praised as a reformer of the science, and whose elegant writings were soon widely circulated." (Hankel, *loc. cit.*, p. 210.) Following on this statement of Hankel and a remark of Prof. H. A. Schwarz, who looks upon Bolzano as the inventor of a line of reasoning further developed by Weierstrass ('Journal für Mathematik,' vol. lxxiv. p. 22, 1872), Prof. O. Stolz published in 1881 ('Math. Ann.,' vol. xviii. p. 255) an account of the several writings of Bolzano, beginning in the year 1810, in so far as they referred to the principles of the Calculus. "All these writings are remarkable inasmuch as they start with an unbiassed and acute criticism of the contributions of the older literature" (*loc. cit.*, p. 257). A posthumous tract by Bolzano, 'Paradoxieen des Unendlichen,' was republished in 1889 in 'Wissenschaftliche Classiker,' vol. ii., Berlin (Meyer and Müller). As stated above, Hankel was also one of the first to draw attention to the originality and importance of Hermann Grassmann's work.

Bolyai in Hungary, Lobatchevski in Kasan, Grassmann in Stettin. Most of these were unknown to each other. However, near the beginning of the last third of the century three distinct publications created a great stir in the mathematical world, brought many scattered but cognate lines of reasoning together, and made them mutually fertile and suggestive. These three were—*first*, the publication in 1860 of Gauss's correspondence with Schumacher, in which two letters of the former, dated May and July 1831,[1] became known, where he referred to his extensive but unwritten and unfinished speculations on the foundations of geometry and the theorem which refers to the sum of the angles in a triangle. The *second* was the publication in 1867 of the first and only part of Hermann Hankel's "Lectures on the Complex Numbers and their Functions." [2] The *third* was the posthumous publication in the same year of Riemann's paper, dated 1854,[3] "On the Hypotheses which lie at the Foundation of Geometry." Almost simultaneously there appeared the first of Helmholtz's two important papers [4] on the

[1] See 'Briefwechsel zwischen Gauss und Schumacher,' ed. Peters, 1860, vol. ii. pp. 260, 268.

[2] The small volume contains so much original and historical matter that I have on several occasions referred to it. See above, pp. 645, 653.

[3] Riemann, 'Math. Werke,' 1st ed., p. 254 *sqq.*

[4] The first publication of Helmholtz was a lecture on "the actual foundations of geometry," which he delivered on the 22nd May 1868 to the Medical Society at Heidelberg. This communication, which

referred to investigations carried on for many years,—notably in connection with the theory of the colour-manifold, — was occasioned by the publication of Riemann's paper in the 'Transactions' of the Göttingen Society. He had heard of this through Schering, to whom he wrote on the 21st April 1868 before having seen Riemann's paper : "I have myself been occupied with the same subject during the last two years, in connection with my researches in physiological optics. . . . I now see, from the few hints which you give as to the

same subject, through which it became more widely known and attracted the attention of other than purely mathematical writers. The small but eminently suggestive volume of Hankel showed the necessity of a revision and extension of the fundamental principles and definitions [1] of general arithmetic and algebra as

result of the investigation, that Riemann has arrived at exactly the same results. My starting-point was the question, How must a magnitude of several dimensions be constituted, if solid bodies are to move in it everywhere continuously, monodromically, and as freely as bodies move in real space?" On receiving from Schering a reply with a copy of Riemann's paper, Helmholtz wrote (18th May), "I enclose a short exposition of that which in my researches on the same subject is not covered by Riemann's work." A fuller paper, with the title "On the Facts which lie at the foundation of Geometry," appeared in the 'Göttinger Nachrichten,' June 3, 1868. See Helmholtz, 'Wiss. Abhandl.,' vol. ii. pp. 610 and 618, &c. ; also 'H. von Helmholtz,' by Leo Koenigsberger (1903), vol. ii. p. 138, &c. In another lecture, " On the origin and meaning of the Axioms of Geometry" (1870, reprinted in abstract in 'The Academy,' vol. i.), as well as in an article in vol. i. of 'Mind' (p. 301), he discussed "the philosophical bearing of recent inquiries concerning geometrical axioms and the possibility of working out analytically other systems of geometry with other axioms than Euclid's" (reprinted in vol. ii. of 'Vorträge und Reden').

[1] In this treatise Hankel introduced into German literature the three terms "distributive," "associative," and "commutative" to define the three principles which

govern the elementary operations of arithmetic, and introduced further what he calls the principle of the permanence of former rules in the following statement: "If two forms, expressed in the general terms of universal arithmetic, are equal to each other, they are to remain equal if the symbols cease to denote simple quantities ; hence also if the operations receive a different meaning." Hankel seems to have been led to his definitions by a study of French and English writers, among whom he mentions Servois ('Gergonne's Ann., v. p. 93, 1814) as having introduced the terms "distributive" and "commutative," and Sir W. R. Hamilton as having introduced the term "associative." He further says (p. 15): "In England, where investigations into the fundamental principles of mathematics have always been treated with favour, and where even the greatest mathematicians have not shunned the treatment of them in learned dissertations, we must name George Peacock of Cambridge as the one who first recognised emphatically the need of formal mathematics. In his interesting report on certain branches of analysis, the principle of permanence is laid down, though too narrowly, and also without the necessary foundation." Other writings, of what he terms Peacock's Cambridge school, such as those of De Morgan, Hankel states that he had not inspected ; mention-

an introduction to the advanced theories of Gauss and
Riemann; and for this purpose he went back to the
unnoticed labours of Grassmann in Germany, to the
writings of Peacock and De Morgan in England, and
incidentally introduced into Germany the elaborate
algebra of quaternions, invented and practised by
Hamilton twenty years before that time. The papers
of Riemann and Helmholtz similarly showed the necessity of a thorough investigation of the principles and
foundations of ordinary or Euclidean geometry, and
showed how consistent systems of geometry could be
elaborated on other than Euclidean axioms. Only

53.
Non-
Euclidean
geometry.

from that moment, in fact, did it become generally
recognised that already, a generation before, two independent treatises on elementary geometry had been
published in which the axiom of parallel lines was
dispensed with and consistent geometrical systems
developed. These were contained — as already stated
— in the 'Kasan Messenger,' under date 1829 and

ing only a short paper by Dr F.
Gregory on Symbolical Algebra
in the Edinburgh 'Transactions.'
Whilst Hankel was delivering
lectures on these fundamentals,
Weierstrass in Berlin was likewise
in the habit of introducing his
lectures on the Theory of Analytic
Functions by a discussion of the
theory of Complex Numbers. This
introduction was published, with
Weierstrass's permission, in the year
1872 by Dr E. Kossak (in a programme of the Friedrichs-Werder
Gymnasium), after lectures delivered by Weierstrass in 1865-66.
To what extent Hankel may have
been influenced by Weierstrass's
lectures, which he seems to have
attended after leaving Göttingen,
is uncertain, for in spite of his very
extensive references he does not
mention Weierstrass. In Kossak's
'Elemente der Arithmetik' the
term "permanence of formal rules"
is not used, but the treatment of
the extended arithmetic is carried
on along the same lines—i.e., not
by an attempt to represent the
complex quantities, but on the
ground of maintaining the rules
which govern the arithmetic of
ordinary numbers. Great importance is also attached to the
principle of inversion as having
shown itself of value in the theory
of elliptic functions, and being not
less valuable in arithmetic. As
stated above (p. 640, note), this principle is also insisted on by Peacock.

1830, the author being Lobatchevski; and in the appendix to an Introduction to Geometry, published by Wolfgang Bolyai at Maros Vasarheli, a town of Transylvania, the appendix being by the author's son, Johann Bolyai. The elder Bolyai having been a friend and correspondent of Gauss, and his speculations evidently of the same nature as those indicated by the latter in the above-mentioned correspondence, conjectures have been made as to which of the two originated the whole train of thought.[1] The independent investigations of Riemann and Helmholtz started from a differ-

[1] See above, p. 652, note. What is important from our point of view in the investigations of both Riemann and Helmholtz lies in the following points : First, Neither Riemann nor Helmholtz refers to the non-Euclidean geometry of Lobatchevski or Bolyai. This is not surprising in the case of Helmholtz, whose interest was originally not purely mathematical; in fact, we may incidentally remark how, in spite of his profound mathematical ability, he on various occasions came into close contact with mathematical researches of great originality and importance without recognising them — e.g., the researches of Grassmann and Plücker. As regards Riemann, his paper was read before Gauss, who certainly knew all about Bolyai, and latterly also about Lobatchevski, of whom he thought so highly that he proposed him as a foreign member of the Göttingen Society. Gauss could therefore easily have pointed out to Riemann the relations of his speculations with his own and those of the other mathematicians named. Since the publication of the latest volume of Gauss's works, it has become evident that Gauss corresponded a good deal, and more than one would have supposed from reading Sartorius's obituary memoir, on the subject of non-Euclidean (astral or imaginary) geometry, notably with Gerling; and that several contemporary mathematicians, such as Schweikart, came very near to Gauss's own position. Second, although Riemann, and subsequently also Helmholtz, made use of the term "manifold" (Mannigfaltigkeit), it does not appear in the course of their discussion that they considered the space-manifold from any other than a metrical point of view. In fact, the manifold becomes in their treatment a magnitude (Grösse). It is true that Riemann does refer to certain geometrical relations not connected with magnitude but only with position, as being of great importance. These two points through which the researches of Riemann and Helmholtz stand in relation to other, and at the time isolated, researches, were dwelt on, the first by Beltrami, and the second by Cayley and Prof. Klein.

ent origin: both made use of the more general conception of an extended magnitude, introduced the notion of the curvature of space by analogy with Gauss's measure of curvature of a surface, and tried to express in algebraical formulæ the general and necessary properties of a magnitude which should form the foundation of a geometry. The relation of these algebraical results to those arrived at by the critical and purely geometrical methods of Lobatchevski and Bolyai were set out by Beltrami, who showed clearly that three geometries of two dimensions are possible— the Euclidean, that of Lobatchevski, where the three angles of a triangle are less than two right angles, and a third where they are more. He showed the analogy of the third with geometry on the sphere, and suggested the pseudo-sphere as a surface on which the second could be similarly represented. At the same time he indicated the generalisation through the algebraical formula of the conception of dimensions, and introduced the symbolical term geometry of four or more dimensions, as Grassmann and Cayley had done before him.[1] Through all these investigations a habit

[1] The geometry of non-Euclidean space, as well as the geometry of four or more dimensions (both usually comprised under the term "non-Euclidean geometry"), can now boast of an enormous literature, the enumeration of which alone would fill many pages. A complete bibliography up to the year 1878 is given in vols. i. and ii. of the American 'Journal of Mathematics' by Prof. Bruce Halsted, who has done much to make known to English readers the original writings of the pioneers in this subject. Later publications are referred to in Dr Victor Schlegel's papers ('Leopoldina,' xxii., 1886, Nos. 9-18): "Ueber Entwickelung und Stand der n-dimensionalen Geometrie," &c., &c. In France Houël published (beginning with the year 1866) translations of memoirs referring to this subject; in fact, he was almost the first to draw attention to this important modern departure. But it is almost exclusively owing to the various writings of Prof. Felix Klein that

has been introduced into mathematical writings which has not a little puzzled outsiders, and even exposed the logically rigorous deductions of mathematicians to the ridicule—not to say the contempt—of eminent philosophical authorities. The complete parallelism or correspondence of geometrical with algebraical notions —the possibility of expressing the former with perfect accuracy by the latter, and of retranslating the latter into the former, and this in more than one way, according to the choice of the space element (point, line, sphere), led to the habit of using purely geometrical presentable ideas as names for algebraical relations which had been generalised by the addition of more than a limited number of variables. Thus the conception of curvature, easily defined for a plane curve, and extended by Gauss to surfaces, was, by adding a third variable in the algebraic formula, applied to space. We are then told that it is necessary to understand what is meant by the curvature of space, this being a purely algebraical relation, not really presentable, but only formed by analogy from the geometrically presentable relations of geometry on a surface. In a similar

54.
Curvature
of space.

the different points of origin of this most recent mathematical speculation, which are to be found in the mathematical literature of all the principal nations, have been put in the true light and brought into connection. In fact, here, as in several other subjects, his publications, including his lithographed lectures on non-Euclidean geometry (delivered at Göttingen, 1893-94), serve as the best guide through the labyrinth and controversies of this intricate subject. See especially his article "Ueber die so-genannte nicht-Euclidische Geometrie" in vol. iv., 'Math. Ann.,' 1871. In this paper he connects the independent researches of Cayley (following Laguerre, 'Nouv. Ann. de Math.,' 1853), who in his sixth memoir on Quantics showed how metrical geometry can be included in projective geometry by referring figures to a fundamental fixed figure in space called by him the "Absolute," with the independent researches of Lobatchevski, Bolyai, Riemann, and Beltrami.

way the idea of the dimensions of space was extended, and four and more dimensions freely spoken of when really only a limited number is geometrically presentable. In the hands of mathematicians these terms are useful, and we may discard the criticism of philosophers and laymen as based on misunderstanding.[1] The introduction, however, into geometrical work of conceptions such as the infinite, the imaginary, and the relations of hyperspace, none of which can be directly imaged, has a psychological significance well worthy of examination.[2] It gives a deep insight into the resources and working of the mind. We arrive at the borderland of mathematics and philosophy.

[1] The most important philosophical criticism of the non-Euclidean geometry is that of Lotze, contained in the second book, chap. ii., of the 'Metaphysik' (1879, p. 249, &c.) It must not be forgotten that Lotze wrote at a time when the novel and startling conceptions put forward by popular writers on the subject had been employed in the interest of a spiritualistic philosophy, to the delusions of which some even of Lotze's friends had fallen a prey. This explains the severity of Lotze's criticisms, which are of the very same nature as those he pronounced many years earlier on similar aberrations (see 'Kleine Schriften,' vol. iii. p. 329). Those who are interested in following up the subject should refer to the writings of Friedr. Zöllner as collected in the four vols. of his 'Wissenschaftliche Abhandlungen' (Leipzig, 1878-81). They belong to the curiosities of the philosophical and scientific literature of that age, but can hardly claim a place in the history of thought.

[2] See the remark of Cayley in his Presidential Address ('Coll. Works,' vol. xi. p. 434): "The notion, which is really the fundamental one (and I cannot too strongly emphasise the assertion), underlying and pervading the whole of modern analysis and geometry, is that of imaginary magnitude in analysis and of imaginary space (or space as a *locus in quo* of imaginary points and figures) in geometry. I use in each case the word imaginary as including real. This has not been, so far as I am aware, a subject of philosophical discussion or inquiry. As regards the older metaphysical writers, this would be quite accounted for by saying that they knew nothing, and were not bound to know anything, about it; but at present, and considering the prominent position which the notion occupies—say even that the conclusion were that the notion belongs to mere technical mathematics or has reference to nonentities, in regard to which no science is possible—still it seems to me that (as a subject of philosophical discussion) the notion ought not to be thus ignored; it should at least be shown that there is a right to ignore it."

There exists, moreover, an analogy between the manner in which these novel and extended ideas have been historically introduced and the mode of reasoning which led Sir W. R. Hamilton to the invention of a new and extended algebra—the algebra of quaternions. This analogy becomes evident if we study the small volume of Hermann Hankel, which appeared about the same time as Riemann's and Beltrami's fundamental geometrical dissertations.

The extension of Hamilton was only possible by dropping one of the fundamental principles of general arithmetic, the commutative principle of multiplication, which is symbolically expressed by saying that $a \times b$ is equal to $b \times a$. By assuming that $a \times b$ is equal to $-b \times a$, Hamilton founded a new general arithmetic on an apparently paradoxical principle. Similarly Lobatchevski and Bolyai constructed new geometries by dropping the axiom of parallel lines. Hankel made clear the significance of the new algebra, Riemann and Beltrami that of the new geometry. The practical performance anticipated and led up to the theoretical or philosophical exposition of the underlying principles. But there was a third instance in which a new science had been created by abandoning the conventional way of looking at things. This was the formation of a consistent body of geometrical teaching by disregarding the metrical properties and studying only the positional or projective properties, following Monge and Poncelet. The two great minds who worked out this geometry independently of the conception of number or measurement, giving a purely geometrical definition of distance and number, were Cayley in Eng-

55.
Generalised
conceptions

land and Von Staudt in Germany. It was reserved for
Prof. Felix Klein of Göttingen to show how the generalised notions of distance introduced into geometry by
Cayley and Von Staudt opened out an understanding of
the three geometries of Euclid, of Lobatchevski, and of
Riemann.[1] We have to go back to the purely projective
properties of space to understand these different possibilities. Lobatchevski attacked the problem practically,
Riemann analytically, Klein geometrically. Through the
labours of Klein the subject has arrived at a certain
finality. And what was still wanting after he had
written his celebrated memoir (which was approved and

56.
Klein's
exposition.

[1] See the note on p. 714, above;
also 'Math. Ann.,' vol. iv. p. 573,
and vol. vi. p. 112. Prof. Klein
—following a usage in mathematical language — distinguishes
three different geometries, the
hyperbolic, the elliptic, and the
parabolic geometry, corresponding to the possession by the straight
line at infinity of two real or two
imaginary (that is, none) or two
coincident points. The whole
matter turns upon the fact that,
although metrical relations of
figures are in general changed
by projection, there is one metrical relation—known in geometry
as the "anharmonic ratio" (in
German *Doppelverhältniss*)—which
in all projective transformations
remains unchanged. As this anharmonic ratio of points or lines
can be geometrically constructed
without reference to measurement (Von Staudt, ' Geometrie
der Lage,' 1847 and 1857), a
method is thus found by which,
starting from a purely descriptive
property or relation, distance and
angles—*i.e.*, metrical quantities—
can be defined. Some doubts have

been expressed whether, starting
from the purely projective properties of space and building up
geometry in this way (arriving at
the metrical properties by the
construction suggested by Von
Staudt), the ordinary idea of
distance and number is not tacitly
introduced from the beginning.
This may be of philosophical,
but is not of mathematical,
importance, as the main object
in the mathematical treatment is
to gain a starting-point from
which the several possible consistent systems of geometry can
be deduced and taken into view
together. See on this point,
inter alia, Cayley's remarks in
the appendix to vol. ii. of ' Collected Works' (p. 604 *sqq.*), also
Sir R. S. Ball's paper (quoted
there), and more recently the discussion on the subject in Mr
Bertrand Russell's ' Essay on the
Foundations of Geometry' (1897,
p. 31, &c.; p. 117, &c.) See
also the same author's article on
non-Euclidean Geometry in the
supplement of the 'Ency. Brit.,'
vol. xxviii.

commented on by Cayley) was later on supplied in consequence of a suggestion of his.   The researches of
Riemann, and still more those of Helmholtz, had not
merely a mathematical, they had also a logical and a
psychological, meaning.   Space was conceived to be a
threefold - extended manifold.   There are other mani-
folds besides space—such, for instance, as the threefold-
extended manifold of colours.   Helmholtz came from the
study of this manifold to that of space.   Now the
question arises as to the conditions or data which are
necessary and sufficient for the foundations of a science
like geometry.   We have seen that the axiom of parallel
lines is not required; we have also seen that the notion
of distance and number can be generalised.   What other
data remain which cannot be dispensed with ?   Helmholtz had attempted to answer this question.   But
neither he nor Riemann had considered the possibility
of a purely projective geometry.   Now it is the merit of
Prof. Klein to have seen that there exists a purely algebraical method by which this problem can be attacked.
This is the method of groups referred to above, and
applied by Sophus Lie to assemblages of continuously
variable quantities.   Klein was one of the first to recognise the power of this new instrument.   He saw that
the space problem was a problem of transformations, the
possible motions in space forming a group with definite
elements (the different freedoms of motion) which were
continuously variable—*i.e.*, in infinitesimal quantities—
and which returned into themselves under certain well-
defined conditions.   They possessed, moreover, in the
maintenance of distance the algebraic property of in-

57.
Sophus Lie.

variance. He also expressed some doubt regarding the logical consistency of the assumptions of Helmholtz. Sophus Lie undertook this investigation, and thus brought the logical side of the labours of Riemann and Helmholtz to a final conclusion.[1] This is one of the celebrated instances where the rigorous algebraical methods have detected flaws in the more intuitional or purely geometrical process, and extended our knowledge of hidden possibilities.

But there is yet another branch of the great science of number, form, and interdependence, the principles and foundations of which had been handed down from earlier ages, where the critical and sifting process of the nineteenth century has led to an expansion and revolution of our fundamental ideas. Here also, as in so many other directions, the movement begins with Gauss. Hitherto I have spoken mainly of algebra or general arithmetic, of geometry, of the connections of both in the

---

[1] " Lie was early made aware by Klein and his "program" that the space problem belonged to the theory of groups. . . . Ever since 1880 he had been pondering over these questions ; he published his views first in 1886 on the occasion of the Berlin meeting of natural philosophers. Helmholtz's conception was itself unconsciously (but remarkably so, inasmuch as it dates from 1868) one belonging to the theory of groups, trying, as it did, to characterise the groups of the sixfold infinite motions in space, which led to the three geometries, in comparison with all other groups. He did this by fixing on the free mobility of rigid bodies—i.e., on the existence of an invariant between two points as the only essential invariant. When Lie took up this problem in principle, as one belonging to the theory of groups, he recognised that for our space that part of the axiom of monodromy was unnecessary which added periodicity to the free mobility round a fixed axis. . . . The value of these investigations lies mainly in this, that they permit of our fixing for every kind of geometry the most appropriate system of axioms. . . . And they justly received in the year 1897 the first Lobatchevski prize awarded by the Society of Kasan" (M. Nöther, 'Math. Ann.,' vol. liii. p. 38). A lucid exposition of Lie's work will be found in Mr B. Russell's ' Essay,' &c., p. 47 sqq.

theory of forms and functions : there remains the science of numbers—of number in the abstract and also of the named numbers of ordinary arithmetic. Gauss's earliest labours were connected with this branch. Superseding the work of Fermat, Euler, and Legendre, he produced that great book with seven seals, the 'Disquisitiones Arithmeticæ.' The seals were only gradually broken. Lejeune Dirichlet did much in this way : others followed, notably Prof. Dedekind, who published the lectures of Dirichlet and added much of his own. The question may be asked, Have we gained any new ideas about numbers ?

58.
Theory of numbers.

In this abstract inquiry we can again facilitate our survey by distinguishing between the practical and the purely theoretical interests which stimulated it. Looking at the matter as well as the formal treatment by which it was rendered accessible, we may say Gauss not only taught us some very remarkable new properties of numbers—he also invented a new instrument or calculus for their investigation. Let us consider his work and that of his followers from these different points of view.

First, then, there were certain definite problems connected with the properties of numbers which had been handed down from antiquity. Such were the division of the circle into equal parts by a ready geometrical construction, the duplication of the cube, and the quadrature of the circle or the geometrical construction of the number π.[1] To the latter may be attached the

---

[1] See above, vol. i. p. 181, note. The student will find much interesting matter referring to these problems in Prof. Klein's little volume entitled 'Famous Problems in Elementary Geometry,' transl. by Beman and Smith, Boston and London, 1879. In it is also given

properties of the number *e*, the basis of the Napierian or natural logarithms, this number having been shown by Euler to stand in a remarkable arithmetical relation to the number π—a relation which could be very simply expressed if one had the courage to make use of the imaginary unit. As in the instance referred to above, when I dealt with the problem of the solution of the higher order of equations, so also in the case of the three celebrated problems now under review, the reasoning of the mathematicians of the nineteenth century lay largely in proving why these problems were insoluble or in defining those special cases in which they were soluble. Moreover, the labours of Gauss and the class of mathematicians who followed or read him were directed towards the defining and fixing of general conceptions, the study and elaboration of which embraced these single problems as special cases. Prime numbers had always been the object of special attention. Division and par-

an account of several mechanical contrivances for the solution of transcendental problems, or of those where the use of the compass and the ruler do not suffice. Although accurate constructions with a ruler and compass, or with either alone, were known to the ancients only in comparatively small numbers, approximations, and sometimes very close ones, seem to have been known. A very interesting example is Röber's construction of the regular heptagon, of which we read in the correspondence of Sir W. R. Hamilton with De Morgan (Life of Hamilton, by Graves, vol. iii. pp. 141, 534), and which was described by him in the 'Phil. Mag.,' February 1864. The approximation to the correctly calculated figure of the true septisection of the circle was so close that he could not discover, up to the 7th decimal, whether the error was in the direction of more or less. On carrying the calculation further, he found the approximation to be such that a heptagon stepped round a circle equal in size to the equator would reach the starting-point within 50 feet. The inventor or discoverer of this method — Röber, an architect of Dresden—supposed that it was known to the ancient Egyptians, and in some form or other connected with the plans of the temple at Edfu, but on this point I have obtained no information. The question is not referred to in Prof. Cantor's 'History of Mathematics.'

tition of numbers had been studied, and many interesting formulæ had been found by induction, and subsequently proved—or not proved—by a multitude of ingenious devices. As in so many other directions of research so also here, the genius of Gauss gave a great impetus to progress by the invention of a definite calculus and an algorithm. This invention referred to the solution of what used to be known as indeterminate equations: to find two or more numbers—notably integers, which obey a certain algebraical relation. For one large class of these problems (which already occupied the ancient geometers), viz., those of the divisibility of one number by another (called the modulus) with or without residue, Gauss invented the conception and notation of a congruence. Two numbers are congruent if when divided by a certain number they leave the same remainder. "It will be seen," says Henry Smith, "that the definition of a congruence involves only one of the most elementary arithmetical conceptions—that of the divisibility of one number by another. But it expresses that conception in a form so suggestive of analysis, so easily available in calculation and so fertile in new results, that its introduction into arithmetic has proved a most important contribution to the progress of the science."[1] Notably the analogy with ordinary algebraic equations and the possibility of transferring the properties and treatment of these was at once evident. It became a subject of

59.
Gauss's
theory of
congru-
ences.

[1] See Henry J. S. Smith in his most valuable 'Report on the Theory of Numbers' (Brit. Assoc., 1859-65, six parts. Reprinted in 'Collected Math. Papers,' vol. i. pp. 38-364). It gives a very lucid account of the history of this department of mathematical science up to the year 1863.

interest to determine the residues of the powers of numbers. A number is said to be a quadratic, cubic, or biquadratic residue of another (prime) number (the modulus) if it is possible to find a square, cube, or bi-quadratic number which is congruent with the first number. The theory of congruences was a new calculus: as such it was, like the theory of determinants or of in-variants or the general theory of forms, a tactical device for bringing order and simplicity into a vast region of very complicated relations. Gauss himself wrote about it late in life to Schumacher.[1] " In general the position as regards all such new calculi is this—that one cannot attain by them anything that could not be done without them: the advantage, however, is, that if such a cal-culus corresponds to the innermost nature of frequent wants, every one who assimilates it thoroughly is able—without the unconscious inspiration of genius which no one can command—to solve the respective problems, yes, even to solve them mechanically in complicated cases where genius itself becomes impotent. So it is with the invention of algebra generally, so with the differential calculus, so also—though in more restricted regions—with Lagrange's calculus of variations, with my calculus of congruences, and with Möbius's calculus. Through such conceptions countless problems which otherwise would remain isolated and require every time (larger or smaller) efforts of inventive genius, are, as it were, united into an organic whole." But a new calculus frequently does more than this. In the course of its

<hr/>

[1] See 'Briefwechsel,' &c., vol. iv. p. 147 ; also Gauss's 'Werke,' vol. viii. p. 298.

application it may lead to a widening of ideas, to an enlargement of views, to a removing of artificial and conventional barriers of thought.   As I stated early in this chapter, the attempts of Gauss to prove the fundamental theorem of algebra, that every equation has a root, suggested to him the necessity of introducing complex numbers; the development of the theory of congruences and of residues—notably of the higher residues—confirmed this necessity.   In the year 1831, in his memoir on biquadratic residues, he announces it as a matter of fundamental importance.   In the earlier memoir he had treated this extension of the field of higher arithmetic as possible, but had reserved the full exposition.   And before he redeemed this promise the necessity of doing so had been proved by Abel and Jacobi, who had created the theory of elliptic functions, showing that the conception of a periodic function (such as the circular or harmonic function) could be usefully extended into that theory, if a double period—a real and an imaginary one—were introduced.   A simplification similar to that which this bold step led to in the symbolic representation of those higher transcendents, had been discovered by Gauss to exist in the symbolical representation of the theory of biquadratic residues which only by the simultaneous use of the imaginary and the real unit "presented itself in its true simplicity and beauty."   In this theory it was necessary to introduce not only a positive and negative, but likewise a lateral system of counting—*i.e.*, to count not only in a line backwards and forwards, but also sideways in two directions, as Gauss showed very plainly in the now familiar manner.   At the

60. Generalised conception of number.

same time a metaphysical question presented itself—viz., Can such an extension into more than two dimensions be consistently and profitably carried out? Gauss had satisfied himself that it could not;[1] but the proof of this was only given in more recent times by Weierstrass, who definitely founded the whole discussion of the subject on the logical principle "that the legitimacy of introducing a number into arithmetic depends solely on the definition of such number." And this leads me to another extension in the region of number suggested by Gauss's treatment, which has also become fundamental, and, in the hands of Dirichlet, Kummer, Liouville, Dedekind, and others, has remodelled the entire science of higher arithmetic. It is based on the logical process of the

---

[1] A concise history of this subject is given by Kossak in the Program referred to above, p. 712, note. Gauss had promised to answer the question, "Why the relations between things which have a manifoldness of more than two dimensions would not admit of other" (than the ordinary complex numbers introduced by him) "fundamental quantities being introduced into general arithmetic?" He never redeemed his promise. In consequence of this, several eminent mathematicians, notably Hankel, Weierstrass, and Prof. Dedekind, have attempted to reply to this question, and to establish the correctness of the implied thesis according to which any system of higher complex numbers becomes superfluous and useless. Prof. Stolz, in the first chapter of the second volume of his 'Allgemeine Arithmetik,' gives an account of these several views, which do not exactly coincide. In general, however, the proof given by Weierstrass, and first published by Kossak, has been adopted. This proof is based upon the condition that the product of several factors cannot disappear except one of its factors is equal to zero. "We must, therefore, exclude from general arithmetic complex numbers consisting of three fundamental elements. This is, however, not necessary if the use of them be limited" by some special conditions (Kossak, *loc. cit.*, p. 27). In the course of the further development of this matter Weierstrass arrives at the fundamental thesis "that the domain of the elementary operations in arithmetic is exhausted by addition and multiplication, including the inverse operations of subtraction and division." "There are," says Weierstrass, "no other fundamental operations — at least it is certain that no example is known in analysis where, if an analytical connection exists at all, this cannot be analysed into and reduced to those elementary operations" (p. 29).

inversion of operations in the most general manner. In the direct process we build up algebraical formulæ—called equations or forms—by a combination of addition and multiplication. We can omit subtraction and division, as through the use of negative quantities and fractions these are reduced to the former. Now, given the most general algebraical equation or form, we can search out and define the simple factors or forms into which it can be split up, and these factors and their products we can take to serve as the definition of numbers. The question then arises, What are the properties of numbers thus inversely defined? and, secondly, Do these numbers exhaust or cover the whole extent of number as it is defined by the uses of practical life? The answer to the former question led to the introduction of complex and subsequently of ideal numbers; the discovery by Liouville that the latter is not the case has led to the conception of transcendental, *i.e.*, non-algebraic, numbers.

61.
Process of inversion.

The idea of generalising the conception of number, by arguing backward from the most general forms into which ordinary numbers can be cast by the processes of addition and multiplication, has led to a generalised theory of numbers. Here, again, the principal object is the question of the divisibility of such generalised algebraical numbers and the generalised notion of prime numbers—*i.e.*, of prime factors into which such numbers can be divided. Before the general theory was attempted by Prof. Dedekind, Kronecker, and others, the necessity of some extension in this direction had already been discovered by the late Prof. Kummer of

Berlin when dealing with a special problem. This was no other than the celebrated problem of the division of the circle into equal parts, which had been reduced by Gauss to an arithmetical question. Gauss had shown that the accurate geometrical solution of this problem depended on the solution of certain simple binomial forms or equations. The study of such forms accordingly became of special interest: it necessitated the employment of the extended notion of number called by Gauss that of complex numbers. Now it is one of the fundamental laws in the theory of ordinary numbers that every integer can be divided only in one way into prime numbers. This law was found to break down at a certain point if complex numbers were admitted. Kummer, however, suggested that the anomaly disappeared if we introduced along with the numbers he was dealing with other numbers, which he termed ideal numbers— i.e., if we considered these complex factors to be divisible into other prime factors. The law of divisibility was thus again restored to its supreme position. These abstract researches led to the introduction of a very useful conception—the conception not only of generalised numbers, but also of a system (body, corpus, or region) of numbers;[1] comprising all numbers which, by the

---

[1] The idea of a closed system or domain of generalised numbers has revolutionised the theory of numbers. Originally the theory of numbers meant only the theory of the common integers, excluding complex numbers. Gauss, in the introduction to the 'Disquisitiones,' limits the doctrine in this way. He excludes also the arithmetical theories which are implied in cyclotomy—i.e., the theory of the division of the circle; stating at the same time that the principles of the latter depend on theories of higher arithmetic. This connection of algebraical problems with the theory of numbers became still more evident in the labours of Gauss's successors — Jacobi and Lejeune Dirichlet, and was surprising to them. "The

ordinary operations of arithmetic, can be formed out of the units or elements we start with. Thus all rational integers form a system; we can compound them, but also resolve them into their elements. Where we introduce new elements or units we only arrive at correct laws if we are careful to cover the whole field or system which is measured by the application of the fundamental operations of arithmetic. Throughout all our abstract reasoning it is the fundamental operations which remain permanent and unaltered,—a rule which,

reason for this connection is now completely cleared up. The theory of algebraical numbers and Galois's 'theory of equations' have their common root in the general theory of algebraical systems; especially the theory of the system of algebraical numbers has become at the same time the most important province of the theory of numbers. The merit of having laid down the first beginnings of this theory belongs again to Gauss. He introduced complex numbers, he formulated and solved the problem of transferring the theorems of the ordinary theory of numbers, above all, the properties of divisibility and the relation of congruence, to these complex numbers. Through the systematic and general development of this idea,—based upon the far-reaching ideas of Kummer,— Dedekind and Kronecker succeeded in establishing the modern theory of the system of algebraical numbers" (Prof. Hilbert in the preface to his "Theorie der Algebraischen Zahlkörper," 'Bericht der Math. Ver.,' vol. iv. p. 3). In the further course of his remarks Prof. Hilbert refers to the intimate connection in which this general or analytical theory of numbers stands with other regions of

modern mathematical science, notably the theory of functions. "We thus see," he says, "how arithmetic, the queen of mathematical science, has conquered large domains and has assumed the leadership. That this was not done earlier and more completely, seems to me to depend on the fact that the theory of numbers has only in quite recent times arrived at maturity." He mentions the spasmodic character which even under the hands of Gauss the progress of the science exhibited, and says that this was characteristic of the infancy of the science, which has only in recent times entered on a certain and continuous development through the systematic construction of the theory in question. This systematic treatment was given for the first time in the last supplement to Dedekind's edition of Dirichlet's lectures (1894, 4th ed., p. 134). A very clear account will also be found in Prof. H. Weber's 'Lehrbuch der Algebra' (vol. ii., 1896, p. 487, &c.) He refers (p. 494) to the different treatment which the subject has received at the hands of its two principal representatives — Prof. Dedekind (1871 onwards) and Kronecker (1882)—and tries to show the connection of the two methods.

as we saw above, was vaguely foreshadowed by Peacock, and expressly placed at the head of all mathematical reasoning by Hermann Hankel. In passing it may also be observed how the notion of a system of algebraical numbers, which belong together as generated in certain defined ways, prepares us for the introduction of that general theory of groups which is destined to bring order and unity into a very large section of scattered mathematical reasoning. The great importance of this aspect is clearly and comprehensively brought out in Prof. H. Weber's Algebra. Nothing could better convince us of the great change which has come over mathematical thought in the latter half of the nineteenth century than a comparison of Prof. Weber's Algebra with standard works on this subject published a generation earlier.

63.
Modern
algebra.

I have shown how the definition of algebraical numbers has led to an extension and generalisation of the conception of number. Another question simultaneously presented itself, Does this extension cover the whole field of numbers as we practically use them in ordinary life? The reply is in the negative. Practice is richer than theory. Nor is it difficult to assign the reason of this. Numbering is a process carried on in practical life for two distinct purposes, which we distinguish by the terms counting and measuring. Numbering must be made subservient to the purpose of measuring. Thus difficulties arising out of this use of numbers for measuring purposes presented themselves early in the development of geometry in what are called the incommensurable quantities: taking the side of a square as ten, what is the number which measures the

64.
Algebraical
and trans-
cendental
numbers.

diagonal ? Assume that we prolong the side of the square indefinitely, we have a clear conception of the position of the numbers 15, 20, 30, &c. ; but what is the exact number corresponding to the length of the diagonal ? This led to the invention of irrational numbers : it became evident that by introducing the square root of the number 2 we could accurately express the desired number by an algebraical operation. But there are other definite measurements in practical geometry which do not present themselves in the form of straight lines, such as the circumference of a circle with a given radius. Can they, like irrational quantities, be expressed by definite algebraical operations ? Practice had early invented methods for finding such numbers by enclosing them within narrower and narrower limits; and an arithmetical algorithm, the decimal fraction, was invented which expressed the process in a compact and easily intelligible form. Among these decimal fractions there were those which were infinite—the first instances of infinite series—progressing by a clearly defined rule of succession of terms ; others there were which did not show a rule of succession that could be easily grasped. Much time was spent in devising methods for calculating and writing down, e.g., the decimals of the numbers π and e.[1]

It will be seen from this very cursory reference to the practical elements of mathematical thought how the ideas or mental factors which we deal with and

[1] The transcendent nature of the numbers e and π was first proved by Hermite and Prof. Lindemann. The proofs have been gradually simplified. A lucid statement will be found in Klein's 'Famous Problems,' p. 49 sqq.

string together in mathematical reasoning are derived from various and heterogeneous sources. We begin

with counting, then we introduce measuring; in both cases we have definite elements or units which may serve to express order or quantity or both, and we have definite conventional operations; then we have symbols which may denote order or quantity or operation. With these devices we perform on paper certain changes, and we get accustomed to use indiscriminately these heterogeneous conceptions, arithmetical, geometrical, algebraical—nay, even dynamical, as when Newton introduced the conception of a flow or fluxion. As mathematics is an instrument for the purpose of solving practical problems, skill in alternately and promiscuously using these incongruous methods goes a very long way. Geometrical, mechanical evidence helps frequently where pure logic comes to a standstill, and pure logic must help and correct where apparent evidence might deceive us. Mathematics and science generally have always progressed by this alternate use of heterogeneous devices, and will probably always do so. The straight line of pure logic has but very meagre resources, and resourcefulness is the soul of all progress. But though this may be so in practice, there are two other interests which govern scientific reasoning. There is the love of consistency and accuracy, and of clean and transparent, as distinguished from muddled and scamped, work. The latter leads inevitably into serious errors and paradoxes, as the great mathematicians, Gauss, Cauchy, Abel, pointed out early in the century. Mathematics then frequently exhibited the slovenliness of a man who talks at the same time in more than one language, because he is too negligent to arrange his thoughts clearly. Then there come in the demands of the teacher who has to introduce abstract and difficult subjects in a clear, consistent, and simple manner, taking heed that with the elements he does not introduce the sources of future error. The same interest that led in ancient times to the composition of the Elements of Euclid has led, in the higher education of the nineteenth century, beginning with the École Polytechnique and ending with Weierstrass's famous courses of lectures at Berlin, to a revision and recasting of the whole elementary framework of mathematics. In the mean time the resourcefulness in applied mathematical thought which ever since the age of Newton has characterised the individual research of this country, has opened out new vistas and afforded much material for critical siftings and strict definitions. Both qualities were united in the great mind of Gauss with a regrettable absence of the love of teaching and the communicative faculty. Like Newton's 'Principia,' his greatest works will always remain great storehouses of thought; while his unpublished remains might be compared to the Queries appended to the 'Opticks' and to the 'Portsmouth Papers.'

Several eminent mathematicians in France, Germany, and Italy have been for many years [1] working at the

[1] The literature of this subject has been rapidly increasing since the year 1872, — the approximate date of the following publications, which created an epoch : R. Dedekind, 'Stetigkeit und irrationale Zahlen' (Braunschweig, 1872) ; E. Heine, " Die

clearer enunciation of the fundamental conceptions of
the science, and though the ways in which they
approach the subject are different, a general consensus
seems to be within view as to the elementary definitions.
The main difficulty lies in the introduction into pure
arithmetic of the ideas which are forced upon us when

Elemente der Functionenlehre"
('Journal für Mathematik,' vol.
lxxiv. p. 172, 1872). This paper
refers both to Weierstrass's and
Cantor's theories ; H. Kossak, in
the pamphlet referred to above
(p. 712, note). This contains the
principles of Weierstrass's theory ;
C. H. Méray, 'Nouveau Précis
d'Analyse infinitésimale' (Paris,
1872). The first comprehensive
publication of Georg Cantor belongs to the year 1883, 'Grundlagen einer allgemeinen Mannig-
faltigkeitslehre' (Leipzig, Teubner). It was preceded by various
articles in the 'Journal für Mathematik,' vol. lxxvii. p. 257, vol.
lxxxiv. p. 82, and 'Math. Ann.,'
vol. xv. p. 1, in which he had introduced and defined several of the
terms and conceptions that have
since become generally accepted in
writings on this subject. These
earlier publications, by—or referring to—the pioneers in this new
province of mathematical thought,
were followed by a number of
further expositions by Cantor,
Dedekind, and Weierstrass. The
principal writings of Cantor have
been republished in the 'Acta
Mathematica,' vol. ii. Prof. Dedekind published in the year 1888 an
important pamphlet, 'Was sind
und was sollen die Zahlen,' and has
incorporated many of the results of
his researches in his later editions
of Dirichlet's 'Lectures'; whilst the
lines of reasoning peculiar to Weier-

strass have become better known
through the writings of his pupils
and the collected edition of his
mathematical works which is now
in progress. A complete bibliography is given in three important
articles in vol. i. of the German
'Math. Encyc.' by Profs. Schu-
bert (p. 1, &c.), Pringsheim (p.
48, &c.), and Schönflies (p. 184,
&c.) Important works, giving a
summary and analysis of these
various researches, now exist in
the mathematical and philosophical
literature of France, Germany,
Italy, and England. Like the non-
Euclidean geometry, the subject
has attracted considerable attention also outside purely mathematical circles. Notably Cantor's
writings have been exhaustively
dealt with from a philosophical
point of view — in Germany by
Walter Brix (Wundt's 'Philosophische Studien,' vol. v. p. 632,
vol. vi. pp. 104 and 261), and by
B. Kerry, 'System einer Theorie
der Grenz-begriffe' (Leipzig und
Wien, 1890); in France by M.
Louis Couturat, 'De l'Infini mathématique' (Paris, 1896); and
latterly in this country by Mr
Bertrand Russell, 'The Principles
of Mathematics,' vol. i. (Cambridge,
1903). Italian mathematicians have
also dealt largely with the subject,
notably G. Peano, who published
an important work, 'Arithmetices
principia nova methodo exposita'
(Turin, 1889).

we apply the counting process to the needs of geometry and physics. We are here confronted with notions which require to be arithmetically defined — the infinite and the continuous. The same notions at the beginning of the century attracted the attention of eminent analysts like Cauchy. It is now clear, thanks to the labours of Prof. Georg Cantor of Halle, that for mathematical purposes we must distinguish between the indefinitely great and the actually infinite in the sense of the transfinite. To deal with the actually infinite, as distinguished from the immeasurably or indefinitely great, we have to introduce new notions and a new vocabulary. For instance, in dealing with infinite aggregates, the proposition that the part is always less than the whole is not true. Infinities, indeed, differ, but not according to the idea of greater and smaller, of more or less, but according to their order, grade, or power (in German *Mächtigkeit*). Two infinities are equal, or of the same power, if we can bring them into a one-to-one correspondence. Prof. Cantor has shown that the extended range of numbers termed algebraic have the same power as the series of ordinary integers— one, two, three, &c.—because we can establish a one-to-one correspondence between the two series—*i.e.*, we can count them. He has further shown that if we suppose all numbers arranged in a straight line, then in any portion of this line, however small, there is an infinite number of points which do not belong to a countable or enumerable multitude. Thus the continuum of numerical values is not countable—it belongs to a different

66.
Georg Cantor's theory of the transfinite.

grade of infinity; it has a higher, perhaps the second, power.[1]

In all these, and in many similar investigations, a conception has gradually emerged which was foreign to older mathematics, but which plays a great and useful part in modern mathematical thought. Older mathematics, ever since the introduction of general arithmetic or algebra, centred in the conception of equality and in the solution of equations. Everything was reduced to magnitude. But there are other relations besides those of magnitude, of more or less. Often in practical pursuits, if we cannot find a counterpart or write down an exact numerical equation, we can gain information by a correspondence. This conception of correspondence plays a great part in modern mathematics. It is the fundamental notion in the science of order as distinguished from the science of magnitude. If older mathematics were mostly dominated by the needs of mensuration, modern mathematics are dominated by the conception of order and arrangement. It may be that this tendency of thought or direction of reasoning goes hand in hand with the modern discovery in physics, that the changes in nature depend not only or not so much on the quantity of mass and energy as on their distribution or arrangement.

With these reflections we touch the limits of mathe-

67.
Correspond-
ence.

---

[1] A summary of Prof. Cantor's work is given by Prof. Schönflies in the 'Encyklop. Math. Wiss.,' vol. i. p. 184 *sqq.* The importance of accurate definitions and distinctions regarding the infinite and the continuous is dwelt on and the different recent theories set forth in a very lucid address to the London Math. Society by Prof. Hobson, "On the Infinite and Infinitesimal in Mathematical Analysis," November 1902.

matical thought and enter the region of metaphysics. Like other lines of reasoning which have occupied us in former chapters, the exact and rigid definitions and deductions of arithmetic and geometry lead us up to that other large department of our subject—philosophic thought. Many eminent mathematicians of recent years have noticed this tendency, and have urged the mutual help which arithmetic and geometry on this side, logic and psychology on that, may derive from each other. The names of Helmholtz, Georg Cantor, and Dedekind in Germany; of M. Tannery and M. Poincaré in France; of Peano and Veronese in Italy, stand prominently forward abroad; while England can boast of having cultivated, much earlier, by the hands of De Morgan and Boole, a portion at least of this borderland, and of having in recent years taken up the subject again in an original and independent manner.[1] Cayley, in his address to the British Association in 1883, has said: "Mathematics connect themselves on the one side with common life and the physical sciences; on the other

---

[1] I refer to the important but unfinished works of Mr Whitehead on 'Universal Algebra' (vol. i., 1898), and of Mr Bertrand Russell on 'The Principles of Mathematics' (vol. i., 1903). I must defer a more detailed appreciation of these and other writings of this class, such as those of the late Prof. Ernst Schröder ('Algebra der Logik,' 3 vols., 1890-95) and of Prof. Gottlob Frege (see an account of his writings in the appendix to Mr Russell's 'Principles'). They belong largely to a department of philosophical thought which may be termed "the Philosophy of the Exact Sciences." This deals with two great questions—the logical foundations of scientific reasoning, and the general outcome and importance of scientific thought, not for technical purposes, but in the great edifice of human thought which we may term Philosophy. It deals with what has been called "the Creed of Science" and its value. Stanley Jevons and Prof. Karl Pearson in this country, Prof. Mach in Germany, and M. Poincaré in France, have treated the philosophy of science in one or both of these aspects.

side with philosophy in regard to our notions of space and time, and in the questions which have arisen as to the universality and necessity of the truths of mathematics and the foundation of our knowledge of them"; and he subsequently refers specially to the "notion which is really the fundamental one underlying and pervading the whole of modern analysis and geometry," meaning the complex magnitude, as deserving to be specially discussed by philosophers. Beginnings of the philosophical treatment of this and other questions indeed exist. The questions are still *sub judice*, and the historian can merely refer to their existence and importance.

There is, however, one controversy which has arisen out of these and similar speculations, and out of the desire to bring unity and consistency into the fundamental notions of elementary as well as higher mathematics, which deserves to be specially mentioned, because it occupies a prominent place in foreign literature, having given rise to a special term, and thus commanding more general attention. Prof. Klein of Göttingen, under whose master-hand many abstract and obscure subjects have become plain and transparent, has prominently brought the subject before the scientific public in a recent address.[1] I refer to the tendency represented in its extreme form by the late Prof. Kronecker of Berlin, to reduce all mathematical conceptions to the fundamental arithmetical operations with integral numbers, banishing not only all geometrical and dynamical conceptions, such as those of continuity and flow, but

68.
Arithmetising tendency in mathematics.

---

[1] 'Ueber Arithmetisirung der Mathematik' (Göttingen, 1895).

also such apparently algebraical notions as those of irrational and complex quantities. This attempt is an outcome of the school of Weierstrass, which has done so much to banish vagueness and introduce precision into modern text-books.

Opposed to this so-called arithmetising [1] tendency is the equally emphatic view, strongly urged by the late Prof. Paul Du Bois-Reymond in his general theory of Functions, that the separation of the operations of counting and measuring is impossible, and, if it were possible (as, since the publication of his work, the fuller expositions of Kronecker and his followers have tried to show that it is), would degrade mathematics to a mere play with symbols.[2] He tries to show that such is philosophically impossible, and finds a support for his view in the historical genesis of the idea of irrational numbers in the incommensurable magnitudes of Euclid and ancient geometry. Prof. Klein in his address favours the arithmetical tendency as destined to introduce logical

---

[1] The term seems to have been coined by Kronecker. See Prof. Pringsheim in the 'Encyklop. Math. Wiss.,' vol. i. p. 58, note 40. Kronecker's position is set forth in Journal für Math., vol. ci. pp. 337-355, 1887.

[2] "The separation of the conception of number and of the analytical symbols from the conception of magnitude would reduce analysis to a mere formal and literal skeleton. It would degrade this science, which in truth is a natural science, although it only admits the most general properties of what we perceive into the domain of its researches ultimately to the rank of a mere play with symbols, wherein arbitrary meanings would be attached to the signs as if they were the figures on the chessboard or on playing-cards. However amusing such a play might be, nay, however useful for analytical purposes the solution would be of the problem,—to follow up the rules of the signs which emanated from the conception of magnitude into their last formal consequences,—such a literal mathematics would soon exhaust itself in fruitless efforts; whereas the science which Gauss called with so much truth the science of magnitude possesses an inexhaustible source of new material in the ever-increasing field of actual perceptions," &c., &c. ('Allgemeine Functionen-Theorie,' 1882, p. 54).

precision and consistency into the foundations of mathematics, and everywhere to further the very necessary process of critical sifting; but he denies that pure logic can do all, and points to the valuable assistance and suggestive power of geometrical construction and representation.[1] Most of my readers will no doubt agree with this view. Indeed the perusal of the foregoing chapters must have produced on their minds the conviction that, so far as the advance of science and also of mathematics is concerned, it largely depends upon the introduction of different aspects leading to different courses of reasoning. The unification of all of these into one consistent and uncontradictory scheme, though it remains a pious hope and far-off ideal, has not been the prominent work of the nineteenth century. Rather, wherever it has been attempted it has had a narrowing effect, and has resulted in a distinct curtailment of the great and increasing resources of Scientific Thought.

[1] Prof. Klein summarises the opinion which he holds as to the present task of mathematical science as follows : "Whilst I everywhere demand the fullest logical elaboration, I at the same time emphasise that *pari passu* with it the intuitive representation of the subject should be furthered in every possible manner. Mathematical developments which have their origin in intuition cannot count as a firm possession of science unless they have been reduced to a strict logical form. On the other side, the abstract statement of logical relations cannot satisfy us until their importance for every form of representation has been clearly demonstrated, so that we recognise the manifold connections in which the logical scheme stands to other departments of knowledge according to the field of application which we select. I compare mathematical science to a tree which stretches its roots ever deeper into the soil, and at the same time expands its branches freely upwards. Are we to consider the root or the branches as the more important part ? The botanist will tell us that the question is wrongly put, and that the life of an organism consists in the interaction of its various parts" (*loc. cit.*, p. 91).

RETROSPECT AND PROSPECT.

IN the foregoing chapters I have attempted to set forth the chief conceptions which are contained in the scientific literature of the nineteenth century. Upon these the scientific work of that period has been founded or they are the results to which its scientific reasoning has led. The most important outcome of the scientific work of the century does not lie in the region of thought, but rather in that of practical application; and this I have only incidentally referred to. Only in so far as it has reacted upon scientific thought, suggesting or modifying scientific ideas, has it been necessary to allude to it.

My readers who have so far accompanied me may be struck by one feature which, indeed, is characteristic of scientific thought. Our survey has presented such thought as broken up into a series of different aspects; and although certain connections between these aspects have been occasionally pointed out, no attempt has been made to combine them into one comprehensive or united view. The reason for this is to be found in the nature of scientific thought itself, which, proceeding by a definite method, starts from the great variety of phenomena which surround us in time and space; the only assumption which science is obliged to make being the inevitable one that Nature is intelligible to the human mind, which is the same as saying that we must assume the existence of some kind of Order.

There exists, indeed, in the human mind a further demand, which may be defined by saying that the conception of order in Nature or of its intelligibility should not be held merely as a formal iteration, but should be expressed as a highest Unity by some term which conveys to our minds something more than the idea of an empty form. From this demand there have further arisen at all times various attempts to give expression to the ideas of unity, of simplicity, and of the significance of the whole scheme of existence which we call Nature. Such attempts do not form part of purely scientific thought. They are speculations for which those principles of science that are capable of exact enunciation do not suffice. They have, indeed, frequently appeared in the literature of the nineteenth century. But although there are isolated cases where scientific authorities of the first order have indulged in them, such authorities have, as a rule, shown an increasing reluctance to deal with fundamental questions or with principles which extend beyond the limits of scientific thought. We have no examples in the nineteenth century of such intellects as those of Leibniz or Newton. However different these two great thinkers of an earlier age may have been, they had this in common, that for them the scientific and the religious aspects were not only equally important, but equally occupied their attention. The characteristic difference was that Leibniz apparently strove after a unification of scientific and religious reasoning, frequently to the disadvantage of both, whereas Newton kept them so distinctly apart that his immortal scientific works can be studied without any reference whatever to his theological writings.

The two positions represented by these two great men — namely, the attempt on the one side to unify or combine the scientific and the religious aspects, and on the other to keep them apart or contrast them— have, indeed, been adopted by many thinkers in the course of our period; but an attempt to do justice to such problems has been more usually considered the duty of philosophy *par excellence*. In the rare instances in which scientific authorities of the first order have ventured upon a solution of these problems, they have stepped outside of the limits of scientific reasoning; having, as it were, attempted to occupy the more impartial if not more elevated position of judges who assign to scientific reasoning its position and its value in the connected whole of human thought and interests.[1]

Consistently with the division of thought which underlies the present history, and which has been explained in the third part of the Introduction, I relegate the exposition of such theories to the second part of this work, which deals with philosophical thought. The fact that in the course of the nineteenth century there have still appeared scientific thinkers who have not only attacked special scientific problems, but also the great universal world-problem, may well be

2. Philosophical problems.

[1] Examples of this will be found in the writings of André Marie Ampère, of Emil Du Bois-Rey- mond, and of Gustav Theodor Fechner.

noted as a connection, a bond of union, between those two great realms of systematic thought which, for the sake of convenience, I have kept apart in this historical survey.

There are other features in the scientific thought of the period, as it has become known to us, which naturally lead up to a different treatment from that which is peculiar to science. In almost every instance, in following up the various aspects of scientific thought, I have had to show how they have brought us to problems which cannot be solved by the means which we call scientific or exact; and in many instances I have shown how the foremost scientific thinkers themselves have been led up to inquiries which they have variously termed philosophical, metaphysical, logical, or psychological. Such has notably been the case with the ultimate conceptions of the atomic theory, of the doctrine of energy, and, still more, with the conceptions which underlie the scientific treatment of the phenomena of life and consciousness. The further we have advanced from the simple mechanical conceptions of motion and inertia or mass, into the phenomena of the actual world of natural objects which exhibit order, development, purpose, and consciousness, the more we have been obliged to make use of terms not capable of being defined by the simple categories of exact or mathematical thought; and with whatever zeal some of the foremost thinkers have in the course of the century attempted to express these more indefinite conceptions in terms of mechanical science, they have only partially succeeded, and have certainly failed in banishing them from the scientific vocabulary. Such conceptions have always crept in again, proving that they are indispensable even to the purely scientific comprehension or description of natural objects, or of nature as a whole.

It is not surprising, therefore, that an independent examination of the ultimate conceptions which science makes use of, or which it evolves, should have been a task which has occupied some of the greatest intellects of our period, and that the problem arising from this should form a fitting transition from the purely scientific to the philosophical portion of this history.

Now, if we try to characterise in the briefest possible manner the general problems which scientific thought as a whole has definitely formulated and placed before the philosophical thinker, there are two words which stand out prominently as indicating the two grand and complementary conceptions which either underlie all scientific inquiry or result from it. The first of these has already been stated. We saw that exact or scientific thought assumes that there exists in Nature an intelligible ORDER. The closer definition of this order in the so-called laws of the cosmos has to be ascertained by experience, and has been the subject of the foregoing narrative. The subject which remains for philosophical discussion is not any special form of order, but the fact that any kind of order exists at all, and that it is accessible to the human intellect. Clearly this is a question which affects Nature, the object, as much as the human Intellect, the subject.

But if the idea of Order underlies all scientific thought,

standing as it were at the entrance of scientific reasoning, there is another idea which stands at the end of all scientific thought. This is the idea of UNITY in its most impressive form as Individuality. It remains over as an ultimate empirical fact to which scientific reasoning advances, of equal importance with order.

These two conceptions of Order and Individuality likewise govern the two great divisions under which scientific thought has been studied by us—Physics and Biology. After reviewing in the first three chapters the characteristic attitudes taken up by the three leading nations in scientific thought, I entered upon the four abstract conceptions—namely, Attraction, Atomism, Kinetics, and Energy—which are capable of strict mathematical definition, and which form the skeleton or framework around or in which the sciences of Astronomy, Dynamics, Physics, and Chemistry have arranged their various doctrines. They serve together to define more precisely the conception of the general order of things, appropriately termed the Cosmos. In the four chapters following upon these I dealt with the different conceptions under which a comprehension, not so much of the general order as of the special events and things of our world, has been gained. These conceptions, referring to the actual forms, the history, the life and soul of things natural, have been likewise dealt with in four chapters. On them the physics of the universe and of our earth, the sciences dealing with the organised and animated creations, have been built up. Beginning with a special kind of order—namely, that indicated by external figure—these sciences

have advanced through the study of the changes of figure
to an increasing appreciation of an underlying unity.
In many of the organs of living creatures the unity
seems to lie outside the organs themselves, as the unity
of a machine which exists in the design of the maker
adapting it to a certain purpose; whereas in the animated world it seems to be inside the objects of Nature.
The sciences of life have accordingly forced upon us
more and more the conception not only of orderly
arrangement, but also of a unifying principle — that
is, Individuality.

These two conceptions of Order and Individuality are
as little new as are the various conceptions of purely
scientific thought, most of which, as has been shown,
have been handed down to us from earlier times.   They
have accordingly been defined and studied by philosophers from antiquity.   The various positions which
thinkers have taken up with regard to them during the
nineteenth century have, however, been characteristic
of the age, and have been very largely influenced
by the conceptions of Order and Unity which science
itself has elaborated.   In this connection it is of
importance to note that the idea of Order or
arrangement has only within the nineteenth century
met with a comprehensive mathematical treatment; and,
so far as that of Unity is concerned, it can also be
said that the mathematical sciences have in the course
of the nineteenth century for the first time approached
the analysis of the allied idea of Continuity, which
indeed plays an increasingly important part in many
scientific theories.   It may even be held that the

scientific mind advances from the idea of Order or arrangement to that of Unity through the idea of Continuity.

If, however, these highest conceptions had been introduced to us by scientific thought in the form only of limiting ideas or highest abstractions, it is doubtful whether the special discussion of them would have attracted so much attention or occupied so many minds as has actually been the case. In many instances we found it to be quite sufficient for the purposes of science that fundamental principles should be dogmatically asserted, and that their usefulness should be the only proof of their correctness. If no other interest attached to the conceptions of order and unity than attaches, for instance, to the ultimate principles of dynamics, to atomism, or to the axioms of geometry, the number of persons who take up these refined studies would probably be exceedingly small. The reason why the conceptions of order, unity, and individuality have received so much attention lies in this, that they have not only a logical meaning as instruments of thought, but also, as the words themselves indicate, a practical meaning, being bound up with the highest ethical and æsthetical, as well as with our social and religious, interests. The word order means something more than arrangement when we speak of the social or moral order; the word unity is more than an arithmetical conception when we speak of the unity of action or of purpose, or the unity of design in art; the word individuality acquires a higher meaning in the term personality. Those thinkers who in the nine-

4.
Practical
interests
attaching to
Order and
Unity.

teenth century, as well as in former ages, have dealt exhaustively with these the most abstract and highest conceptions of which human thought is capable, have not been, or have only very rarely been, led to their inquiries from the side of purely scientific interests; they have approached them with a full appreciation of the great moral and religious interests which lie hidden in the deeper significance which we attach to the words. In starting, therefore, on the survey of philosophical thought, it would be quite inadequate to take scientific ideas as a suitable introduction. Whatever future ages may bring, the philosophy of the nineteenth century has certainly not been exclusively, or even pre-eminently, scientific or exact. If philosophy has assumed the name of a science, it has done so in that larger sense of the word which, as we have seen, is peculiar to the German language. In this connection scientific treatment means simply methodical treatment, whereas there is an increasing tendency in many circles to identify the word science with exact mathematical or positive treatment. The exact treatment of philosophical problems, such as has been attempted but only very partially carried out in the systems of Auguste Comte in France and of Herbert Spencer in England, belongs almost entirely to a later part of that century, and forms, even then, only one side of its large philosophical literature. Philosophical thought had a brilliant history in the earlier part of the century before the ideas of Positivism or of modern Evolution were much thought of. It will therefore be necessary in any account of philosophical thought to ascertain and clearly define the positions occupied by the great thinkers who governed and revolutionised the thought of earlier generations before the great generalisations of science, notably those connected with the ideas of energy and the theory of descent, could have had any influence whatever. Though the latter have acquired in recent times a great, perhaps an undue, importance, it will only be after becoming acquainted with an earlier and different phase of philosophic thought that we shall have once more to return to those conceptions and trains of reasoning which must be uppermost in the mind of the writer as well as of the reader of the foregoing chapters.

5.
The geographical centre of philosophic thought.

But in starting on the historical account of an entirely different realm of thought, I shall not only have to ask my readers to enter into a new circle of ideas, which for a long time during the course of the nineteenth century lay entirely outside of that circle of ideas with which we have become acquainted so far; we shall be assisted also by finding an entirely different geographical centre from which these ideas emanated. It has been repeatedly pointed out that the great volume of scientific thought with which we have hitherto been occupied, emanated in the latter part of the eighteenth century from the French capital; and in the course of narration I have had to go back almost in every single instance to the foundations laid in French scientific literature. I shall now have to invite my readers to give their attention to the peculiar features which were characteristic not of French but of German literature at the end of the eighteenth and the beginning of the nineteenth century.

The centre of philosophical thought during the first half of the nineteenth century lay as much in Germany as the centre of scientific thought lay, somewhat earlier, in France. It is true that in both cases, if we trace the movement a little further back, we come upon the powerful influences of English thought. Newton can be considered as marking the beginning of the modern era of scientific thought; Locke can be looked upon as having infused into philosophic thought much of its modern spirit. But though this must be conceded to a large extent, it must also be admitted that the scientific thought of the nineteenth century for a long time received its special colouring through the influence of the French mathematicians and naturalists, with Laplace and Cuvier as their most illustrious representatives; while philosophical thought for a long time received its specific colouring from the idealistic movement which began with Kant and culminated in Hegel. And although it was again the specific influence of English thought which in the latter part of the nineteenth century diverted alike scientific and philosophical thought from the channels in which they ran during the first half of the century, we have only very partially emancipated ourselves from the overwhelming influence which the conceptions of the idealistic school of German philosophy have had upon the deeper philosophical thought of all three nations alike. The features peculiar to that period are still strongly marked on the philosophical countenance of the age: neither the lights nor the shadows thrown by the great luminaries which appeared on the philosophical horizon of Germany a century ago have as yet died away.

It will be the object of the second part of this work to trace in more detail this powerful influence, to define more clearly wherein it consisted, and to discover to what extent it still survives or is mingled with other influences, among which that which we have studied exclusively in the first part of this history will prove to have been one of the most important.

INDEX.

THE END.

CATALOGUE OF DOVER BOOKS

Social Sciences

SOCIAL THOUGHT FROM LORE TO SCIENCE, H. E. Barnes and H. Becker. An immense survey of sociological thought and ways of viewing, studying, planning, and reforming society from earliest times to the present. Includes thought on society of preliterate peoples, ancient non-Western cultures, and every great movement in Europe, America, and modern Japan. Analyzes hundreds of great thinkers: Plato, Augustine, Bodin, Vico, Montesquieu, Herder, Comte, Marx, etc. Weighs the contributions of utopians, sophists, fascists and communists; economists, jurists, philosophers, ecclesiastics, and every 19th and 20th century school of scientific sociology, anthropology, and social psychology throughout the world. Combines topical, chronological, and regional approaches, treating the evolution of social thought as a process rather than as a series of mere topics. "Impressive accuracy, competence, and discrimination . . . easily the best single survey," Nation. Thoroughly revised, with new material up to 1960. 2 indexes. Over 2200 bibliographical notes. Three volume set. Total of 1586pp. 5⅜ x 8.

T901 Vol I Paperbound **$2.35**
T902 Vol II Paperbound **$2.35**
T903 Vol III Paperbound **$2.35**
The set **$7.05**

FOLKWAYS, William Graham Sumner. A classic of sociology, a searching and thorough examination of patterns of behaviour from primitive, ancient Greek and Judaic, Medieval Christian, African, Oriental, Melanesian, Australian, Islamic, to modern Western societies. Thousands of illustrations of social, sexual, and religious customs, mores, laws, and institutions. Hundreds of categories: Labor, Wealth, Abortion, Primitive Justice, Life Policy, Slavery, Cannibalism, Uncleanness and the Evil Eye, etc. Will extend the horizon of every reader by showing the relativism of his own culture. Prefatory note by A. G. Keller. Introduction by William Lyon Phelps. Bibliography. Index. xiii + 692pp. 5⅜ x 8. T508 Paperbound **$2.49**

PRIMITIVE RELIGION, P. Radin. A thorough treatment by a noted anthropologist of the nature and origin of man's belief in the supernatural and the influences that have shaped religious expression in primitive societies. Ranging from the Arunta, Ashanti, Aztec, Bushman, Crow, Fijian, etc., of Africa, Australia, Pacific Islands, the Arctic, North and South America, Prof. Radin integrates modern psychology, comparative religion, and economic thought with first-hand accounts gathered by himself and other scholars of primitive initiations, training of the shaman, and other fascinating topics. "Excellent," NATURE (London). Unabridged reissue of 1st edition. New author's preface. Bibliographic notes. Index. x + 322pp. 5⅜ x 8.
T393 Paperbound **$1.85**

PRIMITIVE MAN AS PHILOSOPHER, P. Radin. A standard anthropological work covering primitive thought on such topics as the purpose of life, marital relations, freedom of thought, symbolism, death, resignation, the nature of reality, personality, gods, and many others. Drawn from factual material gathered from the Winnebago, Oglala Sioux, Maori, Baganda, Batak, Zuni, among others, it does not distort ideas by removing them from context but interprets strictly within the original framework. Extensive selections of original primitive documents. Bibliography. Index. xviii + 402pp. 5⅜ x 8. T392 Paperbound **$2.25**

A TREATISE ON SOCIOLOGY, THE MIND AND SOCIETY, Vilfredo Pareto. This treatise on human society is one of the great classics of modern sociology. First published in 1916, its careful catalogue of the innumerable manifestations of non-logical human conduct (Book One); the theory of "residues," leading to the premise that sentiment not logic determines human behavior (Book Two), and of "derivations," beliefs derived from desires (Book Three); and the general description of society made up of non-elite and elite, consisting of "foxes" who live by cunning and "lions" who live by force, stirred great controversy. But Pareto's passion for isolation and classification of elements and factors, and his allegiance to scientific method as the key tool for scrutinizing the human situation made his a truly twentieth-century mind and his work a catalytic influence on certain later social commentators. These four volumes (bound as two) require no special training to be appreciated and any reader who wishes to gain a complete understanding of modern sociological theory, regardless of special field of interest, will find them a must. Reprint of revised (corrected) printing of original edition. Translated by Andrew Bongiorno and Arthur Livingston. Index. Bibliography. Appendix containing index-summary of theorems. 48 diagrams. Four volumes bound as two. Total of 2063pp. 5⅜ x 8½. The set Clothbound **$15.00**

THE POLISH PEASANT IN EUROPE AND AMERICA, William I. Thomas, Florian Znaniecki. A seminal sociological study of peasant primary groups (family and community) and the disruptions produced by a new industrial system and immigration to America. The peasant's family, class system, religious and aesthetic attitudes, and economic life are minutely examined and analyzed in hundreds of pages of primary documentation, particularly letters between family members. The disorientation caused by new environments is scrutinized in detail (a 312-page autobiography of an immigrant is especially valuable and revealing) in an attempt to find common experiences and reactions. The famous "Methodological Note" sets forth the principles which guided the authors. When out of print this set has sold for as much as $50. 2nd revised edition. 2 vols. Vol. 1: xv + 1115pp. Vol. 2: 1135pp. Index. 6 x 9.
T478 Clothbound 2 vol. set **$12.50**

Art, History of Art, Antiques, Graphic Arts, Handcrafts

ART STUDENTS' ANATOMY, E. J. Farris. Outstanding art anatomy that uses chiefly living objects for its illustrations. 71 photos of undraped men, women, children are accompanied by carefully labeled matching sketches to illustrate the skeletal system, articulations and movements, bony landmarks, the muscular system, skin, fasciae, fat, etc. 9 x-ray photos show movement of joints. Undraped models are shown in such actions as serving in tennis, drawing a bow in archery, playing football, dancing, preparing to spring and to dive. Also discussed and illustrated are proportions, age and sex differences, the anatomy of the smile, etc. 8 plates by the great early 18th century anatomic illustrator Siegfried Albinus are also included. Glossary. 158 figures, 7 in color. x + 159pp. 5⅝ x 8⅜. **T744 Paperbound $1.50**

AN ATLAS OF ANATOMY FOR ARTISTS, F Schider. A new 3rd edition of this standard text enlarged by 52 new illustrations of hands, anatomical studies by Cloquet, and expressive life studies of the body by Barcsay. 189 clear, detailed plates offer you precise information of impeccable accuracy. 29 plates show all aspects of the skeleton, with closeups of special areas, while 54 full-page plates, mostly in two colors, give human musculature as seen from four different points of view, with cutaways for important portions of the body. 14 full-page plates provide photographs of hand forms, eyelids, female breasts, and indicate the location of muscles upon models. 59 additional plates show how great artists of the past utilized human anatomy. They reproduce sketches and finished work by such artists as Michelangelo, Leonardo da Vinci, Goya, and 15 others. This is a lifetime reference work which will be one of the most important books in any artist's library. "The standard reference tool," AMERICAN LIBRARY ASSOCIATION. "Excellent," AMERICAN ARTIST. Third enlarged edition. 189 plates, 647 illustrations. xxvi + 192pp. 7⅞ x 10⅝. **T241 Clothbound $6.00**

AN ATLAS OF ANIMAL ANATOMY FOR ARTISTS, W. Ellenberger, H. Baum, H. Dittrich. The largest, richest animal anatomy for artists available in English. 99 detailed anatomical plates of such animals as the horse, dog, cat, lion, deer, seal, kangaroo, flying squirrel, cow, bull, goat, monkey, hare, and bat. Surface features are clearly indicated, while progressive beneath-the-skin pictures show musculature, tendons, and bone structure. Rest and action are exhibited in terms of musculature and skeletal structure and detailed cross-sections are given for heads and important features. The animals chosen are representative of specific families so that a study of these anatomies will provide knowledge of hundreds of related species. "Highly recommended as one of the very few books on the subject worthy of being used as an authoritative guide," DESIGN. "Gives a fundamental knowledge," AMERICAN ARTIST. Second revised, enlarged edition with new plates from Cuvier, Stubbs, etc. 288 illustrations. 153pp. 11⅜ x 9. **T82 Clothbound $6.00**

THE HUMAN FIGURE IN MOTION, Eadweard Muybridge. The largest selection in print of Muybridge's famous high-speed action photos of the human figure in motion. 4789 photographs illustrate 162 different actions: men, women, children—mostly undraped—are shown walking, running, carrying various objects, sitting, lying down, climbing, throwing, arising, and performing over 150 other actions. Some actions are shown in as many as 150 photographs each. All in all there are more than 500 action strips in this enormous volume, series shots taken at shutter speeds of as high as 1/6000th of a second! These are not posed shots, but true stopped motion. They show bone and muscle in situations that the human eye is not fast enough to capture. Earlier, smaller editions of these prints have brought $40 and more on the out-of-print market. "A must for artists," ART IN FOCUS. "An unparalleled dictionary of action for all artists," AMERICAN ARTIST. 390 full-page plates, with 4789 photographs. Printed on heavy glossy stock. Reinforced binding with headbands. xxi + 390pp. 7⅞ x 10⅝. **T204 Clothbound $10.00**

ANIMALS IN MOTION, Eadweard Muybridge. This is the largest collection of animal action photos in print. 34 different animals (horses, mules, oxen, goats, camels, pigs, cats, guanacos, lions, gnus, deer, monkeys, eagles—and 21 others) in 132 characteristic actions. The horse alone is shown in more than 40 different actions. All 3919 photographs are taken in series at speeds up to 1/6000th of a second. The secrets of leg motion, spinal patterns, head movements, strains and contortions shown nowhere else are captured. You will see exactly how a lion sets his foot down; how an elephant's knees are like a human's—and how they differ; the position of a kangaroo's legs in mid-leap; how an ostrich's head bobs; details of the flight of birds—and thousands of facets of motion only the fastest cameras can catch. Photographed from domestic animals and animals in the Philadelphia zoo, it contains neither semiposed artificial shots nor distorted telephoto shots taken under adverse conditions. Artists, biologists, decorators, cartoonists, will find this book indispensable for understanding animals in motion. "A really marvelous series of plates," NATURE (London). "The dry plate's most spectacular early use was by Eadweard Muybridge," LIFE. 3919 photographs; 380 full pages of plates. 440pp. Printed on heavy glossy paper. Deluxe binding with headbands. 7⅞ x 10⅝. **T203 Clothbound $10.00**

CATALOGUE OF DOVER BOOKS

ART ANATOMY, William Rimmer, M.D. Often called one of America's foremost contributions to art instruction, a work of art in its own right. More than 700 line drawings by the author, first-rate anatomist and dissector as well as artist, with a non-technical anatomical text. Impeccably accurate drawings of muscles, skeletal structure, surface features, other aspects of males and females, children, adults and aged persons show not only form, size, insertion and articulation but personality and emotion as reflected by physical features usually ignored in modern anatomical works. Complete unabridged reproduction of 1876 edition slightly rearranged. Introduction by Robert Hutchinson. 722 illustrations. xiii + 153pp. 7¾ x 10¾.
T908 Paperbound **$2.00**

ANIMAL DRAWING: ANATOMY AND ACTION FOR ARTISTS, C. R. Knight. The author and illustrator of this work was "the most distinguished painter of animal life." This extensive course in animal drawing discusses musculature, bone structure, animal psychology, movements, habits, habitats. Innumerable tips on proportions, light and shadow play, coloring, hair formation, feather arrangement, scales, how animals lie down, animal expressions, etc., from great apes to birds. Pointers on avoiding gracelessness in horses, deer; on introducing proper power and bulk to heavier animals; on giving proper grace and subtle expression to members of the cat family. Originally titled "Animal Anatomy and Psychology for the Artist and Layman." Over 123 illustrations. 149pp. 8¼ x 10½.
T426 Paperbound **$2.00**

DESIGN FOR ARTISTS AND CRAFTSMEN, L. Wolchonok. The most thorough course ever prepared on the creation of art motifs and designs. It teaches you to create your own designs out of things around you — from geometric patterns, plants, birds, animals, humans, landscapes, and man-made objects. It leads you step by step through the creation of more than 1300 designs, and shows you how to create design that is fresh, well-founded, and original. Mr. Wolchonok, whose text is used by scores of art schools, shows you how the same idea can be developed into many different forms, ranging from near representationalism to the most advanced forms of abstraction. The material in this book is entirely new, and combines full awareness of traditional design with the work of such men as Miro, Léger, Picasso, Moore, and others. 113 detailed exercises, with instruction hints, diagrams, and details to enable you to apply Wolchonok's methods to your own work. "A great contribution to the field of design and crafts," N. Y. SOCIETY OF CRAFTSMEN. More than 1300 illustrations. xv + 207pp. 7⅞ x 10¾.
T274 Clothbound **$4.95**

HAWTHORNE ON PAINTING. A vivid recreation, from students' notes, of instruction by Charles W. Hawthorne, given for over 31 years at his famous Cape Cod School of Art. Divided into sections on the outdoor model, still life, landscape, the indoor model, and water color, each section begins with a concise essay, followed by epigrammatic comments on color, form, seeing, etc. Not a formal course, but comments of a great teacher-painter on specific student works, which will solve problems in your own painting and understanding of art. "An excellent introduction for laymen and students alike," Time. Introduction. 100pp. 5⅜ x 8.
T653 Paperbound **$1.00**

THE ENJOYMENT AND USE OF COLOR, Walter Sargent. This book explains fascinating relations among colors, between colors in nature and art; describes experiments that you can perform to understand these relations more thoroughly; points out hundreds of little known facts about color values, intensities, effects of high and low illumination, complementary colors, color harmonies. Practical hints for painters, references to techniques of masters, questions at chapter ends for self-testing all make this a valuable book for artists, professional and amateur, and for general readers interested in world of color. Republication of 1923 edition. 35 illustrations, 6 full-page plates. New color frontispiece. Index. xii + 274pp. 5⅜ x 8.
T944 Paperbound **$2.25**

DECORATIVE ALPHABETS AND INITIALS, ed. by Alexander Nesbitt. No payment, no permission needed to reproduce any one of these 3924 different letters, covering 1000 years. Crisp, clear letters all in line, from Anglo-Saxon mss., Luebeck Cathedral, 15th century Augsburg; the work of Dürer, Holbein, Cresci, Beardsley, Rossing Wadsworth, John Moylin, etc. Every imaginable style. 91 complete alphabets. 123 full-page plates. 192pp. 7¾ x 10¾.
T544 Paperbound **$2.25**

THREE CLASSICS OF ITALIAN CALLIGRAPHY, edited by Oscar Ogg. Here, combined in a single volume, are complete reproductions of three famous calligraphic works written by the greatest writing masters of the Renaissance: Arrighi's OPERINA and IL MODO, Tagliente's LO PRESENTE LIBRO, and Palatino's LIBRO NUOVO. These books present more than 200 complete alphabets and thousands of lettered specimens. The basic hand is Papal Chancery, but scores of other alphabets are also given: European and Asiatic local alphabets, foliated and art alphabets, scrolls, cartouches, borders, etc. Text is in Italian. Introduction. 245 plates. x + 272pp. 6⅛ x 9¼.
T212 Paperbound **$2.25**

CALLIGRAPHY, J. G. Schwandner. One of the legendary books in the graphic arts, copies of which brought $500 each on the rare book market, now reprinted for the first time in over 200 years. A beautiful plate book of graceful calligraphy, and an inexhaustible source of first-rate material copyright-free, for artists, and directors, craftsmen, commercial artists, etc. More than 300 ornamental initials forming 12 complete alphabets, over 150 ornate frames and panels, over 200 flourishes, over 75 calligraphic pictures including a temple, cherubs, cocks, dodos, stags, chamois, foliated lions, greyhounds, etc. Thousand of calligraphic elements to be used for suggestions of quality, sophistication, antiquity, and sheer beauty. Historical introduction. 158 full-page plates. 368pp. 9 x 13.
T475 Clothbound **$10.00**

CATALOGUE OF DOVER BOOKS

THE HISTORY AND TECHNIQUE OF LETTERING, A. Nesbitt. The only thorough inexpensive history of letter forms from the point of view of the artist. Mr. Nesbitt covers every major development in lettering from the ancient Egyptians to the present and illustrates each development with a complete alphabet. Such masters as Baskerville, Bell, Bodoni, Caslon, Koch, Kilian, Morris, Garamont, Jenson, and dozens of others are analyzed in terms of artistry and historical development. The author also presents a 65-page practical course in lettering, besides the full historical text. 89 complete alphabets; 165 additional lettered specimens. xvii + 300pp. 5⅜ x 8. **T427 Paperbound $2.00**

FOOT-HIGH LETTERS: A GUIDE TO LETTERING (A PRACTICAL SYLLABUS FOR TEACHERS), M. Price. A complete alphabet of Classic Roman letters, each a foot high, each on a separate 16 x 22 plate—perfect for use in lettering classes. In addition to an accompanying description, each plate also contains 9 two-inch-high forms of letter in various type faces, such as "Caslon," "Empire," "Onyx," and "Neuland," illustrating the many possible derivations from the standard classical forms. One plate contains 21 additional forms of the letter A. The fully illustrated 16-page syllabus by Mr. Price, formerly of the Pratt Institute and the Rhode Island School of Design, contains dozens of useful suggestions for student and teacher alike. An indispensable teaching aid. Extensively revised. 16-page syllabus and 30 plates in slip cover, 16 x 22. **T239 Clothbound $6.00**

THE STYLES OF ORNAMENT, Alexander Speltz. Largest collection of ornaments in print— 3765 illustrations of prehistoric, Lombard, Gothic, Frank, Romanesque, Mohammedan, Renaissance, Polish, Swiss, Rococo, Sheraton, Empire, U. S. Colonial, etc., ornament. Gargoyles, dragons, columns, necklaces, urns, friezes, furniture, buildings, keyholes, tapestries, fantastic animals, armor, religious objects, much more, all in line. Reproduce any one free. Index. Bibliography. 400 plates. 656pp. 5⅝ x 8⅜. **T557 Paperbound $2.50**

HANDBOOK OF DESIGNS AND DEVICES, C. P. Hornung. This unique book is indispensable to the designer, commercial artist, and hobbyist. It is not a textbook but a working collection of 1836 basic designs and variations, carefully reproduced, which may be used without permission. Variations of circle, line, band, triangle, square, cross, diamond, swastika, pentagon, octagon, hexagon, star, scroll, interlacement, shields, etc. Supplementary notes on the background and symbolism of the figures. "A necessity to every designer who would be original without having to labor heavily," ARTIST AND ADVERTISER. 204 plates. 240pp. 5⅜ x 8. **T125 Paperbound $1.90**

THE UNIVERSAL PENMAN, George Bickham. This beautiful book, which first appeared in 1743, is the largest collection of calligraphic specimens, flourishes, alphabets, and calligraphic illustrations ever published. 212 full-page plates are drawn from the work of such 18th century masters of English roundhand as Dove, Champion, Bland, and 20 others. They contain 22 complete alphabets, over 2,000 flourishes, and 122 illustrations, each drawn with a stylistic grace impossible to describe. This book is invaluable to anyone interested in the beauties of calligraphy, or to any artist, hobbyist, or craftsman who wishes to use the very best ornamental handwriting and flourishes for decorative purposes. Commercial artists, advertising artists, have found it unexcelled as a source of material suggesting quality. "An essential part of any art library, and a book of permanent value," AMERICAN ARTIST. 212 plates. 224pp. 9 x 13¾. **T20 Clothbound $10.00**

1800 WOODCUTS BY THOMAS BEWICK AND HIS SCHOOL. Prepared by Dover's editorial staff, this is the largest collection of woodcuts by Bewick and his school ever compiled. Contains the complete engravings from all his major works and a wide range of illustrations from lesser-known collections, all photographed from clear copies of the original books and reproduced in line. Carefully and conveniently organized into sections on Nature (animals and birds, scenery and landscapes, plants, insects, etc.), People (love and courtship, social life, school and domestic scenes, misfortunes, costumes, etc.), Business and Trade, and illustrations from primers, fairytales, spelling books, frontispieces, borders, fables and allegories, etc. In addition to technical proficiency and simple beauty, Bewick's work is remarkable as a mode of pictorial symbolism, reflecting rustic tranquility, an atmosphere of rest, simplicity, idyllic contentment. A delight for the eye, an inexhaustible source of illustrative material for art studios, commercial artists, advertising agencies. Individual illustrations (up to 10 for any one use) are copyright free. Classified index. Bibliography and sources. Introduction by Robert Hutchinson. 1800 woodcuts. xiv + 247pp. 9 x 12. **T766 Clothbound $10.00**

A HANDBOOK OF EARLY ADVERTISING ART, C. P. Hornung. The largest collection of copyright-free early advertising art ever compiled. Vol. I contains some 2,000 illustrations of agricultural devices, animals, old automobiles, birds, buildings, Christmas decorations (with 7 Santa Clauses by Nast), allegorical figures, fire engines, horses and vehicles, Indians, portraits, sailing ships, trains, sports, trade cuts — and 30 other categories! Vol. II, devoted to typography, has over 4000 specimens: 600 different Roman, Gothic, Barnum, Old English faces; 630 ornamental type faces; 1115 initials, hundreds of scrolls, flourishes, etc. This third edition is enlarged by 78 additional plates containing all new material. "A remarkable collection," PRINTERS' INK. "A rich contribution to the history of American design," GRAPHIS. Volume I, Pictorial. Over 2000 illustrations. xiv + 242pp. 9 x 12. **T122 Clothbound $10.00** Volume II, Typographical. Over 4000 specimens. vii + 312pp. 9 x 12. **T123 Clothbound $10.00** Two volume set, **T121 Clothbound, only $18.50**

Dover Classical Records

Now available directly to the public exclusively from Dover: top-quality recordings of fine classical music for only $2 per record! Almost all were released by major record companies to sell for $5 and $6. These recordings were issued under our imprint only after they had passed a severe critical test. We insisted upon:

First-rate music that is enjoyable, musically important and culturally significant.

First-rate performances, where the artists have carried out the composer's intentions, in which the music is alive, vigorous, played with understanding and sensitivity.

First-rate sound—clear, sonorous, fully balanced, crackle-free, whir-free.

Have in your home music by major composers, performed by such gifted musicians as Elsner, Gitlis, Wührer, Beveridge Webster, the Barchet Quartet, Gimpel, etc. Enthusiastically received when first released, many of these performances are definitive. The records are not seconds or remainders, but brand new pressings made on pure vinyl from carefully chosen master tapes. "All purpose" 12" monaural 33⅓ rpm records, they play equally well on hi-fi and stereo equipment. Fine music for discriminating music lovers, superlatively played, flawlessly recorded: there is no better way to build your library of recorded classical music at remarkable savings. There are no strings; this is not a come-on, not a club, forcing you to buy records you may not want in order to get a few at a lower price. Buy whatever records you want in any quantity, and never pay more than $2 each. Your obligation ends with your first purchase. And that's when ours begins. Dover's money-back guarantee allows you to return any record for any reason, even if you don't like the music, for a full, immediate refund—no questions asked.

MOZART: STRING QUARTETS: IN A (K. 464) AND C ("DISSONANT") (K. 465), Barchet Quartet. The final two of the famous Haydn Quartets, high-points in the history of music. The A Major was accepted with delight by Mozart's contemporaries, but the C Major, with its dissonant opening, aroused strong protest. Today, of course, the remarkable resolutions of the dissonances are recognized as major musical achievements. "Beautiful warm playing," MUSICAL AMERICA. "Two of Mozart's loveliest quartets in a distinguished performance," REV. OF RECORDED MUSIC. (Playing time 58 mins.) HCR 5200 **$2.00**

MOZART: STRING QUARTETS: IN G (K. 80), D (K. 156), and C (K. 157), Barchet Quartet. The early chamber music of Mozart receives unfortunately little attention. First-rate music of the Italian school, it contains all the lightness and charm that belongs only to the youthful Mozart. This is currently the only separate source for the composer's work of this period. "Excellent," HIGH FIDELITY. "Filled with sunshine and youthful joy; played with verve, recorded sound live and brilliant," CHRISTIAN SCI. MONITOR. (playing time 51 mins.) HCR 5201 **$2.00**

MOZART: SERENADES: #9 IN D ("POSTHORN") (K. 320), #6 IN D ("SERENATA NOTTURNA") (K. 239), Pro Musica Orch. of Stuttgart, under Edouard van Remoortel. For Mozart, the serenade was a highly effective form, since he could bring to it the immediacy and intimacy of chamber music as well as the free fantasy of larger group music. Both these serenades are distinguished by a playful, mischievous quality, a spirit perfectly captured in this fine performance. "A triumph, polished playing from the orchestra," HI FI MUSIC AT HOME. "Sound is rich and resonant, fidelity is wonderful," REV. OF RECORDED MUSIC. (Playing time 51 mins.) HCR 5202 **$2.00**

MOZART: DIVERTIMENTO FOR VIOLIN, VIOLA AND CELLO IN E FLAT (K. 563); ADAGIO AND FUGUE IN F MINOR (K. 404a), Kehr Trio. The divertimento is one of Mozart's most beloved pieces, called by Einstein "the finest and most perfect trio ever heard." It is difficult to imagine a music lover who will not be delighted by it. This is the only recording of the lesser known Adagio and Fugue, written in 1782 and influenced by Bach's Well-Tempered Clavichord. "Extremely beautiful recording, strongly recommended," THE OBSERVER. "Superior to rival editions," HIGH FIDELITY. (Playing time 51 mins.) HCR 5203 **$2.00**

SCHUMANN: KREISLERIANA (OPUS 16) AND FANTASIA IN C (OPUS 17), Vlado Perlemuter, Piano. The vigorous Romantic imagination and the remarkable emotional qualities of Schumann's piano music raise it to a special eminence in 19th-century creativity. Both these pieces are rooted to the composer's tortuous romance with his future wife, Clara, and both receive brilliant treatment at the hands of Vlado Perlemuter, Paris Conservatory, proclaimed by Alfred Cortot "not only a great virtuoso but also a great musician." "The best Kreisleriana to date," BILLBOARD. (Playing time 55 mins.) HCR 5204 **$2.00**

Music

A GENERAL HISTORY OF MUSIC, Charles Burney. A detailed coverage of music from the Greeks up to 1789, with full information on all types of music: sacred and secular, vocal and instrumental, operatic and symphonic. Theory, notation, forms, instruments, innovators, composers, performers, typical and important works, and much more in an easy, entertaining style. Burney covered much of Europe and spoke with hundreds of authorities and composers so that this work is more than a compilation of records . . . it is a living work of careful and first-hand scholarship. Its account of thoroughbass (18th century) Italian music is probably still the best introduction on the subject. A recent NEW YORK TIMES review said, "Surprisingly few of Burney's statements have been invalidated by modern research . . . still of great value." Edited and corrected by Frank Mercer. 35 figures. Indices. 1915pp. 5⅜ x 8. 2 volumes.   T36 The Set, Clothbound **$12.50**

A DICTIONARY OF HYMNOLOGY, John Julian. This exhaustive and scholarly work has become known as an invaluable source of hundreds of thousands of important and often difficult to obtain facts on the history and use of hymns in the western world. Everyone interested in hymns will be fascinated by the accounts of famous hymns and hymn writers and amazed by the amount of practical information he will find. More than 30,000 entries on individual hymns, giving authorship, date and circumstances of composition, publication, textual variations, translations, denominational and ritual usage, etc. Biographies of more than 9,000 hymn writers, and essays on important topics such as Christmas carols and children's hymns, and much other unusual and valuable information. A 200 page double-columned index of first lines — the largest in print. Total of 1786 pages in two reinforced clothbound volumes. 6¼ x 9¼.
The set, T333 Clothbound **$15.00**

MUSIC IN MEDIEVAL BRITAIN, F. Ll. Harrison. The most thorough, up-to-date, and accurate treatment of the subject ever published, beautifully illustrated. Complete account of institutions and choirs; carols, masses, and motets; liturgy and plainsong; and polyphonic music from the Norman Conquest to the Reformation. Discusses the various schools of music and their reciprocal influences; the origin and development of new ritual forms; development and use of instruments; and new evidence on many problems of the period. Reproductions of scores, over 200 excerpts from medieval melodies. Rules of harmony and dissonance; influence of Continental styles; great composers (Dunstable, Cornysh, Fairfax, etc.); and much more. Register and index of more than 400 musicians. Index of titles. General Index. 225-item bibliography. 6 Appendices. xix + 491pp. 5⅝ x 8¾.   T705 Clothbound **$10.00**

THE MUSIC OF SPAIN, Gilbert Chase. Only book in English to give concise, comprehensive account of Iberian music; new Chapter covers music since 1941. Victoria, Albéniz, Cabezón, Pedrell, Turina, hundreds of other composers; popular and folk music; the Gypsies; the guitar; dance, theatre, opera, with only extensive discussion in English of the Zarzuela; virtuosi such as Casals; much more. "Distinguished . . . readable," Saturday Review. 400-item bibliography. Index. 27 photos. 383pp. 5⅜ x 8.   T549 Paperbound **$2.00**

ON STUDYING SINGING, Sergius Kagen. An intelligent method of voice-training, which leads you around pitfalls that waste your time, money, and effort. Exposes rigid, mechanical systems, baseless theories, deleterious exercises. "Logical, clear, convincing . . . dead right," Virgil Thomson, N.Y. Herald Tribune. "I recommend this volume highly," Maggie Teyte, Saturday Review. 119pp. 5⅜ x 8.   T622 Paperbound **$1.25**

WILLIAM LAWES, M. Lefkowitz. This is the definitive work on Lawes, the versatile, prolific, and highly original "King's musician" of 17th century England. His life is reconstructed from original documents, and nearly every piece he ever wrote is examined and evaluated: his fantasias, pavans, violin "sonatas," lyra viol and bass viol suites, and music for harp and theorbo; and his songs, masques, and theater music to words by Herrick ("Gather Ye Rosebuds"), Jonson, Suckling, Shirley, and others. The author shows the innovations of dissonance, augmented triad, and other Italian influences Lawes helped introduce to England. List of Lawes' complete works and several complete scores by this major precursor of Purcell and the 18th century developments. Index. 5 Appendices. 52 musical excerpts, many never before in print. Bibliography. x + 320pp. 5⅜ x 8.   T706 Clothbound **$10.00**

THE FUGUE IN BEETHOVEN'S PIANO MUSIC, J. V. Cockshoot. The first study of a neglected aspect of Beethoven's genius: his ability as a writer of fugues. Analyses of early studies and published works demonstrate his original and powerful contributions to composition. 34 works are examined, with 143 musical excerpts. For all pianists, teachers, students, and music-minded readers with a serious interest in Beethoven. Index. 93-item bibliography. Illustration of original score for "Fugue in C." xv + 212pp. 5⅝ x 8⅜.   T704 Clothbound **$6.00**

CATALOGUE OF DOVER BOOKS

JOHANN SEBASTIAN BACH, Philipp Spitta. The complete and unabridged text of the definitive study of Bach. Written some 70 years ago, it is still unsurpassed for its coverage of nearly all aspects of Bach's life and work. There could hardly be a finer non-technical introduction to Bach's music than the detailed, lucid analyses which Spitta provides for hundreds of individual pieces. 26 solid pages are devoted to the B minor mass, for example, and 30 pages to the glorious St. Matthew Passion. This monumental set also includes a major analysis of the music of the 18th century: Buxtehude, Pachelbel, etc. "Unchallenged as the last word on one of the supreme geniuses of music," John Barkham, SATURDAY REVIEW SYNDICATE. Total of 1819pp. 2 volumes. Heavy cloth binding. 5⅜ x 8. T252 The set, Clothbound **$12.50**

THE LIFE OF MOZART, O. Jahn. Probably the largest amount of material on Mozart's life and works ever gathered together in one book! Its 1350 authoritative and readable pages cover every event in his life, and contain a full critique of almost every piece he ever wrote, including sketches and intimate works. There is a full historical-cultural background, and vast research into musical and literary history, sources of librettos, prior treatments of Don Juan legend, etc. This is the complete and unaltered text of the definitive Townsend translation, with foreword by Grove. 5 engraved portraits from Salzburg archives. 4 facsimiles in Mozart's hand. 226 musical examples. 4 Appendixes, including complete list of Mozart's compositions, with Köchel numbers (fragmentary works included). Total of xxviii + 1352pp. Three volume set. 5⅜ x 8.
T85 Vol. I Clothbound **$5.00**
T86 Vol. II Clothbound **$5.00**
The set **$10.00**

BEETHOVEN'S QUARTETS, J. de Marliave. The most complete and authoritative study ever written, enjoyable for scholar and layman alike. The 16 quartets and Grand Fugue are all analyzed bar by bar and theme by theme, not over-technically, but concentrating on mood and effects. Complete background material for each composition: influences, first reviews, etc. Preface by Gabriel Fauré. Introduction and notes by J. Escarra. Translated by Hilda Andrews. 321 musical examples. xxiii + 379pp. 5⅜ x 8. T694 Paperbound **$1.85**

STRUCTURAL HEARING: TONAL COHERENCE IN MUSIC, Felix Salzer. Written by a pupil of the late Heinrich Schenker, this is not only the most thorough exposition in English of the Schenker method but also extends the Schenker approach to include modern music, the middle ages, and renaissance music. It explores the phenomenon of tonal organization by means of a detailed analysis and discussion of more than 500 musical pieces. It casts new light for the reader acquainted with harmony upon the understanding of musical compositions, problems of musical coherence, and connection between theory and composition. "Has been the foundation on which all teaching in music theory has been based at this college," Leopold Mannes, President of The Mannes College of Music. 2 volumes. Total of 658pp. 6½ x 9¼. The set, T418 Clothbound **$8.00**

ANTONIO STRADIVARI: HIS LIFE AND WORK (1644-1737), W. Henry Hill, Arthur F. Hill, and Alfred E. Hill. Still the only book that really delves into life and art of the incomparable Italian craftsman, maker of the finest musical instruments in the world today. The authors, expert violin-makers themselves, discuss Stradivari's ancestry, his construction and finishing techniques, distinguished characteristics of many of his instruments and their locations. Included, too, is story of introduction of his instruments into France, England, first revelation of their supreme merit, and information on his labels, number of instruments made, prices, mystery of ingredients of his varnish, tone of pre-1684 Stradivari violin and changes between 1684 and 1690. An extremely interesting, informative account for all music lovers, from craftsman to concert-goer. Republication of original (1902) edition. New introduction by Sydney Beck, Head of Rare Book and Manuscript Collections, Music Division, New York Public Library. Analytical index by Rembert Wurlitzer. Appendixes. 68 illustrations. 30 full-page plates. 4 in color. xxvi + 315pp. 5⅜ x 8½. T425 Paperbound **$2.25**

THREE CLASSICS IN THE AESTHETIC OF MUSIC, Claude Debussy, Ferrucio Busoni, and Charles Ives. Three very different points of view by three top-ranking modern composers. "M. Croche, the Dilettante-Hater" consists of twenty-five brief articles written by Debussy between the years 1901 and 1905, a sparkling collection of personal commentary on a wide range of topics. Busoni's "Toward a New Aesthetic of Music" considers the nature of absolute music in an attempt to suggest answers to the question, What are the aims of music?, and discusses modern systems of tonality and harmony, the concept of unity of keys, etc. Ives's "Essays Before a Sonata," a literary complement to the movements of the author's "Concord, 1845" piano sonata, contains his most mature analysis of his art. Stimulating reading for musicians, music lovers, and philosophers of the arts. iv + 188pp. 5⅜ x 8½.
T320 Paperbound **$1.45**

CATALOGUE OF DOVER BOOKS

ROMAIN ROLLAND'S ESSAYS ON MUSIC, ed. by David Ewen. 16 best essays by great critic of our time, Nobel Laureate, discuss Mozart, Beethoven, Gluck, Handel, Berlioz, Wagner, Wolf, Saint-Saëns, Metastasio, Lully, Telemann, Grétry, "Origins of 18th Century 'Classic' Style," and musical life of 18th century Germany and Italy. "Shows the key to the high place that Rolland still holds in the world of music," Library Journal. 371pp. 5⅜ x 8.
T550 Paperbound **$1.50**

A GENERAL HISTORY OF THE SCIENCE AND PRACTICE OF MUSIC, Sir John Hawkins. Originally published in 1776, long regarded a genuine classic of musicology. Traces the origin and development of music theory, harmonic and contrapuntal processes, polyphony, musical notation, orchestration, instrumentation, etc. from earliest recorded evidence of music experiment to the author's own time, taking into account a score of musical forms—plainsong, motet, ballad, oratorio, opera, madrigal, canon, cantata, many more—and the particular contributions of various peoples. Still extremely valuable for its consideration of musical theorists and their work and detailed summaries and exact quotes from historically important works unavailable except in largest libraries. Biographical and critical information about hundreds of musicians undeservedly forgotten and now being rediscovered. A unique and significant work of music scholarship, prized by musicologists, composers, performers, historians of culture, and musical amateurs. Reproduction of 1853 edition. New introduction by Charles Cudworth, Curator, Pendlebury Library of Music, Cambridge, England. 315 illustrations; 60 full-page plates. 153 musical excerpts. 20 facsimiles of ancient manuscripts. Memoir of author. Index. Two volumes. Total of 1020pp. of text. 7⅞ x 10¾.
T1048-49 The set, Clothbound **$15.00**

THE GIFT TO BE SIMPLE, Edward Deming Andrews. Students of American history and culture, hymnologists, musicians, historians of religion, and anyone interested in reading about unusual peoples and customs will welcome this unique and authoritative account of Shaker music. Examines the origin of verses and of numerous Shaker dances; the rituals and gestures that accompanied singing; the unusual music theory developed by Shaker musicians and the melodies that were produced. Captures the spirit of an humble and devout people as expressed in many actual texts of hymns, dance songs, ritualistic songs, songs of humility, etc. Includes musical notations of about eighty melodies. A short introduction shows the development of the Shaker movement from its origins (about 1750), through the period of its greatest influence in the 1840's, to its post-Civil War decline. Index of first lines and melodies. Bibliography. 17 illustrations. ix + 170pp. 5⅜ x 8.
T22 Paperbound **$1.50**

BEETHOVEN AND HIS NINE SYMPHONIES, George Grove, editor of Grove's Dictionary of Music and Musicians. In this modern middle-level classic of musicology Grove not only analyzes all nine of Beethoven's symphonies very thoroughly in terms of their musical structure, but also discusses the circumstances under which they were written, Beethoven's stylistic development, and much other background material. This is an extremely rich book, yet very easily followed; it is highly recommended to anyone seriously interested in music. Over 250 musical passages. Index. viii + 407pp. 5⅜ x 8.
T334 Paperbound **$2.00**

AIDA BY GIUSEPPI VERDI, translated and introduced by Ellen H. Bleiler. Full handbook to the most popular opera of all; everything the operagoer (or listener) needs except the music itself. Complete Italian libretto, with all repeats, with new, modern English translation in parallel columns; biography of Verdi and librettists; background to composition of Aida; musical history; plot summary; musical excerpts; pictorial section of 76 illustrations showing Verdi, famous singers, famous performances, etc. Large clear type for easy reading. 147pp. 5⅝ x 8½.
T405 Paperbound **$1.00**

LA BOHEME BY GIACOMO PUCCINI, translated and introduced by Ellen H. Bleiler. Complete handbook for the operagoer, with everything needed for full enjoyment except the musical score itself. Complete Italian libretto, with new modern English line-by-line translation—the only libretto printing all repeats; biography of Puccini; the librettists; background to the opera, Murger's La Boheme, etc.; circumstances of composition and performances; plot summary; and pictorial section of 73 illustrations showing Puccini, famous singers and performances, etc. Large clear type for easy reading. 124pp. 5⅜ x 8½. T404 Paperbound **$1.00**

Prices subject to change without notice.

Dover publishes books on art, music, philosophy, literature, languages, history, social sciences, psychology, handcrafts, orientalia, puzzles and entertainments, chess, pets and gardens, books explaining science, intermediate and higher mathematics, mathematical physics, engineering, biological sciences, earth sciences, classics of science, etc. Write to:

Dept. catrr.
Dover Publications, Inc.
180 Varick Street, N.Y. 14, N.Y.